Contents

Page

◆ Quick Ref Map   (inner front cover)
◆ Contents   1
◆ Publisher's Details / Copyright Notice   2
◆ Useful Telephone Numbers   3
◆ Legend   4
◆ Abbreviations Used   5
◆ How to Use This Directory   6
◆ Electronic Road Pricing (ERP)   7
◆ MRT & LRT System Map   8
◆ Information on Expressway Exits   10

Road Index (Pages with blue edge)   12–52

Places Index (Pages with orange edge)

◆ Bus Interchanges, Terminals, Depot   54
◆ Camping, Adventure   54
◆ Cemeteries, Columbaria, Crematoria   54
◆ Clubs, Country Clubs, Associations   55
◆ Community Clubs / Centres   56
◆ Driving Test Centres   57
◆ Educational Institutions
    • Primary Schools   57
    • Secondary Schools   59
    • Polytechnics, Junior Colleges,   61
      Centralised Institutes
    • Technical Institutes   61
    • Institutions of Higher Learning   61
    • Special Education Schools, Minds   61
    • Foreign Schools   62
    • Islamic Religious Schools   62
    • Language Centres   63
    • Other Institutions, Academia   63
◆ Embassies, High Commissions, Consulates   64
◆ Entry / Exit Points for Travel / Goods   65
◆ Fire Stations / Fire Posts   66
◆ Flyovers, Underpasses, Viaducts, Tunnels   66
◆ Government Offices, Statutory Boards   67
◆ HDB Branch Offices / Service Centres   73
◆ Historical Sites, National Monuments   73

Page

Places Index (cont'd)

◆ Homes for the Aged, Welfare Homes, Hospice   76
◆ Hospitals, Medical Centres, Polyclinics,   77
    First Aid Points
◆ Hostels, Dormitories, Staff Accomodation   79
◆ Hotels   80
◆ Industrial Parks / Estates   82
◆ Libraries   82
◆ MRT & LRT Stations   83
◆ NKF Dialysis Centres   84
◆ Park Connectors   85
◆ Parks, Gardens   85
◆ Places of Interest / Leisure   85
◆ Places of Worship   87
◆ Police Organisations / Units   94
◆ Post Offices, Philatelic Counters   96
◆ Prisons, Drug Rehabilitation Centres   96
◆ Private Housing, Condos, Apartments   96
◆ Public / Commercial Buildings,   115
    Industrial Buildings
◆ Reservoirs   129
◆ SAF Camps and Facilities   130
◆ SCDF Camps and Facilities   130
◆ Stadia, Sports Complexes, Fields,   131
    Golf Driving Ranges
◆ Swimming Complexes   132
◆ Theatres / Cinemas   132
◆ Town Councils   133
◆ Veterinary Centres   133
◆ Visitors Information   133

S'pore Map Pages   134
◆ Whole of Singapore
    Sentosa & Pulau   147
◆ Pulau Tekong &   148
◆ Kusu Island & St   149

Consumer Guide   CG23
◆ Contents (last page)   CG23

Mighty Minds®

Street
Directory

Latest 2009 Edition

14th Edition - Published and distributed by:

Mighty Minds Publishing Pte Ltd

Blk 1008 Toa Payoh North
#06-18 Singapore 318996
Company reg. no. 199806419Z
e-mail : mighty@singnet.com.sg
website :www.mightyminds.com.sg
TEL: 6353 5035 FAX: 6353 5414

Whilst we try to ensure that all the information is accurate and up to-date, the Publisher accepts no liability for any inconvenience, injury or loss sustained by any person using this directory. However we apologise for any inconvenience that may be caused and shall be grateful if any errors, omissions or updated information can be brought to our attention.

The information cut-off date for this directory is 1st September 2008.

TRAVEL HOTLINE

TransitLink Service Hotline for info on Buses & MRT **1800 225 5663**

EMERGENCY

• Police	999
• Fire	995
• Ambulance (Emergency Only)	995
• Non Emergency Ambulance	1777
• Marine Accident	6325 2488
• Johor Bahru Police Hotline	60-7-2212999

TRANSPORT SERVICES
TAXIS

• **Common Taxi Booking Number**	**6342 5222**
	(6 DIAL CAB)
• Comfort & Yellow Top Cab	**6552 1111**
• City Cab	**6552 2222**
• Prime	**6778 0808**
• Silver Cab	**6363 6888**
• Smart Cab	**6485 7777**
• SMRT Taxis	**6555 8888**
• Trans Cab	**6555 3333**

BUSES

• SBS	
- General Information, Feedback & Complaints	1800 287 2727
- Lost & Found	6383 7211
• SMRT Buses	
- Lost & Found and General Enquiries	1800 336 8900

TRAINS

• North South Line & East West Line	1800 336 8900
• North East Line	1800 287 2727
• Bukit Panjang LRT	1800 336 8900
• Punggol & Sengkang LRT	1800 287 2727
• KTM Berhad (Malayan Railway)	6222 5165

BREAKDOWN OF SERVICES

• Street Lighting	1800 225 5582
• Traffic Lights	1800 225 5582
• Water Supply, Drainage & Sewerage System	1800 284 6600
• Electricity	1800 778 8888
• Piped Gas Supply	1800 752 1800

TOURIST INFORMATION

• Singapore Tourism Board Information Service Line	1800 736 2000

VEHICLE SERVICING, REPAIRS, WARRANTY & TEST

• Kar Engineering Pte Ltd	6456 5200

GENERAL

• Police Hotline	1800 255 0000
• Traffic Police	6547 0000
• Traffic Police Hotline	1800 547 1818
• Mindef E-Services Centre (NS Men Notification Centre)	1800 ENSNSNS
• SPCA (Society for Prevention of Cruelty to Animals)	6287 5355

INFORMATION SERVICES

• Tuas and Woodlands Checkpoint Traffic Information	6863 0117
• Changi Airport Flight Information (Voice Prompt)	1800 542 4422
• Weather and Tide	6542 7788
• Time	1711
• Postal Enquiry (General)	1605
• Currency Exchange Rates (DBS Bank-Voice Prompt)	1800 111 1111
• LTA (Land Transport Authority) 24 Hrs Service Line (To report problems on traffic lights or bus stops, to enquire about COE, ERP, Road Tax or vehicle inspection)	1800 225 5582

BOOKING OF TICKETS-EVENT/ PERFORMANCE ENQUIRIES

• SISTIC	6348 5555
• Ticketcharge	6296 2929

VEHICLE BREAKDOWN & TOWING SERVICE

• EMAS (For Expressways Only)	1800 225 5582
• Automobile Association of Singapore (For AAS Members Only)	6748 9911

ACCIDENT DAMAGE ASSESSMENT

• IDAC Hotline	1800 887 5151

SOCIAL SERVICES

• ComCare Call (Help Hotline)	1800 222 0000

CREDIT CARD EMERGENCY ASSISTANCE

• American Express (Office Hrs)	6299 8133
(After Office Hrs)	6294 3113
• Diners Club	6416 0900
• Master Card	800 110 0113
• VISA	800 448 1250

Legend

For speedy and easy search, instead of just words and colours, icons/symbols have been used. For example, if you are searching for a Hotel, the search can be speedily done by looking out for the "hotel" symbol **H** and instantly narrowing down to that locality.

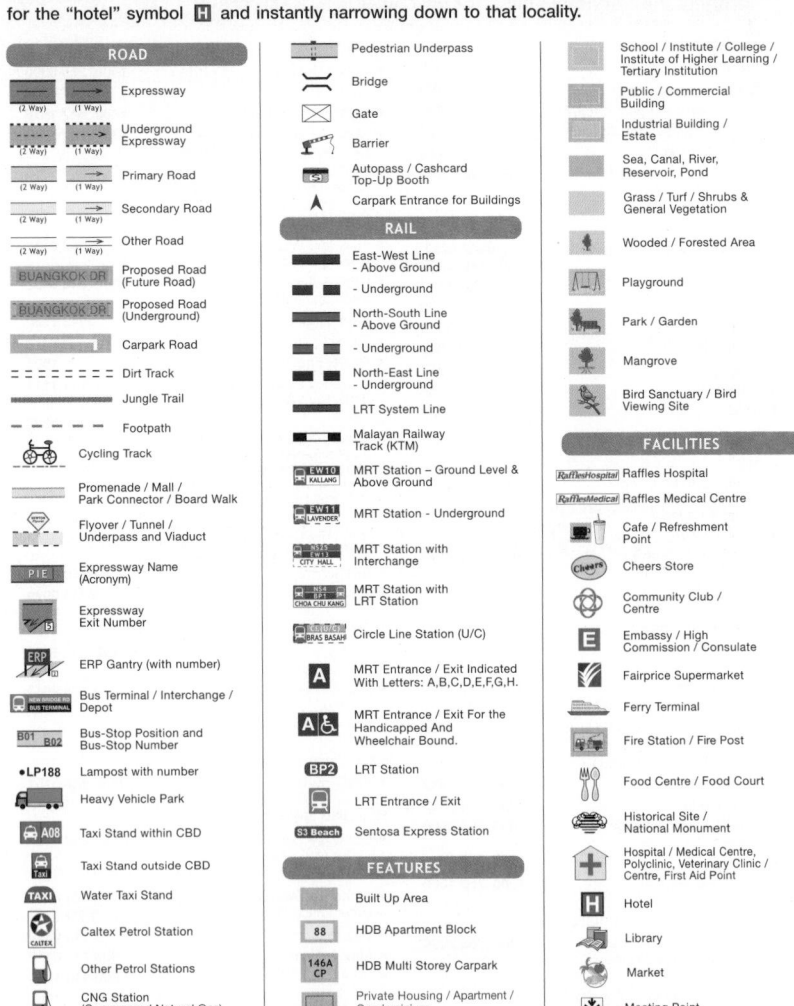

ROAD

Expressway (2 Way) (1 Way)

Underground Expressway (2 Way) (1 Way)

Primary Road (2 Way) (1 Way)

Secondary Road (2 Way) (1 Way)

Other Road (2 Way) (1 Way)

BUANGKOK DR — Proposed Road (Future Road)

BUANGKOK DR — Proposed Road (Underground)

Carpark Road

Dirt Track

Jungle Trail

Footpath

Cycling Track

Promenade / Mall / Park Connector / Board Walk

Flyover / Tunnel / Underpass and Viaduct

PIE — Expressway Name (Acronym)

Expressway Exit Number

ERP — ERP Gantry (with number)

Bus Terminal / Interchange / Depot

B01 B02 — Bus-Stop Position and Bus-Stop Number

●LP188 — Lampost with number

Heavy Vehicle Park

A08 — Taxi Stand within CBD

Taxi — Taxi Stand outside CBD

TAXI — Water Taxi Stand

Caltex Petrol Station

Other Petrol Stations

CNG Station (Compressed Natural Gas)

Pedestrian Overhead Bridge

Pedestrian Underpass

Bridge

Gate

Barrier

Autopass / Cashcard Top-Up Booth

Carpark Entrance for Buildings

RAIL

East-West Line - Above Ground

- Underground

North-South Line - Above Ground

- Underground

North-East Line - Underground

LRT System Line

Malayan Railway Track (KTM)

EW10 KALLANG — MRT Station – Ground Level & Above Ground

EW11 LAVENDER — MRT Station - Underground

NS10 EW17 CITY HALL — MRT Station with Interchange

NS4 EP1 CHOA CHU KANG — MRT Station with LRT Station

CC2 BRAS BASAH — Circle Line Station (U/C)

A — MRT Entrance / Exit Indicated With Letters: A,B,C,D,E,F,G,H.

A — MRT Entrance / Exit For the Handicapped And Wheelchair Bound.

BP2 — LRT Station

LRT Entrance / Exit

S3 Beach — Sentosa Express Station

FEATURES

Built Up Area

88 — HDB Apartment Block

146A CP — HDB Multi Storey Carpark

Private Housing / Apartment / Condominium

Hostel / Dormitory Staff Quarters

School / Institute / College / Institute of Higher Learning / Tertiary Institution

Public / Commercial Building

Industrial Building / Estate

Sea, Canal, River, Reservoir, Pond

Grass / Turf / Shrubs & General Vegetation

Wooded / Forested Area

Playground

Park / Garden

Mangrove

Bird Sanctuary / Bird Viewing Site

FACILITIES

RafflesHospital — Raffles Hospital

RafflesMedical — Raffles Medical Centre

Cafe / Refreshment Point

Cheers — Cheers Store

Community Club / Centre

E — Embassy / High Commission / Consulate

Fairprice Supermarket

Ferry Terminal

Fire Station / Fire Post

Food Centre / Food Court

Historical Site / National Monument

Hospital / Medical Centre, Polyclinic, Veterinary Clinic / Centre, First Aid Point

H — Hotel

Library

Market

Meeting Point

NKF — National Kidney Foundation Dialysis Centre

4

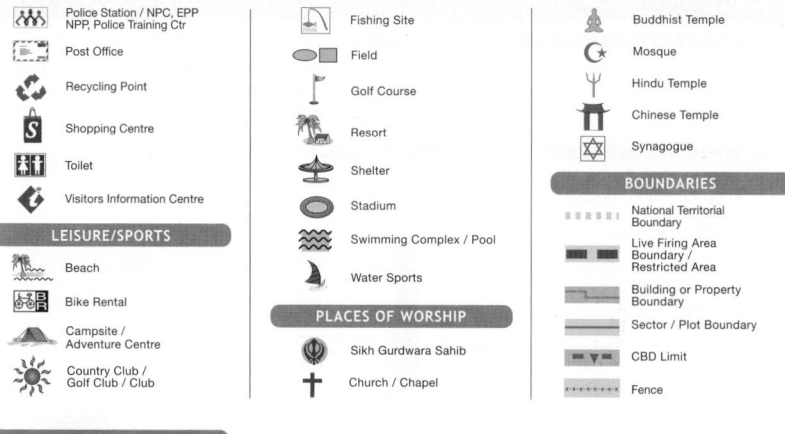

Police Station / NPC, EPP NPP, Police Training Ctr	Fishing Site	Buddhist Temple
Post Office	Field	Mosque
Recycling Point	Golf Course	Hindu Temple
Shopping Centre	Resort	Chinese Temple
Toilet	Shelter	Synagogue

Police Station / NPC, EPP NPP, Police Training Ctr
Post Office
Recycling Point
Shopping Centre
Toilet
Visitors Information Centre

LEISURE/SPORTS

Beach
Bike Rental
Campsite / Adventure Centre
Country Club / Golf Club / Club

Fishing Site
Field
Golf Course
Resort
Shelter
Stadium
Swimming Complex / Pool
Water Sports

PLACES OF WORSHIP

Sikh Gurdwara Sahib
Church / Chapel

Buddhist Temple
Mosque
Hindu Temple
Chinese Temple
Synagogue

BOUNDARIES

National Territorial Boundary
Live Firing Area Boundary / Restricted Area
Building or Property Boundary
Sector / Plot Boundary
CBD Limit
Fence

SCALE

(For Maps With Scale Of 1:18,382)

0   75m   150m   250m   500m   750m   1Km

(To measure distances on the map, kindly use the bookmark magnifier)

SINGAPORE			
1:18,382	All Maps (Except those indicated below)		
1:9,191	Maps 109A,B,C,D Maps 111A,B,C,D Maps 112A,B 113A,B		Maps 110A,B,C,D Maps 132A,B,C,D Map 133A
1:92,700 1:228,000	Map 148	1:8,500 1:14,300	Map 149

The scale is approximate and a rough guide. Some contents and symbols may not be to scale as these have been highlighted for easy identification. For example expressways, roads, MRT stations, etc.

Abbreviations Used

Ably	Assembly	Ctr	Centre	Lk	Link	Rd	Road
Admin	Administration	Ctrl	Central	Ln	Lane	Sch	School
Aft	After	CTY	Countryside	L. / Lor	Lorong	Sec.	Sector
AMK	Ang Mo Kio	Dept	Department	LP	Lamp Post	Sec	Secondary
Apt	Apartment	Div	Division	Man/s	Mansion/s	Sg	Sungei
Assn	Association	Dr	Drive	Med	Medical	SLE	Seletar Expressway
Ave	Avenue	ECP	East Coast Parkway	Meth	Methodist	S'pore	Singapore
AYE	Ayer Rajah Expressway	EPP	Extended Police Post	Mfg	Manufacturing	Sq	Square
		Est	Estate	Min	Ministry	St	Street
Bef	Before	E'way	Expressway	Mjd	Masjid	St.	Saint
Bet	Between	FC	Food Centre	Mkt	Market	Sth	South
BKE	Bukit Timah Expressway	Fty	Factory	Mohd	Mohammad	Stn	Station
Bldg	Building	Gdn/s	Garden/s	Mt	Mount	TC	Town Council
Blk	Block	Grn	Green	Nat'l	National	Tech	Technical
Blvd	Boulevard	Gr	Grove	Nth	North	Temp	Temporary
BO	HDB Branch Office	Hosp	Hospital	N'hood	Neighbourhood	Ter	Terrace
Br	Branch	H./Hts	Heights	NPC	Neighbourhood Police Centre	Term	Terminal
Bt	Bukit	Hq/Hqrs	Headquarters			Tg	Tanjong
Budh	Buddhist	HS	Historical Site	NPP	Neighbourhood Police Post	Tmn	Taman
CC	Community Club / Centre	Hse	House	Ofc	Office	Tp	Temple
		Ind	Industrial	O/S	Open Space	TPE	Tampines Expressway
CCK	Choa Chu Kang	Inst	Institute	Opp	Opposite	TW	Teck Whye
Cemy	Cemetery	Int	Interchange	P/G	Playground	Twr	Tower
Ch	Church	Int'l	International	PIE	Pan Island Expressway	U/C	Under Construction
Chr	Christian	JC	Junior College	Pk	Park	Upp	Upper
C/Cl	Close	J / Jln	Jalan	Pl	Place	Wk	Walk
Comm	Community	Jnr	Junior	PO	Post Office	W'lands	Woodlands
Condo	Condominium	JOC	Join Operations Centre	Poly	Polyclinic	YCK	Yio Chu Kang
CP	Carpark	Kg	Kampong	Pr	Primary	Yn	Yishun
Cplx	Complex	KJE	Kranji Expressway	Presby	Presbyterian		
Cres	Crescent	Km	Kilometre	Pstrn	Pedestrian		
Ct	Court	KPE	Kallang Paya Lebar Expressway	Pt	Point		
CTE	Central Expressway	Lib	Library	R	Rise		

DOING A SEARCH USING THE QUICK REFERENCE MAP:

If you're looking for a road or place and you know the general area it is located at, turn to the **Quick Reference Map** at the inner front cover and locate the general area or refer to the list of place names at the bottom of the **Quick Reference Map**. Note the map number for that area and refer to that map to find the road or place.

DOING A SEARCH USING THE ROAD OR PLACES INDEX:

Refer to the index pages (pages 12 to 52 with **blue** edge for **roads** and pages 54 to 133 with orange edge for features and places).

The **Road Index** has a small square box that appears before the road name.

- This box indicates the colour of the road as it appears in the maps. (See the Legend on page 4 for information on the type of road that the colours represent.)

- Some roads have certain stretches in different colours. Both colours are shown in the box.

ROADS		MAP	GRID
☐ Aida Street	爱达街	115	1 A
☐ Airline Road	航空公司路	54	2 C
▶☐ Airport Boulevard	机场林荫道	75	1 C
☐ Airport Cargo Road	机场货运路	54	2 D
▶☐ Airport Road	机场路	91	1 B
☐ Akyab Road	爱业路	88	2 D
☐ Albert Street	亚巴街	111	1 C

To locate your search destination (eg. Airline Road), turn to the **Map** indicated for Airline Road (**Map 54**) and narrow down to the **Grid** Box indicated in the **Grid** column (**2C**).

For roads, you can also speed up your search by looking out for the road having the same colour as the small coloured box at the Road Index. In the example above, the colour for Airline Road is pale yellow. In the grid box, there are only two roads in pale yellow.

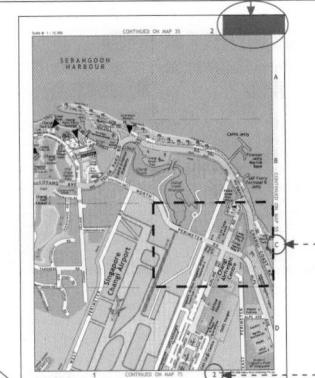

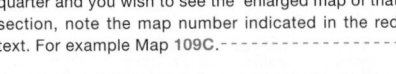

Due to the density of roads, buildings and features in the city area, maps comprising the city area are accompanied by ENLARGED sections.

The maps with enlarged sections are maps 109, 110, 111, 132 and part of maps 112, 113, and 133. These maps can be recognised easily as there is additional information given under the map number and lightened boxes with **red** text on the map. The **red** text indicates the enlarged map number of that quarter section of the particular map. The sections are divided by a thicker dotted line.

If the road or feature you're searching for is in that quarter and you wish to see the enlarged map of that section, note the map number indicated in the red text. For example Map **109C**.

Turn to Map **109C** to locate your search destination.

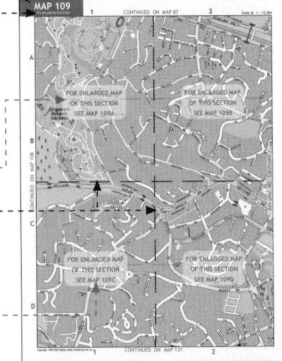

ERP was introduced to prevent congestion on the roads and to maintain smooth traffic flow. The system works on a **"pay per entry"** basis, whereby motorists are charged only if they pass through the ERP gantries. The rates vary according to the type of vehicle, place and time (peak/off peak) and are adjusted from time to time in response to changing traffic patterns. Kindly check the **"Legend"** on page 4 to see the icons used in the maps for ERP gantries and ERP related features.

The system consists of an **In-Vehicle Unit (IU)**, a prepaid **Cashcard** (which is inserted into the IU), the **Gantry** (which has electronic detectors and cameras) and the **Central Computer System**. The appropriate ERP charges are deducted automatically when a vehicle passes through the ERP gantry. The cameras mounted on the ERP gantries record images of vehicles entering without an IU, without a cashcard or with an insufficient balance in the cashcard. This is followed up by enforcement action.

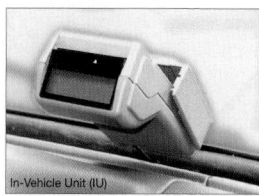

In-Vehicle Unit (IU)

In-Vehicle Unit (IU)

All vehicles (including foreign registered motorcycles, buses and goods vehicles intending to use ERP Roads during ERP hours) are required to be fitted with an IU. Foreign registered passenger cars can either fit a permanent IU and use a cashcard or choose not to install an IU. For this option, the foreign registered passenger car can enter the ERP Zone as many times in a day and need pay only S$5.00 at the point of exit (Immigration counter) using the Autopass Card. The S$5.00 fee will be automatically deducted from the Autopass Card.

Owners of foreign registered motor cycles, buses and goods vehicles intending to install an IU in their vehicles can purchase the IU from the IU centres. Kindly call the **LTA** (Land Transport Authority) **Hotline: 1800-2255582 (24 Hours) or 1800 CALL LTA** for more information on IU installation centres or visit the LTA Website : **www.lta.gov.sg**

Cashcards are available and can be topped up at 7-Eleven convenience stores, selected petrol stations and selected banks. The value of the Cashcard can also be topped up at:
• any ATM displaying the Cashcard logo (If you have an account with that bank - UOB, OCBC, POSBank/DBS) or Autopass top up booths. Kindly call LTA to check the booth locations.

There are penalties for driving through an ERP gantry during ERP hours without an IU installed in your vehicle, without a cashcard inserted or using a cashcard with an insufficient balance. Kindly call the LTA Hotline to check on existing ERP rates for the gantries that you'll be passing through. Quote the gantry number when making your enquiry.

Foreign vehicles entering Singapore are also required to pay **VEP fees** (Vehicle Entry Permit) and toll charges using an Autopass Card which can be purchased at the checkpoint. It costs S$10 (comprising a pre-loaded cash value of S$4 and a non-refundable card cost of S$6). The Autopass can also be inserted in the IU to pay ERP charges and can be topped up at the Autopass/Cashcard Top-up Booths/Centres.

An administrative fee of $10.00 will be imposed if you pay VEP fees and/or charges in cash at any Singapore Checkpoint.

The VEP Fee is S$20.00 per day for cars and S$4.00 per day for motorcycles from Mondays to Fridays from 2am to 5pm. VEP is not charged for all other days and times.

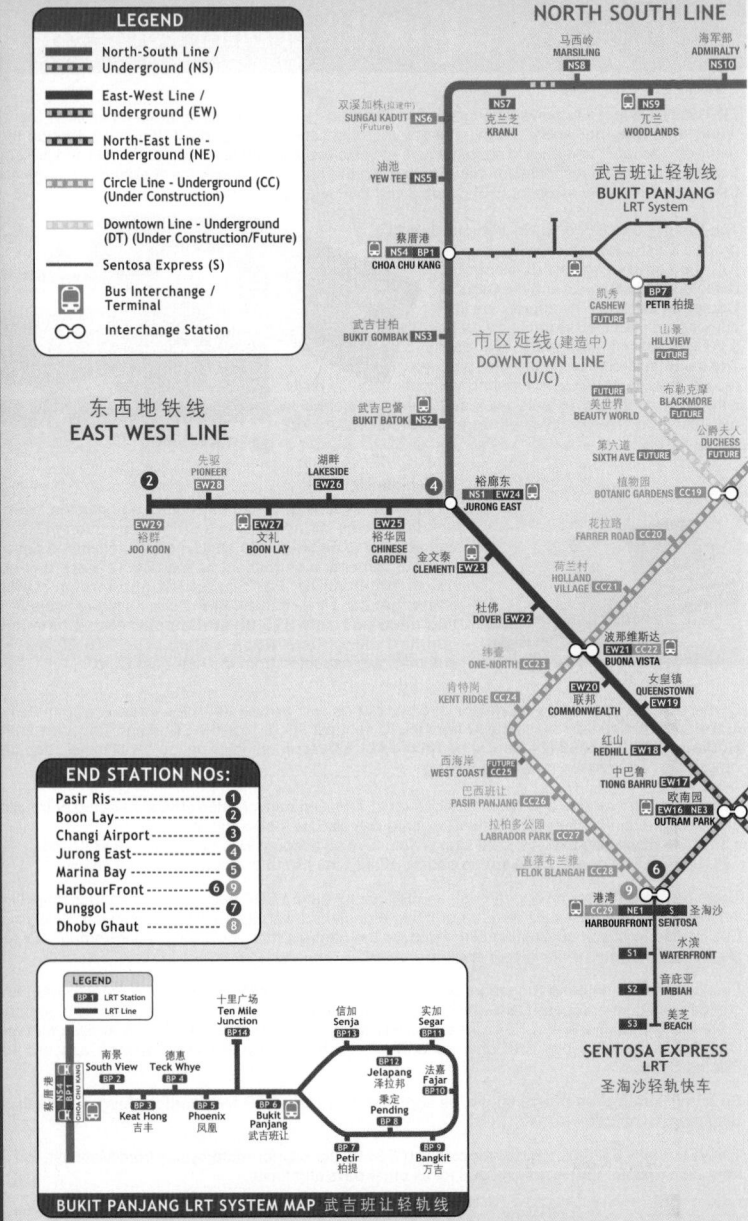

NORTH SOUTH LINE

LEGEND

North-South Line / Underground (NS)

East-West Line / Underground (EW)

North-East Line - Underground (NE)

Circle Line - Underground (CC) (Under Construction)

Downtown Line - Underground (DT) (Under Construction/Future)

Sentosa Express (S)

Bus Interchange / Terminal

Interchange Station

EAST WEST LINE
东西地铁线

市区延线(建造中)
DOWNTOWN LINE (U/C)

武吉班让轻轨线
BUKIT PANJANG LRT System

马西岭 MARSILING NS8
海军部 ADMIRALTY NS10
双溪加株(发展中) SUNGAI KADUT NS6 (Future)
克兰芝 KRANJI NS7
兀兰 WOODLANDS NS9
油池 YEW TEE NS5
凯秀 CASHEW FUTURE
裴提 PETIR BP7 柏提
慕厝港 CHOA CHU KANG NS4 BP1
山景 HILLVIEW FUTURE
武吉甘柏 BUKIT GOMBAK NS3
美世界 BEAUTY WORLD FUTURE
布勒克摩 BLACKMORE FUTURE
武吉巴督 BUKIT BATOK NS2
第六道 SIXTH AVE FUTURE
公爵夫人 DUCHESS FUTURE
先驱 PIONEER EW28
湖畔 LAKESIDE EW26
裕廊东 JURONG EAST NS1 EW24
植物园 BOTANIC GARDENS CC19
裕群 JOO KOON EW29
文礼 BOON LAY EW27
裕华园 CHINESE GARDEN EW25
金文泰 CLEMENTI EW23
花拉路 FARRER ROAD CC20
杜佛 DOVER EW22
荷兰村 HOLLAND VILLAGE CC21
纬壹 ONE-NORTH CC23
波那维斯达 BUONA VISTA EW21 CC22
肯特岗 KENT RIDGE CC24
女皇镇 QUEENSTOWN EW19
联邦 COMMONWEALTH EW20
红山 REDHILL EW18
西海岸 WEST COAST CC25 FUTURE
中巴鲁 TIONG BAHRU EW17
巴西班让 PASIR PANJANG CC26
欧南园 OUTRAM PARK EW16 NE3
拉柏多公园 LABRADOR PARK CC27
直落布兰雅 TELOK BLANGAH CC28
港湾 HARBOURFRONT CC29 NE1
圣淘沙 SENTOSA S
水滨 WATERFRONT S1
音茂亚 IMBIAH S2
美芝 BEACH S3

END STATION NOs:

SENTOSA EXPRESS LRT
圣淘沙轻轨快车

BUKIT PANJANG LRT SYSTEM MAP 武吉班让轻轨线

LEGEND
BP1 LRT Station
LRT Line

十里广场 Ten Mile Junction BP14
南景 South View BP2
德惠 Teck Whye BP4
信加 Senja BP13
实加 Segar BP11
贞加 Jelapang 泽拉邦 BP12
法嘉 Fajar BP10
秉定 Pending BP8
吉丰 Keat Hong BP3
凤凰 Phoenix BP5
武吉班让 Bukit Panjang BP6
裴提 Petir BP7 柏提
万吉 Bangkit BP9

8

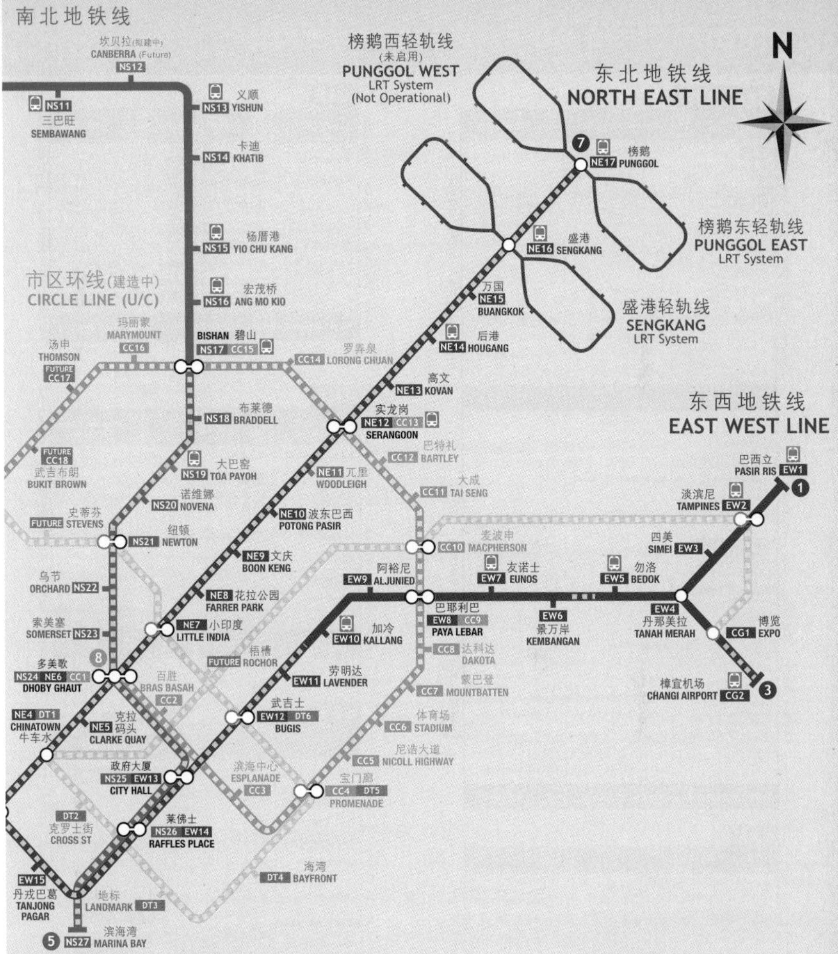
南北地铁线
坎贝拉(规建中) CANBERRA (Future) NS12
NS11 三巴旺 SEMBAWANG
义顺 NS13 YISHUN
卡迪 NS14 KHATIB
杨厝港 NS15 YIO CHU KANG
宏茂桥 NS16 ANG MO KIO
BISHAN 碧山 NS17 CC15
布莱德 NS18 BRADDELL
大巴窑 NS19 TOA PAYOH
诺维娜 NS20 NOVENA
纽顿 NS21 NEWTON
乌节 ORCHARD NS22
索美塞 SOMERSET NS23
多美歌 NS24 NE6 CC1 DHOBY GHAUT
政府大厦 NS25 EW13 CITY HALL
莱佛士 NS26 EW14 RAFFLES PLACE
滨海湾 NS27 MARINA BAY
榜鹅西轻轨线 (未启用) PUNGGOL WEST LRT System (Not Operational)
东北地铁线 NORTH EAST LINE
N
榜鹅 NE17 PUNGGOL
榜鹅东轻轨线 PUNGGOL EAST LRT System
盛港 NE16 SENGKANG
盛港轻轨线 SENGKANG LRT System
万国 NE15 BUANGKOK
后港 NE14 HOUGANG
高文 NE13 KOVAN
实龙岗 NE12 CC13 SERANGOON
NE11 兀里 WOODLEIGH
NE10 波东巴西 POTONG PASIR
NE9 文庆 BOON KENG
NE8 花拉公园 FARRER PARK
NE7 小印度 LITTLE INDIA
NE5 克拉码头 CLARKE QUAY
NE4 DT1 CHINATOWN 牛车水
市区环线(建造中) CIRCLE LINE (U/C)
玛丽蒙 MARYMOUNT CC16
汤申 THOMSON FUTURE CC17
FUTURE CC18 武吉布朗 BUKIT BROWN
史蒂芬 FUTURE STEVENS
罗弄泉 CC14 LORONG CHUAN
巴特礼 CC12 BARTLEY
大成 CC11 TAI SENG
麦波申 CC10 MACPHERSON
CC8 达科达 DAKOTA
蒙巴登 CC7 MOUNTBATTEN
体育场 CC6 STADIUM
尼诰大道 CC5 NICOLL HIGHWAY
宝门廊 CC4 DT5 PROMENADE
滨海中心 ESPLANADE CC3
百胜 BRAS BASAH CC2
梧槽 FUTURE ROCHOR
DT2 克罗士街 CROSS ST
海湾 DT4 BAYFRONT
地标 LANDMARK DT3
东西地铁线 EAST WEST LINE
巴西立 PASIR RIS EW1
淡滨尼 TAMPINES EW2
四美 SIMEI EW3
EW4 丹那美拉 TANAH MERAH
勿洛 EW5 BEDOK
EW6 景万岸 KEMBANGAN
友诺士 EW7 EUNOS
巴耶利巴 EW8 CC9 PAYA LEBAR
EW9 阿裕尼 ALJUNIED
加冷 EW10 KALLANG
劳明达 EW11 LAVENDER
武吉士 EW12 DT6 BUGIS
EW15 丹戎巴葛 TANJONG PAGAR
博览 CG1 EXPO
樟宜机场 CHANGI AIRPORT CG2
1
3
5
7
8

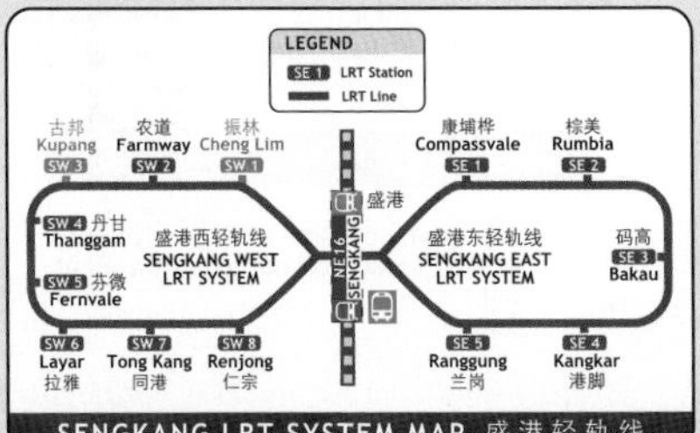
LEGEND
SE 1 LRT Station
LRT Line
古邦 Kupang SW 3
农道 Farmway SW 2
振林 Cheng Lim SW 1
SW 4 丹甘 Thanggam
SW 5 芬微 Fernvale
盛港西轻轨线 SENGKANG WEST LRT SYSTEM
SW 6 Layar 拉雅
SW 7 Tong Kang 同港
SW 8 Renjong 仁宗
NE 16 SENGKANG 盛港
康埔桦 Compassvale SE 1
棕美 Rumbia SE 2
盛港东轻轨线 SENGKANG EAST LRT SYSTEM
码高 SE 3 Bakau
SE 5 Ranggung 兰岗
SE 4 Kangkar 港脚
SENGKANG LRT SYSTEM MAP 盛港轻轨线

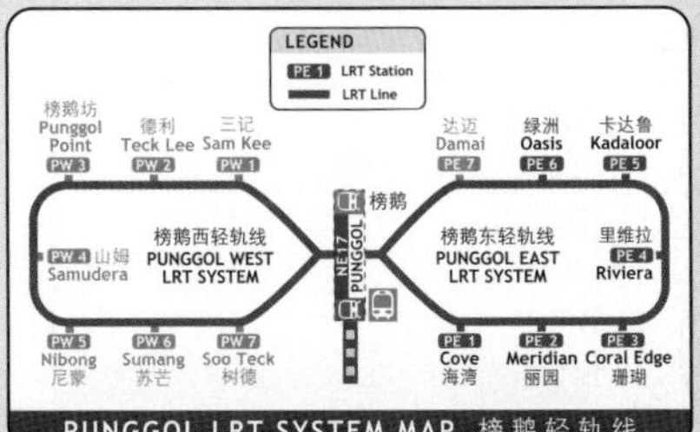
LEGEND
PE 1 LRT Station
LRT Line
榜鹅坊 Punggol Point PW 3
德利 Teck Lee PW 2
三记 Sam Kee PW 1
PW 4 山姆 Samudera
榜鹅西轻轨线 PUNGGOL WEST LRT SYSTEM
PW 5 Nibong 尼蒙
PW 6 Sumang 苏芒
PW 7 Soo Teck 树德
NE 17 PUNGGOL 榜鹅
达迈 Damai PE 7
绿洲 Oasis PE 6
卡达鲁 Kadaloor PE 5
榜鹅东轻轨线 PUNGGOL EAST LRT SYSTEM
里维拉 PE 4 Riviera
PE 1 Cove 海湾
PE 2 Meridian 丽园
PE 3 Coral Edge 珊瑚
PUNGGOL LRT SYSTEM MAP 榜鹅轻轨线

SLE/CTE

	To BKE (Woodlands)	Exit No.	Flyover/ Map & Grid	Exit No.	From BKE (Woodlands)	
FROM WOODLANDS TO SELETAR	BKE (PIE) Mandai Rd Turf Club Ave Kranji Rd	11	Woodlands South Flyover – 23 2A	–		**FROM WOODLANDS TO SELETAR**
	Woodlands Ave 2 Admiralty Rd	10	Marsiling Flyover – 11 2D	10	Woodlands Ave 2 Admiralty Rd	
	Woodlands Ave 12	9	Ulu Sembawang Flyover – 29 1A	9	Woodlands Ave 12	
	Mandai Rd Zoo Night Safari	8A	Sembawang Flyover – 25 2B	8B	Mandai Ave	
	Upper Thomson Rd	5	Upper Thomson Flyover – 45 1A	5	Upper Thomson Rd	
	Lentor Ave	3	Lentor Flyover – 46 1A	3	Yishun	
		–	Seletar Flyover – 47 1A	1B	TPE	
				1A	Yio Chu Kang Rd	
	TPE	1	47 1A			

SLE is above this row
CTE is below this row

		Exit No.		Exit No.		
FROM SELETAR TO CITY (DELTA) FROM CITY	Yio Chu Kang Rd	15	Yio Chu Kang Flyover – 47 1B	–		**FROM SELETAR TO CITY (DELTA)**
		–	Ang Mo Kio North – 47 1D	14	Ang Mo Kio Ave 5 Ang Mo Kio Ave 3	
	Ang Mo Kio Ave 5 Ang Mo Kio Ave 3	12B 12A	Ang Mo Kio Central – 68 2A	–		
	Ang Mo Kio Ave 1	11	Ang Mo Kio South – 68 1C	11	Ang Mo Kio Ave 1	
					ERP – 35	
	Braddell Rd	10	Braddell Flyover – 89 2A	10	Braddell Rd	
					ERP – 31	
	ERP – 46					
	Upper Serangoon Rd PIE (Changi Airport)	8B	Whampoa Flyover – 89 2C	8B	Upper Serangoon Rd PIE (Changi Airport)	
				8A	PIE (Jurong)	
	ERP – 51					
	Jalan Bahagia	7B	Moulmein Flyover – 111 1A	7D	Balestier Rd (Kallang)	
	Moulmein Rd	7A		7C	Balestier Rd (Thomson) Moulmein Rd	
		–	110 2B	6	Bukit Timah Rd Cavenagh Rd	
		–	Kg Java Tunnel – 110 2B	5	Cairnhill Circle	
		–	110 2C	4	Orchard Rd	
	Merchant Rd Clemenceau Ave	2	Chin Swee Tunnel – 132 2A	2	Havelock Rd	
	Tiong Bahru Outram Rd	1B	Outram Flyover – 132 1B	1B	Outram Rd	
		–	Bukit Merah Flyover 131 2C	1A	Jalan Bukit Merah	
	From AYE (Delta)	Exit No.	Flyover/ Map & Grid	Exit No.	**To AYE (Delta)**	

TPE

	To PIE (Changi Airport)	Exit No.	Flyover/ Map & Grid	Exit No.	From PIE (Changi Airport)	
FROM SELETAR TO CHANGI		–	73 2C	1	PIE (Jurong) Upper Changi Rd North Upper Changi Rd East	**FROM CHANGI TO SELETAR**
	Tampines New Town Loyang Ave Changi Village	2	Loyang Flyover – 73 2B	1	Tampines New Town Loyang Ave Changi Village	
	Tampines Ave 12 Pasir Ris Drive 8	3C	Pasir Ris Flyover – 73 1A	3A	Tampines Ave 12	
				3B	Pasir Ris Drive 8	
	Elias Rd	4	72 1A	4	Tampines Rd	
	Tampines Ave 10 Pasir Ris Drive 12	5	Api Api Flyover – 51 1D	5	Tampines Ave 10 Pasir Ris Drive 12	
	Tampines Rd Lorong Halus	7	Tampines Flyover – 50 1C	6	Tampines Rd	
	Punggol New Town Sengkang New Town	9	Punggol Flyover – 49 2A	9	Punggol New Town Sengkang New Town	
		–	Sengkang Flyover – 30 1D	–	Sengkang New Town (under construction)	
	Jalan Kayu	12	Jalan Kayu Flyover – 29 1D	12	Jalan Kayu	
		–	Seletar Flyover – 28 1D	14	CTE (City)	
	From SLE (Woodlands)	Exit No.	Flyover/ Map & Grid	Exit No.	**To SLE (Woodlands)**	

KJE

	To BKE	Exit No.	Flyover/ Map & Grid	Exit No.	From BKE	
FROM TENGAH TO BUKIT PANJANG	BKE (Mandai, Woodlands)	1	Gali Batu Flyover – 42 2B	–		**FROM BUKIT PANJANG TO TENGAH**
	Woodlands Rd	2	Yew Tee Flyover – 42 1B	2	Woodlands Rd	
		–	Choa Chu Kang East Flyover – 41 1B	3	Choa Chu Kang Way Choa Chu Kang Drive	
	Choa Chu Kang Way Choa Chu Kang Drive	4	Choa Chu Kang West Flyover – 41 1B	–		
	Sungei Tengah Rd Choa Chu Kang Rd	5	Lam San Flyover – 40 2D	5	Sungei Tengah Rd Choa Chu Kang Rd	
		–	Tengah Flyover – 60 1B	7	PIE (Changi Airport) Corporation Rd	
	From PIE (Tengah)	Exit No.	Flyover/ Map & Grid	Exit No.	**To PIE (Tengah)**	

BKE

	To Woodlands Checkpoint	Exit No.	Flyover/ Map & Grid	Exit No.	From Woodlands Checkpoint	
FROM BUKIT TIMAH TO WOODLANDS	Woodlands Centre Rd	10B	10 2B	–		**FROM WOODLANDS TO BUKIT TIMAH**
	Woodlands Rd	10A	Woodlands Flyover – 10 2C	–		
	Turf Club Ave Kranji Rd SLE (TPE, CTE)	8	Woodlands South Flyover 23 2A	9	SLE (TPE, CTE) Turf Club Ave Kranji	
	Mandai Rd	7	Mandai Flyover – 23 2C	7	Mandai Rd	
	KJE	5	Gali Batu Flyover – 42 2B	5	KJE	
	Bukit Panjang Rd	3	Zhenghua Flyover – 43 1D	3	Bukit Panjang Rd	
	Dairy Farm Rd	2	Dairy Farm Flyover – 64 1B	2	Dairy Farm Rd	
					ERP – 54	
		–	Chantek Flyover – 64 2D	1	PIE (Changi Airport)	
	From PIE (Bukit Timah)	Exit No.	Flyover/ Map & Grid	Exit No.	**To PIE (Bukit Timah)**	

KPE

	To TPE	Exit No.	Map & Grid	Exit No.	From TPE	
FROM ECP (TG RHU) TO TPE		–	50 1D	10	Exit to Buangkok Dr / Tampines Rd	**FROM TPE TO ECP (TG RHU)**
	Exit to Buangkok Drive	9B	70 2B	–		
	Exit to Tampines Rd	9A	70 2B	9A	Exit to Tampines Rd	
	Exit to Bartley Rd East	6	91 2A	6	Exit to Bartley Rd East	
	Exit to Upper Paya Lebar Rd	5	91 1B	–		
			112 1A	3	Exit to PIE Tuas	
			112 1A	2C	Exit to Sims Avenue	
	ERP – 82					
	Exit to PIE, Changi Airport & Tuas	2B	112 1A	–		
			112 1B	2A	Exit to Nicoll Highway	
			112 1D	1	ECP - Exit to Changi Airport	
					ERP – 81	
			112 1D	1	ECP - Exit to City	
					ERP – 80	
	From ECP (Tg Rhu)	Exit No.	Map & Grid	Exit No.	**To ECP (Tg Rhu)**	

Note: Information on other ERP Gantries sited at KPE Exits was not available as at print date.

PIE

To ECP & Changi Airport	Exit No.	Flyover/ Map & Grid	Exit No.	From ECP & Changi Airport
	–	95 1B	1	Changi South Ave 3 Changi Business Park Singapore Expo
Upp Changi Rd North Upp Changi Rd East TPE (SLE) Pasir Ris Town Changi Village	2	Upper Changi Flyover – 73 2D	2	Upper Changi Rd North Upper Changi Rd East TPE (SLE) Pasir Ris Town Changi Village
Tampines St 31 Tampines Ave 2 Tampines New Town	3B	Simei Flyover – 73 2D	3A	Simei Rd Simei New Town Changi General Hospital
Simei Ave Simei New Town Changi General Hospital Singapore Expo	4A	Tampines South Flyover 94 1A		
Tampines Ave 5 Tampines Central Tampines New Town Tampines Polytechnic	4B		4B	Tampines Ave 5 Tampines Central Tampines New Town Tampines Polytechnic
Bedok North Rd Bedok New Town	8A	Bedok North Flyover – 92 2C		
Bedok Reservoir Road Tampines Ave 10 Bedok North Rd	8B			
Jalan Eunos Eunos Link Kaki Bukit Still Rd	9	Eunos Flyover – 91 2D	9	Jalan Eunos Eunos Link Kaki Bukit Still Rd
Paya Lebar Rd Geylang Rd Airport Rd	11	Paya Lebar Flyover – 91 1D	11	Paya Lebar Rd Geylang Rd Airport Rd
Kallang Way Aljunied Rd	13B	90 1D	13A	Kallang Bahru
ERP – 32				**ERP – 32**
	–	90 1D	14A	Bendemeer Rd
	–	Woodsville Flyover – 89 2C	15A	CTE (City)
CTE (Ang Mo Kio) Braddell Rd Upper Serangoon Rd Macpherson Rd Bendemeer Rd	15	Whampoa Flyover – 89 2C	15B	CTE (Ang Mo Kio) Braddell Rd
Toa Payoh Kim Keat Link	16A	Kim Keat Flyover – 89 1D	16	Toa Payoh Kim Keat Link
Thomson Rd Toa Payoh Balestier Rd	17D	Thomson Flyover – 88 2C	17	Balestier Rd Thomson Rd Whitley Rd Upper Thomson Rd
Stevens Rd	19	Mount Pleasant Flyover 87 2D	19	Stevens Rd
ERP – 37				
Lornie Rd MacRitchie Reservoir	20B	Adam Flyover – 87 1C	20A	Adam Rd Farrer Rd
Eng Neo Ave Dunearn Rd	22	Eng Neo Flyover – 86 2B	22	Eng Neo Ave Bukit Timah Rd
BKE (Woodlands)	24	Chantek Flyover – 64 2D	24	BKE (Woodlands)
Upper Bukit Timah Rd	26B	Anak Bukit Flyover – 85 1B	26A	Clementi Rd Bukit Timah Rd Dunearn Rd
Clementi Ave 6 AYE	27	Clementi North Flyover 84 1B	27	Clementi Ave 6 AYE
Toh Tuck Ave Bukit Batok East Ave 3	28	Toh Tuck Flyover – 84 1B	28	Toh Tuck Ave Bukit Batok East Ave 3
Bukit Batok Rd Jurong Town Hall Rd Jurong East	31	Bukit Batok Flyover – 62 1D	31	Bukit Batok Rd Jurong Town Hall Rd Jurong East
	–	61 2D	32	Jurong Canal Drive Jurong East Ave 1 Jurong West Ave 1
Jurong West Ave 2 Jurong Rd Corporation Rd	34	Hong Kah Flyover – 60 2C	34	Jurong West Ave 2 Jurong Rd Corporation Rd
KJE (BKE)	35	Tengah Flyover – 60 1B	35	KJE (BKE)
Jalan Bahar Jurong West Boon Lay Choa Chu Kang	36	Bahar Flyover – 59 2C	36	Jalan Bahar Jurong West Boon Lay Choa Chu Kang
Pioneer Rd North NTU NIE	38	Nanyang Flyover – 59 1D	38	Pioneer Rd North NTU NIE
Pasir Laba Upper Jurong Rd Benoi Rd	40	Pasir Laba Flyover – 79 2B	40	Pasir Laba Upper Jurong Rd Benoi Road
AYE Tuas Checkpoint	41	Tuas Underpass – 79 1D	41	AYE Tuas Checkpoint
From Tuas Road	**Exit No.**	**Flyover/ Map & Grid**	**Exit No.**	**To Tuas Road**

ECP/AYE

To Changi Airport	Exit No.	Flyover/ Map & Grid	Exit No.	From Changi Airport
PIE (Jurong) TPE (SLE)	1	Changi Flyover – 95 2B	1	PIE (Jurong) TPE (SLE)
Changi Coast Road Tanah Merah Coast Rd Tanah Merah Ferry Terminal Changi Village	2A	Tanah Merah Flyover 95 1D	2A	Changi Coast Rd Tanah Merah Coast Rd Tanah Merah Ferry Terminal Changi Village
Xilin Ave Singapore Expo	2B			
	–	116 1B	5	Carpark F3 East Coast Park
Bayshore Rd	6	115 2B	–	
East Coast Road	7A	Laguna Flyover – 115 1B	–	
Bedok South	7B		7B	Bedok South
Siglap Rd	8A	114 2C	–	
Marine Vista	8B			
East Coast Park ECP (City)	10A	Marine Parade Flyover 114 1C	–	
Still Rd Marine Parade	10B		10B	East Coast Park Still Rd Marine Parade
Tanjong Katong Rd	11	Tanjong Katong Flyover 113 1D	–	
East Coast Park Fort Rd Mountbatten Rd	13	Tanjong Rhu Flyover – 112 2D	13	East Coast Park Fort Rd Mountbatten Rd
				ERP – 30
Rochor Rd	15	Benjamin Sheares Bridge 133 2A	15	Rochor Rd
ERP – 53				
	–	133 1C	17A	Marina South
	–	Telok Ayer Flyover – 133 1C	17	Prince Edward Rd
	–	Keppel Viaduct – 132 1D	18	Keppel Rd
ECP is above this row AYE is below this row				
Keppel Rd	2B	Keppel Viaduct – 132 1D	2A	Keppel Rd
CTE	2C	Radin Mas Flyover – 131 2C	–	
Lower Delta Rd	3	Lower Delta Flyover – 131 2C	–	
Alexandra Rd	6	Gillman Flyover – 130 1B	–	
ERP – 36		130 1B	7A	Normanton Park
Portsdown Rd	7B	129 2A	–	
North Buona Vista Rd South Buona Vista Rd NUH Science Park	8	Buona Vista Flyover – 107 2D	8	North Buona Vista Rd South Buona Vista Rd NUH Science Park
Clementi NUS Singapore Polytechnic	9	University Flyover – 106 2C	9	Clementi Rd NUS Singapore Polytechnic
Clementi Ave 2	10B	Clementi Flyover – 106 1B	10A	West Coast Rd Clementi Ave 2
Clementi Ave 6	11	Pandan Flyover – 106 1A	11	Clementi Ave 6 West Coast Way
Jurong Town Hall Rd	13	Teban Flyover – 83 1D	13	Jurong Town Hall Rd
	–	83 1C	14	Penjuru Rd
Yuan Ching Rd	15B	82 1D	–	
	–	Corporation Flyover – 82 1D	15A	Corporation Rd Jurong Port Rd
Boon Lay Jurong Pier Rd Jurong Island Jurong Bird Park Corporation Rd Jurong Port Rd	17	Jurong Hill Flyover – 81 1D	17	Boon Lay Jurong Pier Rd Jurong Island Jurong Bird Park
Pioneer Rd North First Lok Yang Rd	18	Pioneer Flyover – 80 2D	18	Pioneer Rd North Pioneer Rd
Benoi Rd Gul Circle Joo Koon Circle Singapore Discovery Centre	20	Benoi Flyover – 79 2D	20	Benoi Rd Gul Way Joo Koon Circle Singapore Discovery Centre
Tuas Rd PIE	22	Tuas Flyover – 79 1D	22	Tuas Rd PIE Tuas Avenue 2
Tuas West Rd Raffles Country Club	24	Tuas West Underpass – 78 1A	24	Tuas Avenue 8 Tuas West Rd Raffles Country Club
	–	Tuas Checkpoint Viaduct 77 2A	26B	Tuas West Drive Raffles Marina
From Tuas Checkpoint	**Exit No.**	**Flyover/ Map & Grid**	**Exit No.**	**To Tuas Checkpoint**

ROADS		MAP	GRID	ROADS		MAP	GRID
Numerals 1 to 4				☐ Alnwick Road	安尼克路	68	2 B
				☐ ALPS Ave	机场物流园道	54	2 D
☐ 1st Street (Siglap)	第一街(实乞纳)	114	2 B	☐ Ama Keng Road	亚妈宫路	20	1 D
☐ 2nd Street (Siglap)	第二街(实乞纳)	114	2 B	☐ Amber Gardens	安珀花园	113	2 C
☐ 3rd Street (Siglap)	第三街(实乞纳)	114	2 A	☐ Amber Road	安珀路	113	2 C
☐ 4th Street (Siglap)	第四街(实乞纳)	114	2 B	☐ Amoy Street	厦门街	132	2 B
				☐ Ampang Walk	安邦径	86	1 D
A				☐ Anamalai Avenue	亚马来道	86	1 C
☐ Abbotsingh Road	爱博信路	54	1 D	☐ Anchorvale Crescent	安谷弯	49	1 A
☐ Abingdon Road	爱明敦路	74	2 A	☐ Anchorvale Drive	安谷通道	49	1 B
☐ Adam Drive	亚当通道	86	2 B	☐ Anchorvale Lane	安谷巷	48	2 B
☐ Adam Park	亚当园	87	1 C	☐ Anchorvale Link	安谷连路	49	1 A
☐ Adam Road	亚当路	87	1 C	☐ Anchorvale Road	安谷路	48	1 A
☐ Adis Road	爱蒂丝路	110	2 C	☐ Anchorvale Street	安谷街	49	1 A
☐ Admiralty Drive	海军部通道	13	1 A	☐ Anchorvale Walk	安谷径	49	1 A
☐ Admiralty Lane	海军部巷	3	1 C	☐ Anderson Road	安徒生路	109	2 B
☐ Admiralty Link	海军部连路	3	1 D	☐ Andover Road	安多华路	53	2 B
☐ Admiralty Road	海军部路	10	2 B	☐ Andrew Road	安德烈路	88	1 B
☐ Admiralty Road East	海军部东路	3	2 D	☐ Andrews Avenue	安德烈道	4	1 C
☐ Admiralty Road West	海军部西路	3	2 C	☐ Andrews Terrace	安德烈台	4	1 C
(Canberra Road)	(坎拉拉路)			☐ Ang Mo Kio Avenue 1	宏茂桥1道	67	1 A
☐ Admiralty Road West	海军部西路	10	2 A	(Bishan Park)	(碧山公园)		
(Marsiling)	(马西岭)			☐ Ang Mo Kio Avenue 1	宏茂桥1道	68	1 C
☐ Admiralty Road West	海军部西路	2	1 D	(CTE)	(中央快速公路)		
(Senoko)	(圣诺哥)			☐ Ang Mo Kio Avenue 1	宏茂桥1道	66	2 A
☐ Admiralty Street	海军部街	3	1 C	(Upper Thomson)	(汤申路上段)		
☐ Ah Hood Road	亚佛路	88	2 C	☐ Ang Mo Kio Avenue 2	宏茂桥2道	46	1 D
☐ Ah Soo Garden	阿苏花园	69	2 D	☐ Ang Mo Kio Avenue 3	宏茂桥3道	67	1 A
☐ Ah Soo Walk	阿苏径	69	2 D	(AMK Ave 1)	(宏茂桥1道)		
☐ Ahmadiyya Cemetery	阿玛狄亚墳场	59	1 A	☐ Ang Mo Kio Avenue 3	宏茂桥3道	68	1 A
Path 1	第1小径			(CTE)	(中央快速公路)		
☐ Aida Street	爱达街	115	1 A	☐ Ang Mo Kio Avenue 3	宏茂桥3道	69	1 A
☐ Airline Road	航空公司路	54	2 C	(Yio Chu Kang Road)	(杨厝港路)		
☐ Airport Boulevard	机场林荫道	75	1 C	☐ Ang Mo Kio Avenue 4	宏茂桥4道	46	1 C
☐ Airport Cargo Road	机场货运路	54	2 D	☐ Ang Mo Kio Avenue 5	宏茂桥5道	46	1 D
☐ Airport Road	机场路	91	1 B	(AMK Ave 6)	(宏茂桥6道)		
☐ Akyab Road	爱业路	88	2 D	☐ Ang Mo Kio Avenue 5	宏茂桥5道	48	1 D
☐ Albert Street	亚巴街	111	1 C	(Buangkok Green)	(万国埔)		
☐ Alexandra Lane	亚历山大巷	130	1 C	☐ Ang Mo Kio Avenue 5	宏茂桥5道	47	1 D
☐ Alexandra Road	亚历山大路	130	2 A	(CTE)	(中央快速公路)		
(Pasir Panjang)	(巴西班让)			☐ Ang Mo Kio Avenue 6	宏茂桥6道	67	2 A
☐ Alexandra Road	亚历山大路	131	1 A	(AMK Ave 1)	(宏茂桥1道)		
(River Valley)	(里巴巴利)			☐ Ang Mo Kio Avenue 6	宏茂桥6道	46	2 D
☐ Alexandra Terrace	亚历山大台	130	1 C	(Yio Chu Kang Road)	(杨厝港路)		
☐ Aliwal Street	阿里哇街	111	2 C	☐ Ang Mo Kio Avenue 8	宏茂桥8道	46	2 D
☐ Aljunied Avenue 1	阿裕尼1道	90	2 D	☐ Ang Mo Kio Avenue 9	宏茂桥9道	46	1 C
☐ Aljunied Avenue 2	阿裕尼2道	90	2 D	☐ Ang Mo Kio Avenue 10	宏茂桥10道	68	1 A
☐ Aljunied Avenue 3	阿裕尼3道	91	2 D	☐ Ang Mo Kio Avenue 12	宏茂桥12道	68	2 A
☐ Aljunied Avenue 4	阿裕尼4道	91	1 D	☐ Ang Mo Kio Central 1	宏茂桥中1路	67	2 A
☐ Aljunied Avenue 5	阿裕尼5道	91	1 D	☐ Ang Mo Kio Central 2	宏茂桥中2路	46	2 D
☐ Aljunied Crescent	阿裕尼弯	112	2 A	☐ Ang Mo Kio Central 3	宏茂桥中3路	46	2 D
☐ Aljunied Road	阿裕尼路	90	2 C	☐ Ang Mo Kio Ind Park 1	宏茂桥第1工业区	68	1 B
☐ Alkaff Avenue	阿卡夫道	90	1 C	☐ Ang Mo Kio Ind Park 2	宏茂桥第2工业区	47	2 D
☐ Allamanda Grove	阿拉曼达林	85	1 C	☐ Ang Mo Kio Ind Park 2A	宏茂桥第2A工业区	47	2 D
☐ Allanbrooke Road	爱兰布鲁路	142	2 C	☐ Ang Mo Kio Ind Park 3	宏茂桥第3工业区	46	2 B
☐ Allanbrooke Road East	爱兰布鲁东路	143	1 D	☐ Ang Mo Kio Street 11	宏茂桥11街	67	1 A
☐ Allenby Road	爱伦比路	111	1 B	☐ Ang Mo Kio Street 12	宏茂桥12街	67	1 A
☐ Almond Avenue	杏仁道	63	2 A	☐ Ang Mo Kio Street 13	宏茂桥13街	46	1 D
☐ Almond Crescent	杏仁弯	63	2 A	☐ Ang Mo Kio Street 21	宏茂桥21街	67	1 A
☐ Almond Street	杏仁街	63	2 A	☐ Ang Mo Kio Street 22	宏茂桥22街	67	1 A
				☐ Ang Mo Kio Street 23	宏茂桥23街	67	1 A

ROADS		MAP	GRID
☐ Ang Mo Kio Street 24	宏茂桥24街	67	2 A
☐ Ang Mo Kio Street 31	宏茂桥31街	67	2 A
☐ Ang Mo Kio Street 32	宏茂桥32街	67	2 B
☐ Ang Mo Kio Street 41	宏茂桥41街	68	1 B
☐ Ang Mo Kio Street 42	宏茂桥42街	68	1 A
☐ Ang Mo Kio Street 43	宏茂桥43街	68	1 A
☐ Ang Mo Kio Street 44	宏茂桥44街	68	1 B
☐ Ang Mo Kio Street 51	宏茂桥51街	68	1 A
☐ Ang Mo Kio Street 52	宏茂桥52街	68	1 A
☐ Ang Mo Kio Street 53	宏茂桥53街	47	1 D
☐ Ang Mo Kio Street 54	宏茂桥54街	68	1 A
☐ Ang Mo Kio Street 61	宏茂桥61街	46	1 C
☐ Ang Mo Kio Street 62	宏茂桥62街	46	2 B
☐ Ang Mo Kio Street 63	宏茂桥63街	46	2 B
☐ Ang Mo Kio Street 64	宏茂桥64街	46	2 B
☐ Ang Mo Kio Street 65	宏茂桥65街	46	2 B
☐ Ang Mo Kio Street 66	宏茂桥66街	46	2 B
☐ Angklong Lane	安克弄巷	66	2 B
☐ Angora Close	安哥拉弄	130	2 A
☐ Angsana Avenue	安莎娜道	90	1 C
■ Angsana Drive	安莎娜道道	137A	2 D
☐ Angsana Road	安莎娜路	137A	1 B
☐ Angulia Park	安哥烈园	109	1 C
☐ Angus Street	安格士街	132	2 A
☐ Ann Siang Hill	安祥山	132	2 C
☐ Ann Siang Road	安祥路	132	2 C
☐ Anson Road	安顺路	132	2 D
☐ Anthony Road	安东尼路	110	1 B
☐ Arab Street	亚拉街	111	2 C
☐ Arcadia Road	雅凯路	87	1 C
☐ Architecture Drive	建筑通道	106	2 D
☐ Ardmore Park	阿摩园	109	2 B
☐ Armenian Street	亚米尼亚街	132	2 A
☐ Arnasalam Chetty Rd	安娜莎南齐智路	132	1 A
☐ Aroozoo Avenue	阿鲁舒道	69	2 C
☐ Aroozoo Lane	阿鲁舒巷	69	2 C
☐ Arthur Road	阿德路	112	2 C
■ Artillery Avenue		142	2 C
☐ Arts Link	文学连路	106	2 D
☐ Arumugam Road	阿鲁慕甘路	91	1 D
☐ Ascot Rise	爱士阁坡	85	2 B
☐ Ash Grove	白杨林	86	1 C
☐ Ashwood Grove	白杨木林	11	1 D
☐ Asimont Lane	爱西蒙巷	110	1 A
☐ Astrid Hill	爱士特山	85	2 D
☐ Attap Valley Road	亚答谷路	2	1 D
☐ Auckland Road	奥克兰路	3	2 C
☐ Auckland Road East	奥克兰路东	3	2 C
☐ Auckland Road West	奥克兰路西	3	2 C
☐ Ava Road	爱茂路	89	1 D
☐ Ave A Sakra (Jurong Isl)	沙克拉A道 (裕廊岛)	139	1 B
☐ Aviation Drive	航空通道	54	1 B
☐ Aviation Pk Road	航空园路	76	1 A
☐ Avon Road	爱文路	113	1 C
☐ Ayer Chawan Place	亚逸茶碗坊	125	1 C
☐ Ayer Merbau Road	亚逸美宝路	125	2 C
☐ Ayer Rajah Avenue	亚逸拉惹道	107	2 D
☐ Ayer Rajah Crescent	亚逸拉惹弯	107	2 D
■ Ayer Rajah Expressway	亚逸拉惹快速公路	130	1 B
(Alexandra Road)	(亚历山大路)		
■ Ayer Rajah Expressway	亚逸拉惹快速公路	80	1 D
(Benoi Rd to Pioneer Rd)	(贡耐路至先驱路)		
■ Ayer Rajah Expressway	亚逸拉惹快速公路	106	1 A
(Clementi Road)	(金文泰路)		
■ Ayer Rajah Expressway	亚逸拉惹快速公路	82	1 D
(Corporation Road)	(企业路)		
■ Ayer Rajah Expressway	亚逸拉惹快速公路	131	1 C
(Delta Road)	(立达路)		
■ Ayer Rajah Expressway	亚逸拉惹快速公路	107	1 D
(Dover Road)	(杜佛路)		
☐ Ayer Rajah Expressway	亚逸拉惹快速公路	132	2 D
(ECP)	(东海岸公园大道)		
☐ Ayer Rajah Expressway	亚逸拉惹快速公路	132	1 D
(Keppel Road)	(发巴路)		
■ Ayer Rajah Expressway	亚逸拉惹快速公路	83	1 D
(Penjuru Road)	(本茶鲁路)		
☐ Ayer Rajah Expressway	亚逸拉惹快速公路	79	1 D
(PIE to Benoi Road)	(泛岛快速公路至贡耐路)		
■ Ayer Rajah Expressway	亚逸拉惹快速公路	81	1 D
(Pioneer Rd to Corp Rd)	(从先驱路至企业路)		
☐ Ayer Rajah Expressway	亚逸拉惹快速公路	129	2 A
(South Buona Vista Rd)	(南波那维斯达路)		
☐ Ayer Rajah Expressway	亚逸拉惹快速公路	78	1 A
(Tuas West Road)	(大士西路)		

B			
☐ Baboo Lane	巴布路	111	1 B
☐ Baghdad Street	巴格达街	111	2 C
☐ Bah Soon Pah Road	巴顺芭路	26	2 A
☐ Bahtera Track	巴特拉乡道	7	1 C
☐ Bain Street	培英街	111	1 D
☐ Baker Street	贝克街	29	1 C
☐ Balam Road	巴南路	90	2 C
☐ Balestier Road	马里士他路	88	2 D
☐ Bali Lane	巴厘巷	111	2 C
☐ Balmeg Hill	芭美山	129	1 B
☐ Balmoral Crescent	巴慕乐弯	110	1 A
☐ Balmoral Park	巴慕乐园	109	1 A
☐ Balmoral Road	巴慕乐路	110	1 A
☐ Ban San Street	万山街	111	1 C
■ Banda Street	万达街	132	2 C
☐ Bangkit Road	万吉路	42	2 C
☐ Banyan Avenue	巴央道	124	1 D
☐ Banyan Drive	巴央通道	137A	2 B
☐ Banyan Place	巴央坊	137A	2 B
■ Banyan Road	巴央路	137A	2 B
☐ Banyan View	巴央景	138	1 B
☐ Barbary Walk	巴巴里径	130	2 A
☐ Barker Road	巴克路	110	1 A
☐ Bartley Road	巴特礼路	90	1 A
☐ Bartley Road East	巴特礼路东	90	2 A
☐ Bassein Road	百胜路	88	2 D
☐ Bath Road	白士路	25	2 D
☐ Battersea Road	巴德西路	29	1 C
☐ Battery Road	百得利路	133	1 B
☐ Bayfront Avenue	贝弗兰道	133	1 B
■ Bayfront Drive	贝弗兰大道	133	1 B
☐ Bays Water Road	贝士华德路	28	2 C
☐ Bayshore Road	碧湾路	115	2 B
☐ Beach Rd (Bras Basah)	美芝路(勿拉士巴沙路)	133	1 A
☐ Beach Rd(Crawford St)	美芝路(哥罗福街)	111	2 C
☐ Beach View	美芝景	142	1 C

ROADS		MAP	GRID	ROADS		MAP	GRID
Beatty Lane	美智巷	111	2 B	Bencoolen Lane	明古连巷	111	1 D
Beatty Road	美智路	111	1 A	Bencoolen Link	明古连路	111	1 C
Beaulieu Road	柏友里路	4	1 D	Bencoolen Street	明古连街	111	1 C
Bedford Road	培福路	130	1 B	Bendemeer Road	明地迷亚路	89	2 D
Bedok Avenue	勿洛道	116	1 A	Beng Huat Road	明发路	91	1 C
Bedok Central	勿洛中路	93	1 D	Beng Wan Road	明远路	89	2 D
Bedok Close	勿洛弄	94	1 D	Benoi Crescent	贲耐弯	80	1 D
Bedok Garden	勿洛花园	94	1 D	Benoi Lane	贲耐巷	101	2 C
Bedok Industrial Park C	勿洛C工业园	92	1 B	Benoi Place	贲耐坊	101	2 A
Bedok Industrial Park E	勿洛E工业园	93	2 B	Benoi Road	贲耐路	79	2 D
(Blk 3001 to 3010)	(3001至3010座)			Benoi Sector	贲耐段	80	1 D
Bedok Industrial Park E	勿洛E工业园	94	1 B	Beo Crescent	庙弯	131	2 A
(Blk 3011 to 3016)	(3011至3016座)			Berkshire Road	柏莎路	130	1 B
Bedok Junction	勿洛交叉路	116	2 A	Bermuda Road	百慕达路	3	2 C
Bedok Lane	勿洛巷	94	1 C	Bernam Street	柏南街	132	1 C
Bedok North Avenue 1	勿洛北1道	93	1 C	Berrima Road	柏里玛路	87	2 D
Bedok North Avenue 2	勿洛北2道	93	1 C	Berwick Drive	百力通道	68	2 B
Bedok North Avenue 3	勿洛北3道	93	1 B	Bhamo Road	巴摩路	88	2 D
Bedok North Avenue 4	勿洛北4道	93	2 B	Bideford Road	必德福路	110	1 C
Bedok North Drive	勿洛北通道	93	1 D	Biggin Hill Road	美仁山路	53	2 B
Bedok North Int	勿洛北转换站	93	1 D	Bilal Lane	庇老巷	94	1 D
Bedok North Road	勿洛北路	92	2 A	Bin Tong Park	民东园	108	1 A
Bedok North Street 1	勿洛北1街	93	1 D	Binchang Rise	民昌坡	67	2 D
Bedok North Street 2	勿洛北2街	93	2 C	Binchang Walk	民昌径	67	2 D
Bedok North Street 3	勿洛北3街	93	2 C	Binjai Hill	明才山	85	2 A
Bedok North Street 4	勿洛北4街	93	2 C	Binjai Park	明才园	85	2 A
Bedok North Street 5	勿洛北5街	94	1 B	Binjai Rise	明才坡	85	2 A
Bedok Place	勿洛坊	94	1 D	Binjai Walk	明才径	85	2 B
Bedok Reservoir Cres	勿洛蓄水池弯	92	2 B	Biomedical Grove	生物医药林	107	2 C
Bedok Reservoir Road	勿洛蓄水池路	92	1 B	Biopolis Drive	拜奥波利士通道	107	2 C
(Kaki Bukit)	(加基武吉)			Biopolis Link	拜奥波利士连路	107	2 C
Bedok Reservoir Road	勿洛蓄水池路	93	2 A	Biopolis Road	拜奥波利士路	107	2 C
(Tampines Ave 1)	(淡滨尼1道)			Biopolis Street	拜奥波利士街	107	2 C
Bedok Reservoir View	勿洛蓄水池景	93	1 B	Biopolis Way	拜奥波利士大道	107	2 C
Bedok Ria Crescent	勿洛丽雅弯	94	1 D	Birch Road	柏芝路	111	1 B
Bedok Ria Drive	勿洛丽雅通道	94	1 C	Bird Park Drive	飞禽公园通道	81	1 D
Bedok Ria Place	勿洛丽雅坊	94	1 D	Bishan Lane	碧山巷	88	2 A
Bedok Ria Terrace	勿洛丽雅台	94	1 D	Bishan Place	碧山坊	68	1 D
Bedok Ria Walk	勿洛丽雅径	94	1 D	Bishan Road	碧山路	67	2 C
Bedok Rise	勿洛坡	94	1 D	Bishan Street 11	碧山11街	67	2 D
Bedok Road	勿洛路	94	1 C	Bishan Street 12	碧山12街	89	1 A
Bedok South Avenue 1	勿洛南1道	115	1 A	Bishan Street 13	碧山13街	68	1 D
Bedok South Avenue 2	勿洛南2道	93	2 D	Bishan Street 14	碧山14街	67	2 C
Bedok South Avenue 3	勿洛南3道	93	2 D	Bishan Street 21	碧山21街	67	2 D
Bedok South Road	勿洛南路	115	1 A	Bishan Street 22	碧山22街	67	2 C
Bedok Terrace	勿洛台	94	1 D	Bishan Street 23	碧山23街	67	2 C
Bedok Walk	勿洛径	94	1 C	Bishan Street 24	碧山24街	67	2 C
Bee San Avenue	美山道	85	2 B	Bishan Street 25	碧山25街	67	2 B
Beechwood Grove	桦木林	11	1 D	Bishops Place	主教坊	68	1 D
Begonia Crescent	秋海棠弯	47	2 B	Bishopsgate	主教门	109	2 D
Begonia Drive	秋海棠通道	47	2 B	Bishopswalk	主教径	109	2 D
Begonia Lane	秋海棠巷	47	2 C	Blackmore Drive	布朗克摩通道	85	1 B
Begonia Road	秋海棠路	47	2 B	Blair Road	布莱路	132	1 C
Begonia Terrace	秋海棠台	47	2 B	Blandford Drive	布朗福通道	68	2 B
Begonia Walk	秋海棠径	47	2 B	Bloxhome Drive	布乐京通道	68	2 B
Belilios Lane	柏利利奥巷	111	1 B	Bo Seng Avenue	谋盛道	88	1 D
Belilios Road	柏利利奥路	111	1 B	Boat Quay	驳船码头	132	2 A
Belimbing Avenue	百临宾道	90	1 C	Boat Quay Lane	驳船码头巷	132	2 B
Belmont Road	贝蒙路	108	1 A	Bodmin Drive	博明通道	68	2 B
Belvedere Close	贝菲德雅弄	131	1 A	Bond Terrace	蒙台	132	2 A

INDEX • ROADS

ROADS		MAP	GRID	ROADS		MAP	GRID
☐ Bonham Street	蒙咸街	133	1 B	☐ Buangkok Link	万国连路	48	2 C
☐ Boon Keng Road	文庆路	111	2 A	☐ Buangkok View	万国景	48	2 C
☐ Boon Lay Avenue	文礼道	81	2 A	☐ Buckley Road	巴克里路	110	1 A
☐ Boon Lay Drive	文礼通道	81	2 A	☐ Buffalo Road	巴弗罗路	111	1 C
☐ Boon Lay Place	文礼坊	60	2 D	☐ Bugis Street	武吉士街	111	1 D
☐ Boon Lay Way	文礼大道	81	1 B	☐ Bukit Arang Road	武吉阿兰路	69	1 D
(Boon Lay MRT)	(文礼地铁站)			☐ Bukit Ayer Molek	武吉亚逸慕礼	64	2 D
☐ Boon Lay Way	文礼大道	83	1 B	☐ Bukit Batok Avenue 1	武吉巴督1道	62	2 D
(Jurong East)	(裕廊东)			☐ Bukit Batok Central	武吉巴督中路	62	2 D
☐ Boon Lay Way	文礼大道	82	1 A	☐ Bukit Batok Central Lk	武吉巴督中连路	62	2 D
(Jurong Town Hall Rd)	(裕廊镇大会堂路)			☐ Bukit Batok Crescent	武吉巴督弯	84	1 B
☐ Boon Leat Terrace	文烈台	130	1 C	☐ Bukit Batok East Ave 2	武吉巴督东2道	63	1 D
☐ Boon Tat Link	文达连路	132	2 C	☐ Bukit Batok East Ave 3	武吉巴督东3道	84	1 A
☐ Boon Tat Street	文达街	132	2 C	☐ Bukit Batok East Ave 4	武吉巴督东4道	63	1 D
☐ Boon Teck Road	文德路	88	2 D	☐ Bukit Batok East Ave 5	武吉巴督东5道	62	2 C
☐ Boon Tiong Road	文忠路	131	1 C	☐ Bukit Batok East Ave 6	武吉巴督东6道	83	2 A
☐ Borthwick Drive	保威通道	68	2 B	☐ Bukit Batok Ind Park A	武吉巴督工业区	83	2 A
☐ Boscombe Road	慕士康路	113	1 C	☐ Bukit Batok Road	武吉巴督路	62	1 D
☐ Boundary Road	曼德里路	69	1 C	☐ Bukit Batok Street 11	武吉巴督11街	62	1 D
☐ Bournemouth Road	波茂士路	113	1 C	☐ Bukit Batok Street 21	武吉巴督21街	62	2 D
☐ Bowmont Gardens	慕文花园	114	2 A	☐ Bukit Batok Street 22	武吉巴督22街	83	2 A
☐ Braddell Hill	布莱德山	88	2 A	☐ Bukit Batok Street 23	武吉巴督23街	84	1 A
☐ Braddell Road	布莱德路	89	1 A	☐ Bukit Batok Street 24	武吉巴督24街	84	1 A
(CTE)	(中央快速公路)			☐ Bukit Batok Street 25	武吉巴督25街	84	1 A
☐ Braddell Road	布莱德路	88	2 A	☐ Bukit Batok Street 31	武吉巴督31街	62	2 C
(Thomson Road)	(汤申路)			☐ Bukit Batok Street 32	武吉巴督32街	62	2 B
☐ Braemar Drive	白里马通道	68	2 B	☐ Bukit Batok Street 33	武吉巴督33街	62	2 B
☐ Brani Terminal Avenue	布拉尼终站道	142	2 B	☐ Bukit Batok Street 34	武吉巴督34街	62	2 B
☐ Brani Terminal Road P	布拉尼终站P路	142	2 B	☐ Bukit Batok Street 51	武吉巴督51街	62	2 C
☐ Brani Terminal Road Q	布拉尼终站Q路	143	1 A	☐ Bukit Batok Street 52	武吉巴督52街	62	2 C
☐ Brani Terminal Road R	布拉尼终站R路	143	1 B	☐ Bukit Batok West Ave 2	武吉巴督西2道	62	1 B
☐ Brani Terminal Road S	布拉尼终站S路	143	1 B	☐ Bukit Batok West Ave 3	武吉巴督西3道	62	1 D
☐ Brani Terminal Street 8	布拉尼终站8街	142	2 B	☐ Bukit Batok West Ave 4	武吉巴督西4道	62	1 B
☐ Brani Terminal Street 9	布拉尼终站9街	143	1 B	☐ Bukit Batok West Ave 5	武吉巴督西5道	62	2 C
☐ Brani Terminal Street 10	布拉尼终站10街	143	1 B	☐ Bukit Batok West Ave 6	武吉巴督西6道	62	1 D
☐ Brani Way	布拉尼大道	142	2 B	☐ Bukit Batok West Ave 7	武吉巴督西7道	62	1 B
☐ Branksome Road	白兰森路	113	1 C	☐ Bukit Batok West Ave 8	武吉巴督西8道	62	1 D
☐ Bras Basah Road	勿拉士巴沙路	110	2 D	☐ Bukit Chermin Road	武吉慈明路	130	2 D
☐ Brickland Road	碧兰路	40	2 D	☐ Bukit Drive	武吉通道	64	1 D
☐ Bridport Avenue	布里卜道	68	2 A	☐ Bukit Ho Swee Cres	河水山弯	131	2 B
☐ Bright Hill Crescent	光明山弯	67	1 C	☐ Bukit Ho Swee Link	河水山连路	131	2 B
☐ Bright Hill Drive	光明山通道	67	1 B	☐ Bukit Manis Road	武吉玛尼士路	142	2 D
(From Sin Ming Ave)	(从新民道)			☐ Bukit Merah Central	红山中路	131	1 B
☐ Bright Hill Drive	光明山通道	67	1 C	☐ Bukit Merah Lane 1	红山1巷	130	2 B
(From Upp Thomson Rd)	(从汤申路上段)			☐ Bukit Merah Lane 2	红山2巷	130	2 B
☐ Bright Hill Road	光明山路	67	1 B	☐ Bukit Merah Lane 3	红山3巷	130	2 B
☐ Brighton Avenue	布莱顿道	69	1 B	☐ Bukit Merah View	红山景	131	1 B
☐ Brighton Crescent	布莱顿弯	69	1 B	☐ Bukit Mugliston	武吉莫利士顿	48	1 B
☐ Bristol Road	布里斯托路	110	2 B	☐ Bukit Panjang Link	武吉班让连路	63	1 A
☐ Brizay Park	布里赛园	85	2 C	☐ Bukit Panjang Loop	武吉班让环道	63	1 A
☐ Broadrick Close	普洛力弄	113	1 C	☐ Bukit Panjang Ring Rd	武吉班让环路	42	2 B
☐ Broadrick Road	普洛力路	113	1 C	☐ Bukit Panjang Road	武吉班让路	42	1 C
☐ Brockhampton Drive	布洛汉顿通道	68	2 B	☐ Bukit Pasoh Road	武吉巴梳路	132	1 C
☐ Brompton Road	普朗顿路	29	1 D	☐ Bukit Purmei	武吉宝美	131	2 D
☐ Brooke Road	布鲁克路	113	2 C	☐ Bukit Purmei Avenue	武吉宝美道	131	2 D
☐ Brookvale Drive	布鲁克维通道	84	2 C	☐ Bukit Purmei Road	武吉宝美路	131	2 D
☐ Brookvale Walk	布鲁克维径	84	2 C	☐ Bukit Sedap Road	武吉思达路	85	2 D
☐ Buangkok Crescent	万国弯	48	2 C	☐ Bukit Teresa Close	武吉德莉莎弄	131	2 C
☐ Buangkok Drive	万国通道	49	1 C	☐ Bukit Teresa Road	武吉德莉莎路	131	2 D
☐ Buangkok Green	万国埔	48	2 D	☐ Bukit Timah Avenue	武吉知马道	85	1 A

ROADS		MAP	GRID	ROADS		MAP	GRID
■ Bt Timah Expressway (Bukit Panjang)	武吉知马快速公路 (武吉班让)	43	1 D	☐ Camphor Avenue	康富道	90	1 C
■ Bt Timah Expressway (KJE Junction)	武吉知马快速公路 (克兰芝快速公路口)	42	2 A	☐ Canada Road	加拿大路	3	2 D
■ Bt Timah Expressway (PIE Junction)	武吉知马快速公路 (泛岛快速公路口)	64	1 A	☐ Canberra Drive	坎贝拉道	13	2 C
■ Bt Timah Expressway (SLE Junction)	武吉知马快速公路 (实里达快速公路口)	23	2 A	☐ Canberra Lane	坎贝拉巷	13	2 A
■ Bt Timah Expressway (Woodlands)	武吉知马快速公路 (兀兰)	10	2 C	☐ Canberra Link	坎贝拉连路	13	2 A
☐ Bukit Timah Link	武吉知马连路	85	1 A	☐ Canberra Road	坎贝拉路	13	2 A
☐ Bukit Timah Road	武吉知马路	109	2 A	☐ Canberra Square	坎贝拉圈路	13	2 A
☐ Bukit Timah Road (Clementi Road)	武吉知马路 (金文泰路)	85	1 B	☐ Canning Lane	康宁巷	132	2 A
☐ Bukit Timah Road (CTE)	武吉知马路 (中央快速公路)	110	2 B	☐ Canning Rise	康宁坡	132	2 A
☐ Bukit Timah Road (Farrer Road)	武吉知马路 (花拉路)	87	1 D	☐ Canning Walk	康宁径	110	2 D
☐ Bukit Timah Road (Newton Road)	武吉知马路 (纽顿路)	110	1 A	☐ Canterbury Road	坎特布里路	130	1 B
☐ Bukit Timah Road (Sixth Avenue)	武吉知马路 (第6道)	86	1 C	☐ Canton Street	广东街	132	2 A
☐ Bukit Tinggi Road	武吉丁奇路	85	2 A	☐ Cantonment Close	广东民弄	132	1 C
☐ Bukit Tunggal Road	武吉童戈路	88	1 D	☐ Cantonment Link	广东民连路	132	1 D
☐ Bunga Rampai Place	文雅南派坊	90	2 B	☐ Cantonment Road	广东民路	132	1 C
☐ Burghley Drive	柏格礼道通	68	2 C	☐ Capricorn Drive	卡必康通道	66	2 C
☐ Burgundy Crescent	柏雅丽弯	84	1 A	☐ Cardiff Grove	卡迪夫林	68	2 C
☐ Burgundy Drive	柏雅丽通道	84	1 B	☐ Carisbrooke Grove	卡里斯布鲁林	68	2 C
☐ Burgundy Rise	柏雅丽坡	84	1 B	☐ Carlisle Road	卡莱路	110	2 A
☐ Burmah Road	缅甸路	111	1 B	☐ Carlton Avenue	卡尔顿道	114	2 A
☐ Burn Road	贝恩路	90	2 B	☐ Carmen Street	卡门街	114	2 A
☐ Burnfoot Terrace	贝恩弗台	114	2 B	☐ Carmen Terrace	卡门台	114	2 A
☐ Buroh Lane	布罗巷	104	1 A	☐ Carmichael Road	卡迈哥路	89	2 A
☐ Bury Road	貝礼路	130	1 B	☐ Carnation Drive	卡纳申通道	66	2 C
☐ Business Link	商学连路	129	1 A	☐ Carpenter Street	嘉宾街	132	2 A
▥ Bussorah Street	巴梭拉街	111	2 D	☐ Carpmael Road	加美路	113	2 B
☐ Butterfly Avenue	百侠道	90	1 B	☐ Carver Street	嘉华街	111	1 D
☐ Butterworth Lane	巴特卫巷	113	2 D	☐ Caseen Street	卡幸街	132	1 A
☐ Buyong Road	无蓉路	110	2 D	☐ Cashew Crescent	凯秀弯	63	2 A
				☐ Cashew Link	凯秀连路	63	2 A
C				☐ Cashew Road	凯秀路	63	2 A
☐ Cable Road	开宝路	109	2 D	☐ Cashew Terrace	凯秀台	63	2 A
☐ Cactus Crescent	仙人掌弯	47	1 B	☐ Cashin Street	启信街	111	1 D
☐ Cactus Drive	仙人掌通道	47	1 B	☐ Cassia Crescent	加西雅弯	112	2 B
☐ Cactus Road	仙人掌路	47	1 B	☐ Cassia Drive	加西雅通道	86	2 B
▥ Cairnhill Circle	经禧圈	110	1 C	☐ Cassia Link	加西雅连路	112	2 B
☐ Cairnhill Rise	经禧坡	110	1 C	☐ Casuarina Road	佳丝丽娜路	45	2 D
☐ Cairnhill Road (Orchard Road)	经禧路 (乌节路)	110	1 C	☐ Casuarina Walk	佳丝丽娜径	45	2 D
☐ Cairnhill Road (Scotts Road)	经禧路 (史各士路)	110	1 B	☐ Caterick Road	佳德立路	53	2 D
☐ Caldecott Close (formerly Jalan Piala)	加科谷弄 (前称惹兰比亚拉)	87	2 B	☐ Causeway (To Johor Bahru)	长堤 (往柔佛)	10	2 A
☐ Calshot Road	卡索路	74	2 A	☐ Causeway (To Pulau Damar Laut)	长堤 (往达马劳岛)	103	2 B
☐ Camborne Road	肯蒙路	87	1 D	☐ Cavan Road	加文路	111	2 B
☐ Cambridge Road	剑桥路	110	2 B	☐ Cavenagh Road (Bukit Timah Road)	加文纳路 (武吉知马路)	110	2 B
☐ Camden Park	甘登园	87	1 C	☐ Cavenagh Road (Cuppage)	加文纳路 (卡佩芝路)	110	1 C
☐ Camp Road	兵营路	109	1 C	☐ Cavenagh Road (Orchard Road)	加文纳路 (乌节路)	110	1 C
☐ Campbell Lane	甘贝尔巷	111	1 C	☐ Cecil Street	丝丝街	132	2 B
				☐ Cedar Avenue	四德道	90	1 B
				☐ Cedarwood Grove	杉木林	11	1 D
				☐ Cemetery Central St 4	坟场中4街	38	1 D
				☐ Cemetery Central St 6	坟场中6街	38	1 D
				☐ Cemetery Central St 8	坟场中8街	38	1 D
				☐ Cemetery Central St 21	坟场中21街	38	1 D
				☐ Cemetery Central St 25	坟场中25街	38	1 D
				☐ Cemetery North St 1	坟场北1街	38	2 C

ROADS		MAP	GRID
☐ Cemetery South St 10	坟场南10街	59	1 A
☐ Cemetery South St 16	坟场南16街	59	1 A
☐ Cemetery South St 25	坟场南25街	59	1 A
☐ Central Boulevard	中央林荫道	133	1 C
☐ Central Circus	中央圈	132	1 C
☐ Central Exchange Green	中央交通埔	107	2 D
■ Central Expressway (Ang Mo Kio)	中央快速公路 (宏茂桥)	68	2 A
■ Central Expressway (AYE)	中央快速公路 (亚逸拉惹快速公路)	131	2 C
■ Central Expressway (Balestier Road)	中央快速公路 (马里士他路)	111	1 A
■ Central Expressway (Braddell/Balestier Rd)	中央快速公路 (布莱德路/马里士他路)	89	1 A
■ Central Expressway (Chin Swee Road)	中央快速公路 (振瑞路)	132	1 B
■ Central Expressway (Orchard Road)	中央快速公路 (乌节路)	110	2 C
■ Central Expressway (Yio Chu Kang)	中央快速公路 (杨厝港)	47	1 A
☐ Ceylon Lane	锡兰巷	113	2 B
☐ Ceylon Road	锡兰路	113	2 B
☐ Chai Chee Avenue	菜市道	92	2 D
☐ Chai Chee Drive	菜市通道	92	2 D
☐ Chai Chee Lane	菜市巷	92	2 C
☐ Chai Chee Road	菜市路	92	2 D
☐ Chai Chee Street	菜市街	92	2 C
☐ Champions Way	冠军大道	11	2 D
☐ Chancery Hill Road	彰思礼山路	88	1 D
☐ Chancery Hill Walk	彰思礼山径	88	1 D
☐ Chancery Lane	彰思礼巷	110	1 A
☐ Chander Road	彰德路	111	1 B
☐ Chang Charn Road	增产路	130	2 A
☐ Changi Business Park Ave 1	樟宜商业园1道	94	2 B
☐ Changi Business Park Ave 3	樟宜商业园3道	95	1 B
☐ Changi Business Park Central 1	樟宜商业园中1路	95	1 B
☐ Changi Business Park Central 2	樟宜商业园中2路	95	1 A
☐ Changi Business Pk Cres	樟宜商业园弯	95	1 B
☐ Changi Business Park Vista	樟宜商业园景	95	1 B
■ Changi Coast Road (ECP)	樟宜海岸路 (东海岸公园大道)	95	2 D
■ Changi Coast Road (Nicoll Drive)	樟宜海岸路 (尼诂通道)	54	2 C
☐ Changi Coast Walk	樟宜海岸径	95	2 D
☐ Changi East Close	樟宜东弄	118	2 B
☐ Changi East Drive	樟宜东通道	118	2 B
☐ Changi East Road	樟宜东路	118	2 B
☐ Changi East Turn	樟宜东弯路	119	1 A
☐ Changi Ferry Road	樟宜渡轮路	76	1 A
☐ Changi North Crescent	樟宜北弯	74	1 D
☐ Changi North Rise	樟宜北坡	74	1 D
☐ Changi North Street 1	樟宜北1街	74	1 C
☐ Changi North Street 2	樟宜北2街	74	1 D
☐ Changi North Way	樟宜北大道	74	1 D
☐ Changi Road (Still Rd)	樟宜路(史蒂尔路)	113	2 A
☐ Changi Road (Telok Kurau)	樟宜路 (直落古楼)	114	1 A
☐ Changi South Ave 1	樟宜南1道	94	2 C
☐ Changi South Ave 2	樟宜南2道	94	2 B
☐ Changi South Ave 3	樟宜南3道	95	1 B
☐ Changi South Ave 4	樟宜南4道	95	1 B
☐ Changi South Lane	樟宜南巷	94	1 C
☐ Changi South Street 1	樟宜南1街	95	1 B
☐ Changi South Street 2	樟宜南2街	94	2 C
☐ Changi South Street 3	樟宜南3街	95	1 C
☐ Changi Village Road	樟宜村路	54	1 B
☐ Chapel Close	教堂弄	113	2 B
☐ Chapel Road	教堂路	113	2 C
☐ Charlton Lane	爵敦巷	69	2 C
☐ Charlton Road	爵敦路	69	2 C
☐ Chartwell Drive	爵卫通道	68	2 B
☐ Chatsworth Avenue	采士华道	109	1 C
☐ Chatsworth Park	采士华园	109	1 D
☐ Chatsworth Road	采士华街	109	2 D
☐ Chay Yan Street	齐贤街	131	2 B
☐ Cheang Hong Lim Pl	章芳林坊	132	2 B
☐ Cheang Wan Seng Pl	章苑生坊	132	2 B
☐ Chee Hoon Avenue	紫云道	87	1 D
☐ Chempaka Avenue	祯百家道	90	1 C
☐ Chempaka Kuning Link	真巴卡古林连路	94	1 C
☐ Cheng Soon Crescent	正顺弯	84	2 B
☐ Cheng Soon Garden	正顺花园	84	2 B
☐ Cheng Soon Lane	正顺巷	84	2 B
☐ Cheng Yan Place	清渊坊	111	1 D
☐ Cheong Chin Nam Rd	张振南路	84	2 A
☐ Cheow Keng Road	绍经路	113	2 B
☐ Chepstow Close	策士多弄	69	1 B
☐ Cherry Avenue	樱桃道	85	2 C
☐ Chestnut Avenue	策士纳道	63	2 A
☐ Chestnut Close	策士纳弄	63	2 A
☐ Chestnut Crescent	策士纳弯	63	2 A
☐ Chestnut Drive	策士纳通道	63	2 A
☐ Chestnut Gardens	策士纳花园	63	2 A
☐ Chestnut Lane	策士纳巷	63	2 A
☐ Chestnut Terrace	策士纳台	63	2 A
☐ Cheviot Hill	雪菲山	114	2 A
☐ Chia Eng Say Road	谢荣西路	63	2 C
☐ Chia Ping Road	佳品路	81	2 C
☐ Chiap Guan Avenue	捷源道	69	1 B
☐ Chiku Road	赤果路	113	2 B
☐ Chiltern Drive	齐德通道	68	2 D
☐ Chin Bee Avenue	振美道	81	2 B
☐ Chin Bee Crescent	振美弯	81	2 B
☐ Chin Bee Drive	振美通道	81	2 B
☐ Chin Bee Road	振美路	81	2 C
☐ Chin Cheng Avenue	竞争道	113	2 A
☐ Chin Chew Street	珍珠街	132	2 B
☐ Chin Swee Road	振瑞路	132	1 B
☐ Chin Terrace	陈台	74	2 B
☐ China Street	中国街	132	2 B
☐ Chinese Cemy Path 1	华人坟场第1小径	38	2 D
☐ Chinese Cemy Path 2	华人坟场第2小径	59	1 A
☐ Chinese Cemy Path 3	华人坟场第3小径	38	2 D
☐ Chinese Cemy Path 4	华人坟场第4小径	38	1 A

ROADS		MAP	GRID
Chinese Cemy Path 5	华人坟场第5小径	38	1 D
Chinese Cemy Path 6	华人坟场第6小径	38	2 D
Chinese Cemy Path 7	华人坟场第7小径	38	2 D
Chinese Cemy Path 8	华人坟场第8小径	38	2 D
Chinese Cemy Path 9	华人坟场第9小径	38	2 D
Chinese Cemy Path 10	华人坟场第10小径	38	2 D
Chinese Cemy Path 11	华人坟场第11小径	38	2 D
Chinese Cemy Path 12	华人坟场第12小径	38	2 D
Chinese Cemy Path 13	华人坟场第13小径	38	2 C
Chinese Cemy Path 14	华人坟场第14小径	38	2 C
Chinese Cemy Path 15	华人坟场第15小径	38	2 C
Chinese Cemy Path 16	华人坟场第16小径	38	2 C
Chinese Cemy Path 17	华人坟场第17小径	38	1 C
Chinese Cemy Path 18	华人坟场第18小径	38	2 C
Chinese Cemy Path 19	华人坟场第19小径	38	1 C
Chinese Cemy Path 20	华人坟场第20小径	38	2 C
Chinese Cemy Path 21	华人坟场第21小径	38	1 C
Chinese Cemy Path 22	华人坟场第22小径	38	2 C
Chinese Cemy Path 26	华人坟场第26小径	38	2 C
Chinese Cemy Path 28	华人坟场第28小径	38	2 C
Chinese Cemy Path 30	华人坟场第30小径	38	2 C
Chinese Cemy Path 32	华人坟场第32小径	38	2 C
Chinese Cemy Path 34	华人坟场第34小径	38	1 C
Chinese Cemy Path 36	华人坟场第36小径	38	1 C
Chinese Cemy Path 38	华人坟场第38小径	38	1 C
Chinese Garden Road	裕华园路	82	1 B
Chiselhurst Grove	齐斯赫林	68	2 C
Chitty Road	齐智路	111	1 C
Choa Chu Kang Ave 1	蔡厝港1道	41	2 C
Choa Chu Kang Ave 2	蔡厝港2道	41	1 D
Choa Chu Kang Ave 3	蔡厝港3道	41	1 C
Choa Chu Kang Ave 4	蔡厝港4道	41	1 C
Choa Chu Kang Ave 5	蔡厝港5道	41	1 D
Choa Chu Kang Central	蔡厝港中	41	1 C
Choa Chu Kang Cres	蔡厝港弯	22	2 D
Choa Chu Kang Drive	蔡厝港通道	41	2 A
Choa Chu Kang Link	蔡厝港连路	41	2 A
Choa Chu Kang Loop	蔡厝港环道	41	1 B
Choa Chu Kang North 5	蔡厝港北5路	41	1 B
Choa Chu Kang North 6	蔡厝港北6路	41	1 A
Choa Chu Kang North 7	蔡厝港北7路	22	1 D
Choa Chu Kang Road	蔡厝港路	42	1 D
(Woodlands Junction)	(兀兰路口)		
Choa Chu Kang St 51	蔡厝港51街	41	1 B
Choa Chu Kang St 52	蔡厝港52街	41	1 A
Choa Chu Kang St 53	蔡厝港53街	41	2 B
Choa Chu Kang St 54	蔡厝港54街	41	2 A
Choa Chu Kang St 62	蔡厝港62街	41	1 A
Choa Chu Kang St 64	蔡厝港64街	41	2 A
Choa Chu Kang Ter	蔡厝港合	41	1 D
Choa Chu Kang Track 14	蔡厝港第14乡道	40	1 D
Choa Chu Kang Track 33	蔡厝港第33乡道	59	1 A
Choa Chu Kang Walk	蔡厝港径	41	1 C
Choa Chu Kang Way	蔡厝港大道	41	1 A
Chong Kuo Road	忠国路	26	1 D
Choon Guan Street	俊源街	132	2 C
Christian Cemy Path 1	基督教坟场第1小径	38	2 D
Christian Cemy Path 2	基督教坟场第2小径	59	2 A
Christian Cemy Path 3	基督教坟场第3小径	38	2 A
Christian Cemy Path 4	基督教坟场第4小径	59	2 A
Christian Cemy Path 5	基督教坟场第5小径	59	2 A
Christian Cemy Path 6	基督教坟场第6小径	59	2 A
Christian Cemy Path 7	基督教坟场第7小径	59	2 A
Christian Cemy Path 8	基督教坟场第8小径	59	2 A
Christian Cemy Path 9	基督教坟场第9小径	59	2 A
Christian Cemy Path 11	基督教坟场第11小径	59	2 A
Christian Cemy Path 13	基督教坟场第13小径	59	2 A
Christian Cemy Path 15	基督教坟场第15小径	59	2 A
Chu Lin Road	竹林路	63	1 C
Chu Yen Street	竹园街	63	1 C
Chuan Close	泉弄	68	2 D
Chuan Drive	泉通道	68	2 B
Chuan Garden	泉花园	68	2 B
Chuan Hoe Avenue	泉和道	69	1 B
Chuan Link	泉连路	68	2 B
Chuan Place	泉坊	68	2 B
Chuan Terrace	泉台	68	2 B
Chuan View	泉景	68	2 B
Chuan Walk	泉径	68	2 C
Chulia Street	珠烈街	132	2 B
Chun Tin Road	春田路	84	2 A
Chun Tin Terrace	春田台	84	2 A
Church Street	漆街	132	2 B
Chwee Chian Road	推迁路	129	2 C
Chwee Chian View	推迁景	129	2 C
Circuit Link	循环连路	91	1 D
Circuit Road	循环路	90	2 D
Circular Road	沙球劳路	132	2 B
Clacton Road	格莱顿路	113	1 D
Clarence Lane	克连士巷	131	1 A
Clarke Quay	克拉码头	132	2 A
Clarke Street	克拉街	132	2 A
Claymore Drive	克雷摩通道	109	2 B
Claymore Hill	克雷摩山	109	2 C
Claymore Road	克雷摩路	109	2 B
Clemenceau Ave	克里门梭道	132	2 A
Clemenceau Ave	克里门梭北道	110	1 C
North (CTE)	(中央快速公路)		
Clemenceau Ave	克里门梭北道	110	1 B
North (Newton)			
Clementi Avenue 1	金文泰1道	106	2 B
Clementi Avenue 2	金文泰2道	106	2 A
Clementi Avenue 3	金文泰3道	106	1 A
Clementi Avenue 4	金文泰4道	106	1 A
Clementi Avenue 5	金文泰5道	106	1 A
Clementi Avenue 6	金文泰6道	106	1 A
(AYE)	(亚逸拉惹快速公路)		
Clementi Avenue 6	金文泰6道	84	1 C
(PIE)	(泛岛快速公路)		
Clementi Crescent	金文泰弯	84	2 D
Clementi Loop	金文泰环道	84	1 C
Clementi Road	金文泰路	106	2 A
(AYE)	(亚逸拉惹快速公路)		
Clementi Road	金文泰路	85	1 B
(Bukit Timah)	(武吉知马)		
Clementi Service Road	金文泰辅助路	84	1 D
Clementi Street 11	金文泰11街	84	2 D
Clementi Street 12	金文泰12街	84	2 D
Clementi Street 13	金文泰13街	84	2 D
Clementi Street 14	金文泰14街	84	2 D

ROADS		MAP	GRID
Clementi West Street 1	金文泰西1街	106	1 C
Clementi West Street 2	金文泰西2街	106	1 C
Clementi Woods Drive	金文泰林通道	106	2 D
Clifton Vale	克立顿谷	89	2 A
Clive Street	客来富街	111	1 C
Clover Avenue	高华道	67	2 D
Clover Close	高华弄	67	2 D
Clover Crescent	高华弯	67	2 D
Clover Rise	高华坡	67	2 D
Clover Way	高华大道	67	2 D
Club Street	客纳街	132	2 B
Cluny Hill	古鲁尼山	109	1 A
Cluny Park	古鲁尼园	109	1 A
Cluny Park Road	古鲁尼园路	109	1 A
Cluny Road	古鲁尼路	109	1 B
Cochrane Crescent	高琳弯	3	1 C
Colchester Grove	高策士德林	68	2 C
Coldstream Avenue	哥士琳道	114	2 B
Coleman Lane	哥里门巷	132	2 A
Coleman Street	哥里门街	132	2 A
College Green	学院埔	87	1 D
College Road	学院路	132	2 C
Collyer Quay	哥烈码头	133	1 B
Commonwealth Ave	联邦道	108	1 C
Commonwealth Ave West	联邦西道	106	1 A
Commonwealth Close	联邦弄	108	1 C
Commonwealth Cres	联邦弯	108	1 C
Commonwealth Drive	联邦通道	108	1 C
Commonwealth Lane	联邦巷	108	1 C
Commonwealth Link	联邦连路	108	1 C
Compassvale Bow	康埔桦弓形路	49	1 C
Compassvale Cres	康埔桦弯	49	1 A
Compassvale Drive	康埔桦通道	49	1 B
Compassvale Lane	康埔桦巷	49	2 C
Compassvale Link	康埔桦连路	49	1 C
Compassvale Road	康埔桦路	49	1 B
Compassvale Street	康埔桦街	49	1 A
Compassvale Walk	康埔桦径	49	2 B
Coniston Grove	康尼敦林	68	2 C
Connaught Drive	康乐通道	133	1 A
Conway Circle	康卫圈	68	2 B
Conway Grove	康卫林	68	2 C
Cook Street	库街	132	2 C
Cooling Close	古林弄	68	2 C
Corfe Place	高富坊	68	2 C
Cornwall Gardens	康华花园	108	1 A
Cornwall Road	康华路	130	1 B
Coronation Drive	加冕通道	86	2 D
Coronation Road	加冕路	86	2 D
Coronation Road West	加冕西路	86	1 D
Coronation Walk	加冕径	86	2 D
Corporation Drive	企业通道	82	1 B
Corporation Rise	企业坡	81	2 A
Corporation Road (AYE)	企业路 (亚逸拉惹快速公路)	82	1 B
Corporation Road (Jurong West)	企业路 (裕廊西)	60	2 D
Corporation Walk	企业径	82	1 A
Cosford Road	高士福路	74	2 B
Cotswold Close	高士华弄	68	2 D
Cottesmore Road	哥斯摩路	74	2 B
Countryside Grove	乡间林	46	1 B
Countryside Link	乡间路	46	1 B
Countryside Place	乡间坊	46	1 B
Countryside Road	乡间路	46	1 B
Countryside View	乡间景	46	1 B
Countryside Walk	乡间径	46	1 B
Court Road	阁路	68	2 A
Cove Drive	海湾通道	143	2 C
Cove Grove	海湾林	147	1 A
Cove Way	海湾大道	143	2 D
Cowdray Avenue	高德礼道	68	2 A
Cox Terrace	高士台	110	2 D
Craig Road	克力路	132	2 C
Cranborne Road	克兰本路	112	2 C
Crane Road	克琳路	113	2 B
Cranwell Road	克兰卫路	53	2 B
Crawford Lane	哥罗福巷	111	2 C
Crawford Street	哥罗福街	111	2 C
Crescent Lane	蛾眉巷	109	1 D
Crescent Road	蛾眉路	113	1 C
Crichton Close	克莱顿弄	68	2 C
Cross Street	克罗士街	132	2 B
Croucher Road	克劳丝路	89	2 A
Crowhurst Drive	克劳赫斯通道	68	2 B
Cuff Road	加富路	111	1 C
Cumming Street	康民街	132	2 A
Cuppage Road	卡瓒路	110	1 C
Cuscaden Road	卡斯加登路	109	2 C
Cuscaden Walk	卡斯加登径	109	2 C
Cypress Avenue	丝柏波	85	2 C
Cyprus Road	赛普鲁斯路	4	1 C
D			
Da Silva Lane	达斯华巷	69	2 B
Daffodil Drive	水仙通道	66	2 C
Dafne Street	达夫尼街	114	2 A
Dahan Road	达汉路	1	2 D
Dairy Farm Crescent	牛乳场弯	63	2 B
Dairy Farm Road (BKE)	牛乳场路 (武吉知马快速公路)	64	1 B
Dairy Farm Road (Bukit Timah)	牛乳场路 (武吉知马)	63	2 B
Daisy Avenue	丽施道	89	2 A
Daisy Road	丽施路	89	2 A
Dakota Close	达哥打弄	112	2 C
Dakota Crescent	达哥打弯	112	2 C
Dalhousie Lane	达豪施巷	111	1 C
Dalkeith Road	达凯斯路	87	2 D
D'almeida Street	达美打街	133	1 C
Dalvey Estate	大威园	109	1 A
Dalvey Road	大威路	109	1 A
Davidson Road	大卫逊路	90	2 B
Dawson Road	杜生路	130	2 A
De Souza Avenue	狄苏莎道	84	2 A
De Souza Street	狄苏莎街	133	1 B

ROADS		MAP	GRID	ROADS		MAP	GRID
☐ Deal Road	迪尔路	107	1 C	☐ Duke Street	公爵街	28	2 D
☐ Dedap Link	德达连路	47	2 B	☐ Duke's Road	公爵路	86	2 D
☐ Dedap Place	德达坊	47	2 B	☐ Duku Lane	杜果巷	113	2 B
☐ Dedap Road	德达路	47	2 B	☐ Duku Place	杜果坊	113	2 B
☐ Defu Avenue 1	德福1道	70	1 C	☐ Duku Road	杜果路	113	2 B
☐ Defu Avenue 2	德福2道	70	2 B	☐ Dunbar Walk	丹宝径	114	1 B
☐ Defu Lane 1	德福1巷	70	2 B	☐ Dundee Road	丹蒂路	108	2 D
☐ Defu Lane 2	德福2巷	70	2 B	☐ Dunearn Close	杜尼安弄	87	1 D
☐ Defu Lane 3	德福3巷	70	2 C	☐ Dunearn Road	杜尼安路	87	1 D
☐ Defu Lane 4	德福4巷	70	1 C	(Adam Road)	(亚当路)		
☐ Defu Lane 5	德福5巷	70	2 C	☐ Dunearn Road	杜尼安路	85	1 B
☐ Defu Lane 6	德福6巷	70	2 B	(Clementi Road)	(金文泰路)		
☐ Defu Lane 7	德福7巷	70	1 C	☐ Dunearn Road	杜尼安路	86	1 C
☐ Defu Lane 8	德福8巷	70	1 C	(Eng Neo Avenue)	(英娘道)		
☐ Defu Lane 9	德福9巷	70	1 D	☐ Dunearn Road	杜尼安路	110	1 A
☐ Defu Lane 10	德福10巷	70	1 C	(Newton)	(纽顿)		
☐ Defu Lane 11	德福11巷	91	1 A	☐ Dunearn Road	杜尼安路	109	2 A
☐ Defu Lane 12	德福12巷	91	1 A	(Stevens Road)	(史蒂芬路)		
☐ Delhi Road	德里路	3	1 D	☐ Dunkirk Avenue	登克道	87	2 D
☐ Dell Lane	德尔巷	109	1 B	☐ Dunlop Street	南洛街	111	1 C
☐ Delta Avenue	立达道	131	2 A	☐ Dunman Lane	德明巷	113	1 B
☐ Delta Road	立达路	131	2 A	☐ Dunman Road	德明路	113	1 B
☐ Dempsey Road	登布西路	108	2 C	☐ Dunsfold Drive	丹士福通道	89	2 A
☐ Denham Close	登罗弄	85	1 A	☐ Durban Road	德曼路	3	2 D
☐ Denham Road	登罗路	88	1 C	☐ Durham Road	德汉路	111	1 A
☐ Depot Close	德普弄	130	2 B	☐ Duxton Hill	达士敦山	132	2 C
☐ Depot Lane	德普巷	130	2 B	☐ Duxton Road	达士敦路	132	2 C
☐ Depot Road	德普路	130	2 C	☐ Dyson Road	泰顺路	88	1 D
☐ Depot Walk	德普径	131	1 C				
☐ Deptford Road	得福路	3	2 C		**E**		
☐ Derbyshire Road	达比莎路	110	2 A				
☐ Desker Road	德斯加路	111	1 B	☐ Ean Kiam Place	延谦坊	113	2 C
☐ Devonshire Road	德文莎路	110	1 D	☐ East Church Road	东教会路	53	2 C
☐ Dickenson Hill Road	狄更生山路	132	2 C	☐ East Coast Avenue	东海岸道	114	2 B
☐ Dickson Road	狄生路	111	1 C	☐ East Coast Drive	东海岸通道	114	2 B
☐ Dido Street	戴都街	114	2 A	☐ East Coast Pk Service Rd	东海岸公园辅路	115	1 B
☐ Digby Road	狄比路	54	1 C	(Bedok Sth Ave 1)	(勿洛南1道)		
☐ Dinding Place	亭亭坊	23	1 B	☐ East Coast Pk Service Rd	东海岸公园辅路	116	1 B
☐ Din Pang Avenue	定邦道	85	2 B	(PA Campsite)	(人民协会露营地)		
☐ Dix Road	狄斯路	69	1 B	☐ East Coast Pk Service Rd	东海岸公园辅路	113	1 D
☐ Dobbie Rise	多比坡	110	2 D	(Tanjong Katong)	(丹戎加东)		
☐ Dock Road East	船坞东路	3	2 C	☐ East Coast Pk Service Rd	东海岸公园辅路	114	1 D
☐ Dock Road South	船坞南路	3	1 C	(Still Road South)	(史蒂尔南路)		
☐ Dock Road West	船坞西路	3	1 C	☐ East Coast Parkway	东海岸公园大道	132	2 D
☐ Dorset Road	多实路	110	2 B	(AYE)	(亚逸拉惹快速公路)		
☐ Dover Avenue	杜佛道	107	1 B	☐ East Coast Parkway	东海岸公园大道	115	1 B
☐ Dover Close East	杜佛弗东	107	2 C	(Bedok South Ave 1)	(勿洛南1道)		
☐ Dover Crescent	杜佛弯	107	1 B	☐ East Coast Parkway	东海岸公园大道	133	1 C
☐ Dover Drive	杜佛通道	107	1 C	(Marina Bay)	(滨海湾)		
☐ Dover Rise	杜佛坡	107	1 C	☐ East Coast Parkway	东海岸公园大道	116	1 B
☐ Dover Road	杜佛路	106	2 B	(PA Campsite)	(人民协会露营地)		
☐ Draycott Drive	德雷通道	110	1 B	☐ East Coast Parkway	东海岸公园大道	111	2 D
☐ Draycott Park	德雷葛园	109	2 B	(Republic Boulevard)	(共和国林荫道)		
☐ Dryburgh Avenue	德莱堡道	114	2 A	☐ East Coast Parkway	东海岸公园大道	114	1 C
☐ Dublin Road	都柏林路	110	1 D	(Still Road South)	(史蒂尔南路)		
☐ Duchess Avenue	公爵夫人道	86	1 D	☐ East Coast Parkway	东海岸公园大道	113	1 D
☐ Duchess Place	公爵夫人坊	86	1 D	(Tanjong Katong)	(丹戎加东)		
☐ Duchess Road	公爵夫人路	86	2 D	☐ East Coast Parkway	东海岸公园大道	112	1 D
☐ Duchess Walk	公爵夫人径	86	1 D	(Tanjong Rhu)	(丹戎禺)		

INDEX • ROADS

E F

ROADS		MAP	GRID
East Coast Parkway (PIE)	东海岸公园大道 (泛岛快速公路)	95	1 D
East Coast Road (Joo Chiat Road)	东海岸路 (如切路)	113	2 C
East Coast Rd (Siglap)	东海岸路 (实乞纳)	114	1 B
East Coast Terrace	东海岸台	114	2 B
East Lagoon Link	人工湖东连路	133	1 C
East Perimeter Road	东界路	75	2 D
East Sussex Lane	东赛硕斯巷	107	2 A
Eastwood Drive	东林通道	94	2 D
Eastwood Green	东林埔	94	2 D
Eastwood Place	东林坊	94	2 D
Eastwood Road	东林路	94	2 D
Eastwood Terrace	东林台	94	2 D
Eastwood Walk	东林径	94	2 D
Eastwood Way	东林大道	94	2 D
Eaton Place	伊顿坊	69	1 C
Eaton Walk	伊顿径	48	1 B
Eber Road	伊巴路	110	1 D
Eco Garden Way	生态园大道	109	1 A
Eden Grove	伊甸林	90	1 A
Edgedale Plains	埃奇德尔坪	50	1 A
Edgefield Plains	埃奇菲尔坪	31	1 D
Edgefield Walk	埃奇菲径	31	1 D
Edgware Road	爱兹瓦路	29	1 D
Edinburgh Road	爱登堡路	110	2 C
Ee Teow Leng Road	余兆龙路	69	1 C
Elias Green	伊莱雅埔	51	2 D
Elias Road	伊莱雅路	51	2 C
Elias Terrace	伊莱雅台	51	2 D
Elite Park Avenue	谊立园道	114	2 A
Elite Terrace	谊立雅台	114	2 A
Elizabeth Drive	伊丽莎白通道	63	1 B
Ellington Square	艾灵顿广场	67	1 A
Elliot Road	依洛路	115	1 B
Elliot Walk	依洛径	115	1 B
Ellis Road	爱丽斯路	109	2 C
Elm Avenue	依茵道	85	2 C
Emerald Hill Road	翡翠山路	110	1 C
Emerald Link	翡翠连路	110	1 C
Empress Place	皇后坊	133	1 B
Empress Road	皇后路	108	2 A
Eng Hoon Street	英云街	132	1 B
Eng Kong Crescent	永康弯	84	2 B
Eng Kong Drive	永康通道	84	2 B
Eng Kong Garden	永康花园	84	2 B
Eng Kong Lane	永康巷	84	2 B
Eng Kong Place	永康坊	84	2 B
Eng Kong Road	永康路	84	2 B
Eng Kong Terrace	永康台	84	2 B
Eng Neo Avenue	英娘道	86	1 B
Eng Watt Street	永发街	132	1 B
Enggor Street	英我街	132	2 D
Engineering Drive 1	工程通道1	106	2 D
Engineering Drive 2	工程通道2	106	2 D
Engineering Drive 3	工程通道3	106	2 D
Engineering Drive 4	工程通道4	106	2 D
Engku Aman Road	翁姑亚曼路	113	1 A
Enterprise Road	事业路	81	1 B
Ernani Street	厄纳尼街	114	2 A
Erskine Road	厄士金路	132	2 C
Esplanade Drive	海滨公园通道	133	1 A
Essex Road	爱硕斯路	110	2 A
Estate Office Drive	产业处通道	106	2 C
Ettrick Terrace	爱特立台	114	2 B
Eu Chin Street	有进街	132	1 B
Eu Tong Sen Street	余东旋街	132	1 C
Eunos Avenue 3	友诺士3道	91	2 D
Eunos Avenue 4	友诺士4道	91	2 D
Eunos Avenue 5	友诺士5道	113	1 A
Eunos Avenue 5A	友诺士5A道	91	2 D
Eunos Avenue 5B	友诺士5B道	91	1 D
Eunos Avenue 6	友诺士6道	91	1 D
Eunos Avenue 7	友诺士7道	91	1 D
Eunos Avenue 7A	友诺士7A道	91	1 D
Eunos Avenue 8	友诺士8道	91	2 D
Eunos Avenue 8A	友诺士8A道	91	2 D
Eunos Crescent	友诺士弯	91	2 D
Eunos Link	友诺士连路	91	1 B
Eunos Road 1	友诺士1路	91	2 D
Eunos Road 2	友诺士2路	113	2 A
Eunos Road 3	友诺士3路	91	2 D
Eunos Road 4	友诺士4路	91	1 D
Eunos Road 5	友诺士5路	113	1 A
Eunos Road 6	友诺士6路	91	1 D
Eunos Road 7	友诺士7路	91	1 D
Eunos Road 8	友诺士8路	113	1 A
Eunos Terrace	友诺士台	113	2 A
Evans Road	爱文士路	109	1 A
Evelyn Road	伊芙琳路	110	1 A
Evergreen Avenue	常青道	115	1 A
Evergreen Gardens	常青花园	115	1 A
Everitt Road	艾弗烈路	113	2 B
Everitt Road North	艾弗烈北路	113	2 A
Everton Road	艾弗顿路	132	1 C
Ewart Park	友和园	85	1 D
Ewe Boon Road	有文路	109	2 A
Exeter Road	爱斯特路	110	1 D
Expo Drive	博览通道	94	2 B
Expo Link	博览连路	94	2 B

F

Faber Avenue	花柏道	106	1 A
Faber Crescent	花柏弯	106	1 A
Faber Drive	花柏通道	106	1 A
Faber Green	花柏埔	106	1 A
Faber Grove	花柏林	83	2 D
Faber Heights	花柏岭	83	2 D
Faber Park	花柏园	84	1 D
Faber Terrace	花柏台	83	2 D
Faber Walk	花柏径	83	2 D
Faculty Avenue	儒林道	59	1 D
Fairways Drive	美丽道通道	86	1 A
Fairy Point Hill	菲利波山	53	2 B
Fajar Road	法嘉路	42	2 C
Falkland Road	福克兰路	3	2 C
Fan Yoong Road	繁荣路	81	1 C
Farleigh Avenue	华丽路	68	2 B
Farnborough Road	范波洛路	54	1 B

21

ROADS		MAP	GRID
Farrer Court	花拉阁	108	2 A
Farrer Drive	花拉道	108	2 A
Farrer Road	花拉路	108	2 A
Farrer Park Road	花拉园路	111	1 B
Farrer Park Station Rd	花拉园站路	111	1 B
Fernhill Close	苏禧弄	109	2 B
Fernhill Crescent	苏禧弯	109	2 B
Fernhill Road	苏禧路	109	2 B
Fernvale Crescent	苏维尔弯	29	1 D
Fernvale Lane	苏维尔巷	48	1 B
Fernvale Link	苏维尔连路	48	1 B
Fernvale Road	苏维尔路	48	1 B
Fernvale Street	苏维尔街	48	1 A
Fernwood Terrace	苏木台	114	2 B
Fidelio Circus	菲地利奥圈	114	2 A
Fidelio Street	菲地利奥街	114	2 A
Fifth Avenue	第5道	86	1 C
Fifth Lok Yang Road	第5洛阳路	80	1 D
Figaro Gardens	菲格罗园	114	2 A
Figaro Street	菲格罗街	114	2 A
Fiji Road	菲芝路	3	2 C
Finlayson Green	苏礼逊埔	133	1 B
Fir Avenue	福尔道	85	2 C
First Avenue	第1道	86	1 C
First Hospital Avenue	第1医院道	132	1 C
First Lok Yang Road	第1洛阳路	80	2 D
Fisher Street	菲沙街	132	2 A
Fishery Port Road	渔港路	104	1 B
Flanders Square	富兰德广场	111	1 B
Flint Street	富林街	133	1 B
Flora Drive	弗洛拉通道	74	1 B
Flora Road	弗洛拉路	74	1 B
Florence Close	佛罗伦弄	69	2 B
Florence Road	佛罗伦路	69	2 A
Florida Road	富罗里达路	66	2 C
Florissa Park	富罗里莎园	46	1 B
Flower Road	富罗华路	69	2 B
Foch Road	福士路	111	1 B
Folkestone Road	福斯顿路	106	2 B
Foo Kim Lin Road	符建连路	91	2 C
Ford Avenue	福特道	107	2 A
Fort Canning Link	福康宁连路	110	2 D
Fort Canning Road	福康宁路	110	2 D
Fort Road	炮台路	112	2 D
Fourth Avenue	第4道	86	1 C
Fourth Chin Bee Road	第4振美路	81	2 B
Fourth Lok Yang Road	第4洛阳路	80	1 D
Fourth Street Sakra (Jurong Island)	沙克拉第4街 (裕廊岛)	139	1 B
Fowlie Road	法礼路	113	2 C
Francis Thomas Drive	法姆士通道	89	2 C
Frankel Avenue	富兰克道	114	1 A
Frankel Close	富兰克弄	114	1 A
Frankel Drive	富兰克通道	114	1 A
Frankel Place	富兰克坊	114	2 B
Frankel Street	富兰克街	114	1 A
Frankel Terrace	富兰克台	114	1 A
Frankel Walk	富兰克径	114	1 A
Fraser Street	费列later街	111	1 D
French Road	法士西路	111	2 B
Fudu Park	富都园	46	1 B

ROADS		MAP	GRID
Fudu Walk	富都径	46	1 B
Fullerton Road	浮尔顿路	133	1 B
Fullerton Sq	浮尔顿广场	133	1 B
Fulton Avenue	福登道	67	1 B
Fulton Road	福登路	67	1 B
Fusion Link	启汇连路	107	2 D
Fusion Place	启汇坊	107	2 D
Fusion View	启汇景	107	2 D
Fusion Walk	启汇径	107	2 D
Fusionopolis Way	启汇园大道	107	2 D

	G		
Galistan Avenue	格里士坦路	42	1 D
Gallop Circus	格洛圈	108	2 A
Gallop Park	格洛园	108	2 A
Gallop Park Road	格洛园路	108	2 A
Gallop Road	格洛路	108	2 A
Gallop Walk	格洛径	108	2 A
Gambas Avenue (Sembawang)	甘巴士道 (三巴旺)	13	1 B
Gambas Avenue (Woodlands)	甘巴士道 (兀兰)	12	2 A
Gambir Walk	甘必径	90	1 A
Ganges Avenue	恒河道	131	2 C
Gangsa Road	岗沙路	42	2 D
Gardenia Road	加丁尼亚路	66	2 C
Garlick Avenue	加立克道	85	2 C
Gateway Avenue	桥门道	142	2 C
Gemmill Lane	仁美里	132	2 B
Genting Lane	定巷	90	1 C
Genting Link	仁定连路	90	1 C
Genting Road	定路	90	1 C
Gentle Drive	仁德通道	110	1 A
Gentle Road	仁德路	110	1 A
George Street	乔治街	132	2 B
Gerald Crescent	日乐弯	48	1 B
Gerald Drive	日乐通道	48	1 B
Gerald Park	日乐园	48	1 B
Gerald Terrace	日乐台	48	1 B
Geylang Bahru (Bendemeer)	芽笼巴鲁 (明地迷亚)	90	1 D
Geylang Bahru (Kallang Bahru)	芽笼巴鲁 (加冷巴鲁)	112	1 A
Geylang Bahru Lane	芽笼巴鲁巷	90	1 D
Geylang Bahru Terrace	芽笼巴鲁台	112	1 A
Geylang Drive	芽笼巴通道	112	1 B
Geylang East Avenue 1	芽笼东1道	112	2 A
Geylang East Avenue 2	芽笼东2道	112	2 A
Geylang East Avenue 3	芽笼东3道	113	1 A
Geylang East Central	芽笼东中路	112	2 A
Geylang Road	芽笼路	112	1 A
Geylang Serai	芽笼士乃	113	1 A
Geylang Square	芽笼广场	112	1 A
Ghim Moh Link	锦茂连路	107	1 B
Ghim Moh Road	锦茂路	107	2 B
Gibraltar Crescent	直布罗陀弯	4	1 D
Gillman Heights	吉门岭	130	2 B
Gilstead Road	吉士德路	110	1 A
Gladiola Drive	格地拉通道	66	2 C
Glasgow Road	格拉士哥路	69	1 B
Gloucester Road	格罗士特路	111	1 B

ROADS		MAP	GRID	ROADS		MAP	GRID
☐ Golden Drive	金岭通道	68	2 C	☐ Guillemard Lane	基里玛巷	112	2 B
☐ Golden Rise	金岭坡	68	2 C	☐ Guillemard Road	基里玛路	112	2 B
☐ Golden Walk	金岭径	68	2 C	☐ Gul Avenue	卡尔道	101	2 A
☐ Goldhill Avenue	金岭道	110	1 A	☐ Gul Circle	卡尔圈	79	1 D
☐ Goldhill Drive	金岭通道	88	1 D	☐ Gul Crescent	卡尔弯	100	2 A
☐ Goldhill Place	金岭坊	88	1 D	☐ Gul Drive	卡尔通道	101	1 A
☐ Goldhill Plaza	金岭广场	110	2 A	☐ Gul Lane	卡尔巷	100	2 A
☐ Goldhill Rise	金岭坡	110	1 A	☐ Gul Link	卡尔连路	100	2 A
☐ Goldhill View	金岭景	110	1 A	☐ Gul Road	卡尔路	101	1 C
☐ Gombak Drive	甘柏通道	63	1 A	☐ Gul Street 1	卡尔1街	101	1 A
☐ Gombak Rise	甘柏坡	63	1 A	☐ Gul Street 2	卡尔2街	101	1 A
☐ Goodlink Park	月岭园	13	2 D	☐ Gul Street 3	卡尔3街	101	1 A
☐ Goodman Road	月眠路	112	2 C	☐ Gul Street 4	卡尔4街	101	1 A
☐ Goodwood Hill	良木山	110	1 B	☐ Gul Street 5	卡尔5街	101	1 A
☐ Gopeng Street	高平街	132	2 C	☐ Gul Way	卡尔大道	79	1 D
☐ Gordon Road	戈登路	74	2 A	☐ Guok Avenue	郭氏道	128	2 C
☐ Gosport Road	哥士卜路	53	2 B	☐ Gymkhana Avenue	因干纳道	87	2 C
☐ Grace Park	玉丽园	68	2 C				
☐ Grace Walk	玉丽径	68	2 C	**H**			
☐ Graham White Drive	格汉怀德通道	89	2 C	☐ Hacienda Grove	哈生达林	115	1 B
☐ Grange Garden	格兰芝花园	109	2 C	☐ Hai Sing Crescent	海星弯	70	1 B
☐ Grange Road	格兰芝道	110	1 C	☐ Hai Sing Road	海星路	70	1 B
(Orchard Road)	(乌节路)			☐ Haig Avenue	海格道	113	2 B
☐ Grange Road	格兰芝路	109	2 C	☐ Haig Lane	海格巷	113	2 B
(Paterson Hill)	(巴德申山)			☐ Haig Road	海格路	113	1 B
☐ Gray Lane	格烈巷	113	1 B	☐ Haigsville Drive	海格威通道	113	1 B
☐ Green Lane	格林巷	113	1 B	☐ Haji Lane	哈芝巷	111	1 C
☐ Greenbank Park	青岸园	64	2 D	☐ Halifax Road	赫利法斯路	110	2 B
☐ Greendale Avenue	青谷道	86	2 C	☐ Halton Road	贺敦路	53	2 B
☐ Greendale Rise	青谷坡	86	2 C	☐ Hamilton Place	翰密顿坊	28	2 C
☐ Greenfield Drive	格林菲通道	114	1 B	☐ Hamilton Road	翰密顿路	111	2 B
☐ Greenleaf Avenue	绿叶道	85	2 D	☐ Hampshire Road	翰莎路	110	2 B
☐ Greenleaf Drive	绿叶通道	85	2 D	☐ Hampstead Gardens	翰士德花园	29	1 C
☐ Greenleaf Grove	绿叶林	85	2 D	☐ Handy Road	汉地路	110	2 D
☐ Greenleaf Lane	绿叶巷	85	2 D	☐ Happy Avenue Central	安乐道中	90	2 C
☐ Greenleaf Place	绿叶坊	85	2 D	☐ Happy Avenue East	安乐道东	90	2 C
☐ Greenleaf Rise	绿叶坡	85	2 D	☐ Happy Avenue North	安乐道北	90	2 C
☐ Greenleaf Road	绿叶路	85	2 D	☐ Happy Avenue West	安乐道西	90	2 C
☐ Greenleaf View	绿叶景	85	2 D	☐ Harbour Drive	海港通道	128	2 A
☐ Greenleaf Walk	绿叶径	85	1 D	☐ Harbour Lane	海港巷	128	2 B
☐ Greenmead Avenue	青美道	86	2 B	☐ Harbour Link	海港连路	128	2 B
☐ Greenpark Avenue	青园道	86	2 B	☐ HarbourFront Ave	港湾道	142	1 A
☐ Greenridge Crescent	翠绿岗弯	84	1 B	☐ HarbourFront Place	港湾坊	142	1 A
☐ Greenview Crescent	青景弯	86	2 B	☐ HarbourFront Walk	港湾径	142	1 A
☐ Greenwood Avenue	青木道	86	2 B	☐ Harding Lane	哈丁巷	109	1 C
☐ Greenwood Crescent	青木弯	86	2 B	☐ Harding Road	哈丁路	109	1 C
☐ Greenwood Grove	青木林	86	2 B	☐ Harlyn Road	哈林路	87	2 D
☐ Greenwood Lane	青木巷	86	2 B	☐ Harper Road	哈波路	90	2 B
☐ Greenwood Link	青木连路	86	2 B	☐ Harrison Road	哈里逊路	90	2 B
☐ Greenwood Place	青木坊	86	2 C	☐ Hartley Grove	哈特礼林	114	1 A
☐ Greenwood Terrace	青木台	86	2 B	☐ Harvey Avenue	哈威道	94	1 B
☐ Greenwood Walk	青木径	86	2 B	☐ Harvey Close	哈威弄	94	1 A
☐ Grove Avenue	小林道	107	1 B	☐ Harvey Crescent	哈威弯	94	1 A
☐ Grove Crescent	小林弯	107	1 A	☐ Harvey Road	哈威路	90	2 B
☐ Grove Drive	小林通道	107	1 A	☐ Hastings Road	赫士汀斯路	111	1 C
☐ Grove Lane	小林巷	107	1 A	☐ Havelock Link	合乐连路	132	1 A
☐ Guan Chuan Street	源全街	132	1 B	☐ Havelock Road	合乐路	131	2 A
☐ Guan Soon Avenue	源顺道	94	1 B	(Outram Road)	(欧南路)		
☐ Guards Avenue	守卫道	116	1 A	☐ Havelock Road	合乐路	132	2 B
☐ Guillemard Crescent	基里玛弯	112	2 B	(Upper Cross Street)	(克罗士街上段)		

ROADS		MAP	GRID	ROADS		MAP	GRID
☐ Havelock Square	合乐广场	132	2 B	☐ Holland Rise	荷兰坡	107	2 B
☐ Hawkinge Road	贺肯芝路	54	1 C	■ Holland Road	荷兰路	108	2 B
☐ Hay Market	赫马克	28	2 C	(Farrer Road)	(花拉路)		
☐ Hazel Park Terrace	嘉林台	63	1 A	☐ Holland Road	荷兰路	107	2 A
☐ Hemmant Road	亨门路	113	1 B	(Sixth Avenue)	(第6道)		
☐ Hemsley Avenue	亨士利道	68	2 A	■ Holland Road North	荷兰北路	85	1 C
☐ Henderson Crescent	亨德申弯	131	1 A	■ Holland Road South	荷兰南路	85	1 C
☐ Henderson Road	亨德申路	131	1 B	■ Holland Road West	荷兰西路	85	1 C
(Alexandra Road)	(亚历山大路)			☐ Holland Walk	荷兰径	85	2 C
☐ Henderson Road	亨德申路	130	2 D	☐ Holt Road	贺德路	109	2 D
(Telok Blangah Drive)	(直落布兰雅通道)			☐ Hon Sui Sen Drive	韩瑞生通道	129	1 A
☐ Hendon Road	亨敦路	53	2 B	☐ Hong Lee Place	丰利坊	69	1 C
☐ Hendry Close	亨德利弄	69	2 C	☐ Hong San Terrace	丰山台	41	2 D
☐ Heng Mui Keng Terrace	王美敬台	128	2 A	☐ Hong San Walk	丰山径	41	2 D
☐ Hertford Road	赫褔路	110	2 B	☐ Hongkong Street	香港街	132	2 B
☐ High Street	谐街	132	2 A	☐ Hooper Road	胡柏路	110	2 B
☐ Highgate Crescent	高门弯	84	1 A	☐ Hoot Kiam Road	佛谦路	109	2 D
☐ Highgate Walk	高门径	84	2 A	☐ Hornchurch Road	丰泽路	54	1 C
☐ Highland Close	高原弄	69	2 C	☐ Horne Road	贺恩路	111	2 B
☐ Highland Road	高原路	69	1 C	☐ Hospital Drive	医院通道	132	1 C
☐ Highland Terrace	高原台	69	2 C	☐ Hougang Avenue 1	后港1道	70	1 C
☐ Highland Walk	高原径	69	2 C	☐ Hougang Avenue 2	后港2道	69	2 A
■ Hill Street	禧街	132	2 A	☐ Hougang Avenue 3	后港3道	70	1 B
☐ Hillcrest Road	翠林路	86	2 B	☐ Hougang Avenue 4	后港4道	70	1 A
☐ Hillside Drive	山傍通道	69	1 B	☐ Hougang Avenue 5	后港5道	70	1 A
☐ Hillside Terrace	山傍台	69	1 C	☐ Hougang Avenue 6	后港6道	49	1 D
☐ Hillview Avenue	山景道	63	1 B	☐ Hougang Avenue 7	后港7道	70	1 B
☐ Hillview Crescent	山景弯	63	1 C	☐ Hougang Avenue 8	后港8道	69	2 A
☐ Hillview Drive	山景通道	63	1 C	☐ Hougang Avenue 9	后港9道	48	2 D
☐ Hillview Link	山景连路	63	1 A	☐ Hougang Avenue 10	后港10道	70	1 A
☐ Hillview Road	山景路	63	1 B	☐ Hougang Central	后港中路	70	1 A
☐ Hillview Terrace	山景台	63	1 C	☐ Hougang Street 11	后港11街	69	2 D
☐ Hillview Way	山景大道	63	1 C	☐ Hougang Street 21	后港21街	69	2 C
☐ Hindhede Drive	海希德通道	64	1 D	☐ Hougang Street 22	后港22街	70	1 C
☐ Hindhede Place	海希德坊	64	1 D	☐ Hougang Street 31	后港31街	70	1 B
☐ Hindhede Road	海希德路	64	1 D	☐ Hougang Street 51	后港51街	48	2 D
☐ Hindhede Walk	海希德径	63	2 D	☐ Hougang Street 52	后港52街	49	1 D
☐ Hindoo Road	兴都路	111	1 B	☐ Hougang Street 61	后港61街	48	2 D
☐ Hindu Cemetery Path 1	兴都坟场第1小径	59	1 A	☐ Hougang Street 91	后港91街	48	2 D
☐ Hindu Cemetery Path 2	兴都坟场第2小径	59	1 A	☐ Hougang Street 92	后港92街	48	2 D
☐ Ho Ching Road	河景路	82	1 B	☐ Hougang Street 93	后港93街	48	2 D
☐ Hobart Road	贺拔路	3	2 C	☐ How Sun Avenue	禾山道	90	2 A
☐ Hoe Chiang Road	和昌路	132	2 D	☐ How Sun Close	禾山弄	90	2 A
☐ Hokkien Street	福建街	132	2 B	☐ How Sun Drive	禾山通道	90	2 A
☐ Holland Avenue	荷兰道	108	1 B	☐ How Sun Road	禾山路	90	2 A
☐ Holland Close	荷兰弄	108	1 B	☐ How Sun Walk	禾山径	90	1 A
■ Holland Drive	荷兰通道	107	2 B	☐ Howard Road	豪华路	90	2 B
☐ Holland Green	荷兰埔	85	2 D	☐ Hoy Fatt Road	开发路	130	2 A
☐ Holland Grove Avenue	荷兰林道	107	1 A	☐ Hu Ching Road	湖景路	82	1 C
■ Holland Grove Drive	荷兰林通道	107	1 A	☐ Hua Guan Avenue	华源道	85	1 A
☐ Holland Grove Lane	荷兰林巷	107	1 A	☐ Hua Guan Crescent	华源弯	85	2 B
☐ Holland Grove Road	荷兰林路	107	1 A	☐ Huddington Avenue	哈定道	68	2 A
☐ Holland Grove Terrace	荷兰林台	107	1 A	☐ Hullet Road	合力路	110	1 C
☐ Holland Grove View	荷兰林景	107	1 B	☐ Hume Avenue	谦道	63	1 C
☐ Holland Grove Walk	荷兰林径	107	1 A	☐ Hun Yeang Road	汉阳路	71	2 A
☐ Holland Heights	荷兰峰	108	1 B	☐ Hyde Park Gate	海德公园门	28	2 C
☐ Holland Hill	荷兰山	108	1 B	☐ Hyderabad Road	海特拉巴路	130	1 C
☐ Holland Link	荷兰连路	85	2 C	■ Hylam Street	海南街	111	1 D
☐ Holland Park	荷兰园	108	2 B	☐ Hythe Road	海士路	68	2 A
☐ Holland Plain	荷兰坪	85	2 C				

ROADS		MAP	GRID
I			
Imbiah Hill Road	音庇亚山路	142	1 B
Imbiah Road	音庇亚路	142	1 C
Imbiah Walk	音庇亚径	141	2 B
Indus Road	印度士路	131	2 A
Inggu Road	因古路	4	1 C
Inner Temple	因纳登柏	28	2 C
Institution Hill	因士迪申山	110	1 D
International Business Pk	国际商业园	83	2 C
International Road (Boon Lay)	国际路 (文礼)	81	1 C
International Road (Corporation Road)	国际路 (企业路)	82	1 C
International Road (Pioneer Road)	国际路 (先驱路)	80	1 C
Ipoh Lane	怡保巷	113	1 B
Iqbal Avenue	益巴尔道	45	2 C
Irau Ave	希劳道	4	1 D
Irau Drive	希劳通道	4	1 C
Irrawaddy Road	依拉瓦底路	88	2 D
Irving Place	尔文坊	90	2 B
Irving Road	尔文路	90	2 B
Irwell Bank Road	尔卫民路	109	2 D
Island Club Road	岛屿俱乐部路	66	2 B
Island Gardens Walk	岛屿花园径	66	2 B

ROADS		MAP	GRID
J			
Jacaranda Road	雅加兰达路	45	2 D
Jago Close	雅哥弄	114	1 C
Jalan Adat	惹兰阿达	87	1 C
Jalan Afifi (Benoi Road)	惹兰亚菲菲 (贡耐路)	91	1 D
Jalan Ahmad Ibrahim (Benoi Road)	惹兰阿末依布拉欣 (贡耐路)	79	1 D
Jalan Ahmad Ibrahim (Bird Park)	惹兰阿末依布拉欣 (飞禽公园)	81	1 D
Jalan Ahmad Ibrahim (Corporation Road)	惹兰阿末依布拉欣 (企业路)	82	1 D
Jalan Ahmad Ibrahim (Pioneer Rd)	惹兰阿末依布拉欣 (先驱路)	80	1 D
Jalan Ahmad Ibrahim (Tuas)	惹兰阿末依布拉欣 (大士)	78	1 A
Jalan Ampang	惹兰安邦	86	1 D
Jalan Ampas	惹兰安柏士	89	1 D
Jalan Anak Bukit	惹兰安娜武吉	85	1 A
Jalan Anak Patong	惹兰安娜巴东	93	2 C
Jalan Anggerek	惹兰安格烈	90	2 C
Jalan Angin Laut	惹兰安因拉兀	94	1 B
Jalan Angklong	惹兰安克弄	66	2 B
Jalan Antoi	惹兰安多依	48	1 C
Jalan Arif	惹兰安立夫	69	2 A
Jalan Arnap	惹兰安纳	109	2 C
Jalan Aruan	惹兰鲁安	110	2 B
Jalan Asas	惹兰安莎士	63	2 C
Jalan Asuhan	惹兰安素罕	87	1 C
Jalan Awang	惹兰阿旺	91	2 D

ROADS		MAP	GRID
Jalan Ayer	惹兰亚逸	112	1 B
Jalan Azam	惹兰阿占	114	2 B
Jalan Bahagia	惹兰巴合宜亚	89	1 D
Jalan Bahar (Jurong West)	惹兰巴哈 (裕廊西)	60	1 C
Jalan Bahar (PIE)	惹兰巴哈 (泛岛快速公路)	59	2 A
Jalan Bahasa	惹兰巴哈沙	87	1 C
Jalan Bahtera	惹兰巴特拉	20	1 A
Jalan Baiduri	惹兰巴都里	114	1 B
Jalan Bangau	惹兰曼高	48	1 C
Jalan Bangket	惹兰万吉	85	1 A
Jalan Bangsawan	惹兰孟沙弯	114	2 A
Jalan Basong	惹兰巴颂	4	1 D
Jalan Batai	惹兰巴泰	66	2 A
Jalan Batalong	惹兰巴达隆	74	1 B
Jalan Batalong East	惹兰巴达隆东	74	1 B
Jalan Batu	惹兰巴株	112	2 C
Jalan Batu Nilam	惹兰巴株尼蓝	63	1 C
Jalan Batu Ubin (P.Ubin)	惹兰巴株乌敏 (乌敏岛)	34	1 C
Jalan Belangkas	惹兰柏拉卡士	90	2 C
Jalan Belibas	惹兰柏利巴士	67	1 C
Jalan Bena	惹兰柏纳	74	1 C
Jalan Benaan Kapal	惹兰百纳安克巴	112	1 D
Jalan Beringin	惹兰柏林茵	113	2 C
Jalan Berjaya	惹兰柏彩雅	67	2 D
Jalan Berseh	惹兰白锡	111	1 B
Jalan Berseri	惹兰柏思礼	60	1 A
Jalan Besar (Lavender Street)	惹兰勿刹 (劳明达街)	111	1 B
Jalan Besar (Sungei Road)	惹兰勿刹 (双溪路)	111	1 C
Jalan Besut	惹兰百树	104	1 A
Jalan Bilal	惹兰庇老	94	1 D
Jalan Binchang	惹兰民昌	67	2 D
Jalan Bingka	惹兰民卡	85	1 A
Jalan Binjai	惹兰明才	113	2 C
Jalan Bintang Tiga	惹兰民三迪卡	92	2 D
Jalan Boon Lay	惹兰文礼	81	1 D
Jalan Bukit Ho Swee	惹兰河水山	132	1 B
Jalan Bukit Merah (Alexandra Road)	惹兰红山 (亚历山大路)	130	2 B
Jalan Bukit Merah (Henderson Road)	惹兰红山 (亨德申路)	131	1 C
Jalan Bukit Merah (Kampong Bahru Rd)	惹兰红山 (甘榜巴鲁路)	132	1 C
Jalan Buloh Perindu	惹兰布洛柏林都	114	2 B
Jalan Bumbong	惹兰万朋	23	1 B
Jalan Bunga Rampai	惹兰文雅南派	90	2 B
Jalan Bunga Raya	惹兰文雅拉耶	88	2 D
Jalan Buroh (Jurong Pier Road)	惹兰布罗 (裕廊渡头路)	103	2 A
Jalan Buroh (Pandan Loop)	惹兰布罗 (班丹环道)	105	2 B
Jalan Buroh (Penjuru Rd)	惹兰布罗(本茱鲁路)	104	1 A
Jalan Buroh (Tanjong Kling)	惹兰布罗 (丹戎吉宁)	102	2 B
Jalan Buroh (West Coast)	惹兰布罗 (西海岸)	106	1 B

ROADS		MAP	GRID
Jalan Chegar	慈兰仄卡	67	1 C
Jalan Chelagi	慈兰芝拉及	74	1 C
Jalan Chempah	慈兰真巴	67	1 C
Jalan Chempaka Kuning	慈兰真巴卡古林	94	1 C
Jalan Chempaka Puteh	慈兰真巴卡布爹	94	1 C
Jalan Chempedak	慈兰真必达	66	2 A
Jalan Chengam	慈兰清庵	46	1 D
Jalan Chengkek	慈兰清吉	90	2 C
Jalan Chermai	慈兰仄迈	48	1 C
Jalan Chermat	慈兰仄默	69	1 D
Jalan Cherpen	慈兰仄本	13	2 B
Jalan Chichau	慈兰基超	61	2 B
Jalan Chorak	慈兰佐叻	69	2 B
Jalan Chulek	慈兰朱乐	68	2 B
Jalan Daliah	慈兰达利亚	113	1 D
Jalan Damai	慈兰达迈	92	1 B
Jalan Datoh	慈兰拿督	88	2 C
Jalan Daud	慈兰达兀	92	1 D
Jalan Demak	慈兰丹	94	2 A
Jalan Dermawan	慈兰德玛万	63	1 B
Jalan Derum	慈兰德润	13	2 B
Jalan Dinding	慈兰亭亭	23	1 B
Jalan Dondang Sayang	慈兰弄朗沙央	114	2 B
Jalan Dua	慈兰都亚	112	2 B
Jalan Durian (P. Ubin)	慈兰榴槤(乌敏岛)	34	2 C
Jalan Dusun	慈兰都顺	88	2 C
Jalan Elok	慈兰益乐	110	1 C
Jalan Emas Urai	慈兰恩马士乌来	63	2 A
Jalan Empat	慈兰安拨	112	2 B
Jalan Enam	慈兰安南	112	2 B
Jalan Endut Senin (P. Ubin)	慈兰安都舍宁(乌敏岛)	33	2 C
Jalan Eunos	慈兰友诺士	91	2 C
Jalan Gaharu	慈兰加哈鲁	85	1 A
Jalan Gajus	慈兰卡朱士	113	2 C
Jalan Gali Batu	慈兰卡巴株	41	2 A
Jalan Gapis	慈兰卡比士	4	1 C
Jalan Gelam	慈兰哥南	4	1 C
Jalan Gelegar	慈兰格里卡	23	1 B
Jalan Gelenggeng	慈兰格林安	45	2 D
Jalan Gemala 2	慈兰哥马拉2	20	1 A
Jalan Gemala 3	慈兰哥马拉3	20	2 B
Jalan Gembira	慈兰肯比拉	90	2 C
Jalan Gendang	慈兰肯当	66	2 B
Jalan Geneng	慈兰更宁	69	2 C
Jalan Girang	慈兰宜兰	68	2 D
Jalan Gotong Royong	慈兰哥东罗央	90	2 A
Jalan Greja	慈兰格列慈	94	2 D
Jalan Grisek	慈兰格里锡	92	2 D
Jalan Gumilang	慈兰古米郎	63	1 C
Jalan Haji Alias	慈兰哈芝阿立亚士	85	2 D
Jalan Haji Salam	慈兰哈芝沙南	116	1 A
Jalan Hajijah	慈兰哈芝慈	115	1 B
Jalan Hang Jebat	慈兰韩日巴	130	1 A
Jalan Hari Raya	慈兰哈里拉耶	67	1 C
Jalan Harom Setangkai	慈兰哈仑史丹开	108	2 A
Jalan Harum	慈兰哈仑	107	2 A
Jalan Hiboran	慈兰依波兰	90	2 C
Jalan Hikayat	慈兰希加耶	13	2 B
Jalan Hitam Manis	慈兰依淡玛尼士	108	1 B
Jalan Hock Chye	慈兰福财	70	1 C
Jalan Hormat	慈兰和麦	79	2 C
Jalan Hussein	慈兰胡申	92	1 D
Jalan Hwi Yoh	慈兰缶窑	69	1 B
Jalan Ibadat	慈兰依巴达	39	2 D
Jalan Ikan Merah	慈兰依干美拉	67	1 C
Jalan Ilmu	慈兰依慕	87	1 C
Jalan Inggu	慈兰因古	4	1 C
Jalan Insaf	慈兰因萨	67	2 D
Jalan Intan	慈兰因丹	63	1 B
Jalan Ishak	慈兰依煞	92	1 D
Jalan Ismail	慈兰依斯迈	91	2 D
Jalan Isnin	慈兰依士宁	67	1 C
Jalan Istimewa	慈兰依士蒂美华	107	2 A
Jalan Jamal	慈兰惹吗	114	2 B
Jalan Jambu Ayer	慈兰占武逸	85	2 B
Jalan Jambu Batu	慈兰占武巴株	85	2 B
Jalan Jambu Mawar	慈兰占武马哇	85	2 B
Jalan Janggus	慈兰詹古士	4	1 D
Jalan Jarak	慈兰惹叻	47	2 C
Jalan Jelita	慈兰芝里达	107	2 A
Jalan Jelutong (P. Ubin)	慈兰日落洞(乌敏岛)	34	1 D
Jalan Jendela	慈兰珍德拉	23	1 B
Jalan Jentera	慈兰仁特拉	81	2 D
Jalan Jermin	慈兰芝敏	90	2 C
Jalan Jeruju	慈兰芝鲁朱	13	2 B
Jalan Jintan	慈兰仁丹	110	1 C
Jalan Jitong	慈兰日东	48	1 C
Jalan Joran	慈兰楚兰	47	2 C
Jalan Jurong Kechil	慈兰裕廊克基	84	2 A
Jalan Kakatua	慈兰卡卡都亚	84	1 A
Jalan Kampong Chantek	慈兰甘榜彰德	85	2 B
Jalan Kampong Siglap	慈兰甘榜实乞纳	115	1 B
Jalan Kandis	慈兰干地士	4	1 D
Jalan Kapal	慈兰卡巴	6	2 C
Jalan Kasau	慈兰卡绍	23	1 B
Jalan Kathi	慈兰卡蒂	94	1 D
Jalan Kayu (TPE)	慈兰加由 (淡滨尼快速公路)	29	1 D
Jalan Kayu (Yio Chu Kang Road)	慈兰加由 (杨厝港路)	47	2 B
Jalan Kayu Manis	慈兰加由马尼士	110	1 C
Jalan Kebaya	慈兰克巴耶	107	1 A
Jalan Kebun Limau	慈兰固本林茂	111	1 A
Jalan Kechil	慈兰克基	113	1 D
Jalan Kechot	慈兰克佐	91	2 D
Jalan Kechubong	慈兰克朱蒙	48	1 B
Jalan Kelabu Asap	慈兰克拉武亚沙	108	1 B
Jalan Kelawar	慈兰克拉哇	109	2 C
Jalan Kelempong	慈兰哥隆邦	74	1 B
Jalan Keli	慈兰克利	67	1 C
Jalan Kelichap	慈兰哥利查	69	2 D
Jalan Kelulut	慈兰克鲁路	48	1 C
Jalan Kemajuan	慈兰克马友	90	2 B
Jalan Kemaman	慈兰甘马挽	88	2 D
Jalan Kembang Melati	慈兰更邦莫拉地	87	1 D
Jalan Kembangan	慈兰景万岸	92	1 D
Jalan Kemboja	慈兰柬埔寨	90	1 C
Jalan Kemuning	慈兰克慕宁	13	2 B

ROADS		MAP	GRID
☐ Jalan Kenarah	惹兰肯那拉	48	1 C
☐ Jalan Kerayong	惹兰克拉容	4	1 D
☐ Jalan Keria	惹兰克里亚	85	1 A
☐ Jalan Keris	惹兰克里士	114	2 B
☐ Jalan Keruing	惹兰克鲁因	48	1 C
☐ Jalan Kesoma	惹兰克索马	90	2 A
☐ Jalan Ketuka	惹兰克都卡	4	1 C
☐ Jalan Ketumbit	惹兰克都密	48	1 C
☐ Jalan Khairuddin	惹兰开鲁丁	114	2 A
☐ Jalan Khamis	惹兰开美士	67	1 C
☐ Jalan Kilang	惹兰奇士	130	2 B
☐ Jalan Kilang Barat	惹兰奇兰巴叻	130	2 B
☐ Jalan Kilang Timor	惹兰奇兰蒂摩	130	2 B
☐ Jalan Klapa	惹兰克拉巴	111	2 C
☐ Jalan Kledek	惹兰克列狄	111	1 A
☐ Jalan Klinik	惹兰克利尼	131	2 A
■ Jalan Kolam Ayer	惹兰哥南亚逸	112	2 A
☐ Jalan Korban	惹兰哥班	90	2 A
☐ Jalan Krian	惹兰克里安	92	1 D
☐ Jalan Kuak	惹兰柯	67	1 C
☐ Jalan Kuala	惹兰瓜拉	110	1 D
☐ Jalan Kuang	惹兰关	73	2 D
☐ Jalan Kubor	惹兰古坡	111	1 C
☐ Jalan Kukoh	惹兰固哥	132	1 A
☐ Jalan Kuning	惹兰坤宁	108	1 B
☐ Jalan Kupang	惹兰古邦	115	2 A
☐ Jalan Kuras	惹兰古拉士	45	2 D
☐ Jalan Kurnia	惹兰古尼亚	90	2 A
☐ Jalan Kwok Min	惹兰国民	24	1 C
☐ Jalan Labu Ayer	惹兰拉武亚逸	90	1 A
☐ Jalan Labu Manis	惹兰拉武玛尼士	90	1 A
☐ Jalan Labu Merah	惹兰拉武美拉	90	1 A
☐ Jalan Lada Puteh	惹兰拉达布爹	110	1 C
☐ Jalan Lakum	惹兰拉贡	48	1 C
☐ Jalan Lam Huat	惹兰南发	9	2 C
☐ Jalan Lam Sam	惹兰南山	61	1 D
☐ Jalan Lana	惹兰拉那	92	2 D
☐ Jalan Langgar Bedok	惹兰加勿洛	94	1 D
☐ Jalan Lanjut	惹兰祝	66	2 A
☐ Jalan Lapang	惹兰拉邦	92	2 D
☐ Jalan Lateh	惹兰拉爹	90	1 A
☐ Jalan Layang Layang	惹兰拉央拉央	84	1 A
☐ Jalan Leban	惹兰利巴	66	2 A
☐ Jalan Lebat Daun	惹兰叻巴达恩	47	2 C
☐ Jalan Legundi	惹兰叻昆迪	13	2 B
☐ Jalan Lekar	惹兰礼卡	40	1 B
☐ Jalan Lekub	惹兰礼谷	48	1 C
☐ Jalan Lembah Bedok	惹兰仑巴勿洛	93	2 A
☐ Jalan Lembah Kallang	惹兰仑巴加冷	111	2 A
☐ Jalan Lembah Thomson	惹兰仑巴汤申	67	1 D
☐ Jalan Lempeng	惹兰仑平	106	1 A
☐ Jalan Lengkok Sembawang	惹兰麟谷三巴旺	13	2 D
☐ Jalan Lepas	惹兰叻巴士	70	1 C
☐ Jalan Lim Tai See	惹兰林太师	85	2 D
☐ Jalan Lima	惹兰利马	112	2 B
☐ Jalan Limau Bali	惹兰柠檬巴里	94	1 D
☐ Jalan Limau Kasturi	惹兰柠檬卡士杜里	94	1 D
☐ Jalan Limau Manis	惹兰柠檬马尼士	94	1 D
☐ Jalan Limau Nipis	惹兰柠檬尼比士	94	1 D
☐ Jalan Limau Purut	惹兰柠檬普鲁特	94	1 D
☐ Jalan Limbok	惹兰林木	69	1 B
☐ Jalan Lokam	惹兰罗甘	90	2 A
☐ Jalan Loyang Besar	惹兰罗央勿利	52	2 D
☐ Jalan Lye Kwee	惹兰来贵	70	1 A
☐ Jalan Machang	惹兰马章	4	1 D
☐ Jalan Mahir	惹兰马希雅	90	2 A
☐ Jalan Malu-Malu	惹兰马鲁马鲁	13	2 B
☐ Jalan Mamam (P. Ubin)	惹兰马蒙 (乌敏岛)	34	2 B
☐ Jalan Ma'mor	惹兰马摩	89	1 C
☐ Jalan Manis	惹兰马尼士	89	2 D
☐ Jalan Mariam	惹兰马莉安	74	1 B
☐ Jalan Mas Kuning	惹兰马士古宁	106	1 B
☐ Jalan Mas Puteh	惹兰马士布爹	106	1 B
☐ Jalan Mashor	惹兰马士和	88	1 B
☐ Jalan Masjid	惹兰马士日	114	1 A
☐ Jalan Mastuli	惹兰马士都利	69	2 C
☐ Jalan Mat Jambol	惹兰默占波	129	2 C
☐ Jalan Mata Ayer	惹兰马达亚逸	13	2 D
☐ Jalan Mawar	惹兰马哇	90	2 C
☐ Jalan Mayaanam	惹兰耶安南	74	1 C
☐ Jalan Melati	惹兰美拉地	90	2 C
☐ Jalan Melor	惹兰美罗	90	2 C
☐ Jalan Membina	惹兰孟比那	131	2 B
☐ Jalan Mempurong	惹兰孟布隆	4	1 C
☐ Jalan Menarong	惹兰孟那弄	66	2 A
☐ Jalan Mengkudu	惹兰孟姑都	67	1 A
☐ Jalan Merah Saga	惹兰美拉沙加	108	1 B
☐ Jalan Merbok	惹兰美柏	84	1 A
☐ Jalan Merdu	惹兰美都	49	2 B
☐ Jalan Merlimau	惹兰美林茂	88	1 D
☐ Jalan Mesin	惹兰美新	90	2 C
☐ Jalan Mesra	惹兰美士拉	90	2 C
☐ Jalan Minggu	惹兰民固	67	1 C
☐ Jalan Minyak	惹兰民亚	132	1 B
☐ Jalan Molek	惹兰茂希	112	2 B
☐ Jalan Muhibbah	惹兰慕希巴	90	2 C
☐ Jalan Mulia	惹兰慕利雅	90	2 B
☐ Jalan Murai	惹兰慕莱	38	2 A
☐ Jalan Mutiara	惹兰慕迪雅拉	109	2 D
☐ Jalan Naga Sari	惹兰那卡沙利	86	1 C
☐ Jalan Naung	惹兰纳翁	70	1 A
☐ Jalan Nipah	惹兰尼巴	94	1 D
☐ Jalan Nira	惹兰尼拉	68	2 B
☐ Jalan Noordin (P. Ubin)	惹兰诺丁 (乌敏岛)	34	1 B
☐ Jalan Novena	惹兰诺维娜	88	2 D
☐ Jalan Novena Barat	惹兰诺维娜巴叻	88	2 D
☐ Jalan Novena Selatan	惹兰诺维娜实拉丹	88	2 D
☐ Jalan Novena Timor	惹兰诺维娜蒂摩	88	2 D
☐ Jalan Novena Utara	惹兰诺维娜乌打拉	88	2 D
☐ Jalan Nuri	惹兰努力	113	1 D
☐ Jalan Pacheli	惹兰巴奇里	68	2 C
☐ Jalan Pakis	惹兰巴吉士	63	2 A
☐ Jalan Pandan	惹兰班丹	86	1 C
☐ Jalan Papan	惹兰巴班	82	2 D
☐ Jalan Paras	惹兰巴拉士	92	1 D
☐ Jalan Pari Burong	惹兰巴里布隆	94	1 B
☐ Jalan Pari Dedap	惹兰巴里德达	93	2 C
☐ Jalan Pari Kikis	惹兰巴里吉济士	93	2 C
☐ Jalan Pari Unak	惹兰巴里乌纳	93	2 C

ROADS		MAP	GRID
☐ Jalan Pasir Ria	惹兰巴西利亚	129	2 C
☐ Jalan Pasiran	惹兰巴西兰	110	1 A
☐ Jalan Payoh Lai	惹兰巴窑内	70	1 A
☐ Jalan Pekan Ubin	惹兰贝干乌敏(乌敏岛)	34	1 D
(P. Ubin)			
☐ Jalan Pelajau	惹兰柏拉乔	48	1 C
☐ Jalan Pelangi	惹兰柏兰宜	107	2 A
☐ Jalan Pelatina	惹兰柏拉地纳	67	1 D
☐ Jalan Pelatok	惹兰柏拉督	94	2 A
☐ Jalan Pelepah	惹兰柏拉巴	130	1 D
☐ Jalan Pelikat	惹兰柏利卡	69	2 C
☐ Jalan Pemimpin	惹兰柏民宾	67	2 D
☐ Jalan Penjara	惹兰本查拉	108	2 D
☐ Jalan Peradun	惹兰柏拉敦	47	2 C
☐ Jalan Perahu	惹兰柏拉乌	6	2 D
☐ Jalan Pergam	惹兰柏甘	94	2 A
☐ Jalan Pernama	惹兰柏沙玛	74	1 C
☐ Jalan Pesawat	惹兰柏沙瓦	81	2 D
☐ Jalan Piala	惹兰比亚拉	87	2 B
(changed to Caldecott Cl)	(已易名为加利谷弄)		
☐ Jalan Pinang	惹兰槟榔	111	1 C
☐ Jalan Pintau	惹兰宾道	67	1 C
☐ Jalan Piring	惹兰碧林	39	2 D
☐ Jalan Pisang	惹兰比山	111	1 C
☐ Jalan Pokok Serunai	惹兰波谷实鲁奈	115	2 B
☐ Jalan Punai	惹兰布乃	91	2 C
☐ Jalan Puteh Jerneh	惹兰布德芝涅	108	1 B
☐ Jalan Puteri Jula Juli	惹兰布德里朱拉朱利	114	2 B
☐ Jalan Puyoh	惹兰布育	19	2 D
☐ Jalan Quee Chew	惹兰贵州	60	1 A
☐ Jalan Rabu	惹兰布	67	1 C
☐ Jalan Rahmat	惹兰拉末	91	2 D
☐ Jalan Rajah	惹兰拉惹	89	1 C
☐ Jalan Raja Udang	惹兰拉惹乌当	88	2 C
☐ Jalan Raja Wali	惹兰拉惹哇利	84	2 A
☐ Jalan Rama-Rama	惹兰拉马拉马	88	2 D
☐ Jalan Rasok	惹兰拉索	23	1 B
☐ Jalan Raya	惹兰拉耶	90	2 C
☐ Jalan Rebana	惹兰礼巴那	66	2 B
☐ Jalan Redop	惹兰礼笃	48	1 C
☐ Jalan Remaja	惹兰仑马惹	63	1 C
☐ Jalan Remis	惹兰礼米士	115	2 A
☐ Jalan Rendang	惹兰仑乃	114	1 C
☐ Jalan Rengas	惹兰玲加士	48	1 C
☐ Jalan Rengkam	惹兰仑甘	70	1 B
☐ Jalan Resak	惹兰礼萨	48	1 C
☐ Jalan Ria	惹兰利亚	89	2 A
☐ Jalan Riang	惹兰利安	68	2 D
☐ Jalan Rimau	惹兰里茅	91	2 C
☐ Jalan Rindu	惹兰林都	90	1 A
☐ Jalan Rukam	惹兰鲁甘	66	2 A
☐ Jalan Rumah Tinggi	惹兰乌马丁宜	130	2 B
☐ Jalan Rumbia	惹兰仑比亚	110	2 D
☐ Jalan Rumia	惹兰鲁米亚	108	1 B
☐ Jalan Sabit	惹兰沙必	60	1 B
☐ Jalan Sahabat	惹兰沙哈拔	69	2 C
☐ Jalan Sajak	惹兰沙甲	13	2 B
☐ Jalan Salang	惹兰沙浪	13	2 B
☐ Jalan Sam Heng	惹兰三兴(乌敏岛)	34	2 B
(P. Ubin)			

ROADS		MAP	GRID
☐ Jalan Sam Kongsi	惹兰三公司	71	2 A
☐ Jalan Samarinda	惹兰沙马林达	69	2 C
☐ Jalan Sampurna	惹兰三布娜	107	2 A
☐ Jalan Samulun	惹兰沙木仑	102	2 B
☐ Jalan Sankam	惹兰甘	4	1 D
☐ Jalan Sappan	惹兰沙班	66	2 A
☐ Jalan Satu	惹兰沙都	112	2 B
☐ Jalan Saudara Ku	惹兰少达拉固	114	2 B
☐ Jalan Sayang	惹兰沙央	114	1 A
(Changi Road)	(樟宜路)		
☐ Jalan Sayang	惹兰沙央	92	1 D
(near Jalan Selamat)	(近惹兰士拉末)		
☐ Jalan Seaview	惹兰海景	113	1 D
☐ Jalan Sedap	惹兰思达	113	1 D
☐ Jalan Segam	惹兰思甘	73	2 D
☐ Jalan Seh Chuan	惹兰树群	84	2 A
☐ Jalan Sejarah	惹兰士惹拉	87	1 C
☐ Jalan Selamat	惹兰士拉末	92	1 D
☐ Jalan Selanting	惹兰士拉汀	84	1 A
☐ Jalan Selaseh	惹兰士拉色	48	1 C
☐ Jalan Selendang Delima	惹兰士玲当蒂利马	114	2 B
☐ Jalan Selimang	惹兰士林曼	4	1 C
☐ Jalan Sembilang	惹兰森美士	67	1 C
☐ Jalan Semerbak	惹兰司马巴	89	2 D
☐ Jalan Sempadan	惹兰森巴丹	115	1 B
☐ Jalan Senandong	惹兰申南通	85	2 B
☐ Jalan Senang	惹兰申南	92	1 C
☐ Jalan Sendudok	惹兰申都督	13	2 B
☐ Jalan Seni	惹兰申尼	87	1 D
☐ Jalan Sentosa	惹兰圣淘沙	92	1 D
☐ Jalan Senyum	惹兰申永	114	1 A
(Changi Road)	(樟宜路)		
☐ Jalan Senyum	惹兰申永	92	1 D
(Jalan Lapang)	(惹兰申邦)		
☐ Jalan Serene	惹兰士林	87	1 D
☐ Jalan Serengam	惹兰士玲甘	13	2 B
☐ Jalan Seruling	惹兰士如林	66	2 B
☐ Jalan Setia	惹兰士地亚	90	2 B
☐ Jalan Shaer	惹兰沙尔	13	2 B
☐ Jalan Siantan	惹兰仙丹	86	1 D
☐ Jalan Siap	惹兰诗雅	63	2 B
☐ Jalan Sikudangan	惹兰司古丹安	90	2 C
☐ Jalan Simpang Bedok	惹兰新邦勿洛	94	1 C
☐ Jalan Sinar Bintang	惹兰西那宾丹	74	1 B
☐ Jalan Sinar Bulan	惹兰西那布兰	74	1 B
☐ Jalan Sindor	惹兰星多	48	1 C
☐ Jalan Singa	惹兰新加	91	2 C
☐ Jalan Songket	惹兰宋格	69	2 C
☐ Jalan Soo Bee	惹兰四美	94	1 B
☐ Jalan Sotong	惹兰苏东	114	1 B
☐ Jalan Suasa	惹兰苏亚沙	63	2 A
☐ Jalan Suka	惹兰苏卡	112	2 B
☐ Jalan Sukachita	惹兰苏卡基打	68	2 D
☐ Jalan Sultan	惹兰苏丹	111	2 C
☐ Jalan Sungei Poyan	惹兰双溪波扬	59	1 A
☐ Jalan Surau	惹兰苏劳	10	1 D
☐ Jalan Taman	惹兰达曼	89	2 D
☐ Jalan Tamban	惹兰丹曼	114	1 B

ROADS		MAP	GRID
Jalan Tambur	惹兰丹坡	66	2 B
Jalan Tampang	惹兰丹邦	13	2 B
Jalan Tan Tock Seng	惹兰陈笃生	110	2 A
Jalan Tanah Puteh	惹兰丹那布德	115	1 A
Jalan Tanah Rata	惹兰丹那拉打	93	2 C
Jalan Tani	惹兰丹尼	69	2 B
Jalan Tanjong	惹兰丹戎	93	2 C
Jalan Tapisan	惹兰大璧山	40	1 D
Jalan Tari Dulang	惹兰达里杜郎	29	1 D
Jalan Tari Lilin	惹兰达里利邻	48	1 A
Jalan Tari Payong	惹兰达里巴容	48	1 A
Jalan Tari Piring	惹兰达里庇邻	29	1 D
Jalan Tari Serimpi	惹兰达里士林庇	48	1 A
Jalan Tari Zapin	惹兰达里查宾	48	1 A
Jalan Tarum	惹兰达仑	46	1 D
Jalan Teck Kee	惹兰德记	69	1 C
Jalan Teck Whye	惹兰德惠	42	1 C
Jalan Tekad	惹兰德卡	63	2 B
Jalan Tekukor	惹兰德固国	84	1 A
Jalan Telang	惹兰德朗	45	2 D
Jalan Telawi	惹兰德拉威	71	1 B
Jalan Telipok	惹兰德利坡	13	2 B
Jalan Teliti	惹兰德利地	70	1 B
Jalan Tembusu	惹兰登布树	113	2 C
Jalan Tempua	惹兰登那亚	87	1 D
Jalan Tenaga	惹兰登那加	91	2 B
Jalan Tenang	惹兰登南	107	2 A
Jalan Tenggiri	惹兰登宜里	114	1 B
Jalan Tenon	惹兰登农	69	2 C
Jalan Tenteram	惹兰登德兰	89	1 C
Jalan Tepong	惹兰登德榜	104	1 B
Jalan Terang Bulan	惹兰德朗布兰	92	2 D
Jalan Terap	惹兰德腊	70	2 B
Jalan Terubok	惹兰德鲁博	67	1 C
Jalan Terusan	惹兰德鲁山	82	1 D
Jalan Tiga	惹兰迪卡	112	2 B
Jalan Tiga Ratus	惹兰迪卡拉都士	94	2 A
Jalan Tiong	惹兰冢	131	1 A
■ Jalan Toa Payoh	惹兰大巴窑	89	1 C
Jalan Todak	惹兰多达	67	1 C
Jalan Tua Kong	惹兰大公	114	2 A
Jalan Tukang	惹兰都干	81	2 C
Jalan Tumpu	惹兰敦布	63	2 B
Jalan Tupai	惹兰都派	109	2 C
Jalan Turi	惹兰都利	113	2 A
Jalan Ubi	惹兰乌美	113	2 A
Jalan Ubin (P. Ubin)	惹兰乌敏(乌敏岛)	34	1 C
Jalan Uji	惹兰乌芝	63	2 C
Jalan Ulu Seletar	惹兰乌鲁实里达	26	1 C
Jalan Ulu Sembawang (Mandai Road)	惹兰乌鲁三巴旺 (万礼路)	24	2 B
Jalan Ulu Sembawang (Sembawang Road)	惹兰乌鲁三巴旺 (三巴旺路)	13	2 B
Jalan Ulu Siglap	惹兰乌鲁实乞纳	115	1 A
Jalan Unggas	惹兰温佳士	87	1 D
Jalan Usaha	惹兰乌沙哈	90	2 A
Jalan Wajek	惹兰华捷	85	1 A
Jalan Wak Selat	惹兰华石呐	9	2 C
Jalan Wakaff	惹兰华卡夫	114	1 A
Jalan Wangi	惹兰万宜	90	1 C
Jalan Waringin	惹兰花林myn	92	2 D
Jalan Wat Siam (P. Ubin)	惹兰暹庙(乌敏岛)	33	1 B
Jalan Yasin	惹兰雅新	91	2 D
Jalan Zamrud	惹兰詹鲁	63	1 B
Jamaica Road	牙买加路	3	2 C
Jambol Place	占波坊	129	2 C
Jambol Walk	占波径	129	2 C
Jansen Close	詹森弄	69	2 C
Jansen Road	詹森路	69	1 B
Japanese Garden Road	星和园路	82	1 B
Jasmine Road	捷士民路	66	2 C
Java Road	爪哇路	111	2 C
Jedburgh Gardens	捷堡花园	114	2 A
Jelapang Road	日拉邦路	42	2 C
Jelebu Road	日叻务路	42	1 C
Jellicoe Road	捷利歌路	111	2 B
Jervois Close	泽维士弄	131	2 A
Jervois Hill	泽维士山	109	1 D
Jervois Lane	泽维士巷	109	1 D
Jervois Road	泽维士路	109	1 D
Jetty Drive	吉地通道	53	1 C
Jetty Link	吉地连路	53	1 C
Jiak Chuan Road	若泉路	132	2 C
Jiak Kim Street	若锦街	132	1 A
Joan Road	贞安路	88	1 B
John Road	约翰路	88	1 B
Joo Avenue	柔道	111	1 A
Joo Chiat Avenue	如切道	114	1 A
Joo Chiat Lane	如切巷	113	2 B
Joo Chiat Place	如切坊	113	2 B
Joo Chiat Road	如切路	113	2 B
Joo Chiat Terrace	如切台	113	2 A
Joo Chiat Walk	如切径	114	1 A
Joo Hong Road	裕丰路	69	2 B
Joo Koon Circle	裕群圈	79	2 C
Joo Koon Crescent	裕群弯	79	2 C
Joo Koon Road	裕群路	79	2 D
Joo Koon Way	裕群大道	79	1 D
Joo Seng Road	裕盛路	90	2 B
Joo Yee Road	如意路	81	2 C
Joon Hiang Road	润亨路	69	1 D
Jubilee Road	朱比丽路	106	1 C
Jupiter Road	朱比德路	66	2 C
Jurong Canal Drive	裕廊水道通道	61	2 D
Jurong East Avenue 1	裕廊东1道	82	1 A
Jurong East Central	裕廊东中路	83	1 A
Jurong East Central 1	裕廊东中1路	83	1 C
Jurong East Street 11	裕廊东11街	83	1 C
Jurong East Street 12	裕廊东12街	83	1 B
Jurong East Street 13	裕廊东13街	82	2 B
Jurong East Street 21	裕廊东21街	83	1 C
Jurong East Street 24	裕廊东24街	83	1 A
Jurong East Street 31	裕廊东31街	82	2 A
Jurong East Street 32	裕廊东32街	82	2 C
Jurong Hill	裕廊山	81	1 D
■ Jurong Island Highway	裕廊岛大道	125	2 A
Jurong Pier Road	裕廊渡头路	81	2 D

J K

ROADS		MAP	GRID
Jurong Pier Way	裕廊渡头大道	103	2 B
Jurong Port Road	裕廊海港路	82	1 D
Jurong Road	裕廊路	61	1 C
Jurong Road Track 18	裕廊路第18乡道	61	2 D
Jurong Road Track 20	裕廊路第20乡道	61	2 C
Jurong Road Track 22	裕廊路第22乡道	61	2 C
Jurong Town Hall Road	裕廊镇大会堂路	83	1 C
Jurong West Avenue 1	裕廊西1道	61	1 D
Jurong West Avenue 2	裕廊西2道	60	1 D
Jurong West Avenue 3	裕廊西3道	60	1 C
Jurong West Avenue 4	裕廊西4道	60	1 D
Jurong West Avenue 5	裕廊西5道	80	2 A
Jurong West Central 1	裕廊西中路	81	1 A
Jurong West Central 2	裕廊西中2路	81	1 A
Jurong West Central 3	裕廊西中3路	81	1 A
Jurong West Street 22	裕廊西22街	60	1 C
Jurong West Street 23	裕廊西23街	60	1 C
Jurong West Street 24	裕廊西24街	60	1 D
Jurong West Street 25	裕廊西25街	60	1 C
Jurong West Street 41	裕廊西41街	61	1 D
Jurong West Street 42	裕廊西42街	60	2 D
Jurong West Street 51	裕廊西51街	61	1 D
Jurong West Street 52	裕廊西52街	60	2 D
Jurong West Street 61	裕廊西61街	80	2 A
Jurong West Street 62	裕廊西62街	81	1 A
Jurong West Street 63	裕廊西63街	80	2 B
Jurong West Street 64	裕廊西64街	81	1 A
Jurong West Street 65	裕廊西65街	81	1 A
Jurong West Street 71	裕廊西71街	80	2 A
Jurong West Street 72	裕廊西72街	59	2 D
Jurong West Street 73	裕廊西73街	60	1 D
Jurong West Street 74	裕廊西74街	59	2 D
Jurong West Street 75	裕廊西75街	60	1 D
Jurong West Street 76	裕廊西76街	60	1 D
Jurong West Street 81	裕廊西81街	80	2 A
Jurong West Street 82	裕廊西82街	59	2 D
Jurong West Street 91	裕廊西91街	80	1 A
Jurong West Street 92	裕廊西92街	80	2 A
Jurong West Street 93	裕廊西93街	80	2 A

K

Kadayanallur Street	卡达耶那鲁街	132	2 C
Kaki Bukit Avenue 1	加基武吉1道	91	2 C
Kaki Bukit Avenue 2	加基武吉2道	91	2 B
Kaki Bukit Avenue 3	加基武吉3道	91	2 B
Kaki Bukit Avenue 4	加基武吉4道	91	2 B
Kaki Bukit Avenue 5	加基武吉5道	92	1 B
Kaki Bukit Avenue 6	加基武吉6道	92	1 A
Kaki Bukit Crescent	加基武吉弯	92	1 B
Kaki Bukit Ind Terrace	加基武吉工业台	91	2 B
Kaki Bukit Place	加基武吉坊	91	2 B
Kaki Bukit Road 1	加基武吉1路	91	2 B
Kaki Bukit Road 2	加基武吉2路	91	2 B
Kaki Bukit Road 3	加基武吉3路	91	2 B
Kaki Bukit Road 4	加基武吉4路	92	1 B
Kaki Bukit Road 5	加基武吉5路	92	1 A
Kaki Bukit View	加基武吉景	92	1 B
Kalidasa Avenue	卡里达沙道	45	2 C

ROADS		MAP	GRID
Kallang Avenue	加冷道	111	2 B
Kallang Bahru	加冷巴鲁	111	2 A
Kallang Junction	加冷交叉路	111	2 B
Kallang Paya Lebar Expressway (KPE)	加冷巴耶利巴快速公路	50	1 D
Kallang Place	加冷坊	111	2 A
Kallang Pudding Road	加冷布丁路	90	1 C
Kallang Sector	加冷段	111	2 B
Kallang Sector	加冷段	90	1 D
Kallang Tengah	加冷登雅	111	2 A
Kallang Walk	加冷径	111	2 C
Kallang Way	加冷大道	90	1 D
Kallang Way 1	加冷第1大道	90	1 D
Kallang Way 2	加冷第2大道	90	1 D
Kallang Way 2A	加冷第2A大道	90	1 D
Kallang Way 3	加冷第3大道	90	2 D
Kallang Way 4	加冷第4大道	90	2 D
Kallang Way 5	加冷第5大道	90	2 D
Kampong Ampat	甘榜安拔	90	2 B
Kampong Arang Road	甘榜阿兰路	112	2 D
Kampong Bahru Road	甘榜巴鲁路	131	2 D
Kampong Bugis	甘榜武吉士	111	2 B
Kampong Eunos	甘榜友诺士	113	2 A
Kampong Java Road	甘榜爪哇路	110	1 B
Kampong Kapor Road	甘榜加卜路	111	1 B
Kampong Kayu Road	甘榜加由路	112	2 C
Kampong Sireh	甘榜思礼	69	2 C
Kampong Wak Hassan	甘榜哇哈山	4	1 C
Kandahar Street	干达哈街	111	1 C
Kandis Lane	甘地士巷	4	1 C
Kandis Walk	甘地士径	4	1 D
Kang Ching Road	岗景路	82	1 B
Kang Choo Bin Road	江子民路	69	2 B
Kang Choo Bin Walk	江子民径	69	2 B
Karikal Lane	卡利加巷	114	1 B
Kasai Road	卡赛路	47	2 C
Katmandu Road	加得满都路	90	2 B
Kay Poh Road	继宝路	109	2 B
Kay Siang Road	继祥路	109	1 D
Kee Choe Avenue	基生道	90	1 C
Kee Seng Street	基生街	132	2 C
Kee Sun Avenue	纪辰道	115	1 B
Kelantan Lane	吉兰丹巷	111	1 C
Kelantan Road	吉兰丹路	111	1 C
Kellock Road	客乐路	131	2 A
Kelopak Road	克罗被路	4	1 C
Kelulut Hill	克鲁路山	48	1 C
Kempas Road	肯巴士路	111	1 A
Kenanga Avenue	肯南卡道	90	1 B
Keng Cheow Street	敬招街	132	2 A
Keng Chin Road	庆振路	109	2 A
Keng Kiat Street	庆吉街	132	2 B
Keng Lee Road	庆利路	110	1 B
Kensington Park Drive	肯新顿园通道	68	2 A
Kensington Park Road	肯新顿园路	68	2 A
Kent Ridge Crescent	肯特岗弯	106	2 D
Kent Ridge Drive	肯特岗通道	106	2 D
Kent Ridge Road	肯特岗路	129	1 A
Kent Road	肯特路	111	1 A
Kenya Crescent	肯雅弯	3	2 D

ROADS		MAP	GRID
☐ Keong Saik Road	恭锡路	132	2 B
☐ Keppel Bay Drive	发巴湾通道	142	1 A
☐ Keppel Bay Vista	发巴湾景	141	1 A
☐ Keppel Bay Walk	发巴湾径	142	1 A
☐ Keppel Hill	发巴山	131	1 D
☐ Keppel Road	发巴路	132	1 D
☐ Keppel Terminal Ave	发巴码头道	142	2 A
☐ Keppel Terminal Rd K	发巴码头K路	132	1 D
☐ Keppel Terminal Rd M	发巴码头M路	143	1 A
☐ Keppel Terminal Rd N	发巴码头N路	142	2 A
☐ Keppel Terminal St 6	发巴码头6街	132	1 D
☐ Keppel Terminal St 7	发巴码头7街	132	1 D
☐ Keramat Road	克拉默路	1	2 D
■ Kerbau Road	加宝路	111	1 B
☐ Keris Drive	卡里斯通道	114	1 A
☐ Kerong Lane	克隆巷	4	1 C
☐ Kerong Walk	克隆径	4	1 C
☐ Kew Avenue	邱道	94	1 D
☐ Kew Crescent	邱弯	116	1 A
☐ Kew Drive	邱通道	94	1 D
☐ Kew Heights	邱岭	116	1 A
☐ Kew Lane	邱巷	94	1 D
☐ Kew Terrace	邱台	116	1 A
☐ Kew Walk	邱径	116	1 A
☐ Khalsa Crescent	卡沙弯	1	1 D
☐ Kheam Hock Road	谦福路	87	1 B
☐ Khiang Guan Avenue	乾元道	110	2 A
☐ Kian Teck Avenue	建德道	80	2 C
☐ Kian Teck Crescent	建德弯	80	2 C
☐ Kian Teck Drive	建德通道	80	2 C
☐ Kian Teck Lane	建德巷	80	2 C
☐ Kian Teck Road	建德路	80	1 C
☐ Kian Teck Way	建德大道	80	2 C
☐ Killiney Road	基里尼路	110	1 D
☐ Kim Cheng Street	金钟街	132	1 B
☐ Kim Chuan Drive	金泉通道	91	1 A
☐ Kim Chuan Lane	金泉巷	91	1 A
☐ Kim Chuan Road	金泉路	91	1 A
☐ Kim Chuan Terrace	金泉台	91	1 A
☐ Kim Keat Avenue	金吉道	89	1 C
☐ Kim Keat Close	金吉弄	89	1 D
☐ Kim Keat Lane	金吉巷	89	1 D
☐ Kim Keat Link	金吉连路	89	1 C
☐ Kim Keat Road	金吉路	89	1 D
☐ Kim Pong Road	金榜路	131	2 B
☐ Kim Seng Promenade	金声河畔道	132	1 A
☐ Kim Seng Road	金声路	132	1 A
☐ Kim Seng Walk	金声径	109	2 D
☐ Kim Tian Place	金殿坊	131	2 B
☐ Kim Tian Road	金殿路	131	2 B
☐ Kim Yam Road	金炎路	110	1 D
■ Kinara Lane	基纳拉巷	132	2 B
☐ King Albert Park	阿尔柏王园	85	1 B
☐ King George's Avenue	乔治王道	111	2 B
☐ King's Avenue	京士道	3	2 D
☐ King's Close	京士弄	108	1 D
☐ King's Drive	京士通道	108	2 A
☐ King's Road	京士路	86	2 D
☐ King's Walk	京士径	108	1 A
☐ Kingsmead Road	京士密路	108	2 A

ROADS		MAP	GRID
☐ Kingswear Avenue	京士卫道	68	2 A
☐ Kinta Road	近打路	111	1 B
☐ Kirk Terrace	客台	110	2 D
☐ Kismis Avenue	吉士美道	84	2 B
☐ Kismis Green	吉士美埔	84	2 B
☐ Kismis Place	吉士美坊	84	1 B
☐ Kismis Road	吉士美路	84	2 B
☐ Kitchener Link	吉真那路路	111	1 B
☐ Kitchener Road	吉真那路	111	1 B
☐ Klang Lane	巴生巷	111	1 B
☐ Klang Road	巴生路	111	1 B
☐ Knights Bridge	奈士桥	28	2 D
☐ Koek Road	谷路 (郭路)	110	1 C
☐ Koh Sek Lim Road	许锡林路	94	2 C
☐ Koon Seng Road	坤成路	113	2 B
☐ Kovan Close	高文弄	69	2 C
☐ Kovan Road	高文路	69	2 C
☐ Kramat Lane	克拉末巷	110	2 C
☐ Kramat Road	克拉末路	110	2 C
☐ Kranji Crescent	克兰芝弯	9	2 C
■ Kranji Expressway (BKE Junction)	克兰芝快速公路 (武吉知马快速公路交叉处)	42	1 B
■ Kranji Expressway (Choa Chu Kang)	克兰芝快速公路 (蔡厝港)	41	2 B
■ Kranji Expressway (Lam San Flyover)	克兰芝快速公路 (南山立交桥)	40	1 D
■ Kranji Expressway (Tengah Flyover)	克兰芝快速公路 (登嘉立交桥)	60	2 A
☐ Kranji Link	克兰芝连路	9	1 C
☐ Kranji Loop	克兰芝环路	9	2 C
☐ Kranji Road	克兰芝路	9	2 C
☐ Kranji Way	克兰芝大道	9	1 B
☐ Kreta Ayer Road	水车路	132	2 C
☐ Kung Chong Road	工厂路	130	2 A
☐ Kuo Chuan Avenue	国专道	114	1 C
☐ Kurau Grove	古鲁林	114	1 B
☐ Kurau Place	古鲁坊	114	1 B
☐ Kurau Terrace	古鲁台	114	1 B
☐ Kwong Avenue	邝道	90	1 C
☐ Kwong Min Road	光明路	81	1 C

	L		
☐ La Salle Street	拉莎街	114	2 A
☐ Labrador Villa Road	拉柏多维拉路	130	1 D
☐ Lady Hill Road	淑女山路	109	2 B
☐ Lagos Circle	拉哥士圈	3	2 D
☐ Laguna Golf Green	礁湖高球埔	95	1 C
☐ Lakepoint Drive	湖滨通道	81	2 A
☐ Lakeshore View	湖岸景	143	1 D
☐ Lakeside Walk	湖岸径	82	1 A
☐ Lakme Street	乐美街	115	1 A
☐ Lakme Terrace	乐美台	114	2 A
☐ Lambeth Walk	蓝柏径	29	1 C
☐ Lancaster Gate	兰卡斯特门	28	2 C
☐ Lange Road	兰芝路	69	1 C
☐ Langsat Road	兰莎路	113	2 A
☐ Lantana Avenue	兰丹娜道	85	2 C
☐ Larut Road	拉律路	111	1 C

L

ROADS		MAP	GRID	ROADS		MAP	GRID
Lasia Avenue	拉西亚道	85	2 C	Lichfield Road	李芝菲路	69	1 B
Laurel Wood Ave	月桂木大道	85	2 D	Lichi Avenue	荔枝道	90	1 C
Lavender Street	劳明达街	111	2 B	Lilac Drive	紫丁香通道	47	2 C
Law Link	法学连路	128	2 A	Lilac Road	紫丁香路	47	2 C
Leedon Heights	礼敦岭	108	1 A	Lilac Walk	紫丁香径	47	2 C
Leedon Park	礼敦园	108	1 A	Lily Avenue	百合道	85	2 C
Leedon Road	礼敦路	108	1 A	Lim Ah Pin Road	林亚柄路	69	2 B
Leicester Road	李斯特路	89	2 C	Lim Ah Woo Road	林亚胡路	113	1 B
Leith Park	李斯园	69	1 B	Lim Chu Kang Lane 1	林厝港1巷	7	1 D
Leith Road	李斯路	69	1 B	Lim Chu Kang Lane 1A	林厝港1A巷	20	2 A
Lembu Road	仑布路	111	1 B	Lim Chu Kang Lane 2	林厝港2巷	7	1 D
Lemon Avenue	柠檬道	86	1 C	Lim Chu Kang Lane 3	林厝港3巷	7	1 D
Lempeng Drive	仑邦道道	84	1 D	Lim Chu Kang Lane 3A	林厝港3A巷	7	1 D
Leng Kee Road	麟记路	130	2 A	Lim Chu Kang Lane 4	林厝港4巷	7	2 C
Lengkok Angsa	麟谷安沙	109	2 C	Lim Chu Kang Lane 5	林厝港5巷	7	2 C
Lengkok Bahru	麟谷巴鲁	130	2 B	Lim Chu Kang Lane 5A	林厝港5A巷	7	2 C
Lengkok Mariam	麟谷马莉安	74	1 B	Lim Chu Kang Lane 6	林厝港6巷	7	2 C
Lengkok Merak	麟谷美叻	109	2 C	Lim Chu Kang Lane 6C	林厝港6C巷	7	2 B
Lengkong Dua	麟光都亚	92	1 D	Lim Chu Kang Lane 6D	林厝港6D巷	7	2 B
Lengkong Empat	麟光安拔	92	1 C	Lim Chu Kang Lane 6F	林厝港6F巷	7	2 B
Lengkong Enam	麟光安南	92	1 C	Lim Chu Kang Lane 8	林厝港8巷	7	2 B
Lengkong Lima	麟光利马	92	1 C	Lim Chu Kang Lane 8A	林厝港8A巷	7	2 B
Lengkong Satu	麟光沙都	92	1 C	Lim Chu Kang Lane 9	林厝港9巷	7	2 A
Lengkong Tiga	麟光地牙	92	1 D	Lim Chu Kang Lane 9A	林厝港9A巷	7	2 A
Lengkong Tujuh	麟光都祝	92	1 C	Lim Chu Kang Road	林厝港路	7	1 D
Lentor Avenue	伦多道	46	1 A	(End)	(林厝港路尾)		
Lentor Crescent	伦多弯	46	1 B	Lim Chu Kang Road	林厝港路	38	2 D
Lentor Drive	伦多通道	46	1 C	(Old Choa Chu Kang)	(蔡厝港路)		
Lentor Green	伦多埔	46	1 B	Lim Chu Kang Road	林厝港路	20	1 D
Lentor Grove	伦多林	46	1 B	(Sungei Gedong)	(当)		
Lentor Lane	伦多巷	46	1 B	Lim Chu Kang Track 11	林厝港第11乡道	20	1 C
Lentor Link	伦多连路	46	1 B	Lim Chu Kang Track 13	林厝港第13乡道	20	1 B
Lentor Loop	伦多环道	46	1 B	Lim Liak Street	林烈街	131	2 B
Lentor Place	伦多坊	46	1 B	Lim Tai See Walk	林太师径	85	2 D
Lentor Plain	伦多坪	46	1 B	Lim Teck Boo Road	林特武路	90	2 A
Lentor Road	伦多路	46	1 B	Lim Teck Kim Road	林德金路	132	2 D
Lentor Street	伦多街	46	1 B	Lim Tua Tow Road	林大头路	69	1 C
Lentor Terrace	伦多台	46	1 B	Limau Garden	柠檬花园	94	1 D
Lentor Vale	伦多谷	46	1 B	Limau Grove	柠檬林	94	1 D
Lentor Walk	伦多径	46	1 B	Limau Rise	柠檬坡	94	1 D
Lentor Way	伦多大道	46	1 B	Limau Terrace	柠檬台	94	1 D
Leo Drive	利奥通道	66	2 C	Limau Walk	柠檬径	94	1 D
Leonie Hill	利安尼山	110	1 D	Limbok Terrace	林木台	69	1 B
Leonie Hill Road	利安尼山路	110	1 D	Lincoln Road	林肯路	110	2 A
Lermit Road	勒密路	109	1 B	Linden Drive	林登通道	86	1 B
Leuchars Road	柳加士路	53	2 B	Link Road	林克路	81	2 C
Lew Lian Vale	榴梿谷	69	1 D	Little Road	立德路	90	2 B
Lewin Terrace	鲁英台	132	2 A	Liu Fang Road	留芳路	102	2 A
Lewis Road	鲁易士路	109	1 A	Lloyd Road	来益路	110	1 D
Leyden Hill	莱敦山	87	1 D	Lock Road	洛克路	130	2 C
Li Hwan Close	丽苑弄	68	2 C	Loewen Road	罗文路	108	2 C
Li Hwan Drive	丽苑通道	68	2 C	Lok Yang Way	洛阳大道	80	1 D
Li Hwan Place	丽苑坊	68	2 C	Loke Yew Street	陆佑街	132	2 A
Li Hwan Terrace	丽苑台	68	2 C	Lompang Road	隆邦路	42	2 C
Li Hwan View	丽苑景	68	2 C	Lornie Road	罗尼路	87	1 B
Li Hwan Walk	丽苑径	68	2 C	Lornie Walk	罗尼径	87	1 B
Li Po Avenue	李白道	45	2 C	Lorong 101 Changi	樟宜罗弄101	113	2 A
Liane Road	丽燕路	109	1 B	Lorong 102 Changi	樟宜罗弄102	113	2 A
Liang Seah Street	连城街	111	1 D	Lorong 104 Changi	樟宜罗弄104	113	2 A
Libra Drive	李柏拉通道	66	2 C	Lorong 105 Changi	樟宜罗弄105	113	2 A

32

INDEX • ROADS

L

ROADS		MAP	GRID
Lorong 106 Changi	樟宜罗弄106	113	2 A
Lorong 107 Changi	樟宜罗弄107	113	2 A
Lorong 108 Changi	樟宜罗弄108	113	2 A
Lorong 110 Changi	樟宜罗弄110	114	1 A
Lorong 1 Geylang	芽笼1巷	112	1 B
Lorong 3 Geylang	芽笼3巷	112	1 B
Lorong 4 Geylang	芽笼4巷	112	1 B
Lorong 6 Geylang	芽笼6巷	112	1 B
Lorong 7 Geylang	芽笼7巷	112	1 B
Lorong 8 Geylang	芽笼8巷	112	1 B
Lorong 9 Geylang	芽笼9巷	112	1 B
Lorong 10 Geylang	芽笼10巷	112	1 B
Lorong 11 Geylang	芽笼11巷	112	1 B
Lorong 12 Geylang	芽笼12巷	112	1 B
Lorong 13 Geylang	芽笼13巷	112	1 B
Lorong 14 Geylang	芽笼14巷	112	2 B
Lorong 15 Geylang	芽笼15巷	112	1 B
Lorong 16 Geylang	芽笼16巷	112	2 B
Lorong 17 Geylang	芽笼17巷	112	1 A
Lorong 18 Geylang	芽笼18巷	112	2 B
Lorong 19 Geylang	芽笼19巷	112	2 A
Lorong 20 Geylang	芽笼20巷	112	2 B
Lorong 21 Geylang	芽笼21巷	112	2 A
Lorong 21A Geylang	芽笼21A巷	112	2 A
Lorong 22 Geylang	芽笼22巷	112	2 B
Lorong 23 Geylang	芽笼23巷	112	2 A
Lorong 24 Geylang	芽笼24巷	112	2 B
Lorong 24A Geylang	芽笼24A巷	112	2 B
Lorong 25 Geylang	芽笼25巷	112	2 A
Lorong 25A Geylang	芽笼25A巷	112	2 A
Lorong 26 Geylang	芽笼26巷	112	2 B
Lorong 27 Geylang	芽笼27巷	112	2 A
Lorong 27A Geylang	芽笼27A巷	112	2 A
Lorong 28 Geylang	芽笼28巷	112	2 B
Lorong 29 Geylang	芽笼29巷	112	2 A
Lorong 30 Geylang	芽笼30巷	112	2 B
Lorong 31 Geylang	芽笼31巷	112	2 A
Lorong 32 Geylang	芽笼32巷	112	2 B
Lorong 33 Geylang	芽笼33巷	112	2 A
Lorong 34 Geylang	芽笼34巷	112	2 B
Lorong 35 Geylang	芽笼35巷	112	2 A
Lorong 36 Geylang	芽笼36巷	112	2 B
Lorong 37 Geylang	芽笼37巷	113	1 A
Lorong 38 Geylang	芽笼38巷	112	2 A
Lorong 39 Geylang	芽笼39巷	113	1 A
Lorong 40 Geylang	芽笼40巷	113	1 B
Lorong 41 Geylang	芽笼41巷	113	1 A
Lorong 42 Geylang	芽笼42巷	113	1 A
Lorong 44 Geylang	芽笼44巷	113	1 A
Lorong 1 Realty Park	实业园1巷	70	1 A
Lorong 2 Realty Park	实业园2巷	70	1 A
Lorong 3 Realty Park	实业园3巷	70	1 A
Lorong 4 Realty Park	实业园4巷	70	1 A
Lorong 5 Realty Park	实业园5巷	70	1 A
Lorong 6 Realty Park	实业园6巷	70	1 A
Lorong 7 Realty Park	实业园7巷	70	1 A
Lorong 1 Toa Payoh	大巴窑1巷	88	2 A
Lorong 1A Toa Payoh	大巴窑1A巷	88	2 B
Lorong 2 Toa Payoh	大巴窑2巷	88	2 B
Lorong 3 Toa Payoh	大巴窑3巷	88	2 B
Lorong 4 Toa Payoh	大巴窑4巷	89	1 B
Lorong 5 Toa Payoh	大巴窑5巷	89	1 B
Lorong 6 Toa Payoh	大巴窑6巷	88	2 C
Lorong 7 Toa Payoh	大巴窑7巷	89	1 B
Lorong 8 Toa Payoh	大巴窑8巷	89	1 A
Lorong 8A Toa Payoh	大巴窑8A巷	89	1 B
Lorong A-Leng	罗弄阿灵	90	2 A
Lorong Abu Talib	罗弄阿武达立	115	1 A
Lorong Ah Soo	罗弄阿苏	69	2 D
Lorong Ampas	罗弄安拔士	89	1 D
Lorong Asrama	罗弄阿士拉马	23	2 B
Lorong Ayam Hutan	罗弄阿炎乌丹	20	2 D
Lorong Ayam Katek	罗弄阿炎加德	20	2 D
Lorong Bachok	罗弄巴祝	112	2 B
Lorong Bakar Batu	罗弄巴卡巴株	90	1 C
Lorong Bandang	罗弄班当	114	1 A
Lorong Batawi	罗弄巴达威	70	1 A
Lorong Bekukong	罗弄柏古岗	54	1 B
Lorong Bengkok	罗弄明国	91	1 D
Lorong Biawak	罗弄比阿华	69	1 D
Lorong Binkiang (P. Ubin)	罗弄敏江(敏乌岛)	34	1 D
Lorong Bistari	罗弄比斯达里	22	1 D
Lorong Buangkok (Gerald Dr)	罗弄万国 (日乐通道)	48	2 C
Lorong BuangKok (Sengkang East Way)	罗弄万国 (盛港东大道)	49	2 B
Lorong Bunga	罗弄文雅	90	1 C
Lorong Chencharu	罗弄真查鲁	26	2 B
Lorong Chuan	罗弄泉	68	2 B
Lorong Danau	罗弄丹闹	59	1 B
Lorong Dangai	罗弄丹开	94	2 C
Lorong G Telok Kurau	直落古楼G巷	114	1 A
Lorong Gambir	罗弄甘必	90	1 A
Lorong H Telok Kurau	直落古楼H巷	114	1 A
Lorong Halus	罗弄哈鲁士	50	2 B
Lorong Halwa	罗弄哈哇	87	2 C
Lorong How Sun	罗弄禾山	90	2 A
Lorong J Telok Kurau	直落古楼J巷	114	1 B
Lorong K Telok Kurau	直落古楼K巷	114	1 B
Lorong Kebasi	罗弄可巴希	41	1 A
Lorong Kembang	罗弄肯邦	90	1 C
Lorong Kembangan	罗弄景万岸	92	1 D
Lorong Kemunchup	罗弄可萌竹	63	1 B
Lorong Kesudian	罗弄可素典	91	1 A
Lorong Kilat	罗弄基叻	84	2 A
Lorong Kismis	罗弄吉士美	84	2 B
Lorong L Telok Kurau	直落古楼L巷	114	1 B
Lorong Lada Hitam	罗弄拉打依淡	25	1 B
Lorong Lew Lian	罗弄榴梿	69	1 D
Lorong Limau	罗弄柠檬	89	1 D
Lorong Liput	罗弄力步	108	1 B
Lorong Low Koon	罗弄刘坤	70	1 A
Lorong M Telok Kurau	直落古楼M巷	114	1 B
Lorong Mambong	罗弄曼蒙	108	1 B
Lorong Marican	罗弄马利计	92	1 D
Lorong Marzuki	罗弄马裕基	92	1 D
Lorong Mega	罗弄美佳	67	1 C
Lorong Melayu	罗弄马来由	92	1 D
Lorong Melukut	罗弄美鲁古	19	2 C
Lorong Mesu	罗弄美默苏	87	2 C

ROADS		MAP	GRID
Lorong Mydin	罗弄迈丁	92	1 D
Lorong N Telok Kurau	直落古楼N巷	114	1 B
Lorong Nangka	罗弄南卡	113	2 B
Lorong Napiri	罗弄纳比利	69	1 A
Lorong Ong Lye	罗弄黄梨	69	2 D
Lorong Panchar	罗弄班查	85	2 D
Lorong Pasu	罗弄巴素	40	2 B
Lorong Paya Lebar	罗弄巴耶利巴	90	2 B
Lorong Payah	罗弄巴牙	110	2 D
Lorong Penchalak	罗弄本查拉	90	1 A
Lorong Pendek	罗弄本德	90	1 C
Lorong Pisang Asam	罗弄比山阿三	84	2 A
Lorong Pisang Batu	罗弄比山巴株	84	2 A
Lorong Pisang Emas	罗弄比山恩玛士	84	2 A
Lorong Pisang Hijau	罗弄比山易照	84	2 A
Lorong Pisang Raja	罗弄比山拉惹	84	2 A
Lorong Pisang Udang	罗弄比山乌当	84	2 A
Lorong Puntong	罗弄本同	66	2 B
Lorong Rusuk	罗弄鲁素	38	2 C
Lorong Salleh	罗弄沙礼	91	2 D
Lorong Samak	罗弄沙末	48	1 A
Lorong Sarhad	罗弄沙哈	129	2 C
Lorong Sari	罗弄莎莉	129	2 C
Lorong Sarina	罗弄莎莉娜	113	2 A
Lorong Selangat	罗弄司兰卡	89	2 A
Lorong Semangka	罗弄司芒卡	40	1 B
Lorong Serambi	罗弄西兰比	38	2 B
Lorong Sesuai	罗弄西素艾	63	2 D
Lorong Siglap	罗弄西乞纳	114	2 A
Lorong Sireh Pinang	罗弄西雷槟榔	113	1 A
Lorong Stangee	罗弄史丹宜	113	2 B
Lorong Tahar	罗弄达哈	112	1 B
Lorong Tanggam	罗弄丹甘	48	1 A
Lorong Tawas	罗弄大华士	59	2 C
Lorong Telok	罗弄直落	132	2 B
Lorong Temechut	罗弄德美珠	64	2 D
Lorong Tukang Dua	罗弄都干亚	81	2 D
Lorong Tukang Empat	罗弄都干安拔	81	2 D
Lorong Tukang Lima	罗弄都干利马	81	2 C
Lorong Tukang Satu	罗弄都干沙都	81	2 D
Lorong Tukang Tiga	罗弄都干迪卡	81	2 D
Lorong Tukol	罗弄杜哥	39	1 A
Lothian Terrace	罗天台	114	2 B
Lotus Avenue	莲花道	85	2 C
Lower Delta Road	立达路下段	131	2 C
Lower Kent Ridge Road	肯特岗路下段	106	2 D
Lower Ring Road	下环路	109	1 B
Lower Seletar Close	实里达下段弄	46	1 A
Lowland Road	罗兰路	69	2 B
Loyang Avenue (Changi Village)	罗央道 (樟宜村)	54	1 B
Loyang Avenue (TPE)	罗央道 (淡滨尼快速公路)	73	2 B
Loyang Besar Close	罗央勿刹弄	52	2 D
Loyang Crescent	罗央弯	53	1 C
Loyang Drive	罗央通道	74	1 A
Loyang Garden	罗央花园	74	1 A
Loyang Lane	罗央巷	74	1 A
Loyang Link	罗央连路	53	1 C
Loyang Place	罗央坊	52	2 C
Loyang Rise	罗央坡	74	1 B
Loyang Street	罗央街	53	1 D
Loyang Terrace	罗央台	52	2 C
Loyang View	罗央景	74	1 B
Loyang Walk	罗央径	53	1 C
Loyang Way	罗央大道	74	1 A
Loyang Way 1	罗央第1大道	53	1 D
Loyang Way 2	罗央第2大道	53	2 D
Loyang Way 4	罗央第4大道	53	2 D
Loyang Way 6	罗央第6大道	53	1 C
Lucky Crescent	幸福弯	115	2 A
Lucky Gardens	幸福花园	115	2 A
Lucky Heights	幸福岭	115	2 A
Lucky Rise	幸福坡	115	2 A
Lucky View	幸福景	115	2 A
Ludlow Place	勒罗坊	68	2 B
Lutheran Road	路德兰路	108	2 C
Lyndhurst Road	林赫士路	112	2 C
Lynwood Grove	陵兀林	89	2 A

M			
MacAlister Road	麦克里斯特路	132	1 C
MacKenzie Road	麦肯西路	110	2 C
MacKerrow Road	麦克罗路	89	2 C
MacPherson Lane	麦波申巷	90	2 C
MacPherson Road	麦波申路	90	1 C
MacTaggart Road	麦打嘉路	90	2 B
Madras Street	马德拉斯街	111	1 C
Magazine Road	马可新路	132	2 A
Maida Vale	美达谷	29	1 D
Maidstone Road	梅斯顿路	107	1 B
Maju Avenue	马裕道	68	2 B
Maju Drive	马裕通道	85	1 C
Makepeace Road	麦比士路	110	2 B
Makeway Avenue	麦克威道	110	2 B
Malabar Street	马拉巴街	111	1 D
Malacca Street	六甲街	132	2 B
Malan Road	马兰路	130	2 C
Malay Street	马来街	111	1 D
Malcolm Park	马康园	87	2 D
Malcolm Road	马康路	87	2 D
Malta Crescent	马尔他弯	4	1 C
Mandai Avenue	万礼道	26	1 B
Mandai Estate	万礼园	23	1 C
Mandai Lake Road	万礼湖路	24	1 C
Mandai Lake Rd Track 15	万礼湖路第15乡道	24	1 C
Mandai Link	万礼连路	23	1 C
Mandai Quarry Road	万礼石场路	23	1 C
Mandai Road (BKE)	万礼路 (武吉知马快速公路)	23	2 C
Mandai Road (SLE)	万礼路 (实里达快速公路)	25	1 B
Mandai Road (Upper Thomsom Rd)	万礼路 (汤申路上段)	26	1 D
Mandai Road (Zoo)	万礼路 (动物园)	24	1 C
Mandai Road Track 3	万礼路第3乡道	26	1 D
Mandai Road Track 7	万礼路第7乡道	25	2 D
Mandai Road Track 16	万礼路第16乡道	23	2 C

ROADS		MAP	GRID
Mandalay Road	曼德礼路	110	2 A
Mangis Road	曼基士路	113	2 B
Manila Street	马尼拉街	111	1 D
Maple Avenue	美柏道	85	2 C
Maple Lane	美柏巷	85	2 C
Mar Thoma Road	玛多玛路	89	2 D
Marang Road	玛朗路	142	1 A
Maranta Avenue	马连达道	109	1 B
Margaret Drive	玛格烈通道	108	1 C
Margate Road	马格德路	113	1 D
Margoliouth Road	马可柳斯路	109	2 A
Maria Avenue	马莉亚道	92	2 D
Mariam Close	马莉安弄	74	1 B
Mariam Walk	马莉安径	74	1 B
Mariam Way	马莉安大道	74	1 B
Marigold Drive	马里哥通道	66	2 C
Marina Boulevard	滨海林荫道	133	2 C
Marina Coastal Drive	滨海岸通道	133	2 D
Marina Coastal E'way	滨海岸快速公路	133	2 D
Marina Green	滨海埔	133	2 C
Marina Grove	滨海林	133	2 C
Marina Lane 1	滨海1巷	133	1 D
Marina Lane 2	滨海2巷	133	1 D
Marina Lane 3	滨海3巷	133	1 D
Marina Lane 4	滨海4巷	133	1 D
Marina Mall	滨海广场	133	2 C
Marina Park	滨海公园	133	2 C
Marina Place	滨海坊	133	1 C
Marina Station Road	滨海站路	133	1 C
Marina Street	滨海街	133	1 C
Marina View	滨海景	133	1 C
Marina View Link	滨海景连路	133	1 C
Marina Way	滨海大道	133	2 C
Marine Crescent	马林弯	114	1 C
Marine Drive	马林道	114	1 C
Marine Parade Central	马林百列中路	113	2 C
Marine Parade Road	马林百列路	113	2 C
Marine Terrace	马林台	114	1 C
Marine Vista	马林风景路	114	2 C
Maritime Square	海事广场	142	1 A
Market Street	马吉街	132	2 B
Marlene Avenue	玛琳道	69	1 B
Marne Road	玛安路	111	1 B
Marshall Lane	马绍尔巷	113	2 B
Marshall Road	马绍尔路	113	2 C
Marsiling Crescent	马西岭弯	10	2 A
Marsiling Drive	马西岭通道	10	2 A
Marsiling Ind Est Rd 1	马西岭工业区1路	11	1 B
Marsiling Ind Est Rd 2	马西岭工业区2路	11	1 B
Marsiling Ind Est Rd 3	马西岭工业区3路	11	1 B
Marsiling Ind Est Rd 4	马西岭工业区4路	11	1 B
Marsiling Ind Est Rd 5	马西岭工业区5路	11	1 B
Marsiling Ind Est Rd 6	马西岭工业区6路	11	1 B
Marsiling Ind Est Rd 7	马西岭工业区7路	11	1 B
Marsiling Ind Est Rd 8	马西岭工业区8路	11	1 B
Marsiling Ind Est Rd 9	马西岭工业区9路	11	1 B
Marsiling Ind Est Rd 10	马西岭工业区10路	11	1 B
Marsiling Lane	马西岭巷	10	2 A
Marsiling Rise	马西岭坡	11	1 B
Marsiling Road	马西岭路	10	2 B
Martaban Road	马达班路	89	1 D
Martia Road	马西雅路	114	1 B
Martin Road	马丁路	132	1 A
Martlesham Road	马德威路	53	2 C
Maryland Drive	玛莉兰通道	107	2 A
Marymount Lane	玛丽蒙巷	67	1 D
Marymount Road	玛丽蒙路	67	1 D
Marymount Terrace	玛丽蒙台	67	1 D
Mas Kuning Terrace	马士古宁台	106	1 B
Mata Road	马答路	4	1 C
Matlock Rise	美乐坡	68	2 D
Mattar Road	玛达路	90	2 D
Maude Road	茂德路	111	1 B
Maxwell Link	麦士威连路	132	2 C
Maxwell Road	麦士威路	132	2 C
May Road	梅路	89	1 D
Mayfield Avenue	梅菲道	113	1 D
Mayflower Avenue	美花道	46	1 D
Mayflower Crescent	美花弯	46	1 D
Mayflower Drive	美花通道	46	1 D
Mayflower Lane	美花巷	67	1 A
Mayflower Place	美花坊	46	1 D
Mayflower Rise	美花坡	67	1 A
Mayflower Road	美花路	67	1 A
Mayflower Terrace	美花台	67	1 A
Mayflower Way	美花大道	67	1 A
Mayne Road	梅茵路	110	2 C
Mayo Street	美瑶街	111	1 C
McCallum Street	麦卡南街	132	2 C
McNair Road	麦奈雅路	111	1 A
McNally Street	麦纳利街	111	1 C
Medical Drive	医学通道	107	1 D
Medway Drive	麦威通道	68	2 B
Mei Chin Road	美景路	130	1 A
Mei Hwan Crescent	美苑弯	68	2 C
Mei Hwan Drive	美苑通道	68	1 C
Mei Hwan Road	美苑路	68	1 C
Mei Hwan View	美苑景	68	2 D
Mei Ling Street	美岭街	130	2 A
Melrose Drive	美乐士通道	68	2 D
Meng Suan Road	明端路	26	1 D
Meragi Close	美拉宜弄	94	2 A
Meragi Road	美拉宜路	94	2 A
Meragi Terrace	美拉宜台	94	2 A
Meranti Ave	美兰地道	137A	2 D
Meranti Crescent	美兰地弯	138	1 D
Meranti Lane	美兰地巷	145A	1 C
Meranti Road	美兰地路	145A	1 A
Merbau Road	蓦宝路	132	2 A
Merbok Crescent	美柏弯	84	1 C
Merchant Loop	马真环道	132	2 C
Merchant Road	马真路	132	2 C
Mergui Road	麦桂路	111	1 A
Merino Crescent	麦林诺弯	130	2 A
Merlimau Place	猛里茂坊	125	2 C
Merlimau Road	猛里茂路	125	2 A
Merlion Walk	鱼尾狮径	142	1 C
Merpati Road	美芭蒂路	90	2 C
Merryn Avenue	美林弄	87	2 D
Merryn Close	美林弄	87	2 D
Merryn Drive	美林通道	87	2 D

ROADS		MAP	GRID	ROADS		MAP	GRID
☐ Merryn Road	美林路	87	2 D	☐ Mount Sinai Rise	西乃山坡	107	1 A
☐ Merryn Terrace	美林台	87	2 D	☐ Mount Sinai Road	西乃山路	107	1 A
☐ Metropole Drive	麦特罗波通道	92	2 D	☐ Mount Sinai View	西乃山景	107	1 A
☐ Meyappa Chettiar Road	麦耶巴齐智亚路	89	2 C	☐ Mount Sinai Walk	西乃山径	107	1 A
☐ Meyer Place	麦雅坊	112	2 D	☐ Mount Sophia	苏菲雅山	110	2 C
☐ Meyer Road	麦雅路	112	2 D	☐ Mount Vernon Road	翡珑山路	90	2 A
☐ Middle Road	密驼路	111	1 D	☐ Mountbatten Road	蒙巴顿路	112	1 B
☐ Middlesex Road	密德塞斯路	109	1 C	☐ Mowbray Road	茂布莱路	41	1 A
☐ Miller Street	米勒街	111	1 D	☐ Mugliston Gardens	莫士顿花园	48	1 C
☐ Miltonia Close	美通弄	27	2 A	☐ Mugliston Park	莫士顿园	48	2 B
☐ Miltonia Link	美通连路	28	1 A	☐ Mugliston Road	莫士顿路	113	2 B
☐ Mimosa Crescent	含羞草弯	47	2 C	☐ Mugliston Walk	莫士顿径	48	2 B
☐ Mimosa Drive	含羞草通道	47	2 C	☐ Mulberry Avenue	百利道	90	1 C
☐ Mimosa Place	含羞草坊	47	2 C	☐ Munshi Abdullah Ave	孟诗阿都拉道	45	2 C
☐ Mimosa Road	含羞草路	47	2 C	☐ Munshi Abdullah Walk	孟诗阿都拉径	45	2 C
☐ Mimosa Terrace	含羞草台	47	2 C	☐ Murai Farmway	慕莱农道	38	2 A
☐ Mimosa Vale	含羞草谷	47	2 C	☐ Murai Path	慕莱小径	38	2 A
☐ Mimosa View	含羞草景	47	2 C	☐ Murray Street	慕理街	132	2 C
☐ Mimosa Walk	含羞草径	47	2 C	☐ Murray Terrace	慕理台	132	2 C
☐ Minaret Walk	米住勒径	94	1 D	☐ Muscat Street	马士吉街	111	1 C
☐ Minbu Road	缅布路	88	2 D	☐ Muslim Cemy Path 1	回教坟场第1小径	38	2 D
☐ Minden Road	民登路	109	1 C	☐ Muslim Cemy Path 2	回教坟场第2小径	38	2 D
☐ Ming Teck Park	明德园	85	2 D	☐ Muslim Cemy Path 3	回教坟场第3小径	38	2 D
☐ Minto Road	民多路	111	2 C	☐ Muslim Cemy Path 4	回教坟场第4小径	38	2 D
☐ Mistri Road	美士特里路	132	2 D	☐ Muslim Cemy Path 5	回教坟场第5小径	59	2 A
☐ Moh Guan Terrace	茂源台	131	2 B	☐ Muslim Cemy Path 6	回教坟场第6小径	59	2 A
☐ Mohamed Ali Lane	莫罕默阿里巷	132	2 B	☐ Muslim Cemy Path 7	回教坟场第7小径	59	2 A
☐ Mohamed Sultan Road	莫罕默苏丹路	132	1 A	☐ Muslim Cemy Path 8	回教坟场第8小径	38	2 D
☐ Monk's Hill Road	蒙克山路	110	1 B	☐ Muslim Cemy Path 9	回教坟场第9小径	59	1 A
☐ Monk's Hill Terrace	蒙克山台	110	1 B	☐ Muslim Cemy Path 10	回教坟场第10小径	59	1 A
☐ Montreal Drive	蒙特利通道	3	2 D	☐ Muslim Cemy Path 11	回教坟场第11小径	59	1 A
☐ Montreal Link	蒙特利连路	3	2 D	☐ Muslim Cemy Path 12	回教坟场第12小径	59	1 A
☐ Montreal Road	蒙特利路	3	2 C	☐ Muslim Cemy Path 12A	回教坟场第12A小径	59	1 B
☐ Moonbeam Drive	月光通道	107	1 A	☐ Muslim Cemy Path 13	回教坟场第13小径	59	1 B
☐ Moonbeam Terrace	月光台	107	1 A	☐ Muslim Cemy Path 15	回教坟场第15小径	38	1 C
☐ Moonbeam View	月光景	107	1 A	☐ Muslim Cemy Path 16	回教坟场第16小径	38	2 C
☐ Moonbeam Walk	月光径	107	1 A	☐ Muslim Cemy Path 17	回教坟场第17小径	38	2 C
☐ Moonstone Lane	蒙士楼巷	89	2 C	☐ Muslim Cemy Path 18	回教坟场第18小径	38	1 C
☐ Moreton Close	慕敦弄	68	2 B	☐ Muslim Cemy Path 19	回教坟场第19小径	38	1 B
☐ Morley Road	莫利路	108	1 A	☐ Muslim Cemy Path 20	回教坟场第20小径	38	2 B
☐ Mornington Crescent	莫宁敦弯	29	1 C	☐ Muslim Cemy Path 21	回教坟场第21小径	38	1 B
☐ Morse Road	莫斯路	131	1 D	☐ Muslim Cemy Path 22	回教坟场第22小径	38	2 B
☐ Mosque Street	摩士街	132	2 B	☐ Muslim Cemy Path 24	回教坟场第24小径	38	2 B
☐ Moulmein Rise	摩绵坡	110	2 A	☐ Muslim Cemy Path 26	回教坟场第26小径	38	1 B
☐ Moulmein Road	摩绵路	110	2 A	☐ Muswell Hill	马士威山	89	2 A
☐ Mount Echo Park	玉高峰	109	1 D	☐ Muthuraman Chetty Rd	穆都拉曼齐地路	132	1 A
☐ Mount Elizabeth	伊丽莎白山	110	1 C				
☐ Mount Elizabeth Link	伊丽莎白山连路	110	1 C		N		
☐ Mount Emily Road	爱美丽山路	110	2 C	☐ Nallur Road	纳乐路	115	1 B
☐ Mount Faber Loop	花柏山环道	131	1 D	☐ Namly Avenue	南利道	86	1 D
☐ Mount Faber Road	花柏山路	131	1 D	☐ Namly Close	南利弄	86	1 D
☐ Mount Pleasant Drive	快乐山通道	87	2 C	☐ Namly Crescent	南利弯	86	1 D
☐ Mount Pleasant Road	快乐山路	88	1 C	☐ Namly Drive	南利通道	86	1 D
☐ Mount Rosie Road	露茜山路	88	1 D	☐ Namly Garden	南利花园	86	1 D
☐ Mount Rosie Terrace	露茜山台	88	1 D	☐ Namly Grove	南利林	86	1 D
☐ Mount Sinai Avenue	西乃山道	107	1 A	☐ Namly Hill	南利山	86	1 D
☐ Mount Sinai Crescent	西乃山弯	107	1 A	☐ Namly Place	南利坊	86	1 D
☐ Mount Sinai Drive	西乃山通道	107	1 A	☐ Namly Rise	南利坡	86	1 D
☐ Mount Sinai Lane	西乃山巷	107	2 A	☐ Namly View	南利景	86	1 D
☐ Mount Sinai Plain	西乃山坪	107	1 A	☐ Nankin Mall	南京广场	132	2 B
				☐ Nanson Road	南森路	132	1 A

ROADS		MAP	GRID
Nanyang Avenue	南洋道	59	1 D
Nanyang Circle	南洋圈	80	1 D
Nanyang Crescent	南洋弯	59	1 C
Nanyang Drive	南洋通道	59	1 D
Nanyang Green	南洋埔	59	1 D
Nanyang Hill	南洋山	59	1 D
Nanyang Link	南洋连路	80	1 A
Nanyang Terrace	南洋台	59	1 D
Nanyang Valley	南洋谷	59	1 D
Nanyang View	南洋景	59	1 D
Nanyang Walk	南洋径	59	1 D
Napier Road	纳比雅路	109	1 C
Narayanan Chetty Rd	那拉耶南齐地路	132	1 A
Narooma Road	那鲁马路	87	2 D
Nassim Hill	那森山	109	2 C
Nassim Road	那森路	109	1 A
Nathan Road	纳丹路	109	2 D
Nee Soon Road	义顺路	26	1 D
Neil Road	尼路	132	1 C
Nemesu Avenue	纳美素道	45	2 D
Neo Pee Teck Lane	梁彼德巷	128	2 A
Neo Tiew Crescent	梁宙弯	8	2 B
Neo Tiew Lane 1	梁宙1巷	20	2 B
Neo Tiew Lane 2	梁宙2巷	20	2 A
Neo Tiew Lane 3	梁宙3巷	8	1 D
Neo Tiew Road	梁宙路	20	1 A
Nepal Circus	尼泊尔圈	107	2 C
Nepal Park	尼泊尔园	107	2 C
Neram Crescent	尼蓝弯	47	2 C
Neram Road	尼蓝路	47	2 C
Netheravon Road	尼德拉文路	53	2 B
New Bridge Road	新桥路	132	2 B
New Bugis Street	新武吉士街	111	1 D
New Industrial Road	新工业路	90	2 A
New Loyang Link	新罗央连路	74	1 B
New Market Road	新巴刹路	132	2 B
New Upper Changi Rd	新樟宜路上段	93	1 D
Newton Circus	纽顿圈	110	1 B
Newton Road	纽顿路	110	1 A
Neythal Road	尼德路	81	1 C
Nicoll Drive	尼诰通道	54	1 B
Nicoll Highway	尼诰大道	133	1 A
(Bras Basah Road)	(勿拉士巴沙路)		
Nicoll Highway	尼诰大道	112	1 C
(Stadium Road)	(体育场路)		
Nim Crescent	尼敏弯	47	2 C
Nim Drive	尼敏通道	47	2 C
Nim Green	尼敏埔	47	2 C
Nim Road	尼敏路	47	2 C
Niven Road	尼文路	110	2 C
Norfolk Road	纳福路	110	2 A
Norma Terrace	娜玛台	114	2 A
Normanton Park	诺曼顿园	129	2 A
Norris Road	诺里士路	111	1 B
North Boat Quay	驳船北码头	132	2 A
North Bridge Road	桥北路	111	1 C
(Bras Basah Road)	(勿拉士巴沙路)		

ROADS		MAP	GRID
North Bridge Road	桥北路	111	2 C
(Crawford Street)	(哥罗福街)		
North Buona Vista Drive	北波那维斯达通道	107	2 C
North Buona Vista Rd	北波那维斯达路	107	2 B
North Canal Road	北干拿路	132	2 B
North Coast Crescent	北海岸弯	1	2 D
North Coast Drive	北海岸通道	1	2 D
North Perimeter Road	北界路	54	1 B
North Road	诺特路	3	2 B
North Woodlands Drive	兀兰北通道	11	1 B
North Woodlands Link	兀兰北连路	11	2 B
North Woodlands Way	兀兰北大道	11	2 B
Northolt Road	诺霍特路	53	2 C
Northumberland Road	诺森伯兰路	110	2 B
Novena Rise	诺维娜坡	88	2 D
Novena Terrace	诺维娜台	88	2 D
Nutmeg Road	纳麦路	110	1 C

	O		
Oak Avenue	奥克道	85	2 C
Oakwood Grove	橡木林	11	1 D
Ocean Drive	海洋通道	143	1 D
Ocean Way	海洋大道	143	1 D
Oei Tiong Ham Park	黄仲涵园	107	2 A
Office Road	公署路	3	2 C
Old Airport Road	旧机场路	112	2 B
Old Bah Soon Pah Rd	旧巴顺芭路	14	2 D
Old Birdcage Walk	旧鸟克芝径	29	1 C
Old Choa Chu Kang Rd	旧蔡厝港路	38	2 D
(Jalan Bahar)	(惹兰巴哈)		
Old Choa Chu Kang Rd	旧蔡厝港路	40	1 D
(Sungei Tengah Road)	(双溪登雅路)		
Old Holland Road	旧荷兰路	85	2 C
Old Jurong Road	旧裕廊路	63	2 D
Old Lim Chu Kang Rd	旧林厝港路	38	2 C
Old Middle Road	旧密驼路	3	2 B
Old Nelson Road	旧尼尔逊路	13	2 A
Old Parliament Lane	旧国会巷	133	1 A
Old Pier Road	旧渡头路	53	2 B
Old Sarum Road	旧沙篮路	54	1 D
Old Tampines Road	旧淡滨尼路	74	1 B
Old Toh Tuck Road	旧道德路	84	1 C
Old Upper Thomson Rd	旧汤申路上段	45	1 B
Old Yio Chu Kang Road	旧杨厝港路	46	1 C
Oldham Lane	奥登巷	110	2 D
Olive Road	奥立夫路	88	1 B
Omar Khayyam Avenue	奥马卡炎道	45	2 C
Onan Road	奥南路	113	2 B
One North Crescent	纬壹弯	107	2 D
One North Gateway	纬壹门道	107	2 C
One North Link	纬壹连道	107	2 C
One Tree Hill	独木山	109	2 C
Onraet Road	安莱益路	88	1 C
Ontario Avenue	安达里奥道	66	2 C
Opal Crescent	奥柏弯	89	2 C
Ophir Road	奥菲亚路	111	1 C
Orange Grove Road	柑林路	109	2 B
Orchard Boulevard	乌节林荫道	110	1 C
Orchard Link	乌节连路	110	1 C

ROADS		MAP	GRID	ROADS		MAP	GRID
☐ Orchard Road (Bideford Road)	乌节路 (必德福路)	110	1 C	■ Pan Island Expressway (KJE)	泛岛快速公路 (克兰芝快速公路)	60	2 C
☐ Orchard Road (Cuscaden Road)	乌节路 (卡斯加登路)	109	2 C	■ Pan Island Expressway (NTU - Jalan Bahar)	泛岛快速公路 (南大-惹芝巴哈)	59	2 D
☐ Orchard Road (Dhoby Ghaut)	乌节路 (多美歌)	110	2 D	■ Pan Island Expressway (Paya Lebar Way)	泛岛快速公路 (巴耶利巴大道)	91	1 D
☐ Orchard Spring Lane	乌节路泉巷	109	2 C	■ Pan Island Expressway (Pioneer Road North)	泛岛快速公路 (先驱北路)	80	1 A
☐ Orchard Turn	乌节弯路	110	1 C	■ Pan Island Expressway (Simei Avenue)	泛岛快速公路 (四美道)	94	1 A
☐ Orchid Club Road	胡姬俱乐部路	27	2 B	■ Pan Island Expressway (Thomson Road)	泛岛快速公路 (汤申路)	88	2 C
☐ Orchid Drive	胡姬通道	66	2 C				
☐ Oriole Crescent	奥里欧弯	86	2 B	■ Pan Island Expressway (Upper Bt Timah Rd)	泛岛快速公路 (武吉知马路上段)	85	1 A
☐ Ottawa Road	鄂大瓦路	3	2 D	☐ Pandan Avenue	班丹道	105	2 C
☐ Outram Hill	欧南山	132	1 B	☐ Pandan Crescent	班丹弯	106	1 C
☐ Outram Park	欧南园	132	1 B	☐ Pandan Gardens	班丹花园	83	2 D
☐ Outram Road	欧南路	132	1 C	☐ Pandan Loop	班丹环道	105	2 B
☐ Owen Road	奥云路	111	1 A	☐ Pandan Road	班丹路	105	2 C
☐ Oxford Road	牛津路	111	1 A	☐ Pandan Valley	班丹谷	85	1 D
☐ Oxford Street	牛津街	29	1 C	☐ Pang Seng Road	冯成路	90	1 B
☐ Oxley Garden	欧思礼花园	110	2 D	☐ Parbury Avenue	巴布利道	115	2 A
☐ Oxley Rise	欧思礼坡	110	2 D	☐ Pari Dedap Walk	巴里德达径	93	2 C
☐ Oxley Road	欧思礼路	110	1 D	☐ Park Crescent	柏弯	132	2 B
☐ Oxley Walk	欧思礼径	110	2 D	☐ Park Lane	柏巷	28	2 C
				■ Park Road	柏路	132	2 B

P

				☐ Park Vale	百美谷	86	2 C
☐ Padang Chancery	巴东彰思礼	88	1 D	☐ Park Villas Green	园林别墅埔	69	2 A
☐ Padang Jeringau	巴东泽令告	111	2 B	☐ Park Villas Rise	园林别墅坡	69	1 A
■ Pagoda Street	宝塔街	132	2 B	☐ Park Villas Terrace	园林别墅台	69	2 A
☐ Pahang Street	彭亨街	111	2 C	☐ Parkstone Road	巴士敦路	113	1 C
☐ Pakistan Road	巴基斯坦路	3	2 D	☐ Parliament Place	国会坊	132	2 A
☐ Palawan Beach Walk	灯塔海滨径	142	1 C	☐ Parry Avenue	培立道	69	1 B
☐ Palm Avenue	棕树道	115	1 B	☐ Parry Road	培立路	69	1 B
☐ Palm Drive	棕树通道	115	1 A	☐ Parry Terrace	培立台	69	1 B
☐ Palm Grove Avenue	棕树林道	69	2 B	☐ Parry View	培立景	69	2 B
☐ Palm Road	棕树路	115	1 B	☐ Parry Walk	培立径	69	1 B
☐ Palm Valley Road	棕谷路	109	1 A	☐ Parsi Road	巴诗路	132	2 D
☐ Palmer Road	巴马路	132	2 D	☐ Pasar Lane	巴刹巷	111	1 C
■ Pan Island Expressway (Adam Road)	泛岛快速公路 (亚当路)	87	1 C	☐ Pasir Laba Road	巴西拉巴路	79	1 A
■ Pan Island Expressway (AYE)	泛岛快速公路 (亚逸拉惹快速公路)	79	1 D	☐ Pasir Panjang Close	巴西班让弄	128	2 A
■ Pan Island Expressway (Bedok)	泛岛快速公路 (勿洛)	92	1 C	☐ Pasir Panjang Drive	巴西班让通道	128	2 A
■ Pan Island Expressway (BKE)	泛岛快速公路 (武吉知马快速公路)	64	2 D	☐ Pasir Panjang Hill	巴西班让山	129	2 B
■ Pan Island Expressway (Clementi Avenue 6)	泛岛快速公路 (金文泰6道)	84	1 B	☐ Pasir Panjang Road (Alexandra Road)	巴西班让路 (亚历山大路)	130	1 D
■ Pan Island Expressway (ECP)	泛岛快速公路 (东海岸公园大道)	95	1 A	☐ Pasir Panjang Road (Clementi Rd)	巴西班让路 (金文泰路)	128	2 A
■ Pan Island Expressway (Eng Neo Ave)	泛岛快速公路 (英娘道)	86	2 B	☐ Pasir Panjang Road (Sth Buona Vista Rd)	巴西班让路 (南波那维斯达路)	129	2 C
■ Pan Island Expressway (Jalan Kolam Ayer)	泛岛快速公路 (惹兰哥南亚逸)	112	1 A	☐ Pasir Panjang Terminal Avenue 2	巴西班让 终站2道	129	1 C
■ Pan Island Expressway (Jalan Toa Payoh)	泛岛快速公路 (惹兰大巴窑)	89	1 C	☐ Pasir Panjang Terminal Avenue 3	巴西班让 终站3道	129	1 C
■ Pan Island Expressway (Jurong Canal Dr)	泛岛快速公路 (裕廊水道通道)	61	1 C	☐ Pasir Panjang Terminal Drive 1	巴西班让 终站1通道	129	2 D
■ Pan Island Expressway (Jurong Town Hall Rd)	泛岛快速公路 (裕廊镇大会堂路)	83	1 A	☐ Pasir Panjang Terminal Drive 2	巴西班让 终站2通道	129	2 D
				☐ Pasir Panjang Terminal Drive 3	巴西班让 终站3通道	129	2 D

ROADS		MAP	GRID	ROADS		MAP	GRID
Pasir Panjang Terminal Drive 4	巴西班让 终点4通道	129	2 D	Pasir Ris Drive 12	巴西立第12通道	51	1 C
Pasir Panjang Terminal Drive 5	巴西班让 终点5通道	129	2 D	Pasir Ris Farmway 1	巴西立第1农道	51	1 B
Pasir Panjang Terminal Drive 7	巴西班让 终站7通道	129	2 D	Pasir Ris Farmway 2	巴西立第2农道	51	1 C
Pasir Panjang Terminal Drive 9	巴西班让 终站9通道	129	2 C	Pasir Ris Farmway 3	巴西立第3农道	51	1 B
Pasir Panjang Terminal Drive 10	巴西班让 终站10通道	129	1 C	Pasir Ris Green	巴西立埔	52	1 D
Pasir Panjang Terminal Drive 11	巴西班让 终站11通道	129	2 C	Pasir Ris Heights	巴西立岭	51	2 C
Pasir Panjang Terminal Drive 12	巴西班让 终站12通道	129	2 C	Pasir Ris Ind Drive 1	巴西立工业1通道	51	1 C
Pasir Panjang Terminal Drive 13	巴西班让 终站13通道	129	2 C	Pasir Ris Lane	巴西立巷	52	1 C
Pasir Panjang Terminal Drive 14	巴西班让 终站14通道	129	1 C	Pasir Ris Road	巴西立路	52	1 C
Pasir Panjang Terminal Road A	巴西班让 终站A路	129	2 D	Pasir Ris Street 11	巴西立11街	73	2 B
Pasir Panjang Terminal Road B	巴西班让 终站B路	129	1 C	Pasir Ris Street 12	巴西立12街	73	2 A
Pasir Panjang Terminal Road C	巴西班让 终站C路	129	2 C	Pasir Ris Street 13	巴西立13街	73	2 B
Pasir Panjang Terminal Road D	巴西班让 终站D路	129	2 C	Pasir Ris Street 21	巴西立21街	73	2 A
Pasir Panjang Terminal Road E	巴西班让 终站E路	129	1 C	Pasir Ris Street 41	巴西立41街	52	2 D
Pasir Panjang Terminal Road F	巴西班让 终站F路	129	1 C	Pasir Ris Street 51	巴西立51街	73	1 A
Pasir Panjang Terminal Road G	巴西班让 终站G路	129	1 C	Pasir Ris Street 52	巴西立52街	52	1 D
Pasir Panjang Terminal Road H	巴西班让 终站H路	129	1 C	Pasir Ris Street 53	巴西立53街	52	1 D
Pasir Panjang Terminal Road J	巴西班让 终站J路	129	1 C	Pasir Ris Street 71	巴西立71街	51	1 D
Pasir Panjang Terminal Road K	巴西班让 终站K路	129	1 C	Pasir Ris Street 72	巴西立72街	51	2 C
Pasir Panjang Terminal Road L	巴西班让 终站L路	129	2 D	Pasir Ris Terrace	巴西立台	51	2 C
Pasir Panjang View	巴西班让景	129	1 B	Pasir Ris View	巴西立景	51	2 C
Pasir Panjang Wharves Avenue 1	巴西班让 码头1道	129	2 D	Pasir Ris Walk	巴西立径	73	2 A
Pasir Ris Avenue	巴西立道	51	2 C	Pasir Ris Way	巴西立大道	51	2 C
Pasir Ris Central	巴西立中路	52	1 D	Paterson Hill	巴德申山	109	2 D
Pasir Ris Central St 3	巴西立中路3街	52	1 D	Paterson Road	巴德申路	109	2 D
Pasir Ris Close	巴西立弄	52	2 D	Pavilion Circle	百比林圈	62	2 A
Pasir Ris Coast Ind Pk 1	巴西立海岸第1工业园	51	1 B	Pavilion Grove	百比林林	62	2 A
Pasir Ris Coast Ind Pk 2	巴西立海岸第2工业园	51	1 A	Pavilion Place	百比林坊	62	2 A
Pasir Ris Coast Ind Pk 3	巴西立海岸第3工业园	51	1 A	Pavilion Rise	百比林坡	62	2 A
Pasir Ris Coast Ind Pk 4	巴西立海岸第4工业园	51	1 A	Pavilion Street	百比林街	62	2 A
Pasir Ris Coast Ind Pk 5	巴西立海岸第5工业园	51	1 A	Pavilion View	百比林景	62	2 A
Pasir Ris Coast Ind Pk 6	巴西立海岸第6工业园	51	1 A	Paya Lebar Crescent	巴耶利巴弯	69	2 D
Pasir Ris Drive 1	巴西立第1通道	73	1 A	Paya Lebar Place	巴耶利巴坊	69	2 D
Pasir Ris Drive 2	巴西立第2通道	73	2 A	Paya Lebar Rise	巴耶利巴坡	69	2 D
Pasir Ris Drive 3	巴西立第3通道	52	1 D	Paya Lebar Rd (Geylang)	巴耶利巴路(芽笼)	113	1 A
Pasir Ris Drive 4	巴西立第4通道	73	2 A	Paya Lebar Road (PIE)	巴耶利巴路 (泛岛快速公路)	91	1 C
Pasir Ris Drive 6	巴西立第6通道	73	2 A	Paya Lebar Street	巴耶利巴街	90	2 B
Pasir Ris Drive 8	巴西立第8通道	73	1 A	Paya Lebar Walk	巴耶利巴径	69	2 D
Pasir Ris Drive 10	巴西立第10通道	51	2 C	Paya Lebar Way	巴耶利巴大道	90	2 D
				Peach Garden	桃花园	113	1 D
				Peakville Avenue	登峰道	93	2 C
				Peakville Grove	登峰林	93	2 C
				Peakville Terrace	登峰台	93	2 C
				Peakville Walk	登峰径	93	2 C
				Pearl Bank	珍珠坂	132	1 B
				Pearl's Hill Road	珍珠山路	132	2 B
				Pearl's Hill Terrace	珍珠山台	132	1 B
				Pebble Lane	培柏巷	113	1 B
				Peck Hay Road	碧爱路	110	1 B
				Peck Seah Street	柏城街	132	2 C
				Peel Road	比尔路	108	2 C
				Pegu Road	白姑路	89	1 D
				Pei Wah Avenue	培华道	85	1 B
				Peirce Drive	贝雅士通道	108	2 C
				Peirce Hill	贝雅士山	108	2 C
				Peirce Road	贝雅士路	108	2 C
				Pekin Street	北京街	132	2 B
				Pemimpin Drive	柏民通道	67	2 D
				Pemimpin Place	柏民宾坊	67	2 D

ROADS		MAP	GRID
Pemimpin Terrace	柏民宾台	67	2 C
Penaga Place	本纳加坊	4	1 C
Penang Lane	槟榔巷	110	2 D
Penang Road	槟榔路	110	2 D
Pender Road	秉德路	131	1 D
Pending Road	秉定路	42	2 D
Peng Kang Avenue	秉光道	80	1 B
Peng Nguan Street	炳源街	131	2 B
Penhas Road	班夏士路	111	2 B
Penjuru Circle	本莱鲁圈	105	1 C
Penjuru Circus	本莱鲁交通圈	104	2 C
Penjuru Close	本莱鲁弄	104	2 B
Penjuru Lane	本莱鲁巷	104	2 B
Penjuru Place	本莱鲁坊	104	2 A
Penjuru Road (AYE)	本莱鲁路 (亚逸拉惹快速公路)	83	1 D
Penjuru Road (Jalan Buroh)	本莱鲁路 (惹本布罗)	104	2 C
Penjuru Street	本莱鲁街	104	2 B
Pennefather Road	彭尼华德路	113	2 B
Penshurst Place	平治士坊	68	2 B
Pepys Road	必比士路	129	2 B
Perahu Road	柏拉湖路	7	1 D
Perak Road	霹雳路	111	1 C
Percival Road	白思华路	110	2 D
Pereira Road	白里拉路	90	2 B
Perumal Road	柏鲁马路	111	1 B
Pesari Walk	柏沙礼径	94	1 D
Pesek Road	百锡路	123	2 B
Petain Road	贝当路	111	1 B
Petir Road	闪电路	42	2 D
Pheng Geck Avenue	平玉道	90	1 C
Phillip Street	菲立街	132	2 B
Phillips Avenue	菲立道	69	1 B
Phoenix Avenue	凤凰道	42	1 D
Phoenix Garden	凤凰花园	42	1 D
Phoenix Park	凤凰园	109	1 D
Phoenix Rise	凤凰坡	42	1 D
Phoenix Road	凤凰路	42	1 D
Phoenix Walk	凤凰径	42	1 D
Piccadilly	必卡利里	29	1 C
Piccadilly Circus	必卡利里圈	29	1 D
Pickering Street	必麒麟街	132	2 B
Pillai Road	裴礼路	69	2 D
Pine Close	松弄	112	2 B
Pine Grove	松林	106	2 A
Pine Lane	松巷	112	2 B
Pine Walk	松径	86	1 B
Pinewood Grove	松木林	11	1 D
Pioneer Circle	先驱圈	80	2 D
Pioneer Crescent	先驱弯	102	2 A
Pioneer Place	先驱坊	101	2 B
Pioneer Road (AYE)	先驱路 (亚逸拉惹快速公路)	80	2 D
Pioneer Road (Benoi Road)	先驱路 (贲耐路)	101	1 B
Pioneer Road (Tanjong Kling Road)	先驱路 (丹戎吉宁路)	102	1 B
Pioneer Road (Tuas Rd)	先驱路(大士路)	100	2 A
Pioneer Road (Tuas West Drive)	先驱路 (大士西通道)	77	2 B
Pioneer Road North	先驱北路	80	2 A
Pioneer Sector 1	先驱路1段	100	2 B
Pioneer Sector 2	先驱路2段	101	1 C
Pioneer Sector 3	先驱路3段	101	1 D
Pioneer Sector Lane	先驱路段巷	101	1 D
Pioneer Sector Walk	先驱路段径	101	1 D
Pioneer Walk	先驱径	102	2 A
Pipit Road	比笔路	90	2 D
Pitt Street	毕德街	111	1 C
Plantation Avenue	种植道	69	1 C
Platina Road	布拉提那路	13	2 D
Playfair Road	贝列菲路	90	2 B
Plumer Road	普兰麦路	111	1 B
Plymouth Avenue	普里睦道	87	2 D
Poh Huat Crescent	宝发弯	69	2 A
Poh Huat Drive	宝发通道	69	2 B
Poh Huat Road	宝发路	69	2 A
Poh Huat Road West	宝发西路	69	1 A
Poh Huat Terrace	宝发台	69	1 A
Ponggol Seventeenth Ave	榜鹅第17道	31	1 B
Ponggol Twenty-Fourth Ave	榜鹅第24道	31	1 A
Poole Road	布尔路	113	1 C
Port Road	波德路	130	1 D
Portchester Avenue	波彻士特道	68	2 A
Portsdown Avenue	波斯陶道	130	1 A
Portsdown Road	波斯陶路	107	2 D
Potong Pasir Avenue 1	波东巴西1道	89	2 B
Potong Pasir Avenue 2	波东巴西2道	89	2 C
Potong Pasir Avenue 3	波东巴西3道	89	2 B
Preston Road	普勒士顿路	130	2 C
Primrose Avenue	必灵乐士道	115	1 A
Prince Charles Crescent	查理士太子弯	131	1 A
Prince Charles Square	查理士太子广场	131	1 A
Prince Edward Link	爱德华太子连路	132	2 C
Prince Edward Road	爱德华太子路	132	2 C
Prince George's Park	乔治太子公园	129	1 A
Prince of Wales Road	威尔斯太子路	86	2 D
Prince Philip Avenue	菲立太子道	131	1 A
Prince Road	太子路	108	2 A
Princess of Wales Rd	威尔斯公主路	86	2 D
Prinsep Link	布连捷连路	110	2 D
Prinsep Street	布连捷街	110	2 D
Prome Road	百乐美路	88	2 D
Puay Hee Avenue	培熙道	90	1 C
Pulasan Road	布拉山路	113	2 B
Punggol Central	榜鹅中心	30	2 D
Punggol Crescent	榜鹅弯	30	1 D
Punggol Drive	榜鹅通道	31	1 D
Punggol East	榜鹅东	50	1 A
Punggol Field	榜鹅城	49	2 A
Punggol Field Walk	榜鹅城径	50	1 A
Punggol Lane	榜鹅巷	30	1 D
Punggol Place	榜鹅坊	30	2 D
Punggol Port Lane	榜鹅港巷	31	1 C
Punggol Port Road	榜鹅港路	31	1 C
Punggol Road (End)	榜鹅路 (尾)	31	1 B

ROADS		MAP	GRID
Punggol Road (Hougang Avenue 10)	榜鹅路 (后港10道)	49	2 A
Punggol Road Track 19	榜鹅路第19乡道	30	2 A
Punggol Road Track 22	榜鹅路第22乡道	31	1 B
Punggol Road Track 24	榜鹅路第24乡道	31	1 A
Punggol Walk	榜鹅径	30	2 D
Punggol Way	榜鹅大道	30	1 D
Purvis Street	巴米士街	111	1 D

Q

Quality Road	品质路	81	2 C
Queen Astrid Gardens	爱士特女皇花园	107	2 A
Queen Astrid Park	爱士特女皇园	107	2 A
Queen Elizabeth Walk	伊丽莎白女皇道	133	1 A
Queen Street	奎因街	111	1 D
Queen's Avenue	女皇道	3	2 D
Queen's Close	女皇弄	130	1 A
Queen's Crescent	女皇弯	130	1 A
Queen's Road	女皇路	108	2 A
Queensway	女皇大道	108	1 B
Quemoy Road	金门路	90	2 A

R

Race Course Lane	跑马埔巷	111	1 B
Race Course Road	跑马埔路	111	1 A
Radin Mas	拉丁马士	131	2 C
Raeburn Park	黎本园	132	1 D
Raffles Avenue	莱佛士道	133	1 A
Raffles Boulevard	莱佛士林荫道	133	1 A
Raffles Institution Lane	莱佛士书院巷	88	2 A
Raffles Link	莱佛士连路	133	1 A
Raffles Place	莱佛士坊	133	1 B
Raffles Quay	莱佛士码头	133	1 B
Raglan Grove	勒格兰林	68	2 B
Rain Tree Drive	雨树通道	109	1 A
Rain Tree Valley	雨树谷	45	2 C
Rakit Road	拉吉路	7	1 D
Rambai Road	兰排路	113	2 B
Rambau Street	兰堡街	132	2 D
Rambutan Road	红毛丹路	113	2 A
Ramsgate Road	兰士格路	113	1 D
Rangoon Lane	仰光巷	111	1 A
Rangoon Road	仰光路	111	1 A
Rasok Drive	拉索通道	23	1 B
Read Crescent	李德弯	132	2 A
Read Street	李德街	132	2 A
Rebecca Road	利百加路	86	1 D
Recreation Lane	立可力生巷	69	1 D
Recreation Road	立可力生路	69	1 D
Red Brick Path	红砖小径	109	1 A
Redhill Close	红山弄	131	1 B
Redhill Lane	红山巷	131	1 B
Redhill Road	红山路	131	1 B
Redwood Avenue	红木道	85	2 C
Redwood Grove	红木林	11	1 D
Refinery Road	炼油厂路	102	2 B
Regent Street	励精街	28	2 D
Republic Avenue	共和国道	111	2 D
Republic Boulevard	共和国林荫道	133	1 A
Republic Crescent	共和国弯	11	2 A
Republic Link	共和国连路	11	2 A
Research Link	研究连路	129	1 A
Reservoir Road	水池路	88	1 A
Rhu Cross	禺十字路	111	2 D
Richards Avenue	李节士道	69	2 B
Richards Place	李节士坊	69	2 B
Ridgewood Close	冈林弄	107	1 A
Ridley Park	李利园	109	1 D
Ridout Road	莱道路	108	2 C
Rienzi Street	黎英芝街	114	2 A
Rifle Range Road	射靶场路	85	1 A
Ringwood Road	环林路	113	1 C
Ripley Crescent	李布礼弯	69	1 B
Ritchie Road	里奇路	109	1 C
River Valley Close	里巴巴利弄	110	1 D
River Valley Green	里巴巴利埔	132	1 A
River Valley Grove	里巴巴利林	110	1 D
River Valley Road (Delta Road)	里巴巴利路 (立达路)	131	2 A
River Valley Road (Hill Street)	里巴巴利路 (禧街)	132	2 A
River Valley Road (Killiney Road)	里巴巴利路 (基里尼路)	110	1 D
Riverina Crescent	丽河弯	51	2 C
Riverina View	丽河景	52	1 C
Riverina Walk	丽河径	51	2 D
Riverside Road	河岸路	11	1 A
Rivervale Close	河谷弄	49	2 C
Rivervale Crescent	河谷弯	49	2 B
Rivervale Drive	河谷通道	49	2 A
Rivervale Lane	河谷巷	49	2 C
Rivervale Link	河谷连路	49	2 C
Rivervale Street	河谷街	49	2 B
Rivervale Walk	河谷径	49	2 C
Riviera Drive	里维拉通道	115	2 A
Roberts Lane	罗拔士巷	111	1 B
Robertson Quay	罗拔申码头	132	1 A
Robey Crescent	罗比弯	69	2 A
Robin Close	罗彬弄	109	2 A
Robin Drive	罗彬通道	109	2 A
Robin Lane	罗彬巷	109	2 A
Robin Road	罗彬路	109	2 A
Robin Walk	罗彬径	109	2 A
Robinson Road	罗敏申路	132	2 C
Rochalie Drive	罗渣利通道	109	1 C
Rochdale Road	罗治路	90	2 A
Rochester Drive	罗彻斯德通道	107	2 C
Rochester Park	罗彻斯德园	107	2 C
Rochor Canal Road	梧槽干弯路	111	1 C
Rochor Road	梧槽路	111	1 C
Rodyk Street	罗泰街	132	1 A
Rose Lane	玫瑰巷	113	1 B
Roseburn Avenue	乐士朋道	114	1 B
Rosewood Drive	花梨木通道	11	1 D
Ross Avenue	罗斯道	87	1 D
Rosyth Avenue	乐赛道	69	1 B
Rosyth Road	乐赛路	69	1 B
Rosyth Terrace	乐赛台	69	1 B
Rotan Lane	罗丹巷	111	1 B
Rowell Road	罗威路	111	1 B

ROADS		MAP	GRID
☐ Royal Road	乐雅路	130	1 B
☐ Ruby Lane	鲁比巷	89	2 C
☐ Russels Road	罗素路	130	1 B
☐ Rutland Road	罗德兰路	110	2 B

S

☐ Sago Lane	硕莪巷	132	2 C
■ Sago Street	硕莪街	132	2 B
☐ Saiboo Street	赛布街	132	1 A
☐ Saint Andrew's Road	圣安德烈路	133	1 A
☐ Saint Anne's Wood	圣安尼林	49	2 B
☐ Saint Barnabas Lane	圣巴那巴士巷	89	2 D
☐ Saint Francis Road	圣法兰西士路	89	2 D
☐ Saint George's Lane	圣乔治巷	89	2 D
☐ Saint George's Road	圣乔治路	89	2 D
☐ Saint Gregory's Place	圣格烈哥利坊	132	2 A
☐ Saint Helena Road	圣海伦娜路	4	1 D
☐ Saint Helier's Avenue	圣海莉尔道	69	1 B
☐ Saint John's Crescent	圣约翰弯	74	2 A
☐ Saint John's Road	圣约翰路	3	2 D
☐ Saint Margaret's Road	圣玛格烈路	106	2 C
☐ Saint Martin Lane	圣马丁巷	29	1 C
☐ Saint Martins Drive	圣马丁通道	109	2 C
☐ Saint Michael's Road	圣迈克路	89	2 D
☐ Saint Nicholas View	圣尼克拉景	46	1 D
☐ Saint Patrick's Road	圣巴特埠路	114	1 B
☐ Saint Thomas Walk	圣多马径	110	1 D
☐ Saint Wilfred Road	圣威菲立路	89	2 D
☐ Saint Xavier's Lane	圣芳济巷	70	2 A
■ Sakra Avenue	莎克拉道	138	2 A
☐ Sakra Place	莎克拉坊	138	2 C
☐ Sakra Road	莎克拉路	139	1 A
☐ Sakra View	莎克拉景	139	1 A
☐ Salam Walk	莎南径	94	1 D
☐ Sallim Road	莎琳路	90	2 D
☐ Sam Leong Road	三龙路	111	1 B
☐ Sampan Place	舢舨坊	112	2 D
☐ Samudera Lane	桑姆特拉巷	30	2 B
☐ Sandilands Road	珊蒂兰路	69	2 B
☐ Sandown Place	珊岛坊	68	2 B
☐ Sandwich Road	桑威芝路	106	2 C
☐ Sandy Lane	沙地巷	113	1 B
☐ Saraca Drive	沙乐卡通道	47	1 C
☐ Saraca Hill	沙乐卡山	47	2 C
☐ Saraca Place	沙乐卡坊	47	2 B
☐ Saraca Road	沙乐卡路	47	2 C
☐ Saraca Terrace	沙乐卡台	47	1 C
☐ Saraca View	沙乐卡景	47	2 B
☐ Saraca Walk	沙乐卡径	47	2 C
☐ Sarimbun Ave	莎琳汶道	20	1 A
☐ Sarkies Road	沙奇士路	110	1 A
☐ Saujana Road	桑加那路	42	2 C
☐ Saunders Road	桑德斯路	110	1 C
☐ Science Centre Road	科学馆路	83	1 C
☐ Science Drive 1	科学通道1	107	1 D
☐ Science Drive 2	科学通道2	107	1 D
☐ Science Drive 3	科学通道3	107	1 D
☐ Science Drive 4	科学通道4	107	1 D
☐ Science Park Drive	科学园通道	129	2 A

ROADS		MAP	GRID
☐ Science Park Road	科学园路	129	1 A
☐ Scotts Road	史各士路	110	1 B
☐ Sea Avenue	海洋道	113	2 C
☐ Sea Breeze Avenue	海风道	94	1 B
☐ Sea Breeze Grove	海风林	94	1 B
☐ Sea Breeze Road	海风路	94	1 B
☐ Sea Breeze Walk	海风径	94	1 B
☐ Seagull Walk	海鸥径	94	2 A
☐ Seah Im Road	声音路	142	1 A
☐ Seah Street	佘街	111	1 D
☐ Sealand Road	西兰路	53	2 B
☐ Sea Town Lane	海镇巷	99	1 A
☐ Second Avenue	第2道	86	1 C
☐ Second Chin Bee Road	第2振美路	81	2 C
☐ Second Hospital Ave	第2医院道	132	1 C
■ Second Link (Tuas)	新马第二通道	56	1 C
☐ Second Lok Yang Road	第2络阳路	80	2 D
☐ Segar Road	实加路	42	2 B
☐ Selarang Park Road	史拉兰园路	74	2 A
☐ Selarang Ring Road	史拉兰环路	74	1 A
☐ Selarang Road	史拉兰路	74	2 A
☐ Selarang Way	史拉兰大道	74	1 A
☐ Selegie Road	实利基路	110	1 D
☐ Seletar Close	实里达弄	47	2 C
☐ Seletar Club Road	实里达俱乐部路	28	2 C
☐ Seletar Court	实里达阁	48	1 B
☐ Seletar Crescent	实里达弯	48	1 B
■ Seletar Expressway (Lentor Avenue)	实里达快速公路 (伦多道)	46	1 A
■ Seletar Expressway (Mandai Road)	实里达快速公路 (万礼路)	25	1 A
■ Seletar Expressway (Marsiling Flyover)	实里达快速公路 (马西岭立交桥)	11	2 D
■ Seletar Expressway (Upper Thomson Rd)	实里达快速公路 (汤申路上段)	45	1 A
☐ Seletar Hills Drive	实里达山道	48	1 C
☐ Seletar Road	实里达路	47	2 C
☐ Seletar Satellite Stn Rd	实里达卫星站路	46	1 A
☐ Seletar Terrace	实里达台	47	2 C
☐ Seletar West Farmway 1	实里达西第1农道	47	2 B
☐ Seletar West Farmway 2	实里达西第2农道	47	2 B
☐ Seletar West Farmway 3	实里达西第3农道	47	2 A
☐ Seletar West Farmway 4	实里达西第4农道	47	2 A
☐ Seletar West Farmway 5	实里达西第5农道	47	2 A
☐ Seletar West Farmway 6	实里达西第6农道	47	2 A
☐ Seletar West Farmway 7	实里达西第7农道	48	1 A
☐ Seletar West Farmway 8	实里达西第8农道	47	2 A
☐ Seletar West Farmway 9	实里达西第9农道	47	2 A
☐ Seletar West Farmway 10	实里达西第10农道	28	2 D
☐ Sembawang Alley	三巴旺小巷	13	1 A
☐ Sembawang Avenue	三巴旺道	13	1 B
☐ Sembawang Close	三巴旺弄	13	1 A
☐ Sembawang Crescent	三巴旺弯	13	1 A
☐ Sembawang Drive	三巴旺通道	13	1 A
☐ Sembawang Hills Drive	三巴旺山道	45	2 D
■ Sembawang Link	三巴旺连路	13	1 B
☐ Sembawang Place	三巴旺坊	13	2 B
☐ Sembawang Rd (End)	三巴旺路(尾)	4	1 C
▥ Sembawang Road (Gambas Avenue)	三巴旺路 (甘巴士道)	13	2 A

ROADS		MAP	GRID
Sembawang Road (Mandai Road)	三巴旺路 (万礼路)	26	2 A
Sembawang Terminal Avenue 1	三巴旺 终站1道	3	2 C
Sembawang Terminal Avenue 2	三巴旺 终站2道	3	2 C
Sembawang Terminal Avenue 3	三巴旺 终站3道	3	2 C
Sembawang Terminal Road A	三巴旺 终站A路	4	1 C
Sembawang Terminal Road B	三巴旺 终站B路	4	1 C
Sembawang Terminal Road C	三巴旺 终站C路	4	1 C
Sembawang Terminal Road D	三巴旺 终站D路	4	1 C
Sembawang Terminal Road E	三巴旺 终站E路	4	1 C
Sembawang Terminal Road F	三巴旺 终站F路	4	1 C
Sembawang Terminal Road G	三巴旺 终站G路	4	1 C
Sembawang Terminal Road H	三巴旺 终站H路	3	2 C
Sembawang Vista	三巴旺景	13	1 A
Sembawang Walk	三巴旺径	13	2 B
Sembawang Way	三巴旺大道	13	1 A
Sembong Road	森榜路	13	2 B
Senang Crescent	申南弯	92	1 C
Seng Poh Lane	成保巷	132	1 B
Seng Poh Road	成保路	132	1 B
Sengkang Central	盛港中路	49	1 C
Sengkang East Avenue	盛港东道	49	1 C
Sengkang East Drive	盛港东通道	49	2 C
Sengkang East Road	盛港东路	49	1 A
Sengkang East Way	盛港东大道	49	1 A
Sengkang Square	盛港广场	49	1 B
Sengkang West Avenue	盛港西道	48	1 B
Sengkang West Way	盛港西大道	48	1 A
Senja Link	信佳连路	42	1 B
Senja Road	信佳路	42	1 B
Senja Way	信佳大道	42	1 C
Sennett Avenue	信立道	115	2 A
Sennett Close	信立弄	115	2 A
Sennett Drive	信立通道	115	2 A
Sennett Lane	信立巷	115	2 A
Sennett Place	信立坊	115	2 A
Sennett Road	信立路	115	2 A
Sennett Terrace	信立台	115	2 A
Senoko Avenue	圣诺哥道	2	2 B
Senoko Crescent	圣诺哥弯	2	2 C
Senoko Drive	圣诺哥通道	2	1 C
Senoko Link	圣诺哥连路	2	1 C
Senoko Loop	圣诺哥环道	2	1 C
Senoko Road	圣诺哥路	2	2 C
Senoko South Road	圣诺哥南路	2	1 D
Senoko Way	圣诺哥大道	2	2 B
Sentosa Gateway	圣淘沙入口	142	2 B
Sentul Avenue	冼都道	30	1 C
Sentul Crescent	冼都弯	30	2 C
Sentul Link	冼都连路	30	2 C
Serangoon Avenue 1	实龙岗1道	69	1 D
Serangoon Avenue 2	实龙岗2道	69	1 D
Serangoon Avenue 3	实龙岗3道	68	2 D
Serangoon Avenue 4	实龙岗4道	69	1 C
Serangoon Central	实龙岗中路	69	1 D
Serangoon Central Dr	实龙岗中通道	69	1 C
Serangoon Garden Circus	实龙岗花园圈	68	2 B
Serangoon Garden Way	实龙岗花园大道	68	2 B
Serangoon Lane	实龙岗巷	90	1 A
Serangoon North Ave 1	实龙岗北1道	69	1 A
Serangoon North Ave 2	实龙岗北2道	69	1 A
Serangoon North Ave 3	实龙岗北3道	69	1 A
Serangoon North Ave 4	实龙岗北4道	69	1 A
Serangoon North Ave 5	实龙岗北5道	48	1 D
Serangoon North Ave 6	实龙岗北6道	48	1 D
Serangoon Road	实龙岗路	111	1 B
Serangoon Terrace	实龙岗台	69	1 D
Serapong Course Road	实拉蓬球场路	142	2 C
Serapong Hill Road	实拉蓬山路	143	1 C
Seraya Avenue (Jurong Island)	西拉雅道 (裕廊岛)	126	1 C
Seraya Crescent	西拉雅弯	45	2 D
Seraya Jetty Road (Jurong Island)	西拉雅码头路 (裕廊岛)	126	2 D
Seraya Lane	西拉雅巷	113	2 C
Seraya Place (Jurong Island)	西拉雅坊 (裕廊岛)	126	1 A
Seraya Road	西拉雅路	113	2 C
Seraya Road (Jurong Island)	西拉雅路 (裕廊岛)	126	1 C
Seraya Road 14 (Jurong Island)	西拉雅14路 (裕廊岛)	126	2 D
Seraya Road 18 (Jurong Island)	西拉雅18路 (裕廊岛)	126	1 C
Seraya Road 25 (Jurong Island)	西拉雅25路 (裕廊岛)	126	1 C
Serenade Walk	西利那德径	46	1 D
Seton Close	薛敦弄	109	2 C
Shamah Terrace	沙马台	84	1 A
Shan Road	珊路	88	2 D
Shanghai Road	上海路	109	2 D
Shangri-La Close	香格里拉路	67	1 A
Shangri-La Walk	香格里拉径	67	1 A
Shaw Road	邵氏路	90	2 B
Sheares Avenue	薛尔思道	133	1 C
Shelford Road	赐福路	86	2 C
Shenton Way	珊顿大道	132	2 C
Shepherds Drive	薛柏斯通道	130	2 A
Sherwood Road	赛武路	109	2 A
Shipyard Crescent	船厂弯	102	1 C
Shipyard Road	船厂路	102	1 B
Short Street	肃街	110	2 D
Shrewsbury Road	思鲁斯布利路	110	2 A
Shunfu Road	顺福路	67	1 D
Siak Kew Avenue	锡九道	90	1 C
Sian Tuan Avenue	祥端道	85	2 A
Siang Kuang Avenue	祥光道	90	1 C
Siglap Avenue	实乞纳道	114	1 A

ROADS		MAP	GRID	ROADS		MAP	GRID
☐ Siglap Avenue South	实乞纳南道	114	2 A	☐ Sixth Avenue (Bt Timah)	第6道(武吉知马)	86	1 C
☐ Siglap Bank	实乞纳坂	114	2 A	☐ Sixth Avenue (Holland)	第6道(荷兰)	107	2 A
☐ Siglap Close	实乞纳弄	114	2 A	☐ Sixth Crescent	第6弯	85	2 D
☐ Siglap Drive	实乞纳通道	114	2 A	☐ Sixth Lok Yang Road	第6洛阳路	80	1 D
☐ Siglap Gardens	实乞纳花园	114	2 B	☐ Slim Barracks Rise	史林兵营坡	107	2 C
☐ Siglap Hill	实乞纳山	114	2 A	☐ Smith Street	史密斯街	132	2 B
☐ Siglap Link	实乞纳连路	114	2 C	☐ Solomon Street	所罗门街	132	2 A
☐ Siglap Plain	实乞纳坪	114	1 A	☐ Somapah Road	索马巴路	94	2 B
☐ Siglap Rise	实乞纳坡	114	2 A	☐ Somerset Road	索美塞路	110	1 C
☐ Siglap Road	实乞纳路	114	2 A	☐ Somme Road	松美路	111	1 B
☐ Siglap Terrace	实乞纳台	114	2 A	☐ Sommerville Estate Dr	索美维村道	108	2 B
☐ Siglap View	实乞纳谷	114	2 A	☐ Sommerville Estate Rd	索美维村路	108	2 B
☐ Siglap View	实乞纳景	114	1 A	☐ Sommerville Road	索美维路	89	2 A
☐ Siglap Walk	实乞纳径	114	2 A	☐ Sommerville Walk	索美维径	90	1 A
☐ Silat Avenue	石叻道	131	2 C	☐ Soo Chow Drive	苏州通道	67	1 C
☐ Silat Road	石叻路	131	2 C	☐ Soo Chow Garden Rd	苏州花园路	66	2 C
☐ Silat Walk	石叻径	131	2 C	☐ Soo Chow Rise	苏州坡	66	2 C
☐ Siloso Beach Walk	西乐索海滩径	142	1 C	☐ Soo Chow View	苏州景	66	2 D
☐ Siloso Road	西乐索路	141	2 B	☐ Soo Chow Walk	苏州径	67	1 C
☐ Sime Park Hill	森园山	86	2 B	☐ Soo Chow Way	苏州大道	66	2 D
☐ Sime Road	森路	87	1 B	☐ Soon Lee Drive	顺利通道	80	2 C
☐ Simei Avenue	四美道	94	1 A	☐ Soon Lee Road	顺利路	80	2 C
☐ Simei Rise	四美坡	73	2 D	☐ Soon Wing Road	顺荣路	90	2 C
☐ Simei Road	四美路	94	2 A	☐ Sophia Road	菲菲雅路	110	2 C
☐ Simei Street 1	四美1街	94	1 A	☐ Sops Avenue	索普斯道	53	1 D
☐ Simei Street 2	四美2街	94	2 A	☐ Sops Boulevard	索普斯林荫道	53	1 C
☐ Simei Street 3	四美3街	94	1 A	☐ Sops Crescent	索普斯弯	53	1 D
☐ Simei Street 4	四美4街	94	2 A	☐ Sops Drive	索普斯通道	53	1 D
☐ Simei Street 5	四美5街	94	1 A	☐ Sops Lane	索普斯巷	53	1 D
☐ Simei Street 6	四美6街	94	1 A	☐ Sops Link	索普斯连路	53	1 D
☐ Simon Lane	西门巷	69	2 B	☐ Sops Place	索普斯坊	53	1 D
☐ Simon Place	西门坊	69	2 B	☐ Sops Street	索普斯街	53	1 D
☐ Simon Road	西门路	69	2 B	☐ Sops Terrace	索普斯台	53	1 C
☐ Simon Walk	西门径	69	2 B	☐ Sops Way	索普斯大道	53	1 C
☐ Sims Avenue (Aljunied)	沈氏道(阿裕尼路)	112	2 A	☐ Sorby Adams Drive	苏比亚当通道	89	2 B
☐ Sims Ave (Paya Lebar)	沈氏道(巴耶利巴)	113	1 A	☐ South Bridge Road	桥南路	132	2 C
☐ Sims Avenue East	沈氏东道	114	1 A	☐ South Buona Vista Rd	武吉那维斯达路	129	1 A
☐ Sims Drive	沈氏通道	112	1 A	☐ South Canal Road	南干拿路	132	2 B
☐ Sims Lane	沈氏巷	112	2 A	☐ South Perimeter Road	南界路	95	2 A
☐ Sims Place	沈氏坊	112	2 A	☐ South Woodlands Drive	兀兰南通道	11	2 C
☐ Sims View	沈氏景	114	1 A	☐ South Woodlands Way	兀兰南大道	11	2 C
☐ Sims Way	沈氏大道	112	1 B	☐ Spooner Road	史布纳路	132	1 C
☐ Sin Ming Avenue	新民道	67	1 B	☐ Sports Drive 1	体育通道1	106	2 D
☐ Sin Ming Drive	新民通道	67	1 B	☐ Sports Drive 2	体育通道2	106	2 D
☐ Sin Ming Ind Est Sector A	新民工业区A段	67	1 C	☐ Spottiswoode Park Rd	史波disco那兀路	132	1 C
☐ Sin Ming Ind Est Sector B	新民工业区B段	67	1 C	☐ Spring Street	史必灵路	132	2 C
				☐ Springleaf Avenue	春叶道	45	1 A
☐ Sin Ming Ind Est Sector C	新民工业区C段	67	1 C	☐ Springleaf Crescent	春叶弯	45	2 A
				☐ Springleaf Drive	春叶通道	26	2 D
☐ Sin Ming Road	新民路	67	1 C	☐ Springleaf Garden	春叶花园	45	2 A
☐ Sin Ming Walk	新民径	67	1 B	☐ Springleaf Height	春叶岭	45	1 A
☐ Sinaran Drive	西赋兰通道	110	2 A	☐ Springleaf Lane	春叶巷	45	1 A
☐ Sing Avenue	星道	111	1 A	☐ Springleaf Link	春叶连路	26	2 D
☐ Sing Joo Walk	星柔径	111	1 A	☐ Springleaf Rise	春叶坡	26	2 D
☐ Siok Wan Close	菽园弄	129	2 C	☐ Springleaf Road	春叶路	45	1 A
☐ Sirat Place	西勒坊	69	1 C	☐ Springleaf View	春叶景	45	1 A
☐ Sirat Road	西勒路	69	1 C	☐ Springleaf Walk	春叶径	45	1 A
☐ Sireh Place	思礼坊	69	2 C	☐ Springside Avenue	泉滨道	26	2 C
☐ Sit Wah Road	薛华路	132	1 B	☐ Springside Crescent	泉滨弯	26	2 D
				☐ Springside Drive	泉滨通道	26	1 D

ROADS		MAP	GRID
☐ Springside Green	泉滨埔	26	1 D
☐ Springside Link	泉滨连路	26	1 C
☐ Springside Place	泉滨坊	26	2 C
☐ Springside Road	泉滨路	26	1 C
☐ Springside View	泉滨景	26	2 C
☐ Springside Walk	泉滨径	26	1 C
☐ Springwood Avenue	春林道	129	2 C
☐ Springwood Close	春林弄	129	2 C
☐ Springwood Crescent	春林弯	129	2 C
☐ Springwood Height	春林岭	129	2 B
☐ Springwood Terrace	春林台	129	2 C
☐ Springwood Walk	春林径	129	2 C
☐ Stadium Boulevard	体育场林荫道	112	1 C
☐ Stadium Crescent	体育场弯	112	1 C
☐ Stadium Drive	体育场通道	112	1 C
☐ Stadium Lane	体育场巷	112	1 C
☐ Stadium Link	体育场连路	112	1 B
☐ Stadium Road	体育场路	112	1 C
☐ Stadium Walk	体育场径	112	1 C
☐ Stagmont Ring	史达蒙环路	41	2 A
(Woodlands Road)	(兀兰路)		
☐ Stagmont Road	史达蒙路	41	2 C
☐ Stamford Road	史丹福路	110	2 D
☐ Stangee Close	实丹宜弄	113	2 B
☐ Stangee Place	实丹宜坊	113	2 B
☐ Stanley Street	史坦利街	132	2 C
☐ Starlight Road	星光路	111	1 A
☐ Starlight Terrace	星光台	111	1 A
☐ Stephen Lee Road	史蒂芬李路	24	2 A
☐ Stevens Close	史蒂芬弄	109	2 A
☐ Stevens Drive	史蒂芬通道	109	2 A
☐ Stevens Road	史蒂芬路	109	2 A
☐ Still Lane	史蒂尔巷	114	1 B
☐ Still Road	史蒂尔路	113	2 A
☐ Still Road South	史蒂尔南路	114	1 C
☐ Stirling Road	史德林路	108	1 D
☐ Stirling Walk	史德林径	130	2 A
☐ Stockport Road	史托波路	129	2 A
☐ Stokesay Drive	史托基通道	68	2 B
☐ Stone Avenue	史吨道	85	2 A
☐ Stores Road	士多路	4	1 B
☐ Straits Boulevard	海峡林荫道	133	1 D
☐ Strathmore Avenue	史达拉摩道	130	2 A
☐ Strathmore Road	史达拉摩路	131	1 A
☐ Stratton Drive	斯特拉顿通道	47	2 C
☐ Stratton Green	斯特拉顿埔	47	2 C
☐ Stratton Place	斯特拉顿坊	47	2 C
☐ Stratton Road	斯特拉顿路	47	2 C
☐ Stratton Walk	斯特拉顿径	47	2 C
☐ Student Walk	学生径	59	1 D
☐ Sturdee Road	史德蒂路	111	1 B
☐ Sturdee Road North	史德蒂北路	111	1 A
☐ Sudan Road	苏丹路	3	2 D
☐ Suffolk Road	萨福路	110	2 A
☐ Suffolk Walk	萨福径	110	2 A
☐ Sultan Gate	苏丹门	111	2 C
☐ Summer Place	夏坊	68	2 C
☐ Summit Lane	顶峰巷	83	1 C
☐ Sunbird Avenue	桑柏道	94	2 B
☐ Sunbird Circle	桑柏圈	94	2 B

ROADS		MAP	GRID
☐ Sunbird Road	桑柏路	94	2 B
☐ Sundridge Park Road	善立志园路	68	2 D
☐ Sungei Gedong Road	双溪格当路	20	1 A
☐ Sungei Kadut Avenue	双溪加株道	22	2 C
☐ Sungei Kadut Crescent	双溪加株弯	22	1 C
☐ Sungei Kadut Drive	双溪加株通道	22	1 C
☐ Sungei Kadut Loop	双溪加株环道	22	1 C
☐ Sungei Kadut Street 1	双溪加株1街	22	2 A
☐ Sungei Kadut Street 2	双溪加株2街	22	2 B
☐ Sungei Kadut Street 3	双溪加株3街	22	2 B
☐ Sungei Kadut Street 4	双溪加株4街	22	2 A
☐ Sungei Kadut Street 5	双溪加株5街	22	2 A
☐ Sungei Kadut Street 6	双溪加株6街	9	2 D
☐ Sungei Kadut Way	双溪加株大道	22	2 C
☐ Sungei Road	双溪路	111	1 C
☐ Sungei Tengah Road	双溪登雅路	40	2 A
☐ Sunrise Avenue	朝阳道	47	1 B
☐ Sunrise Close	朝阳弄	47	1 B
☐ Sunrise Drive	朝阳通道	47	1 B
☐ Sunrise Lane	朝阳巷	47	1 B
☐ Sunrise Place	朝阳坊	47	1 B
☐ Sunrise Terrace	朝阳台	47	1 B
☐ Sunrise Walk	朝阳径	47	1 B
☐ Sunrise Way	朝阳大道	47	1 B
☐ Sunset Avenue	斜阳道	86	2 B
☐ Sunset Close	斜阳弄	84	2 D
☐ Sunset Crescent	斜阳弯	84	2 C
☐ Sunset Drive	斜阳通道	84	2 D
☐ Sunset Grove	斜阳林	84	2 D
☐ Sunset Heights	斜阳岭	84	2 C
☐ Sunset Lane	斜阳巷	84	2 D
☐ Sunset Place	斜阳坊	84	2 D
☐ Sunset Square	斜阳广场	84	2 C
☐ Sunset Terrace	斜阳台	84	2 D
☐ Sunset Vale	斜阳谷	84	2 C
☐ Sunset View	斜阳景	84	2 C
☐ Sunset Walk	斜阳径	84	2 D
☐ Sunset Way	斜阳大道	84	2 C
☐ Sunshine Terrace	日光台	90	1 A
☐ Supreme Court Lane	最高法院巷	133	1 A
☐ Surin Avenue	树林道	69	2 C
☐ Surin Lane	树林巷	69	2 C
☐ Surin Road	树林路	69	2 C
☐ Surrey Road	萨立路	110	2 A
☐ Sussex Garden	塞硕斯花园	28	2 D
☐ Sut Avenue	苏特道	139	1 D
☐ Swallow Street	燕子街	28	2 C
☐ Swan Lake Avenue	天鹅湖道	114	2 A
☐ Swanage Road	士温纳路	113	1 B
☐ Swettenham Close	瑞登翰弄	108	2 C
☐ Swettenham Green	瑞登翰埔	108	2 C
☐ Swettenham Road	瑞登翰路	108	2 C
☐ Swiss Club Avenue	瑞士俱乐部道	85	2 B
☐ Swiss Club Lane	瑞士俱乐部巷	85	2 B
☐ Swiss Club Link	瑞士俱乐部连路	85	2 A
☐ Swiss Club Road	瑞士俱乐部路	85	2 A
☐ Swiss Cottage Estate	瑞士小屋村	109	2 A
☐ Swiss View	瑞士景	85	2 A
☐ Syed Alwi Road	赛阿威路	111	1 B
☐ Synagogue Street	新那阁街	132	2 B

ROADS		MAP	GRID
T			
☐ T1 Arrival Crescent (Changi Airport)	第1机场终站入境弯 (樟宜机场)	75	1 B
☐ T1 Basement Drive (Changi Airport)	第1机场终站地下通道 (樟宜机场)	75	1 B
☐ T1 Boulevard (Changi Airport)	第1机场终站林荫道 (樟宜机场)	75	1 C
☐ T1 Link East (Changi Airport)	第1机场终站东连路 (樟宜机场)	75	1 B
☐ T1 Link West (Changi Airport)	第1机场终站西连路 (樟宜机场)	75	1 B
☐ T1 Passenger Crescent (Changi Airport)	第1机场终站搭客弯 (樟宜机场)	75	1 B
☐ T1 VIP Drive (Changi Airport)	第1机场终站贵宾通道 (樟宜机场)	75	1 B
☐ T2 Arrival Drive (Changi Airport)	第2机场终站入境通道 (樟宜机场)	75	1 C
☐ T2 Basement Drive (Changi Airport)	第2机场终站地下通道 (樟宜机场)	75	1 C
☐ T2 Boulevard (Changi Airport)	第2机场终站林荫道 (樟宜机场)	75	1 C
☐ T2 Departure Drive (Changi Airport)	第2机场终站离境通道 (樟宜机场)	75	1 C
☐ T2 Link North (Changi Airport)	第2机场终站北连路 (樟宜机场)	75	1 C
☐ T2 Link South (Changi Airport)	第2机场终站南连路 (樟宜机场)	75	1 D
☐ T2 VIP Drive (Changi Airport)	第2机场终站贵宾通道 (樟宜机场)	75	1 D
☐ Tagore Avenue	太戈尔道	45	2 C
☐ Tagore Drive	太戈尔通道	45	2 C
☐ Tagore Industrial Ave	太戈尔工业道	45	2 C
☐ Tagore Lane	太戈尔巷	45	2 C
☐ Tagore Road	太戈尔路	45	2 C
☐ Tah Ching Road	塔清路	82	1 B
☐ Tai Gin Road	大人路	88	2 C
☐ Tai Hwan Avenue	大苑道	68	2 C
☐ Tai Hwan Close	大苑弄	68	2 C
☐ Tai Hwan Crescent	大苑弯	68	2 C
☐ Tai Hwan Drive	大苑通道	68	2 C
☐ Tai Hwan Grove	大苑林	68	2 C
☐ Tai Hwan Heights	大苑岭	68	2 C
☐ Tai Hwan Lane	大苑巷	68	2 C
☐ Tai Hwan Place	大苑坊	68	2 C
☐ Tai Hwan Terrace	大苑台	68	2 C
☐ Tai Hwan Walk	大苑径	68	2 C
☐ Tai Keng Avenue	大庆道	69	2 D
☐ Tai Keng Gardens	大庆花园	69	2 D
☐ Tai Keng Lane	大庆巷	69	2 D
☐ Tai Keng Place	大庆坊	90	2 A
☐ Tai Keng Terrace	大庆台	69	2 D
☐ Tai Seng Avenue	大成道	91	1 B
☐ Tai Seng Drive	大成通道	91	1 B
☐ Tai Seng Link	大成连路	91	1 B
☐ Tai Seng Street	大成街	91	1 B
☐ Tai Thong Crescent	大通弯	90	1 C
☐ Tai Yuan Heights	泰园岭	68	2 C
☐ Talma Road	达马路	112	1 B
☐ Taman Bedok	达曼勿洛	94	1 D
☐ Taman Ho Swee	达曼河水	131	2 A
☐ Taman Kembangan	达曼景万岸	92	1 D
☐ Taman Mas Merah	达曼马士美拉	106	1 B
☐ Taman Nakhoda	达曼那哥达	108	2 B
☐ Taman Permata	达曼马马达	67	1 D
☐ Taman Selamat	达曼士拉末	92	1 D
☐ Taman Serasi	达曼史拉西	109	1 B
☐ Taman Siglap	达曼实乞纳	114	2 A
☐ Taman Sireh	达曼思礼	69	2 D
☐ Taman Warna	达曼哇那	108	1 B
☐ Tamarind Road	答淋林络	47	2 B
☐ Tampines Avenue	淡滨尼道	72	1 A
☐ Tampines Avenue 1	淡滨尼1道	93	2 A
☐ Tampines Avenue 2	淡滨尼2道	73	1 D
☐ Tampines Avenue 3	淡滨尼3道	72	1 D
☐ Tampines Avenue 4	淡滨尼4道	73	1 C
☐ Tampines Avenue 5	淡滨尼5道	72	1 C
☐ Tampines Avenue 6	淡滨尼6道	72	2 C
☐ Tampines Avenue 7	淡滨尼7道	73	1 C
☐ Tampines Avenue 8	淡滨尼8道	72	1 D
☐ Tampines Avenue 9	淡滨尼9道	72	1 B
☐ Tampines Avenue 10	淡滨尼10道	72	1 D
☐ Tampines Avenue 12	淡滨尼12道	72	2 B
☐ Tampines Central 1	淡滨尼中1路	72	2 C
☐ Tampines Central 2	淡滨尼中2路	72	2 C
☐ Tampines Central 3	淡滨尼中3路	72	2 C
☐ Tampines Central 4	淡滨尼中4路	73	1 C
☐ Tampines Central 5	淡滨尼中5路	72	2 D
☐ Tampines Central 6	淡滨尼中6路	72	2 D
☐ Tampines Central 7	淡滨尼中7路	72	2 C
☐ Tampines Concourse	淡滨尼总汇	72	2 C
■ Tampines Expressway (Jalan Kayu)	淡滨尼快速公路 (惹兰加由)	29	1 D
■ Tampines Expressway (Lorong Halus)	淡滨尼快速公路 (罗弄哈鲁士)	50	1 B
■ Tampines Expressway (Loyang Avenue)	淡滨尼快速公路 (罗央道)	73	1 A
■ Tampines Expressway (Pasir Ris)	淡滨尼快速公路 (巴西立)	51	1 D
■ Tampines Expressway (Punggol)	淡滨尼快速公路 (榜鹅)	49	2 A
☐ Tampines Grande	淡滨尼宏道	72	2 C
☐ Tampines Ind Ave 1	淡滨尼工业1道	71	2 C
☐ Tampines Ind Ave 2	淡滨尼工业2道	72	1 B
☐ Tampines Ind Ave 3	淡滨尼工业3道	72	1 C
☐ Tampines Ind Ave 4	淡滨尼工业4道	71	2 A
☐ Tampines Ind Ave 5	淡滨尼工业5道	72	1 A
☐ Tampines Ind Crescent	淡滨尼工业弯	50	2 D
☐ Tampines Ind St 61	淡滨尼工业61街	72	1 A
☐ Tampines Ind St 62	淡滨尼工业62街	72	1 A
☐ Tampines Link	淡滨尼连路	72	2 A
☐ Tampines Nth Dr 1 & 2	淡滨尼北1和2通道	72	1 A
☐ Tampines Place	淡滨尼坊	72	
☐ Tampines Road (Hng)	淡滨尼路(后港)	70	1 B
☐ Tampines Road (Tampines New Town)	淡滨尼路 (淡滨尼新镇)	72	1 A
▥ Tampines Road (TPE)	淡滨尼路 (淡滨尼快速公路)	50	1 D
☐ Tampines Street 11	淡滨尼11街	73	1 D
☐ Tampines Street 12	淡滨尼12街	72	2 D

ROADS		MAP	GRID
Tampines Street 21	淡滨尼21街	73	1 C
Tampines Street 22	淡滨尼22街	73	1 C
Tampines Street 23	淡滨尼23街	73	1 C
Tampines Street 24	淡滨尼24街	73	1 C
Tampines Street 31	淡滨尼31街	73	2 D
Tampines Street 32	淡滨尼32街	73	2 C
Tampines Street 33	淡滨尼33街	73	2 D
Tampines Street 34	淡滨尼34街	73	2 C
Tampines Street 41	淡滨尼41街	73	1 C
Tampines Street 42	淡滨尼42街	73	1 C
Tampines Street 43	淡滨尼43街	73	1 C
Tampines Street 44	淡滨尼44街	73	1 C
Tampines Street 45	淡滨尼45街	73	2 B
Tampines Street 71	淡滨尼71街	72	1 C
Tampines Street 72	淡滨尼72街	72	1 C
Tampines Street 73	淡滨尼73街	72	1 C
Tampines Street 81	淡滨尼81街	72	1 D
Tampines Street 82	淡滨尼82街	72	2 D
Tampines Street 83	淡滨尼83街	72	1 C
Tampines Street 84	淡滨尼84街	72	1 D
Tampines Street 91	淡滨尼91街	72	2 D
Tampines Street 92	淡滨尼92街	93	2 A
Tampines Street 93	淡滨尼93街	93	2 A
Tampines Street 94	淡滨尼94街	93	2 A
Tan Boon Chong Ave	陈文宗道	107	2 A
Tan Kim Cheng Road	陈金钟路	86	2 D
Tan Quee Lan Street	陈桂兰街	111	1 D
Tan Sim Boh Road	陈森茂路	88	1 D
Tan Tock Seng Link	陈笃生连路	88	2 D
Tan Tye Place	陈泰坊	132	2 A
Tanah Merah Besar Ln	丹那美拉勿刹巷	74	2 C
Tanah Merah Besar Rd	丹那美拉勿刹路	74	1 B
Tanah Merah Besar Wk	丹那美拉勿刹径	74	2 B
Tanah Merah Coast Rd	丹那美拉海岸路	117	2 A
Tanah Merah Ferry Rd	丹那美拉渡轮路	118	1 A
Tanah Merah Kechil Ave	丹那美拉克基道	94	1 C
Tanah Merah Kechil Lk	丹那美拉克基连路	93	2 C
Tanah Merah Kechil Ridge	丹那美拉克基岗	93	2 C
Tanah Merah Kechil Rise	丹那美拉克基坡	93	2 C
Tanah Merah Kechil Rd	丹那美拉克基路	93	2 C
Tanah Merah Kechil Road South	丹那美拉克基南路	94	1 D
Tanglin Gate Road	东陵门路	109	1 B
Tanglin Halt Close	东陵福弄	108	1 C
Tanglin Halt Road	东陵福路	107	2 C
Tanglin Hill	东陵山	109	1 C
Tanglin Rise	东陵坡	109	1 C
Tanglin Road (Alexandra Road)	东陵路 (亚历山大路)	131	1 A
Tanglin Road (Chatsworth Road)	东陵路 (采士华路)	109	1 C
Tanglin Road (Tomlinson Road)	东陵路 (汤林生路)	109	2 C
Tanglin Walk	东陵径	109	1 C
Tangmere Road	唐美路	53	2 C
Tanjong Beach Walk	丹戎海滨径	142	2 D
Tanjong Katong Road	丹戎加东路	113	1 B
Tanjong Katong Rd Sth	丹戎加东南路	113	1 D
Tanjong Kling Road	丹戎吉宁路	102	2 A
Tanjong Pagar Plaza	丹戎巴葛广场	132	2 C
Tanjong Pagar Road	丹戎巴葛路	132	2 C
Tanjong Pagar Terminal Avenue	丹戎巴葛 终站道	133	1 D
Tanjong Pagar Terminal Road A	丹戎巴葛 终站A路	132	2 D
Tanjong Pagar Terminal Road B	丹戎巴葛 终站B路	132	2 D
Tanjong Pagar Terminal Road C	丹戎巴葛 终站C路	143	2 A
Tanjong Pagar Terminal Road D	丹戎巴葛 终站D路	143	2 A
Tanjong Pagar Terminal Road E	丹戎巴葛 终站E路	132	2 D
Tanjong Pagar Terminal Road F	丹戎巴葛 终站F路	143	2 A
Tanjong Pagar Terminal Road G	丹戎巴葛 终站G路	143	2 A
Tanjong Pagar Terminal Road H	丹戎巴葛 终站H路	143	2 A
Tanjong Pagar Terminal Road J	丹戎巴葛 终站J路	132	2 D
Tanjong Pagar Terminal Street 1	丹戎巴葛 终站1街	143	2 A
Tanjong Pagar Terminal Street 2	丹戎巴葛 终站2街	143	2 A
Tanjong Pagar Terminal Street 3	丹戎巴葛 终站3街	143	2 A
Tanjong Pagar Terminal Street 4	丹戎巴葛 终站4街	132	2 D
Tanjong Pagar Terminal Street 5	丹戎巴葛 终站5街		
Tanjong Penjuru	丹戎本茱鲁	104	2 B
Tanjong Penjuru Cres	丹戎本茱鲁弯	105	1 C
Tanjong Rhu Place	丹戎禺坊	112	1 D
Tanjong Rhu Road	丹戎禺路	112	1 D
Tanjong Rhu View	丹戎禺景	111	2 D
Tank Road	登路	110	2 D
Tannery Lane	登纳利巷	90	1 C
Tannery Road	登纳利路	90	1 C
Tao Ching Road	岛景路	82	1 B
Tasmania Road	塔斯马尼亚路	3	2 C
Tavistock Avenue	达维士笃道	68	2 A
Tay Lian Teck Drive	郑连德道道	115	1 B
Tay Lian Teck Road	郑连德路	115	1 B
Teban Gardens Cres	德曼花园弯	83	1 D
Teban Gardens Road	德曼花园路	83	1 D
Tebing Lane	德明巷	50	1 A
Tebing Walk	德明径	50	1 B
Tech Park Crescent	科技园弯	99	1 B
Technology Crescent	工艺弯	129	2 A
Teck Chye Terrace	德财台	69	1 C
Teck Lim Road	德霖路	132	2 C
Teck Whye Avenue	德惠道	41	2 C
Teck Whye Crescent	德惠弯	41	2 C
Teck Whye Lane	德惠巷	41	2 C
Teck Whye Walk	德惠径	41	2 C
Tekka Lane	德卡巷	110	2 B
Tekong Highway	德光大道	148	

ROADS		MAP	GRID	ROADS		MAP	GRID
Telegraph Street	电报街	133	1 C	Thrift Drive	俭约通道	90	2 A
Telok Ayer Street	直落亚逸街	132	2 B	Tiong Bahru Road	中巴鲁路	131	1 A
Telok Blangah Crescent	直落布兰雅弯	131	1 C	Tiong Poh Avenue	忠坡道	131	2 B
Telok Blangah Drive	直落布兰雅通道	130	2 D	Tiong Poh Road	忠坡路	132	1 B
Telok Blangah Green	直落布兰雅埔	130	2 C	Tiverton Lane	蒂华顿巷	110	1 D
Telok Blangah Heights	直落布兰雅岭	130	2 C	Toa Payoh Central	大巴窑中路	88	2 B
Telok Blangah Rise	直落布兰雅坡	131	1 D	Toa Payoh East	大巴窑东	89	1 B
Telok Blangah Road	直落布兰雅路	130	2 D	Toa Payoh Ind Park	大巴窑工业园	89	2 B
(Pasir Panjang)	(巴西班让)			Toa Payoh North	大巴窑北路	88	2 A
Telok Blangah Road	直落布兰雅路	142	1 A	Toa Payoh Rise	大巴窑坡	88	1 B
(HarbourFront)	(港湾)			Toa Payoh West	大巴窑西路	88	1 B
Telok Blangah Street 31	直落布兰雅31街	130	2 D	Toh Avenue	卓道	74	1 B
Telok Blangah Street 32	直落布兰雅32街	130	2 D	Toh Close	卓弄	74	1 B
Telok Blangah Way	直落布兰雅大道	131	1 C	Toh Crescent	卓弯	74	1 B
Telok Kurau Road	直落古楼路	114	1 A	Toh Drive	卓通道	74	1 B
Telok Paku Road	直落巴古路	54	1 B	Toh Guan Loop	卓源环	83	2 B
Temasek Avenue	淡马锡道	133	2 A	Toh Guan Road	卓源路	83	2 B
Temasek Boulevard	淡马锡林荫道	133	1 A	Toh Guan Road East	卓源东路	84	1 B
Tembeling Lane	登瓦灵巷	113	2 B	Toh Heights	卓岭	74	1 B
Tembeling Road	登瓦灵路	113	2 B	Toh Street	卓街	74	1 B
Tembusu Avenue	登布苏道	123	2 C	Toh Tuck Avenue	道德道	84	1 C
Tembusu Crescent	登布苏弯	123	1 D	Toh Tuck Close	道德弄	84	2 B
Tembusu Drive	登布苏通道	123	1 D	Toh Tuck Crescent	道德弯	84	1 B
Tembusu Lane	登布苏巷	123	1 D	Toh Tuck Drive	道德通道	84	2 A
Tembusu Road	登布苏路	137A	1 A	Toh Tuck Link	道德连路	84	1 C
Temenggong Road	天猛公路	142	2 A	Toh Tuck Place	道德坊	84	1 B
Temple Hill Road	邓波山路	53	2 C	Toh Tuck Rise	道德坡	84	1 B
Temple Street	邓波街	132	2 B	Toh Tuck Road	道德路	84	2 A
Teng Tong Road	庭通路	113	2 B	Toh Tuck Terrace	道德台	84	2 B
Tengah Avenue	登加道	80	1 B	Toh Tuck Walk	道德径	84	1 B
Teo Hong Road	赵芬路	132	1 C	Toh Yi Drive	道义通道	84	2 B
Teo Kim Eng Road	张金荣路	92	1 C	Toh Yi Road	道义路	84	2 B
Teow Hock Avenue	朝福道	69	2 B	Tomlinson Road	汤林生路	109	2 C
Terang Bulan Avenue	德朗布兰道	92	2 D	Tong Lee Road	东利路	29	1 D
Tessensohn Road	德申宋路	111	1 A	Tong Watt Road	东发路	132	1 A
Tew Chew Street	潮州街	132	2 A	Topaz Road	多珀路	89	2 C
Tham Soong Avenue	谭顺道	84	2 A	Toranto Road	托兰多路	26	1 B
The Inglewood	英格林	66	2 B	Toronto Road	多伦多路	66	2 C
The Oval	奥哇街	28	2 C	Tosca Street	托士卡街	114	2 A
Thiam Siew Avenue	添寿道	113	1 B	Tosca Terrace	托士卡台	114	2 A
Third Avenue	第3道	86	1 C	Towner Road	陶纳路	111	1 A
Third Chin Bee Road	第3振美路	81	2 B	Townsend Road	陶胜路	111	1 B
Third Hospital Avenue	第3医院道	132	1 C	Track 24	第24乡道	46	1 A
Third Lok Yang Road	第3络阳路	80	1 D	(Lentor Avenue)	(伦多道)		
Thomson Close	汤申弄	46	1 D	Tractor Road	拖拉机路	81	1 D
Thomson Green	汤申埔	46	1 D	Trafalgar Street	特拉法加街	132	2 D
Thomson Heights	汤申岭	45	2 D	Transit Road	德兰习路	26	1 C
Thomson Hill	汤申山	46	1 D	Tras Street	道拉实街	132	2 C
Thomson Hills Drive	汤申山通道	46	1 D	Trengganu Street	丁加奴街	132	2 B
Thomson Ridge	汤申岗	67	1 D	Trent Way	特伦特大道	53	2 D
Thomson Rd	汤申路(纽顿路)	110	2 A	Trevose Crescent	特利华士弯	87	2 D
(Newton Rd)				Trevose Place	特利华士坊	87	1 C
Thomson Road (PIE)	汤申路(泛岛快速公路)	88	1 A	Truro Road	杜鲁路路	110	2 C
Thomson Terrace	汤申台	46	1 D	Tu Fu Avenue	杜甫道	45	2 C
Thomson View	汤申景	45	2 D	Tua Kong Green	大公埔	114	2 A
Thomson Walk	汤申径	46	1 D	Tua Kong Place	大公坊	114	2 A
Thong Bee Road	通美路	26	1 D	Tua Kong Terrace	大公台	114	2 A
Thong Soon Avenue	通顺道	45	1 A	Tua Kong Walk	大公径	114	2 A
Thong Soon Green	通顺埔	26	1 D	Tuah Road	杜娃路	4	1 C
Thong Soon Road	通顺路	45	1 D	Tuas Avenue 1	大士1道	78	1 B
Three Rings Drive	三环通道	23	1 A	Tuas Avenue 2	大士2道	78	1 D

ROADS		MAP	GRID	ROADS		MAP	GRID
Tuas Avenue 3	大士3道	78	2 D	Tuas View Square	大士景广场	99	1 C
Tuas Avenue 4	大士4道	78	1 D	Tuas View Walk 1	大士景1径	99	1 C
Tuas Avenue 5	大士5道	100	2 A	Tuas View Walk 2	大士景2径	99	1 C
Tuas Avenue 6	大士6道	78	1 C	Tuas West Avenue	大士西道	77	2 B
Tuas Avenue 7	大士7道	78	1 B	Tuas West Drive	大士西通道	77	1 C
Tuas Avenue 8	大士8道	78	1 C	Tuas West Road	大士西路	78	1 B
Tuas Avenue 9	大士9道	78	1 C	Tuas West Street	大士西街	77	2 B
Tuas Avenue 10	大士10道	78	1 C	Tudor Close	都德弄	87	1 D
Tuas Avenue 11	大士11道	78	1 D	Tung Po Avenue	东坡道	46	1 C
Tuas Avenue 12	大士12道	78	1 B	Turf City Road	赛马城路	85	2 B
Tuas Avenue 13	大士13道	77	2 D	Turf Club Avenue	赛马公会道	23	1 A
Tuas Avenue 14	大士14道	78	1 D	Turf Club Road	赛马公会路	86	1 B
Tuas Avenue 16	大士16道	77	2 D	Turnhouse Road	邓豪士路	53	2 B
Tuas Avenue 18	大士18道	77	2 D	Turut Track	都鲁乡道	8	1 D
Tuas Avenue 18A	大士18A道	77	2 D	Tyersall Avenue	泰瑟道	109	1 B
Tuas Avenue 20	大士20道	77	2 C	Tyersall Road	泰瑟路	109	1 A
Tuas Basin Close	大士盆地弄	100	2 A	Tyrwhitt Road	德威路	111	2 B
Tuas Basin Link	大士盆地连路	100	1 A				
Tuas Bay Circle	大士湾圈	99	1 A	**U**			
Tuas Bay Drive	大士湾通道	77	1 D	Ubi Avenue 1	乌美1道	91	2 C
Tuas Bay Lane	大士湾巷	99	2 D	Ubi Avenue 2	乌美2道	91	1 C
Tuas Bay Link	大士湾连路	99	2 D	Ubi Avenue 3	乌美3道	91	1 C
Tuas Bay Street	大士湾街	99	2 C	Ubi Avenue 4	乌美4道	91	1 B
Tuas Bay Walk	大士湾径	99	1 A	Ubi Close	乌美弄	91	2 B
Tuas Crescent	大士弯	77	2 D	Ubi Crescent	乌美弯	91	1 C
Tuas Drive 1	大士通道1	78	2 D	Ubi Link	乌美连路	91	1 C
Tuas Drive 2	大士通道2	78	2 D	Ubi Road 1	乌美1路	91	1 C
Tuas Lane	大士巷	77	2 C	Ubi Road 2	乌美2路	91	1 B
Tuas Link 1	大士连路1	77	2 B	Ubi Road 3	乌美3路	91	2 C
Tuas Link 2	大士连路2	77	2 B	Ubi Road 4	乌美4路	91	2 C
Tuas Link 3	大士连路3	77	2 A	Ubi View	乌美景	91	2 C
Tuas Link 4	大士连路4	77	2 A	Ulu Pandan Road	乌鲁班丹路	106	2 A
Tuas Road	大士路	100	2 D	(Clementi Road)	(金文泰路)		
Tuas South Avenue 1	大士南1道	77	1 D	Ulu Pandan Road	乌鲁班丹路	85	1 D
Tuas South Avenue 2	大士南2道	99	1 A	(Pandan Valley)	(班丹谷)		
Tuas South Avenue 3	大士南3道	77	1 D	Unity Street	团结街	132	2 A
Tuas South Avenue 4	大士南4道	99	2 B	University Road	大学路	87	1 C
Tuas South Avenue 5	大士南5道	99	1 D	University Walk	大学径	87	1 D
Tuas South Avenue 6	大士南6道	99	1 C	Upavon Road	巫爱文路	53	2 B
Tuas South Avenue 7	大士南7道	121	1 A	Upper Aljunied Lane	阿裕尼巷上段	90	2 B
Tuas South Avenue 8	大士南8道	99	1 C	Upper Aljunied Link	阿裕尼路连路上段	90	2 B
Tuas South Avenue 9	大士南9道	99	2 D	Upper Aljunied Road	阿裕尼路上段	90	1 B
Tuas South Avenue 10	大士南10道	121	1 B	Upper Bedok Road	勿洛路上段	94	1 C
Tuas South Avenue 12	大士南12道	121	2 A	Upper Boon Keng Rd	文庆路上段	112	1 A
Tuas South Avenue 14	大士南14道	121	1 D	Upper Bukit Timah Rd	武吉知马路上段	42	1 D
Tuas South Avenue 16	大士南16道	136A	1 A	(Bt Panjang)	(武吉班让)		
Tuas South Street 1	大士南1街	99	1 D	Upper Bukit Timah Rd	武吉知马路上段	63	1 A
Tuas South Street 2	大士南2街	99	1 B	(Hillview Road)	(山景路)		
Tuas South Street 3	大士南3街	99	1 C	Upper Bukit Timah Rd	武吉知马路上段	85	1 A
Tuas South Street 5	大士南5街	98	2 D	(PIE)	(泛岛快速公路)		
Tuas Street	大士街	78	2 D	Upper Bukit Timah View	武吉知马景上段	63	2 D
Tuas Terminal Road	大士终站路	120	2 A	Upper Changi Rd	樟宜路上段	93	2 C
Tuas View Circuit	大士景环	99	1 D	Upper Changi Rd East	樟宜东路上段	73	2 D
Tuas View Close	大士景弄	99	1 C	(PIE)	(泛岛快速公路)		
Tuas View Crescent	大士景弯	99	1 D	Upper Changi Rd East	樟宜东路上段	94	2 A
Tuas View Drive	大士景通道	121	1 A	(Simei Avenue)	(四美道)		
Tuas View Lane	大士景巷	121	2 A	Upper Changi Rd North	樟宜北路上段	74	2 A
Tuas View Link	大士景连路	99	1 C	Upper Changi Rd	樟宜路上段第39乡道	74	1 B
Tuas View Loop	大士景环道	99	1 C	Track 39			
Tuas View Place	大士景坊	99	1 C	Upper Circular Road	沙球劳路上段	132	2 A

ROADS		MAP	GRID
Upper Cross Street	克罗士街上段	132	2 B
Upper Dickson Road	狄生路上段	111	1 C
Upper East Coast Road (Bayshore Road)	东海岸路上段 (碧湾路)	115	2 A
Upper East Coast Road (Bedok South Road)	东海岸路上段 (勿洛南路)	116	1 A
Upper Hokkien Street	福建街上段	132	2 B
Upper Jurong Road (Pasir Laba Road)	裕廊路上段 (巴西拉巴路)	79	2 C
Upper Jurong Road (Pioneer Road North)	裕廊路上段 (先驱北路)	80	1 C
Upper Neram Road	尼蓝路上段	47	2 B
Upper Paya Lebar Rd (Bartley Road)	巴耶利巴路上段 (巴特利路)	90	2 A
Upper Paya Lebar Rd (Upper Serangoon Rd)	巴耶利巴路上段 (实龙岗路上段)	69	1 D
Upper Pickering Street	必麒麟街上段	132	2 B
Upper Ring Road	上环路	109	1 B
Upper Serangoon Road (Bartley Road)	实龙岗路上段 (巴特利路)	90	1 B
Upper Serangoon Rd (Hougang Street 21)	实龙岗路上段 (后港21街)	69	1 D
Upper Serangoon Rd (Punggol Park)	实龙岗路上段 (榜鹅园)	49	2 D
Upper Serangoon Rd (Hougang)	实龙岗路上段 (后港)	70	1 A
Upper Serangoon View	实龙岗景上段	49	2 D
Upper Thomson Road (Ang Mo Kio Avenue 1)	汤申路上段 (宏茂桥1道)	66	2 A
Upper Thomson Road (Mandai Road)	汤申路上段 (万礼路)	26	1 D
Upper Thomson Road (Sin Ming Road)	汤申路上段 (新民路)	67	1 C
Upper Thomson Road (SLE)	汤申路上段 (实里达快速公路)	45	1 A
Upper Toh Tuck Terrace	卫德路上段	84	2 B
Upper Weld Road	卫德路上段	111	1 C
Upper Wilkie Road	威基路上段	110	2 C

V			
Valley Road	华丽路	70	1 B
Vanda Avenue	万达兰道	86	1 B
Vanda Crescent	万达兰弯	86	1 B
Vanda Drive	万达兰通道	86	1 C
Vanda Link	万达兰连络	86	1 C
Vanda Road	万达兰路	86	1 C
Vaughan Road	富安路	69	1 D
Veeragoo Close	维拉古弄	69	2 C
Veerasamy Road	维拉三美路	111	1 B
Venus Drive	维纳士通道	66	2 B
Venus Road	维纳士路	66	2 C
Verde Avenue	丰涛道	41	2 B
Verde Crescent	丰涛弯	41	2 B
Verde Grove	丰涛林	41	2 B
Verde Place	丰涛坊	41	2 B
Verde View	丰涛景	41	2 B
Verde Walk	丰涛径	41	2 B
Verdun Road	凡尔登路	111	1 B
Vernon Park	翡珑园	90	1 B

ROADS		MAP	GRID
Victoria Lane	维多利亚巷	111	1 C
Victoria Park Close	维多利亚园弄	108	1 A
Victoria Park Road	维多利亚园路	108	2 A
Victoria Street	维多利亚街	111	1 D
View Road	美景路	11	2 A
Vigilante Drive	维安通道	129	2 B
Viking Road	维京路	131	1 A
Vista Exchange Green	易舜绿	107	2 C
Vista Terrace	维斯达台	129	2 C

W			
Wajek Walk	华杰径	85	1 A
Wak Hassan Drive	华克哈山通道	4	1 C
Wak Hassan Place	华克哈山坊	4	1 C
Wallace Way	华丽士大道	87	2 B
Wallich Street	华利街	132	2 C
Walmer Drive	华玛通道	68	2 B
Walshe Road	华士路	109	2 B
Walton Road	华敦路	113	1 D
Wan Lee Road	万利路	81	1 C
Wan Shih Road	万世路	102	2 A
Wan Tho Avenue	运涛道	90	1 C
War Cemetery Road	战时坟场路	23	1 A
Wareham Road	卫榜路	113	1 B
Waringin Park	花林荫园	92	2 D
Waringin Walk	花林荫径	92	2 D
Warna Road	华纳路	108	1 B
Warwick Road	沃里克路	130	1 B
Waterloo Street	滑铁卢街	111	1 D
Watten Close	华登弄	86	2 C
Watten Drive	华登通道	86	2 C
Watten Estate Road	华登园路	86	2 C
Watten Heights	华登岭	86	2 C
Watten Park	华登园	86	2 C
Watten Rise	华登坡	86	2 C
Watten Terrace	华登台	86	2 C
Watten View	华登景	86	2 C
Wee Nam Road	伟南路	110	2 A
Weld Road	卫德路	111	1 C
Wellington Circle	威灵顿圈	3	1 D
Wellington Link	威灵顿连络	3	2 D
Wellington Road	威灵顿路	3	2 C
West Camp Road	西兵营路	28	2 C
West Coast Avenue	西海岸道	106	1 A
West Coast Crescent	西海岸弯	106	1 D
West Coast Drive	西海岸通道	106	1 A
West Coast Ferry Road	西海岸渡轮路	128	1 A
West Coast Green	西海岸埔	105	2 A
West Coast Grove	西海岸林	105	2 A
West Coast Highway (Clementi Rd)	西海岸大道 (金文泰路)	128	2 A
West Coast Highway (Jalan Buroh)	西海岸大道 (惹兰布罗')	105	2 B
West Coast Highway (Pasir Panjang Road)	西海岸大道 (巴西班让路)	129	1 A
West Coast Highway (West Coast Park)	西海岸大道 (西海岸园)	106	1 C
West Coast Lane	西海岸巷	106	1 B
West Coast Link	西海岸连络	106	1 D
West Coast Park	西海岸园	105	2 A

ROADS		MAP	GRID
West Coast Place	西海岸坊	106	1 A
West Coast Rise	西海岸坡	105	2 A
West Coast Road (Clementi Avenue 2)	西海岸路 (金文泰2道)	106	1 B
West Coast Road (Clementi Road)	西海岸路 (金文泰路)	128	2 A
West Coast Road (Jurong Town Hall Rd)	西海岸路 (裕廊镇大会堂路)	105	1 A
West Coast Terrace	西海岸台	106	1 A
West Coast View	西海岸景	128	2 A
West Coast Walk	西海岸径	106	1 B
West Coast Way	西海岸大道	105	2 A
West Perimeter Road	西界路	54	1 D
Westbourne Road	威士朋路	108	1 D
Westerhout Road	威士特豪路	112	2 B
Western Avenue	威士登道	29	1 C
Western Link Road	西连路	16	1 D
Westlake Avenue	西湖道	88	1 A
Westridge Walk	西岗径	129	2 C
Westwood Avenue	西林道	60	1 D
Westwood Crescent	西林弯	60	1 D
Westwood Drive	西林通道	59	2 D
Westwood Road	西林路	59	2 D
Westwood Terrace	西林台	59	2 C
Westwood Walk	西林径	59	2 D
Weyhill Close	卫禧弄	107	2 D
Whampoa Drive	黄埔通道	89	1 D
Whampoa East	黄埔东路	89	1 D
Whampoa North	黄埔北路	89	2 D
Whampoa Road	黄埔路	89	1 D
Whampoa South	黄埔南路	89	2 D
Whampoa West	黄埔西路	89	2 D
Whitchurch Road	惠泽芝路	130	1 A
White House Park	白宫园	109	2 A
White House Road	白宫路	109	2 A
Whitley Heights	惠德里岭	88	1 D
Whitley Road (Dunearn Road)	惠德里路 (杜尼安路)	87	1 D
Whitley Road (Thomson Road)	惠德里路 (汤申路)	88	1 D
Wholesale Centre	批发中心	129	1 B
Wilby Road	威美路	85	2 C
Wilkie Road	威基路	110	2 C
Wilkie Terrace	威基台	110	2 C
Wilkinson Road	威京逊路	113	1 C
Willow Avenue	杨柳道	90	1 C
Wilmonar Avenue	威摩纳道	85	1 B
Wilton Close	威尔敦弄	107	2 C
Wilton Gardens	威尔敦花园	114	2 C
Wiltshire Road	威德莎路	115	2 A
Winborne Road	文朋路	112	2 C
Winchester Road	温彻斯特路	130	1 A
Windsor Park Hill	温莎园山	66	2 C
Windsor Park Road	温莎园路	66	2 C
Winstedt Drive	温斯德通道	110	1 D
Winstedt Road	温斯德路	110	2 B
Wishart Road	威芝路	131	1 D
Wittering Road	威德林路	54	1 C
Woking Road	沃京路	108	1 D
Wolskel Road	武生革路	90	1 A
Wong Chin Yoke Rd	王振毓路	88	1 C

ROADS		MAP	GRID
Woo Mon Chew Road	胡文钊路	115	1 A
Woodgrove Avenue	木林道	11	1 D
Woodgrove Drive	木林通道	11	1 D
Woodgrove View	木林景	11	1 D
Woodgrove Walk	木林径	11	1 D
Woodlands Ave 1	兀兰1道	10	1 D
Woodlands Ave 2	兀兰2道	11	2 B
Woodlands Ave 3	兀兰3道	11	1 C
Woodlands Ave 4	兀兰4道	11	2 A
Woodlands Ave 5	兀兰5道	11	1 D
Woodlands Ave 6	兀兰6道	12	1 A
Woodlands Ave 7	兀兰7道	11	2 B
Woodlands Ave 8	兀兰8道	2	1 D
Woodlands Ave 9	兀兰9道	11	2 B
Woodlands Ave 10	兀兰10道	2	1 D
Woodlands Ave 12	兀兰12道	12	1 A
Woodlands Centre Rd	兀兰中心路	10	2 B
Woodlands Circle	兀兰圈	12	1 B
Woodlands Crescent	兀兰弯	12	1 A
Woodlands Drive 14	兀兰14通道	11	2 C
Woodlands Drive 16	兀兰16通道	12	1 D
Woodlands Drive 17	兀兰17通道	12	1 D
Woodlands Drive 19	兀兰19通道	11	2 C
Woodlands Drive 40	兀兰40通道	12	1 B
Woodlands Drive 42	兀兰42通道	12	1 C
Woodlands Drive 43	兀兰43通道	11	2 C
Woodlands Drive 44	兀兰44通道	11	1 C
Woodlands Drive 50	兀兰50通道	11	2 C
Woodlands Drive 52	兀兰52通道	12	1 C
Woodlands Drive 53	兀兰53通道	11	1 C
Woodlands Drive 60	兀兰60通道	12	1 A
Woodlands Drive 61	兀兰61通道	12	1 A
Woodlands Drive 62	兀兰62通道	12	2 C
Woodlands Drive 63	兀兰63通道	12	1 C
Woodlands Drive 64	兀兰64通道	12	1 C
Woodlands Drive 65	兀兰65通道	12	1 C
Woodlands Drive 70	兀兰70通道	12	1 B
Woodlands Drive 71	兀兰71通道	12	1 B
Woodlands Drive 72	兀兰72通道	12	2 B
Woodlands Drive 73	兀兰73通道	12	2 B
Woodlands Drive 75	兀兰75通道	12	2 B
Woodlands Drive 91	兀兰91通道	11	2 B
Woodlands Ind Pk D St 1	兀兰D工业园1街	10	1 D
Woodlands Ind Pk D St 2	兀兰D工业园2街	10	1 D
Woodlands Ind Pk E1	兀兰E1工业园	2	1 D
Woodlands Ind Pk E2	兀兰E2工业园	11	2 A
Woodlands Ind Pk E3	兀兰E3工业园	2	1 D
Woodlands Ind Pk E4	兀兰E4工业园	12	1 A
Woodlands Ind Pk E5	兀兰E5工业园	2	1 D
Woodlands Ind Pk E6	兀兰E6工业园	12	1 A
Woodlands Ind Pk E7	兀兰E7工业园	12	1 A
Woodlands Ind Pk E8	兀兰E8工业园	2	1 D
Woodlands Ind Pk E9	兀兰E9工业园	12	1 A
Woodlands Ind Pk E10	兀兰E10工业园	11	2 D
Woodlands Lane	兀兰巷	12	2 C
Woodlands Link	兀兰连路	2	2 D
Woodlands Loop	兀兰环道	12	2 A
Woodlands Ring Road	兀兰环路	12	1 C
Woodlands Road (Bt Panjang Road)	兀兰路 (武吉班让路)	42	1 B

ROADS			MAP	GRID
Woodlands Road (Stagmont Ring)	兀兰路 (史达蒙环路)	41	2 A
Woodlands Road (Sungei Kadut Drive)	兀兰路 (双溪加株通道)	22	2 C
Woodlands Road (Turf Club Avenue)	兀兰路 (赛马公会道)	23	1 A
Woodlands Road (W'lands Checkpoint)	兀兰路 (兀兰关卡)	10	1 D
Woodlands Sector 1	兀兰1段	2	2 D
Woodlands Square	兀兰广场	11	2 B
Woodlands Street 11	兀兰11街	11	1 C
Woodlands Street 12	兀兰12街	11	1 C
Woodlands Street 13	兀兰13街	10	2 C
Woodlands Street 31	兀兰31街	11	1 C
Woodlands Street 32	兀兰32街	11	1 C
Woodlands Street 41	兀兰41街	10	2 D
Woodlands Street 81	兀兰81街	11	2 B
Woodlands Street 82	兀兰82街	11	2 B
Woodlands Street 83	兀兰83街	11	2 B
Woodlands Terrace	兀兰台	2	2 D
Woodlands View	兀兰景	12	2 B
Woodlands Walk	兀兰径	2	2 D
Woodleigh Close	兀里弄	90	1 B
Woodleigh Park (Braddell Road)	兀里园 (布莱德路)	89	2 A
Woodleigh Park (Upper Serangoon Rd)	兀里园 (实龙岗路上段)	90	1 B
Woodsville Close	兀士维弄	89	2 C
Woollerton Drive	武勒登通道	108	2 A
Woollerton Park	武勒登园	108	2 A
Woolwich Road	武立支路	143	1 D
Worcester Road	武瑟德路	111	1 B
Workshop Road	工场路	3	2 B
Worthing Road	沃丁路	68	2 A
	X		
Xilin Avenue (ECP)	西林道 (东海岸公园大道)	95	1 C
Xilin Avenue (Simei Avenue)	西林道 (四美道)	94	2 C
	Y		
Yan Kit Road	寅杰路	132	2 C
Yarrow Gardens	雅乐花园	114	2 A
Yarwood Avenue	雅兀道	85	1 A
Yew Siang Road	有祥路	129	2 C
Yew Tee Close	油池弄	41	1 A
Yio Chu Kang Drive	杨厝港通道	46	1 C
Yio Chu Kang Gardens	杨厝港花园	46	1 C
Yio Chu Kang Link	杨厝港连路	69	1 C
Yio Chu Kang Road (Buangkok Green)	杨厝港路 (万国埔)	48	1 B
Yio Chu Kang Road (CTE)	杨厝港路 (中央快速公路)	47	1 B
Yio Chu Kang Road (Lentor Avenue)	杨厝港路 (伦多道)	46	2 B
Yio Chu Kang Road (Upper Serangoon Rd)	杨厝港路 (实龙岗上段)	69	1 A

ROADS			MAP	GRID
Yio Chu Kang Road (Upper Thomson Rd)	杨厝港路 (汤申路上段)	45	2 D
Yio Chu Kang Terrace	杨厝港台	69	1 C
Yishun Avenue 1	义顺1道	26	2 B
Yishun Avenue 2	义顺2道	27	1 A
Yishun Avenue 3	义顺3道	27	1 A
Yishun Avenue 4	义顺4道	27	1 B
Yishun Avenue 5	义顺5道	14	1 D
Yishun Avenue 6	义顺6道	14	1 B
Yishun Avenue 7	义顺7道	14	1 B
Yishun Avenue 9	义顺9道	14	1 D
Yishun Avenue 11	义顺11道	14	2 D
Yishun Central	义顺中路	14	1 D
Yishun Central 1	义顺中1路	14	1 D
Yishun Central 2	义顺中2路	27	1 A
Yishun Central Service Rd	义顺中央辅助路	14	1 D
Yishun Industrial Park A	义顺A工业园	14	1 B
Yishun Northview Drive	义顺北景通道	14	2 D
Yishun Ring Road	义顺环路	27	1 A
Yishun Street 11	义顺11街	14	1 C
Yishun Street 20	义顺20街	14	1 C
Yishun Street 21	义顺21街	14	1 C
Yishun Street 22	义顺22街	14	1 C
Yishun Street 23	义顺23街	14	2 B
Yishun Street 31	义顺31街	14	2 D
Yishun Street 41	义顺41街	27	2 A
Yishun Street 61	义顺61街	27	1 A
Yishun Street 71	义顺71街	13	2 D
Yishun Street 72	义顺72街	14	1 D
Yishun Street 81	义顺81街	27	1 B
Yishun Street 101	义顺101街	27	2 B
Yong Siak Street	永锡街	131	2 B
York Hill	约克山	132	1 B
York Place	约克坊	68	2 A
York Road	约克路	130	1 B
Youngberg Terrace	永伯台	90	1 A
Yuan Ching Road	园景路	82	1 A
Yuk Tong Avenue	玉棠道	84	2 A
Yung An Road	永安路	82	1 B
Yung Ho Road	永和路	82	1 C
Yung Kuang Road	永光路	82	1 C
Yung Loh Road	永乐路	82	1 C
Yung Ping Road	永平路	82	1 C
Yung Sheng Road	永升路	82	1 B
Yunnan Crescent	云南弯	80	2 A
Yunnan Drive 1	云南1通道	80	2 B
Yunnan Drive 2	云南2通道	80	2 B
Yunnan Drive 3	云南3通道	80	2 B
Yunnan Road	云南路	80	2 B
Yunnan Walk 1	云南1径	80	2 B
Yunnan Walk 2	云南2径	80	2 B
Yunnan Walk 3	云南3径	80	2 B
	Z		
Zehnder Road	贞德路	129	1 B
Zion Close	锡安弄	131	2 A
Zion Road	锡安路	132	1 A

"We've always been your trusted motoring partner"

More Motoring Benefits...
✓ Discounts on car evaluation, pre-trip inspection and car valuation services
✓ Discounts on AA maintenance-free car batteries with 24-hour delivery service
✓ Free professional motoring advice
✓ Free scrap car service

Call AA Technical Services at **6333 8811**

Other Value-Added Services
✓ Issuance of International Driving Permit, Carnet and road tax renewal
✓ Sale of CashCards, HDB/URA parking coupons and off-peak car supplementary licences

In fact, we offer a lot more...

- Free 24-hour roadside assistance services such as jumpstart, change of battery/punctured tyre etc and towing in Singapore
- Worldwide reciprocal breakdown service in over 120 countries, including Malaysia
- Free worldwide personal accident cover of S$20,000
- Preferential rates and enhanced coverage for motor, travel, home contents, personal accident and group term life insurance policies
- Exclusive rates for Auto-Ventures™, motoring and lifestyle activities, talks and courses
- Attractive petrol rebates

- Discounts at AA Approved workshops and AA Recommended tyre shops
- Discounts on motoring, car grooming and travel products and accessories at AA Shop
- Discounts and exclusive promotions at over 100 motoring, lifestyle and dining outlets
- Savings on accommodation, entertainment, dining and shopping in more than 150,000 merchant locations worldwide under Show Your Card & Save® scheme
- Special daily movie deals at all Cathay Cineplexes
- Attractive member birthday treats

- Discounts on local and overseas Hertz car rental
- Free bi-monthly Highway magazine, exclusively for AA members
- Preferential access to golf clubs in Singapore and Malaysia and exclusive golfing activities and privileges by joining AA Golf Network
- Free entry to Jackpot Rooms at River Valley and Kung Chong

Terms & conditions apply. Please visit www.aas.com.sg for details

AUTOMOBILE ASSOCIATION OF SINGAPORE
More than a motoring partner

Head Office: 336 River Valley Road #03-00 AA Centre Singapore 238366 Tel: 6333 8811 Fax: 6733 5094
Branch Office: 2 Kung Chong Road (off Leng Kee) Singapore 159140 www.aas.com.sg Email: aasmail@aas.com.sg

PLACES		MAP	GRID	PLACES		MAP	GRID

BUS INTERCHANGE / TERMINAL / DEPOT

BUS INTERCHANGE 巴士转换站

Ang Mo Kio	宏茂桥	67	2 A
Bedok	勿洛	93	1 D
Bishan	碧山	67	2 D
Boon Lay	文礼	81	1 B
Bukit Batok	武吉巴督	62	2 D
Bukit Merah	红山	131	1 A
Bukit Panjang	武吉班让	42	1 D
Choa Chu Kang	蔡厝港	41	1 C
Clementi	金文泰	106	1 A
Eunos	友诺士	113	2 A
HarbourFront (WTC)	港湾 (世界贸易中心)	142	1 A
Hougang Central	后港中	70	1 A
Jurong East	裕廊东	83	1 B
Pasir Ris	巴西立	52	1 D
Punggol (Temporary)	榜鹅 (临时)	30	2 D
Sembawang	三巴旺	13	1 A
Sengkang	盛港	49	1 B
Serangoon	实龙岗	69	1 D
Tampines	淡滨尼	72	2 C
Toa Payoh	大巴窑	88	2 C
Woodlands Regional	兀兰区域	11	2 B
Yishun	义顺	14	1 D

TERMINAL 巴士终站

Buona Vista	波那维斯达	107	2 B
Changi Airport Terminal (Basement)	樟宜机场终站 (底层)	75	1 B
Changi Village	樟宜村	54	1 B
Geylang Lorong 1	芽笼1巷	112	1 B
Ghim Moh	锦茂	107	2 B
Jurong Island Checkpoint (Loop)	裕廊岛关口 (环线)	103	2 B
Kent Ridge	肯特岗	106	2 D
Lim Chu Kang	林厝港	7	1 B
Marina Centre	滨海中心	133	2 A
New Bridge Road	新桥路	132	1 C
Queen Street	奎因街	111	1 C
Science Park 1	科学园	129	2 A
Shenton Way	珊顿大道	132	2 D
Sims Place	沈氏坊	112	2 A
Singapore Johor Express	新柔快车	67	1 C
St. Michael's	圣迈克	89	1 D
Tuas	大士	77	2 A
Upper East Coast Road	东海岸路上段	116	1 A
Yio Chu Kang	杨厝港	46	2 C

DEPOT 巴士总站

SBS Braddell Road	新加坡巴士公司 (布莱德路)	89	1 A
SBS Hougang	新加坡巴士公司 (后港)	91	1 A
SBS Transit Bedok North	新捷运巴士公司勿洛北	93	2 B
SBS Transit East District	新捷运巴士公司东区	46	2 B
SBS Transit NEL (Trains)	新捷运东北线 (地铁)	48	2 B
SBS Transit West District	新捷运巴士公司西区	83	2 A
SBS Transit West District Depot	新捷运巴士总站 西区	80	2 C
SMRT - Ang Mo Kio	SMRT巴士公司 (宏茂桥)	46	2 B
SMRT - Bishan (Trains)	SMRT地铁公司 (碧山)	68	1 C
SMRT - Changi (Trains)	SMRT地铁公司 (樟宜)	94	2 C
SMRT - Kranji	SMRT巴士公司 (克兰芝)	9	2 C
SMRT - Ulu Pandan (Trains)	SMRT巴士公司 (乌鲁班丹)	84	1 C
SMRT - Woodlands	SMRT巴士公司 (兀兰)	12	1 A

CAMPING / ADVENTURE

Boys & Girls Brigade Campsite	男女少年旅露营址	4	1 C
Circuit @ Tuas (Motorcross)	大士跑车道 (赛车场)	77	2 A
Forest Adventure	森林探险	93	1 A
Gallop Stables @ Pasir Ris (Horse Riding)	白沙马厩 (骑马)	52	1 C
Girl Guides S'pore & Camp Christine	新加坡女童军 协会营地	7	1 B
HomeTeam Adventure Ctr	内政团队战备人员保险 中心	62	2 A
Karting	小型赛车	82	1 D
Mamam Campsite	马蒙露营地	34	2 B
MOE Changi Coast Walk Adventure Ctr	教育部樟宜海岸径 探险中心	117	2 A
MOE Dairy Farm Adventure Ctr	教育部牛乳场 探险中心	63	2 B
MOE Jalan Bahtera Adventure Ctr	教育部惹兰巴特拉 探险中心	7	1 B
MOE Labrador Adventure Ctr	教育部拉柏多 探险中心	130	1 D
MOE May Adventure Ctr	教育部梅探险中心	89	1 D
NPCC Camp Site	全国学生警察营营地	34	1 B
Outward Bound @ East Coast	东海岸外展中心	116	2 B
Outward Bound Sch Camp 1 (Pulau Ubin)	外展学校 (第1营) (乌敏岛)	32	1 A
Outward Bound Sch Camp 2 (Pulau Ubin)	外展学校 (第2营) (乌敏岛)	32	1 B
Punggol Pt Holiday Camp	榜鹅假似日营	30	2 A
Red Cross Campsite	红十字会营地	92	2 D
SKI 360° (Cable Ski Ctr)	Ski 360° (滑水中心)	115	1 C
S'pore Scout Assn Sarimbun Campsite	新加坡童子军协会 沙林文营地	7	1 C

CEMETERIES / COLUMBARIA / CREMATORIA

CEMETERIES 坟场

Ahmadiyya Jamaath Burial Ground	阿马迪亚朱马艾坟场	59	1 A
Bahai (Chua Chu Kang)	巴哈教坟场 (蔡厝港)	38	2 D
Bukit Brown Chinese	武吉布朗华人坟场	87	2 B
Chinese (Choa Chu Kang)	华人坟场 (蔡厝港)	38	1 D

PLACES

PLACES		MAP	GRID
Chinese (Kheam Hock Road)	华人坟场 (谦福路)	87	1 B
Chinese (Victoria Park Road)	华人坟场 (维多利亚园路)	86	1 D
Christian - Lower (Choa Chu Kang)	基督教坟场 (蔡厝港下段)	59	2 A
Christian - Upper (Choa Chu Kang)	基督教坟场 (蔡厝港上段)	38	2 D
Guang Xiao Shan	广孝山(坟场)	23	1 D
Hindu (Choa Chu Kang)	兴都教坟场 (蔡厝港)	59	1 A
Jewish (Choa Chu Kang)	犹太教坟场 (蔡厝港)	59	2 A
Kranji Commonwealth War Cemetery	克兰芝阵亡战士纪念碑	23	1 A
Lawn (Choa Chu Kang)	蔡厝港坟场	59	2 A
Muslim - Lower (Choa Chu Kang)	回教坟场 (蔡厝港下段)	59	2 A
Muslim - Upper (Choa Chu Kang)	回教坟场 (蔡厝港上段)	38	1 B
Muslim (Jalan Kubor)	回教坟场(惹兰古坡)	111	1 C
Old Malay (Kampong Glam)	旧马来坟场 (甘榜格南)	111	1 C
Parsi (Choa Chu Kang)	印度袄教坟场(蔡厝港)	59	2 A
Pusara Abadi Muslim	回教永生墓地	59	2 A
State - Kranji	克兰芝国家坟场	23	1 A
Tanah Kubor Raja	拉惹墓园	131	2 D
Tanah Kubor Temenggong	天猛公墓园	142	2 A
The Japanese	日本人坟场	69	1 B
Yin Foh Kuan	云福馆坟场	108	1 C

COLUMBARIA 骨灰瓮安置所

An Le Memorial Pk	安乐纪念园	59	1 A
Bright Hill	光明山	67	1 B
Buddhist (Kembangan)	佛教徒 (景万岸)	92	1 D
Choa Chu Kang	蔡厝港	38	1 D
Christian (The Garden Of Remembrance)	基督教骨灰瓮安置所 (怀念园)	38	2 D
Fong Yun Thai Assn's	丰永大公会	85	2 C
Mandai (NEA)	万礼(国家环境局)	25	2 B
Mount Vernon	翡珑山	90	1 B
Peck San Theng	碧山亭	88	2 A
Saint Theresa's Ctr	圣特莉莎中心	131	2 D
Yishun	义顺	14	1 C

CREMATORIA 火化场

Bright Hill	光明山火化场	67	1 B
Bright Hill Funeral Parlour	光明山殡仪馆	67	1 B
Choa Chu Kang (NEA)	蔡厝港火化场 (国家环境局)	59	1 A
Mandai (NEA)	万礼火化场(国家环境局)	25	2 B
Mt Vernon Funeral Parlours	翡珑山殡仪馆	90	1 A
Teochew Funeral Parlour (Ubi)	潮州殡仪馆 (乌美)	91	2 C

CLUBS / COUNTRY CLUBS / ASSOCIATIONS

PLACES		MAP	GRID
American Club, "The"	美国人俱乐部	110	1 B
Aranda Country Club	爱兰特乡村俱乐部	52	1 D
Archery Club	射箭俱乐部	82	1 C
Arena Country Club	阿连纳乡村俱乐部	80	1 C
Automobile Assn of S'pore	新加坡汽车公会	110	1 D
British Club, "The"	英国人俱乐部	85	2 A
Bt Timah Saddle Club	武吉知马骑马俱乐部	86	1 A
Ceylon Sports Club	锡兰体育俱乐部	111	1 A
Changi Beach Club	樟宜海滨俱乐部	53	2 B
Changi Golf Club	樟宜高尔夫球俱乐部	54	1 B
Changi Sailing Club	樟宜帆船俱乐部	53	2 B
Chinese Swimming Club	中华游泳会	113	2 D
Civil Service Aloha Loyang Resort	公务员阿罗哈罗央度假村	52	2 C
Civil Service Club	公务员俱乐部		
- Bt Batok	- 武吉巴督	62	2 C
- Changi	- 樟宜	54	1 B
- Tessensohn	- 德申末路	111	1 A
Eagle Club	鹰队足球俱乐部	3	2 D
Eurasian Assn of S'pore, "The"	新加坡欧亚人公会	112	2 C
Executive Golf Course	执行员高尔夫球场	25	2 D
Fairway Club	花威俱乐部	82	1 C
French Chamber of Commerce in S'pore, "The"	French Chamber of Commerce in S'pore, "The"	109	2 C
Grassroots Club "The"	基层领袖俱乐部	46	2 C
Green Fairways Golf Course	格林花威高球场	86	1 A
Hollandse Club	荷兰俱乐部	87	1 C
HomeTeamNS	内政团队设备人员协会		
- Ah Hood Rd Club House	- 亚佛路俱乐部	88	2 C
- Bt Batok Club House & Adventure Centre	- 武吉巴督俱乐部及探险中心	62	2 B
- Sembawang Resort	- 三巴旺度假村	3	1 C
- Smith St Club House	- 史密斯街俱乐部	132	2 B
- UE Square Club House	- 友乃德广场俱乐部	132	2 A
Japanese Assn of S'pore	新加坡日本协会	87	1 C
Jurong Country Club	裕廊乡村俱乐部	83	1 C
Kallang Water Sports Ctr	加冷水上运动中心	112	1 C
Kampong Glam Constituency Sports Club	甘榜格南选区体育俱乐部	111	2 C
Keppel Club	发巴俱乐部	141	2 A
Keppel Marina	吉宝滨海俱乐部	141	2 A
Laguna National Golf & Country Club	礁湖国家高尔夫球及乡村俱乐部	94	2 D
Legends	Legends俱乐部	110	2 D
Marina at Keppel Bay	发巴湾滨海俱乐部	141	2 A
Marina Bay Golf Course	滨海湾高尔夫球场	130	1 A
Marina Country Club	滨海乡村俱乐部	30	2 B
Marine Parade Boys Club	马林百列男生俱乐部	114	1 C
MOE Sea Sports Ctr	教育部滨海运动中心	116	2 A
MRT Sports & Recreation Club	新加坡地铁体育与康乐俱乐部	68	1 C
National Cadet Corps (Kallang Camp)	全国学生军团(加冷兵营)	111	2 C
(Amoy Quee Camp)	(Amoy Quee兵营)	47	1 B
National Sailing Centre	国家帆船俱乐部	116	2 A

PLACES		MAP	GRID
National Service Resort & Country Club (Safra Resort)	国民服务度假村俱乐部 (战备军协度假村)	117	1 A
NESSEA Club	NESSEA俱乐部	26	1 D
NSRCC Kranji Sanctuary	国民服务克兰芝俱乐部	8	2 D
NSRCC Sea Sports Ctr	国民服务海上运动中心	117	2 C
Orchid Country Club	胡姬乡村俱乐部	27	2 C
PA Water-Venture	人协海上运动俱乐部		
- Changi	- 樟宜	54	1 B
- East Coast	- 东海岸	116	1 B
- Kallang	- 加冷	111	2 C
- Pasir Ris	- 白沙	51	2 B
PA Staff Club	人协职员俱乐部	111	1 D
People's Association	人民协会	112	1 B
People's Association HQ (U/C)	人民协会总部 (建造中)	111	1 B
Pines Club "The"	松林俱乐部	109	2 B
PSA Club "The"	港务局俱乐部	130	2 D
PUB Recreation Club	公用事业局康乐俱乐部	89	2 A
PWD Sports Club	公共工程局体育俱乐部	112	1 C
Raffles Country Club	莱佛士乡村俱乐部	78	2 B
Raffles Marina	莱佛士滨海俱乐部	77	2 A
Raffles Town Club	莱佛士市镇俱乐部	87	2 D
Republic of S'pore Yacht Club	新加坡共和国游艇俱乐部	128	1 A
Riding for the Disabled Assn of S'pore	新加坡复健策骑协会	88	1 B
SAF Yacht Club	新加坡武装部队游艇俱乐部		
- (Admiralty)	- (海军部)	3	1 B
- (Changi)	- (樟宜)	119	1 B
SAFRA Mt Faber	战备军协(花柏山)	131	1 C
SAFRA Tampines	战备军协(淡滨尼)	93	2 A
SAFRA Toa Payoh	战备军协(大巴窑)	89	1 C
SAFRA Town Club	战备军协市区俱乐部	132	2 A
SAFRA Yishun	战备军协(义顺)	27	2 A
Seletar Country Club	实里达乡村俱乐部	28	1 C
Seletar Flying Club	实里达飞行俱乐部	28	2 A
Sembawang Country Club	三巴旺乡村俱乐部	26	1 B
Senja Soka Ctr	圣惹素加中心	42	1 C
Sentosa Golf Club	圣淘沙高尔夫球俱乐部	142	2 D
Serangoon Gdns Country Club	实龙岗花园乡村俱乐部	68	2 B
Shitoryu Karate Assn	系东流空手道协会	111	1 A
SIA Group Sports Club	新航集团体育俱乐部	95	1 A
SIA Sports Club	新航体育俱乐部	95	1 A
Soka Assn (Soka Culture Ctr)	创价学会 (文化中心)	60	1 D
Soka (Tampines)	创价学会(淡滨尼)	72	1 D
Spa Botanica	Botanica Spa俱乐部	142	2 C
S'pore Amateur Rowing Assn	新加坡业余划船公会	105	2 B
S'pore Assn For The Deaf	新加坡聋哑协会	112	2 B
S'pore Chinese Recreation Club	新加坡中华体育会	111	1 A
S'pore Cricket Club	新加坡板球俱乐部	133	1 A
S'pore Dragon Boat Association	新加坡龙舟协会	112	1 C
S'pore Girl Guides Assn(Guide House)	新加坡女童军协会 (总部)	68	1 C
S'pore Gun Club	新加坡枪械俱乐部	85	1 A
S'pore Indian Assn	新加坡印度人公会	111	1 A
S'pore Indian Fine Arts Society	新加坡印度艺术协会	111	1 A
S'pore Island Country Club (Bukit Location)	新加坡岛屿乡村俱乐部(武吉场)	86	2 A
S'pore Island Country Club (Island Location)	新加坡岛屿乡村俱乐部(岛屿场)	66	1 B
S'pore Mariners Club (Maritime House)	新加坡海员俱乐部 (航运大厦)	132	1 C
S'pore Khalsa Assn	卡尔萨学会	111	1 A
S'pore National Wushu Federation	新加坡全国武术总会	113	1 B
S'pore Orchid Country Club	新加坡胡姬乡村俱乐部	15	1 D
S'pore Polo Club	新加坡马球俱乐部	88	1 C
S'pore Recreation Club	新加坡康乐俱乐部	133	1 A
S'pore Sailing Federation	新加坡帆船协会	116	2 A
S'pore Scout Assn	新加坡童子军协会	68	1 D
S'pore Shooting Assn	新加坡射击协会	38	1 D
S'pore Swimming Club	新加坡游泳俱乐部	112	2 D
S'pore Turf Club	新加坡赛马公会	23	1 A
S'pore Youth Flying Club	少年飞行俱乐部	28	2 B
Stardus Clubhouse	史达德斯俱乐部	110	1 D
Swiss Club Singapore	瑞士俱乐部	85	2 A
Tanah Merah Country Club	丹那美拉乡村俱乐部	95	2 C
Tanglin Club	东陵俱乐部	110	1 B
Tanglin Golf Course	东陵高尔夫球场	109	1 C
Temasek Club	淡马锡俱乐部	130	1 A
Terror Club	恐怖俱乐部	3	2 C
Terror Sea Scouts	恐怖海上童军	4	1 D
The Chevrons	军章俱乐部	83	2 C
The Girls Brigade	少女旅	69	2 C
Warren Golf & Country Club	华伦高尔夫球及乡村俱乐部	40	1 D

COMMUNITY CLUBS /CENTRES

ACE The Place	意德坊	12	1 D
Admiral Garden	美雅	12	1 C
Aljunied	阿裕尼	70	1 C
Anchorvale	安谷	48	2 A
Ang Mo Kio	宏茂桥	67	2 A
Ayer Rajah	亚逸拉惹	83	2 D
Bedok	勿洛	93	2 D
Bishan	碧山	68	1 D
Bishan North	碧山北	67	2 C
Boon Lay	文礼	60	2 D
Braddell Heights	布莱德岭	69	1 D
Bukit Batok	武吉巴督	62	2 D
Bukit Batok East	武吉巴督东	63	1 D
Bukit Gombak	武吉甘柏	62	2 B
Bukit Merah	红山	131	1 B
Bukit Panjang	武吉班让	42	2 D

PLACES		MAP	GRID
Bukit Timah	武吉知马	84	2 A
Buona Vista	波那维斯达	107	2 B
Cairnhill	经禧	110	1 B
Changi - Simei	樟宜四美	94	2 A
Cheng San	静山	67	2 A
Choa Chu Kang	蔡厝港	41	2 C
Chong Pang	忠邦	13	2 D
Ci Yuan	茨园	48	2 D
Clementi	金文泰	106	2 A
Dover	杜佛	107	1 C
Eunos	友诺士	92	1 C
Fengshan	凤山	93	2 C
Fuchun	福春	11	1 D
Gek Poh Ville	玉宝苑	59	2 D
Geylang Serai	芽笼士乃	113	1 B
Geylang West	芽笼西	112	1 A
Henderson	亨德申	131	2 B
Hong Kah North	丰嘉北	62	2 C
Hougang	后港	70	1 B
Hwi Yoh	缶窑	48	1 D
Jalan Besar	惹兰勿刹	111	2 B
Joo Chiat	如切	113	2 B
Jurong Green	裕青	61	1 D
Jurong Spring	裕泉	60	2 D
Kaki Bukit	加基武吉	93	1 C
Kallang	加冷	111	2 A
Kampong Glam	甘榜格南	111	2 C
Kampong Ubi	甘榜乌美	113	2 A
Katong	加东	112	2 D
Kebun Baru	哥本巴鲁	46	1 D
Kg Chai Chee	甘榜菜市	93	1 C
Kg Kembangan	甘榜景万岸	92	1 D
Kim Seng	金声	131	2 A
Kolam Ayer	哥南亚逸	90	1 D
Kreta Ayer	牛车水	132	2 C
Lam Soon	南顺	41	1 C
Leng Kee	麟记	131	1 A
Macpherson	麦波申	90	2 D
Marine Parade	马林百列	114	1 C
Marsiling	马西岭	10	2 B
Mountbatten	蒙巴登	112	2 B
Nanyang	南洋	80	2 A
Nee Soon Central	义顺中	14	1 D
Nee Soon East	义顺东	14	1 D
Nee Soon South	义顺南	27	1 B
Pasir Ris East	巴西立东	73	2 A
Pasir Ris Elias	白沙伊莱雅	51	2 D
Paya Lebar Kovan	巴耶利巴高文	69	2 C
Pek Kio	白桥	110	2 A
Potong Pasir	波东巴西	89	2 B
Punggol	榜鹅	49	1 D
Punggol 21	榜鹅北	50	1 A
Punggol Park	榜鹅园	49	1 D
Queenstown	女皇镇	108	2 D
Radin Mas	拉丁马士	131	1 C
Rivervale	立伟	49	2 A
Sembawang	三巴旺	3	2 D
Sengkang	盛港	49	1 B
Senja - Cashew	信佳－凯秀	42	1 C

PLACES		MAP	GRID
Siglap	实乞纳	93	2 D
Siglap South	实乞纳南	115	1 B
Taman Jurong	达曼裕廊	82	1 B
Tampines Central	淡滨尼中	72	1 C
Tampines Changkat	淡滨尼尚育	94	1 A
Tampines East	淡滨尼东	73	2 D
Tampines North	淡滨尼北	73	1 C
Tampines West	淡滨尼西	72	1 D
Tanglin	东陵	87	2 D
Tanjong Pagar	丹戎巴葛	132	2 C
Teck Ghee	德义	68	1 B
Telok Ayer	直落亚逸	132	2 B
Hong Lim Green	芳林公园		
Telok Blangah	直落布兰雅	130	2 D
The Frontier	边境	81	1 A
The Jelutong	日落洞	13	1 A
The Serangoon	实龙岗	69	1 A
Thomson	汤申	67	1 D
Tiong Bahru	中巴鲁	132	1 B
Toa Payoh Central	大巴窑中	88	2 B
Toa Payoh East	大巴窑东	89	1 B
Toa Payoh South	大巴窑南	89	1 B
Toa Payoh West	大巴窑西	88	2 B
Ulu Pandan	乌鲁班丹	107	2 B
West Coast	西海岸	106	1 C
Whampoa	黄埔	89	1 D
Woodlands	兀兰	11	2 B
Yew Tee	油地	41	1 A
Yio Chu Kang	杨厝港	46	2 C
Yuhua	裕华	83	1 A
Zheng Hua	正华	42	2 B

DRIVING TEST CENTRES

		MAP	GRID
Bukit Batok Driving Ctr	武吉巴督驾驶训练中心	62	2 A
Comfort Delgro Driving Ctr (Ubi)	康福德高驾驶中心 (乌美)	91	1 B
Jurong Driving Test Ctr	裕廊驾驶训练中心	82	1 C
Singapore Safety Driving Ctr (Ang Mo Kio)	新加坡安全驾驶训练中心(红茂桥)	46	2 C

PRIMARY SCHOOLS

		MAP	GRID
Admiralty	美雅	12	1 B
Ahmad Ibrahim	依布拉欣	14	1 C
Ai Tong	爱同	67	1 B
Anchor Green	安泰	48	2 B
Anderson	安德逊	46	2 C
Ang Mo Kio	茂乔	67	1 A
Anglo-Chinese (Junior)	英华(经禧)	110	1 B
Anglo-Chinese (Primary)	英华(小学)	110	1 A
Balestier Hill	博理小学	88	2 D
Beacon	崇辉	42	2 C
Bedok Green	务德	93	2 D
Bedok West	尚智	92	2 B

PLACES		MAP	GRID	PLACES		MAP	GRID
Bendemeer	明智	89	2 D	Holy Innocents' High	圣婴	70	1 A
Blangah Rise	布兰雅坡	130	2 C	Hong Kah	丰嘉	62	1 B
Boon Lay Garden	文园	81	2 A	Hong Wen	宏文	111	2 B
Bukit Panjang	武吉班让	42	2 D	Hougang	后港	48	2 D
Bukit Timah	武吉知马	84	2 B	Huamin	华民	14	2 D
Bukit View	百get	83	2 A	Innova	星烁	11	2 D
Canberra	康培	3	1 D	Jiemin	介民	13	2 D
Canossa Convent	嘉诺撒仁爱会	90	2 C	Jing Shan	静山	68	1 A
Casuarina	康源	73	2 A	Junyuan	俊源	94	2 A
Catholic High	公教中学 (附小)	67	2 C	Jurong	裕廊	61	2 D
Cedar	四德	90	1 B	Jurong West	裕廊西	81	1 B
Changkat	尚育	94	1 B	Juying	聚英	80	1 B
CHIJ Katong	圣婴女小 (加东)	93	1 C	Keming	克明	84	1 A
CHIJ Kellock	圣婴女小 (客乐)	131	2 C	Kheng Cheng	擎青	88	2 B
CHIJ Our Lady of Good Counsel	圣婴女小 (良言)	68	2 C	Kong Hwa	光华	112	2 B
CHIJ Our Lady Queen of Peace	圣婴女小 (武区)	63	2 A	Kranji	格致	41	1 D
				Kuo Chuan Presbyterian	国专长老会	68	1 D
CHIJ Our Lady of Nativity	圣母圣诞圣婴女小	49	1 D	Lakeside	湖畔	82	1 B
CHIJ Saint Nicholas Girls	圣尼各拉女小	46	1 D	Lianhua	联华	62	2 C
CHIJ Toa Payoh	圣婴女校 (大巴窑)	88	2 B	Loyang	洛阳	73	2 A
Chongfu	崇福	14	1 B	Macpherson	柏盛	90	2 D
Chongzheng	崇正	73	1 D	Maha Bodhi	菩提	91	1 C
Chua Chu Kang	蔡厝港	41	1 D	Maris Stella High	海星中学 (附小)	90	1 A
Clementi	金文泰	106	1 A	Marsiling	马西岭	10	2 C
Compassvale	康柏	49	2 A	Marymount Convent	玛丽蒙女小	88	1 B
Concord	克勤	40	2 C	Mayflower	美华	46	2 D
Coral	云海	73	1 A	Mee Toh	弥陀	50	1 A
Corporation	德行	60	1 D	Meridian	美廉	51	1 D
Da Qiao	大侨	68	1 A	Methodist Girl's	美以美	85	1 C
Damai	达迈	92	2 B	Montfort Junior	蒙福	49	1 D
Dazhong	大众	62	2 C	Nan Chiau	南侨	49	1 B
De La Salle	德利撒	41	1 A	Nan Hua	南华	106	1 A
East Coast	东岸	92	2 C	Nanyang	南洋	86	2 D
East Spring	东源	73	2 D	Naval Base	军港	27	1 B
East View	东景	72	1 D	New Town	光道	108	1 C
Edgefield	埃奇菲	31	1 D	Ngee Ann	义安	114	2 C
Elias Park	伊莱雅园	51	2 D	North Spring	北源	49	2 B
Endeavour	毅勤	3	1 D	North View	德贤	14	2 D
Eunos	友诺	91	2 D	North Vista	远景	49	1 C
Evergreen	永青	12	1 B	Northland	新华	27	2 A
Fairfield Methodist	花菲卫理	107	2 C	Opera Estate	奥匹拉	114	2 A
Farrer Park	华苑小学	111	1 B	Park View	百惠	51	2 D
Fengshan	凤山	93	1 C	Pasir Ris	思励	52	2 D
Fernvale	丰伟	48	1 B	Paya Lebar Methodist Girls	巴耶利巴美以美女小	89	2 D
First Toa Payoh	大智	89	1 A	Pei Chun Public	公立培群	89	1 B
Fuchun	福春	11	1 D	Pei Hwa Presbyterian	培华长老会	85	1 B
Fuhua	辅华	82	2 B	Pei Tong	培童	84	1 D
Gan Eng Seng	颜永成	131	1 B	Peixin	培新	14	1 C
Geylang Methodist Sch	芽笼美以美	112	2 A	Peiying	培英	26	2 B
Ghim Moh	锦茂	107	2 B	Pioneer	先驱	61	2 D
Gongshang	工商	73	1 C	Poi Ching	培青	72	1 C
Greendale	绿苑	50	1 A	Princess Elizabeth	伊丽沙白公主	62	1 D
Greenridge	群立	42	2 C	Punggol	榜鹅	49	1 D
Greenwood	学林	12	1 B	Qiaonan	侨南	94	1 A
Griffiths	励福	73	1 D	Qifa	启发	106	1 B
Guangyang	光洋	88	2 A	Qihua	启化	11	2 B
Haig Girls	海格女校	113	2 B	Queenstown	女皇镇	108	2 D
Henry Park	恒力	107	1 A	Radin Mas	拉丁马士	131	2 C
				Raffles Girls	莱佛士女子	86	2 C

PLACES		MAP	GRID
Red Swastika	卍慈	93	1 C
River Valley	立化	132	1 A
Rivervale	立伟	49	2 A
Rosyth	乐赛	48	1 D
Rulang	孺廊	61	1 D
Saint Andrew's Junior	圣安德烈	89	2 C
St. Anthony's Canossian	圣安东尼女校	93	2 B
Saint Anthony's	圣安东尼	62	2 B
Saint Gabriel	圣加俾尔	68	2 D
Saint Hilda's	圣希尔达	72	2 D
Saint Margaret's	圣玛格烈	110	2 C
Saint Stephen's	圣斯德望	114	2 A
San Yu Adventist (Private)	三育小学 (私立)	88	1 D
Sembawang	胜宝旺	13	1 A
Seng Kang	成康	49	2 B
Shuqun	树群	61	1 D
Si Ling	士林	11	2 C
SJI Junior School	圣约瑟书院小学	110	2 A
S'pore Chinese Girls	新加坡女子小学	87	2 D
South View	南山	41	2 C
Stamford	史丹福	111	1 C
Tampines North	淡滨尼北	73	1 B
Tampines	淡滨尼	93	2 D
Tanjong Katong	丹绒加东	113	2 C
Tao Nan	道南	114	1 C
Teck Ghee	德义	67	2 B
Teck Whye	德惠	41	2 C
Telok Kurau	直落古楼	92	1 C
Temasek	淡马锡	116	1 A
Townsville	城景	68	1 B
Unity	协和	22	2 D
Wellington	伟林	3	2 D
West Grove	伟群	80	2 A
West View	维新	42	1 C
White Sands	白沙	73	2 B
Woodgrove	林景	11	2 C
Woodlands	辅仁	11	2 C
Woodlands Ring	辅廉	12	1 C
Xinghua	醒华	70	1 C
Xingnan	醒南	80	1 A
Xinmin	新民	69	2 A
Xishan	西山	14	1 C
Yangzheng	养正	68	2 D
Yew Tee	育智	41	2 A
Yio Chu Kang	杨厝港	48	2 D
Yishun	义顺	13	2 C
Yu Neng	育能	93	1 B
Yuhua	裕华	83	1 A
Yumin	育民	73	1 D
Zhangde	漳德	131	2 B
Zhenghua	正华	42	2 C
Zhonghua	中华	69	1 B

PLACES		MAP	GRID
SECONDARY SCHOOLS			
Admiralty	海军部	12	1 A
Ahmad Ibrahim	伊布拉欣	13	2 C
Anderson	安德逊	47	1 D
Ang Mo Kio	茂乔	67	2 B
Anglican High	圣公会	93	2 C
Anglo-Chinese (Barker Road)	英华 (巴克路)	110	1 A
Anglo-Chinese (Independent)	英华 (自主)	107	1 C
Assumption English	圣升英校	63	2 A
Balestier Hill	博理	88	2 D
Bartley	巴特礼	90	2 A
Beatty	培德	89	1 A
Bedok Green	育青	93	1 B
Bedok North	务能	92	1 B
Bedok South	尚义	94	1 D
Bedok Town	务乐	92	2 C
Bedok View	务德	93	2 D
Bendemeer	明智	89	2 D
Bishan Park	碧苑	67	1 B
Boon Lay	文礼	81	1 A
Bowen	博文	69	1 A
Broadrick	务立	112	2 C
Bukit Batok	武吉巴督	84	2 B
Bukit Merah	红山	131	1 B
Bukit Panjang Govt High	武吉班让政府中学	41	2 C
Bukit View	百德	83	2 A
Canberra	康培	3	1 D
Catholic High	公教中学	67	2 C
Cedar Girls'	四德女中	90	1 D
Chai Chee	尚志	115	2 A
Changkat Changi	尚智	94	1 A
Chestnut Drive	励进	63	2 A
CHIJ Katong Convent	加东修道院女中	114	2 C
CHIJ St. Joseph's Convent	圣母女中 (圣若瑟)	49	2 B
CHIJ St. Nicholas Girls	圣尼各拉女校	46	1 D
CHIJ St. Theresa's Convent	圣婴德兰女校	131	2 C
CHIJ Secondary (Toa Payoh)	圣婴女子中学 (大巴窑)	88	2 C
Chong Boon	崇文	68	1 B
Christ Church	基督堂	12	1 D
Chua Chu Kang	蔡厝港	41	2 C
Chung Cheng High (Branch)	中正 (分校)	27	1 A
Chung Cheng High (Main)	中正 (总校)	113	1 C
Clementi Town	锦文	108	1 C
Clementi Woods	金文泰林	106	1 C
Commonwealth	立才	105	1 A
Compassvale	康柏	49	2 A
Coral	云海	73	1 A
Crescent Girls	克信女中	131	1 A
Damai	达迈	93	1 B
Deyi	德义	68	1 A
Dunearn	德能	62	1 B
Dunman High	德明政府中学	107	2 A
Dunman Secondary	德明中学	73	2 B
East Spring	东源	73	2 C

PLACES		MAP	GRID	PLACES		MAP	GRID
East View	东景	73	1 C	Punggol	培道中学	31	1 D
Evergreen	永青	12	1 B	Queenstown	女皇镇	131	1 A
Fairfield Methodist	花菲卫理	107	2 C	Queensway	女皇道	108	1 D
Fajar	法嘉	42	1 D	Raffles Girls	莱佛士女子	109	2 B
First Toa Payoh	大智	89	1 B	Raffles Institution	莱佛士书院	88	2 A
Fuchun	福春	11	1 D	Regent	励正	41	2 A
Fuhua	辅华	61	1 D	River Valley High	立化	130	1 C
Gan Eng Seng	颜永成	131	2 A	Riverside	立德	11	2 B
Geylang Methodist	芽笼美以美	112	2 C	San Yu Adventist Sch	三育	88	1 D
Greendale	绿苑	50	1 A	(Private)	(私立)		
Greenridge	群立	42	2 C	Sembawang	胜宝旺	13	1 A
Greenview	青景	73	2 A	Seng Kang	成康	49	2 B
Guangyang	光洋	89	1 A	Serangoon Garden	实勤	68	2 A
Hai Sing Catholic	海星天主教	52	1 D	Serangoon	实仁	49	2 D
Henderson	达善	131	1 B	Shuqun	树群	83	1 A
Hillgrove	育林	62	2 C	Si Ling	士林	11	1 A
Holy Innocents' High	圣婴	70	1 A	Siglap	实乞纳	51	2 C
Hong Kah	丰嘉	83	1 A	S'pore Chinese Girl's Sch	新加坡女子学校	87	2 D
Hougang	后港	48	2 D	Springfield	泉原	72	1 D
Hua Yi	华义	61	1 D	St. Andrew's	圣安德烈	89	2 C
Junyuan	俊源	72	1 D	St. Anthony's Canossian	圣安东尼女校	93	2 B
Jurong	裕廊	82	1 C	St. Francis Methodist	圣芳济卫理中学	63	2 B
Jurong West	裕廊西	81	1 B	(Private)	(私立)		
Jurongville	裕廊景	61	2 D	St. Gabriel's	圣加俾尔	69	1 D
Juying	聚英	80	1 B	St. Hilda's	圣希尔达	72	2 D
Kent Ridge	岗丽	106	1 C	St. Joseph's Institution	圣约瑟书院	87	2 D
Kranji	科兰芝	41	1 B	St. Margaret's	圣玛格烈	108	2 A
Kuo Chuan Presbyterian	国专长老会	68	1 D	St. Patrick's	圣伯特理	114	1 D
Loyang	洛阳	73	2 A	Swiss Cottage	瑞士村	62	2 B
Macpherson	柏盛	91	1 C	Tampines	淡滨尼	93	1 D
Manjusri	文殊	112	1 A	Tanglin	东林	106	1 C
Maris Stella High	海星中学	90	1 A	Tanjong Katong Girls Sch	丹绒加东女校	113	1 B
Marsiling	马西岭	11	1 C	Tanjong Katong Sec	丹绒加东中学	113	1 B
Mayflower	美华	67	1 A	Teck Whye	德惠	41	2 C
Methodist Girl's	美以美中	85	1 C	Telok Kurau	德乐	113	2 A
Montfort	蒙福	49	1 D	Temasek	淡马锡	116	1 A
Nan Chiau High	南侨	49	1 B	The Chinese High Sch	华侨	86	1 D
Nan Hua	南华	106	2 B	(Hwa Chong Institution)	(华侨中学)		
Nanyang Girl's High	南洋女子中学	86	1 C	Unity	协和	22	1 D
Naval Base	军港	3	1 C	Victoria Sch	维多利亚学校	115	1 B
New Town	光伟	106	2 B	West Spring	伟林	42	1 B
Ngee Ann	义安	73	2 C	Westwood	维林	60	1 C
North View	德贤	14	2 D	Whitley	惠厉	67	2 C
North Vista	德新	49	2 C	Woodgrove	林景	12	1 D
Northbrooks	思源	27	2 A	Woodlands Ring	辅廉	12	1 C
Northland	德景	14	1 C	Woodlands	辅仁	10	2 B
NUS High School	国大中学	106	2 B	Xinmin	新民	69	2 A
Orchid Park	兰景	27	1 B	Yio Chu Kang	永康	46	2 D
Outram	欧南	132	1 B	Yishun	义顺	13	2 D
Pasir Ris Crest	励志	52	2 D	Yishun Town	毅德	14	1 C
Pasir Ris	思励	73	1 C	Yuan Ching	耘青	82	1 A
Paya Lebar	巴耶利巴	69	2 D	Yuhua	裕华	61	1 D
Methodist Girls	美以美女中			Yusof Ishak	尤索夫依萨	84	1 A
Peicai	培才	69	1 B	Yuying	育英	70	1 C
Pei Hwa	培华	48	1 B	Zhenghua	正华	42	2 B
Peirce	培雅	67	1 A	Zhonghua	中华	69	1 D
Ping Yi	平仪	92	2 D				
Pioneer	先驱	59	2 D				
Presbyterian High	长老会	46	2 C				

PLACES		MAP	GRID

POLYTECHNICS / JNR COLL / C INST

PLACES		MAP	GRID
Nanyang Polytechnic	南洋理工学院	46	2 C
Ngee Ann Polytechnic	义安理工学院	85	1 B
Republic Polytechnic	Republic理工学院	11	2 A
Singapore Polytechnic	新加坡理工学院	107	1 B
Temasek Polytechnic	淡马锡理工学院	93	1 A
Anderson JC	安德逊初院	46	2 D
Anglo-Chinese JC	英华初院	107	2 C
Catholic JC	公教初院	88	1 D
Hwa Chong JC	华中初院	86	2 D
(Hwa Chong Institution)	(华侨中学)		
Innova JC	星烁初院	11	2 D
Jurong JC	裕廊初院	60	2 D
Meridian JC	美廉初院	51	2 D
Nanyang JC	南洋初院	68	2 D
National JC	国家初院	86	2 C
Pioneer JC	先驱初院	41	2 C
Raffles JC	莱佛士初院	88	2 A
Saint Andrew's JC	圣安德烈初院	89	2 B
Serangoon JC	实龙岗初院	69	2 B
Tampines JC	淡滨尼初院	73	2 C
Temasek JC	淡马锡初院	115	1 A
Victoria JC	维多利亚初院	114	2 C
Yishun JC	义顺初院	26	2 A
Millennia Institute	励仁高级中学	62	1 D

TECHNICAL INSTITUTES

PLACES		MAP	GRID
Assumption Vocational Institute	圣升职业专科学院	63	2 A
ITE College Central	工艺教育学院中部		
Bishan Campus	碧山校园	68	1 D
Bedok Campus	勿洛校园	92	2 D
Macpherson Campus	麦波申校园	91	1 D
Tampines Campus	淡滨尼校园	93	2 A
Yishun Campus	义顺校园	14	2 C
ITE College East	工艺教育学院东部	94	2 B
ITE College West	工艺教育学院西部		
Ang Mo Kio Campus	宏茂桥校园	47	1 D
Balestier Campus	马里士他校园	111	1 A
Bukit Batok Campus	武吉巴督校园	83	2 A
Clementi Campus	金文泰校园	84	1 D
Dover Campus	杜佛校园	107	1 D
ITE Headquarters	工艺教育学院总部	107	1 C
North Light Sch (Campus 1)	北光学校(校园1)	113	1 B
North Light Sch (Campus 2)	北光学校(校园2)	113	2 A

INSTITUTIONS OF HIGHER LEARNING

PLACES		MAP	GRID
Curtin University	柯丁大学	89	1 D
Digipen Inst of Technology	迪吉笔科技学院	107	2 C
Duke NUS Graduate Medical Sch	Duke国大医学研究院	132	1 C
James Cook University	詹姆斯·库克大学	45	2 D
Management Development Institute Of S'pore (MDIS)	新加坡管理发展学院	113	2 A
MDIS Uni Campus	MDIS 联合校园	108	1 D
Marketing Institute of S'pore (MIS)(Prinsep Hse)	新加坡市场学院 (布连士大厦)	110	2 D
Nanyang Technological University (NTU)	南洋理工大学	59	1 D
National Institute of Education (NIE)	国立教育学院	58	2 D
National University of S'pore (NUS) (Kent Ridge)	新加坡国立大学 (肯特岗)	106	2 D

PLACES		MAP	GRID
- Bt. Timah Campus	- 武吉知马校园	109	1 A
New York University Tisch Sch of the Arts (Asia)	纽约大学Tisch艺术学校(亚洲)	109	1 D
PSB Academy (HDB Hub - Biz 3)	PSB 学院 (HDB Hub - Biz 3)	88	2 C
Queen Margaret University	玛格烈女皇大学	88	2 C
School of The Arts (SOTA)	新加坡艺术学院	110	2 D
SIM University	新跃大学	85	1 C
S'pore Institute of Management (SIM)	新加坡管理学院		
- Clementi	- 金文泰	85	1 C
- Namly	- 南利	86	1 D
S'pore Management University (SMU) - Administration Bldg	新加坡管理大学 - 行政大厦	111	1 D
SMU-Lee Kong Chian Sch of Business	新加坡管理大学 - 李光前商学院	111	1 D
SMU-Sch of Accountancy	新加坡管理大学 - 会计学院	110	2 D
SMU-Sch of Economics & Sch of Social Sciences	新加坡管理大学 经济与社会科学学院	110	2 D
SMU-Sch of Information Systems & Campus Ctr	新加坡管理大学- 资讯系统学校与校园中心	110	2 D
UBS Campus	UBS校园	87	1 D
University of Chicago	芝加哥大学	110	2 D

SPECIAL EDUCATION SCH / MINDS

PLACES		MAP	GRID
APSN Delta Senior Sch	立达高级特别学校	131	2 A
APSN Jervois Special Sch	泽维士特别学校	131	2 A
APSN Katong Special Sch	加东特别学校	93	2 D
APSN Tanglin Special Sch	东陵特别学校	131	1 A
AWWA Special Sch	AWWA特别学校	69	2 A
Chao Yang Sch (Ang Mo Kio)	朝阳学校 (宏茂桥)	46	2 C
Grace Orchard Sch (Presby Community Svcs)	恩典乌节学校 (长老会社区服务)	60	2 D
METTA Sch	弥达学校	73	2 D
Minds - Fernvale Gdns Sch	新加坡智障福利会 芬雅尔园学校	48	1 B
Minds - Guillemard Gdns Sch	新加坡智障福利会 -基里玛园学校	112	2 B
Minds - Jurong Gdns Sch	新加坡智障福利会 -裕廊园学校	84	2 D
Minds - Lee Kong Chian Gdns Sch	新加坡智障福利会 -李光前园学校	109	1 D
Minds - Towner Gardens Ctr	新加坡智障福利会 -陶纳园学校	92	1 D
Minds - Yio Chu Kang Devt Ctr Gdn Sch	新加坡智障福利会 杨厝港发展中心园学校	47	1 B
Mountbatten Vocational Sch	蒙巴登技术学校	112	2 B
Pathlight School (Autism Resource Ctr)	新光学校 (自闭症资源中心)	68	1 B
Rainbow Ctr - Balestier Special Sch	彩虹中心马里士他 特别学校	111	1 A
Rainbow Ctr - Margaret Dr Special Sch	彩虹中心玛格烈通道 特别学校	108	1 D
Rainbow Ctr - Yishun Special Sch	彩虹中心义顺特别 学校	27	1 A
S'pore Autism Sch	新加坡自闭症学校	82	1 A
S'pore Sch for the Deaf	新加坡聋哑学校	109	1 D
S'pore Sch for the Visually Handicapped	新加坡视障学校	88	2 B
Spastic Children's Assn Sch	痉挛儿童协会学校	51	2 D

POLYTECHNICS理工学院 JNR COLL 初级学院 C INST 高级中学 • TECHNICAL INSTITUTES 工艺教育学院 • INSTITUTIONS OF HIGHER LEARNING 高等学府 • SPECIAL EDUCATION SCH 特别学校 MINDS智障学校

FOREIGN SCHOOLS

Anglo Chinese School (International)	英华国际学校	108	1 B
American College	美国学院	130	2 C
Australian International Sch	澳洲国际学校	68	2 D
Canadian International Sch (Elementary)	加拿大国际学校(小学)	84	2 B
Canadian International Sch (Middle)	加拿大国际学校(中级)	64	2 D
Canadian International Sch (Secondary)	加拿大国际学校(中学)	131	2 D
Canadian International Sch	加拿大国际学校	113	1 C
Chatsworth International Sch	采士华国际学校	110	1 C
Chatsworth International Sch East Campus	采士华国际学校东部校园	113	2 C
Chatsworth International Sch (Jalan Kayu)	采士华国际学校(惹兰加由)	47	2 B
Chinese International Sch	汉合国际学校	87	2 D
Deutsche Schule (German Sch)	德国学校	85	2 A
Dover Court Preparatory Sch	杜佛阁补习学校	107	1 C
DPS International School (Delhi Public School)	DPS国际学校(德里公立学校)	69	2 C
Emaar International Sch	埃玛国际学校	107	1 A
ERC Institute	ERC学校	110	1 D
Eton House International Sch	伊顿楼国际学校	113	1 C
Finnish Supplementary Sch (S'pore Land Twr)	芬兰补习学校(新加坡置地大夏)	133	1 B
Global Indian International Sch	环球印度国际学校	130	1 A
Global Indian International Sch (Branch)	环球印度国际学校(分校)	114	2 A
Global Indian International Sch (Branch)	环球印度国际学校(分校)	89	1 C
Hollandse School (Dutch Sch)	荷兰学校	85	2 A
INSEAD (Institute Of European Business Admin)	欧洲工商管理学校	107	2 D
International Community Sch	国际社团学校	106	1 B
ISS International Sch (Preston Campus)	ISS 新加坡国际学校(普勒士顿校园)	130	2 C
ISS International Sch (Elementary Sch)	ISS 新加坡国际学校(小学)	109	2 C
Italian Supplementary Sch (Italian Embassy)	意大利补习学校(意大利大使馆)	110	2 A
Japanese Kindergarten	日本人幼稚园	105	2 A
Japanese Sch (Changi)	日本人学校(樟宜)	74	1 C
Japanese Sch (Primary)	日本人学校(小学)	106	2 C
Japanese Sch (Secondary)	日本人学校(中学)	105	2 B
Japanese Supplementary Sch	日本人补习学校	106	2 D
Korean Church Kindergarten	韩国教会幼稚园	88	1 D
Lock Road Kindergarten	洛克路幼稚园	130	2 C
Lycee Francaise De Singapour	新法国学校	68	2 A
Norwegian Supplementary Sch	挪威补习学校	107	1 C
NPS International Sch	NPS国际学校	92	2 C
Overseas Family Sch	海外家庭学校	110	1 D
Rosemount Kindergarten	罗斯毛特幼稚园	114	2 B
Sekolah Indonesia Singapura	新加坡印尼学校	114	2 B
Shelton College International	谢尔顿国际学院	131	1 C
Singapore American Sch	新加坡美国学校	10	2 D
Singapore Korean Sch	新加坡韩国学校	113	1 B
SJI International Sch	圣约瑟书院国际学校	88	2 C
Swedish Supplementary Sch	瑞典补习学校	110	1 D
Swiss Sch	瑞士学校	85	2 A
Tanglin Trust Sch	东陵托管学校	107	2 D
United World College of South East Asia	东南亚联合世界学院	107	1 C
Waseda Shibuya Senior High Sch	Waseda Shibuya高级中学	106	1 D

ISLAMIC RELIGIOUS SCHOOLS

Al-Khairiah Islamic Sch	阿凯力亚回教学校	113	2 A
Alsagoff Arab School	阿萨戈夫阿拉伯学校	111	2 C
Madrasah Al-Arabiah Al-Islamiah	阿拉伯回教学校	92	1 D
Madrasah Al-Irsyad Al-Islamiah	伊尔塞回教学校	110	1 B
Madrasah Aljunied Al-Islamic Sch	阿裕尼回教学校	111	1 C
Madrasah Al-Ma'arif Al-Islamiah	阿马亚里夫回教学校	113	1 B
Madrasah Al-Tahzibiah Al-Islamiah	达吉比亚回教学校	26	1 C
Madrasah Wak Tanjong Al-Islamiah	华丹戎回教学校	113	1 A
Muhammadiyah Education Centre	穆哈马迪雅教育中心	112	1 B
Sekolah Ugama Radin Mas	拉丁马士回教学校	131	1 C

LANGUAGE CENTRES

Alliance Francaise De Singapour	新加坡法国语文学院	110	1 A
Ministry of Education Language Centre	教育部语言中心	68	1 C
Umar Pulavar Tamil Language Centre	乌马布拉娃淡米尔语言中心	111	1 A

OTHER INSTITUTIONS / ACADEMIA

Bayanihan Ctr (Filipino Training Ctr)	巴廷尼汉中心(菲律宾人训练中心)	130	1 D
BCA Academy of the Built Environment	建设局建筑环境学院	89	1 A
Boy's Brigade Hq	少年旅总部	131	2 A
British Council	英国文化协会	109	1 C
Buddhist College	佛学院	40	2 D
Centre for Urban Greenery and Ecology (NParks HQ)	市区绿化及生态中心(国家公园总部)	109	1 A
Chinese Opera Institute	华乐学院	111	1 D
Civil Defence Academy	民防学校	59	2 A
Civil Service College	民事服务学院	107	2 B
Employment and Employability Institute	雇用与雇用能力学院	131	2 A
Grace Orchard School	Grace Orchard学校	60	2 D
Home Team Academy	内政群英学院	40	1 D
ICA Academy	移民与检查站学院	59	2 A
JTC Academy (JTC Summit)	裕廊学院(顶峰大厦)	83	1 C
Lasalle - SIA College of the Arts	拉萨尔-新航艺术学院(蒙巴登校园)	112	2 C
LTA Academy (Hampshire Rd)	陆路交通管理局学院(翰莎路)	110	2 B
Minds - SIA Employment Devt Centre	新加坡智障福利会-SIA职业发展中心	109	1 D
Nanyang Academy of Fine Arts	南洋艺术学院	111	1 D
- Campus 1 - Middle Rd	- 学院 1 - 密驼路校园	111	1 D
- Campus 2 - Bencoolen Street	- 学院 2 - 明古连街	110	2 D
- Campus 3 - Bencoolen Street	- 学院 3 - 明古连街	111	1 C
National Cadet Corps (Kallang Camp)	全国学生军团部(加冷兵营)	111	2 C
National Community Leadership Institute	国家社区领袖学院	129	2 B
National Library Institute (Marine Parade Community Bldg)	国家图书馆学院(马林百列社区大厦)	114	1 C
Old Thong Chai Medical Institution	旧同济医院	132	2 B
Pacific Economic Cooperation Council	太平洋经济合作理事会	109	2 B
Prisons Staff Training School	监狱官员训练学校	4	1 D
PSB Academy (HDB Hub - Biz 3)	PSB 学院(HDB Hub - Biz 3)	88	2 C
Public Relations Academy (MICA Bldg)	公共关系学院(新闻及艺术部大厦)	132	2 A
Raffles La Salle Institute	拉萨尔设计学校	111	1 D
SAF Education Centre	新加坡武装部队教育中心	26	2 A
Saint Francis Methodist Sch	圣芳济卫理教会学校	63	2 B
SHA Villa	新加坡旅馆协会训练中心	110	1 D
SIA Training Centre	新航训练中心	95	1 A
Singapore Academy of Law (Supreme Court)	新加坡法律学院(最高法院)	133	1 A
Singapore Aviation Academy	新加坡航空学院	54	1 B
Singapore Hotel Assn Training & Educational Ctr (SHATEC)	新加坡酒店协会训练与教育中心	83	2 A
Singapore Power Training Institute	新加坡能源培训中心	89	2 A
Singapore Sikh Education Foundation (Central Sikh Tp)	新加坡锡克人教育基金(中央锡克庙)	111	2 A
Singapore Sports Sch	新加坡体育学校	11	2 D
SP Jain Ctr of Management	SP Jain管理中心	130	1 C
Tourism Academy	旅游学院	142	1 C
Trinity Theological College	三一神学院	63	2 B
Tropical Marine Science Institute	热带海洋学院总办事处	106	2 D

• LANGUAGE CENTRES 语言中心 • OTHER INSTITUTIONS/ACADEMIA 其他专修及研究团体

EMBASSIES / HIGH COMMISSIONS / CONSULATES

PLACES			MAP	GRID
Angola (Suntec Tower 2)	安哥拉大使馆 (新达城大厦2)		111	1 D
Australia (25 Napier Road)	澳洲最高专员公署 (25纳比雅路)		109	1 C
Austria (Parkview Square)	奥地利大使馆 (百威广场)		111	1 D
Bangladesh (Sunshine Plaza)	孟加拉国最高专员 公署 (金光大厦)		110	2 C
Barbados (31B Kreta Ayer Rd)	巴巴多斯大使馆 (31B 水车路)		132	2 C
Belarus (S'pore Land Tower)	贝拉鲁斯大使馆 (新加坡置地大厦)		133	1 A
Belgium (8 Shenton Way)	比利时大使馆 (8珊顿大道)		132	2 C
Belize (Tong Eng Building)	贝利兹领事馆 (同荣大厦)		132	2 C
Botswana (Beach Ctr)	波札那大使馆 (美芝中心)		111	1 D
Brazil (United Square)	巴西大使馆 (大华广场)		110	2 A
Brunei Darussalam (325 Tanglin Road)	汶莱最高专员公署 (325东陵路)		109	1 C
Cambodia (Orchard Towers)	柬埔寨大使馆 (豪杰大厦)		109	1 C
Cameroon (Afro Asia Bldg)	客麦隆山领事馆 (亚非大厦)		132	2 C
Canada (One George St)	加拿大最高专员公署 (乔治街一号)		132	2 B
Chile (The Octagon)	智利大使馆 (建春大厦)		132	2 C
China (150 Tanglin Road)	中华人民共和国大使馆 (150东陵路)		109	1 C
Colombia (Republic Plaza)	哥伦比亚大使馆 (共和大厦)		132	2 B
Comoros (Cairnhill Plaza)	科摩罗领事馆 (经禧大厦)		110	1 C
Costa Rica (Balmoral Plaza)	哥斯达黎加大使馆 (百慕乐商场)		110	1 A
Cote d'Ivoire (HarbourFront Centre)	象牙海岸领事馆 (港湾中心)		142	1 A
Cyprus (102F Pasir Panjang Rd)	赛普鲁斯总领事馆 (102F 巴西班让路)		130	1 C
Czech Republic (Suntec Tower 1)	捷克共和国大使馆 (新达城大厦1)		111	1 D
Denmark (United Square)	丹麦大使馆 (大华广场)		110	2 A
Djibouti (30 Gul Crescent)	吉布提共和国大使馆 (30 卡尔弯)		100	2 A
Dominican Republic (S'pore Land Tower)	多明尼加共和国大使馆 (新加坡置地大厦)		133	1 A
Ecuador (Costa Rhu Condo)	厄瓜多尔领事馆 (禺渚苑)		111	2 D
Egypt (75 Grange Road)	埃及阿拉伯共和国 大使馆 (75格兰芝路)		109	2 D
Estonia (UIC Bldg)	爱沙尼亚大使馆 (联合工业大厦)		132	2 C
Ethiopia (Chin Bee Avenue)	埃塞俄比亚领事馆 (振美道)		81	2 C
European Union (Raffles City Tower)	欧洲联盟大使馆 (莱佛士城大厦)		133	1 A
Fiji (Ngee Ann City Twr B)	飞枝群岛领事馆 (义安城B大厦)		110	1 C
Finland (United Square)	芬兰大使馆 (大华广场)		110	2 A
France (Cluny Park Road)	法国大使馆 (古鲁尼园路)		87	1 D
Germany (S'pore Land Tower)	德国大使馆 (新加坡置地大厦)		133	1 B
Ghana (Pomo Paradiz)	加纳共和国领事馆 (百乐市)		110	2 D
Greece - Consulate (Sime Darby Centre)	希腊领事馆 (森那美中心)		85	1 B
Hungary (Raffles City Twr)	匈牙利大使馆 (莱佛士城大厦)		133	1 A
Iceland (Bank of China Bldg)	冰岛大使馆 (中国银行大厦)		133	1 B
India (31 Grange Road)	印度最高专员公署 (31格兰芝路)		110	1 D
Indonesia (7 Chatsworth Road)	印尼大使馆 (7采士华路)		109	2 D
Ireland (Liat Towers)	爱尔兰总领事馆 (烈大厦)		109	2 C
Israel (24 Stevens Close)	以色列大使馆 (24 史蒂芬弄)		109	2 A
Italy (United Square)	意大利大使馆 (大华广场)		110	2 A
Jamaica (Lippo Ctr)	牙买加大使馆 (立宝中心)		132	2 D
Japan (16 Nassim Road)	日本大使馆 (16那森路)		109	2 B
Kazakhstan (Ocean Towers)	哈萨克大使馆 (海洋大厦)		133	1 B
Korea - North (The Plaza)	朝鲜民主主义人民共 和国大使馆 (文雅大厦)		111	2 D
Korea - South (Goldbell Tower)	大韩民国大使馆 (慕金钟大厦)		110	1 B
Kuwait (Ritz-Carlton Millenia S'pore)	科威特大使馆 (丽嘉登酒店)		133	1 A
Lao PDR (Goldhill Plaza)	寮国大使馆 (金岭商场)		110	2 A
Lebanon (Centennial Tower)	黎巴嫩领事馆 (百年大厦)		133	2 A
Lithuania (Manhattan House)	立陶宛领事馆 (万豪登大厦)		132	1 B
Luxembourg (Great Eastern Ctr)	卢森堡总领事馆 (大东方保险中心)		132	2 B
Madagascar (Technopreneur Ctr)	马达加斯加共和国 领事馆 (科技企业中心)		131	1 B
Malaysia (301 Jervois Rd)	马来西亚最高专员 公署 (301号泽维士路)		109	2 D
Maldives (United Square)	马尔代夫大使馆 (大华广场)		110	2 A
Mali (City House)	马里领事馆 (城市大厦)		132	2 C
Malta (International Plaza)	马尔他领事馆 (凯联大厦)		132	2 C
Mauritius (Orchard Towers)	毛里求斯领事馆 (豪杰大厦)		109	1 C
Mexico (The Gateway East Twr)	墨西哥大使馆 (新门广场, 东大厦)		111	1 D
Monaco (720 Mounbatten Rd)	摩纳哥大使馆 (720号蒙巴登路)		112	2 D
Mongolia (Parkview Square)	蒙古大使馆 (百威广场)		111	1 D
Morocco (The Concourse)	摩洛哥名誉领事馆 (鸿福中心)		111	2 C
Myanmar (15 St. Martin's Drive)	缅甸大使馆 (15圣马丁通道)		109	2 C
Nepal (High Street Centre)	尼泊尔王国总领事馆 (水仙门商业大厦)		132	2 A
Netherlands (Liat Towers)	荷兰大使馆 (烈大厦)		109	2 C
New Zealand (Ngee Ann City Twr A)	纽西兰最高专员公署 (义安城A座)		110	1 C
Nigeria (Anson House)	尼日利亚大使馆 (安盛大厦)		132	2 D
Norway (Hong Leong Building)	挪威大使馆 (丰隆大厦)		132	2 C

PLACES		MAP	GRID
Pakistan (Shaw Centre)	巴基斯坦回教共和国 最高专员公署(邵氏大厦)	109	2 C
Panama (Hong Leong Building)	巴拿马大使馆 (丰隆大厦)	132	2 C
Papua New Guinea (146 Robinson Rd)	巴布亚新几内亚大使馆 (146号罗敏申路)	132	2 C
Peru (Palais Renaissance)	秘鲁大使馆 (文艺复兴广场)	109	2 C
Philippines (20 Nassim Road)	菲律宾大使馆 (20号那森路)	109	2 B
Poland (Wisma Atria)	波兰大使馆 (威士马广场)	110	1 D
Portugal (55 Waterloo Street)	葡萄牙领事馆 (55号滑铁卢街)	111	1 D
Qatar (Shangri-la Hotel)	卡塔尔大使馆 (香格里拉大酒店)	109	2 B
Romania (48 Jln Harom Setangkai)	罗马尼亚大使馆 (48号惹兰哈仑史丹开开)	108	2 A
Russia Federation (51 Nassim Road)	俄罗斯大使馆 (51号那森路)	109	1 A
Samoa (Winsland House II)	萨摩亚领事馆 (温斯兰大厦2)	110	1 D
Saudi Arabia (Winsland House II)	沙地阿拉伯大使馆 (温斯兰大厦2)	110	1 D
Seychelles (22 Cavenagh Road)	塞舌尔总领事馆 (22号加文纳路)	110	1 C
Slovakia (South Point)	斯洛伐克大使馆 (南坊大厦)	132	1 D
Slovenia (Singapore Land Tower)	斯洛文尼亚共和国领事馆 (新加坡置地大厦)	133	1 B
South Africa (Odeon Towers)	南非最高专员公署 (奥迪安大厦)	111	1 D
Spain (Suntec Tower 1)	西班牙大使馆 (新达城大厦1)	111	1 D
Sri Lanka (Goldhill Plaza)	斯里兰卡最高专员公署(金岭商场)	110	2 A
Sweden (S'pore Power Building)	瑞典大使馆 (新加坡能源大厦)	110	1 D
Switzerland (1 Swiss Club Link)	瑞士领事馆 (1号瑞士俱乐部连路)	85	2 A
Thailand (370 Orchard Road)	泰国大使馆 (370号乌节路)	109	2 C
Tonga (Changi Airport Term 2)	汤加群岛领事馆 (樟宜机场第二搭客大厦)	75	1 C
Tunisia (Thong Teck Building)	突尼西亚领事馆 (同德大厦)	110	1 B
Turkey (SGX Centre 1)	土耳其大使馆 (新加坡交易中心1)	132	2 C
Tuvalu (Aljunied Ind Complex)	图瓦卢领事馆 (阿裕尼工业大厦)	90	2 D
Uganda (Crocodile House)	乌干达领事馆 (鳄鱼大厦)	91	1 C
Ukraine (S'pore Land Tower)	乌克兰共和国领事馆 (新加坡置地大厦)	133	1 B
United Arab Emirates (Parkview Square)	阿拉伯联合酋长国 大使馆(百威广场)	111	1 D
United Kingdom (100 Tanglin Road)	英国大使馆 (100号东陵路)	110	1 C
United States Of America (27 Napier Road)	美国大使馆 (27号纳比雅路)	109	1 C
Uruguay (UIC Bldg)	乌拉圭领事馆 (联合工业大厦)	132	2 C
Uzbekistan (United House)	乌兹别克领事馆 (华业大厦)	110	2 C
Vanuatu (Golden Mile Tower)	梵奴亚达共和国领事馆 (黄金大厦)	111	2 C
Venezuela (Winsland House I)	委内瑞拉大使馆 (温斯兰大厦1)	110	1 D
Vietnam (10 Leedon Park)	越南大使馆 (10号礼敦园)	108	1 A

PLACES		MAP	GRID
Yemen (United House)	叶门共和国领事馆 (华业大厦)	110	2 C
Zambia (Biztech Centre)	赞比亚大使馆 (Biztech中心)	90	2 D

ENTRY / EXIT POINTS FOR TRAVEL / GOODS

AIR 航空

Changi Airport	樟宜机场	75	1 B
- Budget Terminal	廉价飞机终站	96	1 B
- Terminal 1	第一终站	75	1 B
- Terminal 2	第二终站	75	1 C
- Terminal 3	第三终站	75	1 C
Seletar Airport	实里达机场	28	2 A

RAIL 铁路

Tanjong Pagar Railway Stn	丹戎巴葛火车站	132	1 D
Woodlands Station (Disembarkation Only)	兀兰关卡 (只限抵达)	10	2 A

ROAD 陆路

Tuas Checkpoint	大士关卡	56	2 D
Woodlands Checkpoint	兀兰关卡	10	2 A

SEA 海路

Ferry Terminals/Jetties/Marinas/Piers 渡轮码头 / 码头 / 滨海

Bedok Jetty	勿洛码头	115	2 C
CAFHI Jetty	CAFHI码头	54	1 B
Changi Ferry Terminal	樟宜渡轮码头	76	1 A
Changi Point Ferry Terminal	樟宜尾渡轮码头	54	1 B
Esplanade Jetty	滨海剧场码头	133	1 A
Jurong Pier	裕廊码头	103	2 B
Lighter Jetty	驳船码头	129	2 D
Loyang Jetty	洛阳码头	53	1 C
Marina Country Club Marina	滨海乡村俱乐部	30	2 B
Marina South Pier	滨海南码头	133	2 D
Outward Bound Ubin Camp 1 & 2 Jetties	外展学校第1&2营码头	32	1 B
Pasir Panjang Ferry Terminal	巴西班让渡轮码头	130	1 D
Pulau Ubin - Main Jetty	乌敏岛 - 主要码头	34	1 D
- Resort Jetty	- 度假屋码头	33	1 D
Raffles Marina	莱佛士滨海	77	2 A
Raffles Place Jetty	莱佛士坊码头	133	1 B
SAF Ferry Terminal & Jetty	武装部队渡轮终站&码头	54	2 B
S'pore Cruise Ctr	新加坡渡轮中心	142	1 A
Tanah Merah Ferry Terminal	丹那美拉渡轮码头	118	1 B
Tuas Jetty	大士码头	120	1 A
West Coast Pier	西海岸码头	128	1 A

Gates 闸门

Brani Gate 2	布拉尼闸门2	142	2 A
Jurong Port Gate	裕廊海港闸门	103	2 B
Jurong Port West Gate	裕廊西海港闸门	103	2 B
Keppel Distripark Gate	发尼分销园闸门	131	2 D
Pasir Panjang Terminal Gate 4	巴西班让码头闸门4	129	1 B
Pasir Panjang Wharves Gate 3	巴西班让码头闸门3	129	2 C
Sembawang Shipyard Gate 1	三巴旺船坞闸门1	3	2 C
Sembawang Wharves Gate	三巴旺码头闸门	3	2 C
Tg Pagar Terminal Gate 1	丹戎巴葛码头闸门1	132	2 D

FIRE STATIONS / FIRE POSTS

PLACES		MAP	GRID
Airport 1	机场1	74	2 A
Airport 2	机场2	75	2 D
Airport Fire Sub-Stn 3	机场消防分局3	75	2 A
Alexandra Stn	亚历山大	130	1 A
Ang Mo Kio Stn	宏茂桥	46	2 C
Banyan Jurong Island Stn	巴央榕廊岛	137A	2 C
Bishan Stn	碧山	67	1 D
Boon Keng Fire Post	文庆消防岗	112	1 A
Braddell Heights Fire Post	布莱德岭消防岗	69	1 D
Bukit Batok Station	武吉巴督	41	2 D
Bukit Merah View Fire Post	红山景消防岗	131	2 B
Bukit Panjang Fire Post	武吉班让消防岗	42	2 D
Bukit Timah Fire Post	武吉芝马消防岗	84	2 A
Cairnhill Fire Post	经禧消防岗	110	1 B
Central Stn	中央	132	2 A
Chai Chee Fire Post	菜市消防岗	92	2 C
Changi Stn	樟宜	94	1 B
Choa Chu Kang Fire Post	蔡厝港消防岗	41	1 C
Clementi Stn	金文泰	84	1 D
Clementi West Fire Post	金文泰西消防岗	106	1 C
Eunos Fire Post	友诺士消防岗	113	2 A
Geylang East Fire Post	芽笼东消防岗	112	1 A
Jurong East Fire Post	裕廊东消防岗	61	2 D
Jurong Island Stn	裕廊岛	125	1 D
Jurong Stn	裕廊	81	2 A
Jurong West Fire Post	裕廊西消防岗	80	2 A
Loyang Fire Post	罗央消防岗	74	1 B
Marine Parade Fire Post	马林百列消防岗	114	1 C
Mountbatten Fire Post	蒙巴登消防岗	112	2 D
Nee Soon Ctrl Fire Post	义顺中消防岗	27	1 A
Pasir Ris Fire Post	巴西立消防岗	73	2 A
Paya Lebar Stn	巴耶利巴	91	1 B
Punggol North Fire Post	榜鹅北消防岗	50	1 A
Sengkang Stn	盛港	49	1 C
Sentosa Fire Post	圣淘沙消防岗	142	2 C
Sungei Kadut Fire Post	双溪加株消防岗	22	2 B
Tampines Stn	淡滨尼	72	1 C
Teck Ghee Fire Post	德义消防岗	68	1 B
Telok Blangah Fire Post	直落布兰雅消防岗	130	2 D
Toa Payoh Fire Post	大巴窑消防岗	89	1 B
Tuas Checkpoint Fire Post	大士关卡消防岗	56	2 D
Tuas Stn	大士	78	2 D
Woodlands Fire Post	兀兰消防岗	11	2 B
Woodlands Stn	兀兰	10	1 D
Yishun Stn	义顺	14	1 A

FLYOVERS / UNDERPASSES / VIADUCTS / TUNNELS

FLYOVERS 立交桥

		MAP	GRID
Adam	亚当	87	1 C
Aljunied	阿裕尼	90	2 D
Anak Bukit	安娜武吉	85	1 B
Ang Mo Kio Central	宏茂桥中	68	2 A
Ang Mo Kio North	宏茂桥北	47	1 D
Ang Mo Kio South	宏茂桥南	68	1 C
Api Api	阿比阿比	51	1 D
Bahar	巴哈	59	2 C
Bishan	碧山	88	2 A
Bedok North	勿洛北	92	2 C
Bedok Reservoir	勿洛蓄水池	93	1 B
Benjamin Sheares	薛尔思	133	2 A

PLACES		MAP	GRID
Benoi	贲耐	79	2 B
Braddell	布莱德	89	2 A
Buangkok	万国	50	1 D
Bukit Batok	武吉巴督	62	1 D
Bukit Merah	红山	131	2 C
Bukit Timah Seven Mile	武吉芝马七英里	85	1 B
Buona Vista	波那维斯达	107	2 C
Changi Airport	樟宜机场	96	1 A
Changi	樟宜	95	2 B
Chantek	彰德	64	2 D
Choa Chu Kang East	蔡厝港东	41	1 B
Choa Chu Kang West	蔡厝港西	41	1 B
Clementi	金文泰	106	1 D
Clementi North	金文泰北	84	1 B
Corporation	企业	82	1 D
Dairy Farm	牛乳场	64	1 D
Defu	德福	70	2 B
Eng Neo	英娘	86	2 B
Eunos	友诺士	91	2 D
Farrer	花拉	87	1 D
Gali Batu	卡利巴株	42	2 D
Gillman	吉门	130	1 B
Henderson	亨德申	131	1 C
Holland	荷兰	108	2 B
Hong Kah	丰嘉	60	2 C
Jalan Kayu	惹兰加由	29	1 D
Jurong East	裕廊东	83	1 A
Jurong Hill	裕廊山	81	2 D
Kampong Bahru	甘榜巴鲁	131	2 C
Kampong Java	甘榜爪哇	110	2 A
Kim Keat	金吉	89	1 C
Laguna	礁湖	115	1 B
Lam San	南山	40	2 D
Lentor	伦多	46	1 A
Lower Delta	立法下段	131	2 C
Loyang	罗央	73	2 B
Mandai	万礼	23	2 C
Mandai Lake	万礼湖	25	2 B
Marine Parade	马林百列	114	1 C
Marsiling	马西岭	11	2 D
Marymount	玛丽蒙	88	1 A
Moulmein	摩绵	111	1 A
Mount Pleasant	快乐山	87	2 D
Nanyang	南洋	59	1 D
Nee Soon	义顺	25	2 D
Newton	纽顿	110	1 B
Ophir	奥菲亚路	111	2 D
Outram	欧南	132	1 B
Oxley	欧思礼	110	2 D
Pandan	班丹	106	1 A
Pasir Laba	巴西拉巴	79	2 B
Pasir Ris	巴西立	73	1 A
Paya Lebar	巴耶利巴	91	1 D
Penjuru	本鲁	104	2 B
Pioneer	先驱	80	2 D
Punggol	榜鹅	49	2 A
Punggol East	榜鹅东	50	1 B
Punggol West	榜鹅西	30	1 D
Queensway	女皇大道	130	1 A
Radin Mas	拉丁玛士	131	2 C
Rifle Range	射靶场	64	2 C
Rochor	梧槽	111	1 D
Seletar (CTE)	实里达(中央快速公路)	47	1 A

PLACES		MAP	GRID
Sembawang	三巴旺	25	2 B
Simei	四美	73	2 D
Tampines	淡滨尼	50	1 C
Tampines South	淡滨尼南	94	1 A
Tanah Merah	丹那美拉	95	1 D
Tanjong Katong	丹戎加东	113	1 D
Tanjong Rhu	丹戎禺	112	2 D
Teban	德曼	83	1 D
Telok Ayer	直落亚逸	133	1 C
Tengah	登嘉	60	1 B
Thomson	汤申	88	2 C
Toa Payoh North	大巴窑北	89	1 A
Toa Payoh South	大巴窑南	88	2 C
Toh Guan	卓源	83	2 A
Toh Tuck	道德	84	1 B
Tuas	大士	79	1 D
Turf Club	赛马公会	23	1 B
Ulu Sembawang	乌鲁三巴旺	25	1 A
University	大学	106	2 C
Upper Changi	樟宜上段	73	2 D
Upper Seletar	实里达上段	25	2 D
Upper Thomson	汤申上段	45	1 A
Wayang Satu (Whitley)	哇央沙都(惠德里)	109	2 A
Whampoa	黄埔	89	2 C
Woodlands	兀兰	10	2 C
Woodlands South	兀兰南	23	2 A
Woodsville	兀士维	89	2 C
Yew Tee	油池	42	1 B
Yio Chu Kang	杨厝港	47	1 B
Zhenghua	正华	43	1 D

UNDERPASSES 地下通道

PLACES		MAP	GRID
Anak Bukit Underpass	安娜武吉地下通道	85	1 A
Ang Mo Kio Underpass	宏茂桥地下通道	69	1 A
Bartley Underpass	巴特礼地下通道	90	1 A
Braddell Underpass	布莱德地下通道	89	2 A
Bukit Timah Underpass	武吉知马地下通道	87	1 D
Clementi Ave 6 Underpass	金文泰6道地下通道	106	1 A
Dunearn Underpass	杜尼安地下通道	86	2 D
Queensway Underpass	女皇大道地下通道	108	1 D
Tuas Underpass	大士地下通道	79	1 D
Tuas West Underpass	大士西地下通道	78	2 A

VIADUCTS 高架桥

PLACES		MAP	GRID
Kaki Bukit Viaduct	加基武吉高架桥	92	1 B
Keppel Viaduct	发巴高架桥	132	1 D
Lornie Viaduct	罗尼高架桥	88	1 A
MacRitchie Viaduct	麦里芝高架桥	88	1 A
Paya Lebar Viaduct	巴耶利峇高架桥	90	2 A
Telok Blangah Viaduct	直落布兰雅高架桥	142	2 A
Tuas Checkpoint Viaduct	大士关卡高架桥	56	2 D
Upper Serangoon Viaduct	实龙岗上段高架桥	90	1 A

TUNNELS 隧道

PLACES		MAP	GRID
Chin Swee Tunnel	振瑞隧道	110	2 D
Fort Canning Tunnel	福康宁隧道	110	2 D
Kampong Java Tunnel	甘榜爪哇隧道	110	2 B
KPE Tunnel	加冷巴耶利峇快速公路隧道		
- ECP	东海岸公园大道	112	1 D
- PIE	泛岛快速公路	112	1 A
- Tampines	淡滨尼	70	2 C

GOVERNMENT OFFICES / STATUTORY BOARDS

		MAP	GRID
3P Network Division (Environment Bldg)	3P网络署(环境发展部大厦)	110	1 B
A* STAR (Agency for Science, Technology & Research) (Centros Bldg)	A* STAR(科学, 文艺及研究机构) (Centros大厦)	107	2 C
Accountant General's Department (The Treasury)	总会计司(财务大厦)	132	2 A
ACRA - Accounting and Corporate Regulatory Authority (International Plaza)	商业中心注册局 (凯联大厦)	132	2 C
Agri-Food & Veterinary Authority of S'pore (AVA) (MND Complex-Tower Blk)	农业食品与兽医局 (国家发展部大厦-大厦座)	132	2 C
(AVA-Sembawang Research Stn)	(农粮与兽医局三巴旺研究站)	26	2 B
Airport Health Ofc (Changi Airport T1 #14-08)	机场卫生署 (樟宜机场第一搭客大厦 #14-08)	75	1 B
Animal & Plant Health Ctr	动植物卫生中心	7	1 D
Animal Welfare & Control Division (Ctr for Animal Welfare)	动物福利及管制组(动物福利中心)	130	1 D
Appeals Board (Land Acquisition) (Supreme Court Bldg)	上诉局(土地征用)(最高法院大厦)	133	1 A
Attorney General's Chambers (The Adelphi)	总检察署(雅达辉购物中心)	133	1 A
Auditor General's Office (MND Cplx-Tower Blk)	总审计署(国家发展部大厦-大厦座)	132	2 C
Bailliffs Section (Subordinate Courts)	法警组(初级法庭)	132	2 B
BioInformatics Institute (Biopolis-Matrix)	生物资讯科学院(启奥生物医药研究园-Matrix)	107	2 C
BioLab (Biopolis-Chromos)	生物实验室(启奥生物医药研究园Chromos)	107	2 C
Biomedical Research Council (Centros Bldg)	生物医学研究理事会(Centros大厦)	107	2 C
Bioprocessing Technology Institute (Biopolis-Centros)	生物处理科学院(启奥生物医药研究园-Centros)	107	2 C
BioSpace (Biopolis-Helios)	生物空间学院(启奥生物医药研究园-Helios)	107	2 C
Board of Architects (MND Complex - Tower Blk)	新加坡建筑师管理局(国家发展部大厦-大厦座)	132	2 C
Building and Construction Authority (MND Complex-Tower Blk)	建设局 (国家发展部大厦-大厦座)	132	2 C
Buroh Lane Abattoir	布罗巷屠场	104	1 A
Casino Regulatory Authority (PSA Building)	赌场管制局(港务集团大厦)	130	1 D
Central Manpower Base (CMPB-SAF)	中央人力司(CMPB-武装部队)	131	1 C
Central Narcotics Bureau (Cantonment Complex)	中央肃毒局(广东民大厦)	132	1 C
Central Singapore CDC (HDB Hub Bizthree)	中区社理会(建屋发展局中心商业大厦)	88	2 C

Centre for Analytical Science (HSA Bldg)	分析科学中心 (卫生科学局大厦)	132	1 C
Centre for Drug Administration (Biopolis-Helios)	药物管制中心 (Biopolis-Helios)	107	2 C
Centre for Forensic Medicine (HSA Bldg)	法医学中心 (卫生科学局大厦)	132	1 C
Centre for Forensic Science (HSA Bldg)	法医科学中心 (卫生科学局大厦)	132	1 C
Centre for Medical Device Regulation (Biopolis-Helios)	医疗器械管制中心 (Biopolis-Helios)	107	2 C
Centre for Radiation Protection and Nuclear Science (HSA Bldg)	预防辐射及核子科学中心 (卫生科学局大厦)	132	1 C
Centre for Transfusion Medicine (HSA Bldg)	输血医学中心 (卫生科学局大厦)	132	1 C
Centre for Urban Greenery and Ecology (CUGE)	市区绿化及生态中心	109	1 A
(NParks Hq - Raffles Bldg)	(国家公园总部 - 莱佛士大厦)		
Certis Cisco	Certis Cisco工商保安机构	91	1 D
Charities Unit (MCYS Bldg)	慈善组 (社会发展及体育部大厦)	88	1 B
Changi Animal & Plant Quarantine Unit	樟宜动植物检疫组 (樟宜空中货运中心C7闸门)	54	2 D
(Changi Airfreight Ctr Gate C7)			
Chinese Development Assistance Council (CDAC Bldg)	华社自助会 (华社自助会大厦)	113	1 B
Choa Chu Kang Gov't Cemeteries Office	蔡厝港政府坟场办事处	38	2 D
Citizen Services Centre (ICA Bldg)	公民服务中心 (ICA大厦)	111	2 C
City Hall	政府大厦	133	1 A
Civil Aviation Authority of Singapore	新加坡民航局	75	1 B
(Changi Airport - Terminal 2)	(新加坡樟宜机场–第2搭客大厦)		
Civil & Criminal Justice Division (Subordinate Courts)	民事与刑事司法处 (初级法庭)	132	2 B
Civil Service College	民事服务学院	107	2 C
Comcare and Social Support Division (SLF Bldg)	社会支援处 (新加坡劳工基金大厦)	88	1 B
Commercial Affairs Department (Cantonment Complex)	商业事务局 (广东民大厦)	132	1 C
Communicable Disease Centre	传染病中心	110	2 A
Community Mediation Centres	社区调解中心		
CMC Central (URA Ctr - East Wing)	中心 (市区重建局中心–东座)	132	2 C
CMC Regional North (Woodlands Civic Ctr)	北区 (兀兰民事中心)	11	2 C
CMC Subordinate Courts	初级法庭	132	2 B
Community Mediation Unit (URA Ctr - East Wing)	社区调解组 (市区重建局中心东座)	132	2 C
Competition Commission of S'pore (MND Complex - Twr Blk)	新加坡竞争委员会 (国家发展部大厦–大厦座)	132	2 C
Consumer Product Safety Division (SPRING S'pore Bldg)	消费产品安全组 (标准、生产力与创新局大厦)	131	1 B
Contact S'pore (Raffles City Tower 28th Storey)	联系新加坡事务所 (莱佛士城大厦28楼)	133	1 A
Copyright Tribunal (Plaza By The Park)	版权评审局 (新苑大厦)	110	2 D
Corrupt Practices Investigation Bureau	贪污调查局	130	2 B
CPF Board (Hd Ofc) (CPF Building)	中央公积金局 (总办事处) (公积金大厦)	132	2 C
CPF Board - Bishan Office	中央公积金局–碧山办事处	67	2 D
CPF Board - Jurong East Office	中央公积金局–裕廊东办事处	83	1 B
CPF Board - Tampines Office	中央公积金局–淡滨尼办事处	72	2 C
CPF Board - Woodlands Office (Civic Ctr)	中央公积金局–兀兰办事处 (民事中心)	11	2 C
CPG Airport Development Division	CPG机场发展组	74	2 A
Creative Community Singapore (MICA Bldg)	新加坡创意处 (新闻及艺术部大厦)	132	2 A
Criminal Investigation Department	刑事侦查组	132	1 C
(Cantonment Complex)	(广东民大厦)		
Currency Dept (MAS Bldg)	货币组 (金融管理局大厦)	132	2 D
Customs Headquarters (Revenue House)	关税总部 (税务大厦)	110	2 A
Customs Operations Centre	关税行动中心	132	2 D
Data Storage Institute (E5 NUS)	数据储存学院 (E5 新加坡国立大学)	106	2 D
Deep Tunnel Sewerage System Dept (Environment Bldg)	深地道排水系统组 (环境发展部大厦)	110	1 B
Defence Science & Technology Agency - Hq (DSTA Bldg)	国防科技局–总部 (国家电脑局大厦)	129	2 A
Department of Statistics (The Treasury)	统计局 (财务大厦)	132	2 A
Design Singapore Office (MICA Bldg)	新加坡设计局 (新闻及艺术部大厦)	132	2 A
Destitute Persons Service (MCYS Bldg)	贫困人士服务 (社会发展及体育部大厦)	88	1 B
DNA Database Laboratory (MND Bldg-Annex B)	DNA数据库实验室 (国家发展部大厦-附录B)	132	2 C
Economic Development Board (Raffles City Tower)	经济发展局 (莱佛士城大厦)	133	1 A
Elderly, Disability and Gambling Safeguards Division (SLF Bldg)	年老无助及防赌援助组 (新加坡劳工基金大厦)	88	1 B
Elections Department	选举局	110	2 D
Employment Agency Licensing Branch (Kim Seng Rd - MOM)	职业介绍所执照分行 (金声路 - 人力部)	132	2 B
Employment and Employability Institute	就业及就业能力研究	131	1 C
Energy Market Authority (S'pore Power Bldg)	能源市场管理局 (新加坡能源大厦)	110	1 D
Environmental Health Department (Environment Bldg)	环境卫生局 (环境发展部大厦)	110	1 B
Environmental Health Institute (Biopolis-Helios)	环境卫生学院 (启奥生物医药研究园-Helios)	107	2 C

Family & Child Protection and Welfare Branch (MCYS Bldg)	家庭及保护儿童与福利分部(社会发展及体育部大厦)	88	1 B
Family and Juvenile Court	家庭少年法庭	132	2 B
Family Development Group (MCYS Bldg)	家庭发展组(社会发展及体育部大厦)	88	1 B
Family Services Division (SLF Bldg)	家庭服务组(新加坡劳工基金大厦)	88	1 B
Financial Industry Disputes Ctr (Fidrec) (HB Robinson Bldg)	金融业纠纷中心(HB罗敏申楼)	132	2 B
Fire Safety Certification & Enforcement Branch (Hq SCDF)	消防安全准证及执法组(民防总部)	91	1 B
Food & Veterinary Administration (MND Complex - Tower Blk)	食品与兽医局 (国家发展部大厦-大厦座)	132	2 C
Foreign Manpower Management Division (120 Kim Seng Rd)	客工管理组 (120 金声路)	132	1 A
Gifted Education Branch (Teachers Network)	天才教育组(教师网络)	109	2 D
Genome Inst. of S'pore (Biopolis-Genome)	新加坡基因学校(启奥生物医药研究园-基因科技)	107	2 C
Hawkers Dept (Environment Bldg)	小贩局(环境发展部大厦)	110	1 B
Health Promotion Board	保健促进局	132	1 C
Health Sciences Authority	卫生科学局	132	1 C
Hindu Endowments Board (Perumal Temple)	印度教基金信托会(实里尼维沙伯鲁玛庙)	111	1 B
Hindu Advisory Board (Perumal Temple)	印度教咨询局(实里尼维沙伯鲁玛庙)	111	1 B
HortPark	HortPark公园	130	1 C
Hotels Licensing Board (Tourism Court)	酒店执照局(旅游阁)	109	2 C
Housing & Development Board (HDB Hub)	建屋发展局(建屋局新总部)	88	2 C
ICA ALPS Custom Checkpoint	ICA ALPS 关税检查站	55	1 D
ICA Coastal Command (Pulau Brani)	移民关税局海岸指挥部(布拉尼岛)	142	2 B
Immigration & Checkpoints Authority (ICA Bldg)	移民关卡局(ICA大厦)	111	2 C
Industrial Arbitration Court (Supreme Court)	工业仲裁庭(最高法院)	133	1 A
Infocomm Development Authority Of S'pore (Suntec Tower 3)	资讯通信发展管理局(新达城大厦3)	111	1 D
Inland Revenue Authority (Revenue House)	国内税务局(税务大厦)	110	2 A
Insolvency and Public Trustee's Office (The URA Ctr East Wing)	破产及公众受托人办事处 (市区重建局中心-东座)	132	2 C
Institute for Infocomm Research (2 Heng Mui Keng Terrace)	资讯通讯研究学院(2号王美敬台)	128	2 A
Institute of BioEngineering & Nanotechnology (Biopolis-Nanos)	生物工程及毫微科技学院(启奥生物医药研究园-Nanos)	107	2 C
Institute of Chemical and Engineering Sciences	化学及工程学院	123	2 B
Institute of High Performance Computing (The Capricorn)	高性能电脑学院(The Capricorn)	129	1 A
Institute of Materials Research & Engineering (IMRE)	材料研究及工程学院(IMRE)	129	1 A
Institute of Medical Biology (Biopolis-Proteos)	医药生物学院(启奥生物医药研究园-Proteos)	107	2 C
Institute of Mental Health	精神健康学院	48	2 C
Institute of Microelectronics	微电子学研究院	129	1 A
Institute of Molecular & Cell Biology (Biopolis-Proteos)	分子及细胞生物学院(启奥生物医药研究园-Proteos)	107	2 C
Institute of Public Admin & Management (Science Park)	公共行政与管理学院(科学园)	129	1 A
Institute of Public Administration and Management (Civil Service College)	公共行政与管理研究所 (民事服务学院)	107	2 B
Institute of South East Asian Studies	东南亚研究所	129	1 A
Intellectual Property Office of Singapore (Plaza By the Park)	新加坡知识产权局 (新苑大厦)	110	2 D
Internal Security Department (Ministry of Home Affairs)	内部安全局(内政部)	88	2 D
International Enterprise S'pore (Bugis Junction Ofc Tower)	新加坡国际企业局(白沙浮商业城办公楼)	111	1 D
International Manpower Division (Ministry of Manpower Bldg)	国际人力部(人力部大厦)	132	2 B
Istana	总统府	110	2 C
JTC Corporation (The JTC Summit)	裕廊集团总部(顶峰大厦)	83	1 C
Kent Ridge Digital Lab	肯特岗数码实验所	129	1 A
Labour Relations Department (Ministry of Manpower)	劳资关系处 (人力部)	132	2 B
Land Information Centre (8 Shenton Way - SLA)	土地资讯中心(珊顿大道八号 - 新加坡土地管理局)	132	2 C
Land Surveyors Board (8 Shenton Way c/o SLA)	土地测量师管理局(珊顿大道八号c/o新加坡土地管理局)	132	2 C
Land Transport Authority (Hq)	陆路交通管理局(总部)	110	2 B
- Transit Regulation Div	-交通规则署	67	1 C
- Bus & Taxi Regulation Div	-巴士与德士规则署	67	1 C
- Road Pricing Div	-公路收费署	67	1 C
Legal Aid Bureau (URA Ctr East Wing)	法律援助局(市区重建局中心-东座)	132	2 C
Legal Service Commission (Supreme Court)	法律服务委员会(最高法院)	133	1 A
Licensing Division (S'pore Police Force)(Cantonment Cplx)	执照组(新加坡警察部队)(广东民大厦)	132	1 C
Majlis Ugama Islam Singapura (MUIS) (Islamic Religious Council Of Singapore)	新加坡回教理事会 (新加坡回教理事会)	89	1 B

PLACES		MAP	GRID
Marine Environment & Safety Department (Tg Pagar Cplx)	海域环境及安全局 (丹戎巴葛大厦)	132	2 D
Maritime and Port Authority (PSA Bldg)	海事及港务管理局(港务集团大厦)	130	1 D
Maritime and Port Authority - One Stop Document Ctr (Tanjong Pagar Complex)	海事及港务管理局－一站式文件中心 (丹戎巴葛大厦)	132	2 D
Media Development Authority	传媒发展局	132	2 A
- Main Office (MICA Bldg)	总部(新闻及艺术部大厦)	132	2 A
- Customer & Licensing Services (Novena Sq - Tower A)	客户及执照服务(诺维娜广场 – A座)	110	2 A
- Media Content Division - MICA (MICA Bldg)	媒体内容组–新闻及艺术部(新闻及艺术部大厦)	132	2 A
Meteorological Services Division	气象局	75	1 C
(Changi Airport - Terminal 2, 4th Storey Rm 048-033)	(新加坡樟宜机场，第二搭客大厦，第四楼, 048-033号房)		
Ministry of Community Development, Youth and Sports (MCYS Bldg)	社区发展, 青年及体育部 (社会发展及体育部大厦)	88	1 B
Ministry of Defence	国防部	63	1 A
Ministry of Education	教育部	107	2 C
Ministry of The Environment and Water Resources	环境及水源部	110	1 B
Ministry of Finance (The Treasury)	财政部(财务大厦)	132	2 A
Ministry of Foreign Affairs (Tanglin)	外交部(东陵)	109	1 C
Ministry of Health (College of Medicine Bldg)	卫生部(医学院大厦)	132	1 C
Ministry of Home Affairs (New Phoenix Park)	内政部(新凤凰园)	88	2 D
Ministry of Information, Communications and the Arts (MICA Building)	交通及资讯科技部 (新闻及艺术部大厦)	132	2 A
Ministry of Law (The Treasury)	律政部(财务大厦)	132	2 A
Ministry of Manpower	人力部	132	2 B
Ministry of National Development (MND Cplx - Tower Blk)	国家发展部(国家发展部大厦–大厦座)	132	2 C
Ministry of Trade & Industry (The Treasury)	贸易与工业部(财务大厦)	132	2 A
Ministry of Transport (PSA Building)	交通部(PSA大厦)	130	1 D
Monetary Authority of Singapore (MAS Bldg)	新加坡金融管理局(金融管理局大厦)	132	2 D
National Archives of Singapore	新加坡国家档案局	132	2 A
National Arts Council (MICA Bldg)	国家艺术理事会(新闻及艺术部大厦)	132	2 A
National Cancer Ctr	国立癌症中心	132	1 C
National Council of Social Service (Ulu Pandan CC)	全国社会福利理事会(乌鲁班丹民众俱乐部)	107	2 B
National Community Leadership Institute	全国社区领袖训练学院	129	2 B
National Crime Prevention Council (New Phoenix Park)	全国防止犯罪理事会(新凤凰园)	88	2 D
National Dental Centre	全国牙科中心	132	1 C
National Environment Agency (Environment Bldg)	国家环境局(环境发展大厦)	110	1 B
National Fire and Civil Emergency Prepardness (Central Fire Station)	全国防火及紧急民防组(中央消防局)	132	2 A
National Healthcare Group (GMTI Bldg)	国立健保集团综合诊所(肯特岗侧楼)	108	1 C
National Heart Ctr	全国心脏中心	132	1 C
National Heritage Board (MICA Bldg)	国家文物局(新闻及艺术部大厦)	132	2 A
National Library Board (National Library Bldg)	国家图书馆管理局(国家图书馆大厦)	111	1 D
National Medical Research Council Office (Biopolis-Helios)	国家医学研究理事会办事处(启奥生物医药研究园-Helios)	107	2 C
National Neuroscience Institute (Tan Tock Seng Hospital)	国立神经学院(陈笃生医院)	88	2 D
National Parks Board Hq	国家公园局总部	109	1 A
National Population Secretariat (MND Complex - Tower Blk)	国家人口秘书处(国家发展部大厦–大厦座)	132	2 C
National Registry of Diseases Office (HPB Bldg)	国家疾病登记局(建屋局大厦)	132	1 C
National Research Foundation (The Treasury)	国家研究基金(财务大厦)	132	2 A
National Security Co-ordination Secretariat (MND Cplx - Tower Blk)	国家安全协调秘书处 (国家发展部大厦)	132	2 C
National Skin Centre	国立皮肤诊疗中心	110	2 A
National Youth Council (HDB Hub Biz Three)	全国青年理事会(建屋局总部)	88	2 C
NEA Central Regional Office	国家环境局中区办事处	130	2 B
NEA North East Regional Office	国家环境局东北区办事处	67	1 B
NEA North West Regional Office	国家环境局西北区办事处	2	1 C
NEA South East Regional Office	国家环境局东南区办事处	90	2 C
NEA South West Regional Office	国家环境局西南区办事处	84	2 D
North East CDC (AIA Tampines Bldg)	东北社理会(AIA淡滨尼大厦)	72	2 C
North West CDC (Woodlands Civic Ctr)	西北社理会(兀兰民事中心)	11	2 C
Occupational Safety & Health Inspectorate Dept (Blk C - 120 Kim Seng Rd)	职业安全及卫生检查局 (大牌C - 120 金声路)	132	1 A

Ong Teng Cheong Institute of Labour Studies (One Marina Boulevard)	王鼎昌劳工研究所 (滨海林荫道一号)	133	1 B
Overseas Singaporean Unit (MND Complex - Tower Blk)	海外新加坡人事务组 (国家发展部大厦-大厦座)	132	2 C
Parliament Of Singapore (Parliament House)	国会大厦 (国会大厦)	132	2 A
Parliament Secretariat (Parliament House)	国会秘书处 (国会大厦)	132	2 A
People's Association	人民协会	112	1 B
Pollution Control Department (Environment Bldg)	污化管制处 (环境发展部大厦)	110	1 B
Port Health Office (NEA Central Regional Ofc)	海港卫生署 (国家环境局中区办事处)	130	2 B
Port Master's Office (Tanjong Pagar Cplx)	港务长署 (丹戎巴葛大厦)	132	2 D
Preservation of Monuments Board (RELC Bldg)	古迹保存局 (区域语言中心大厦)	109	2 B
Primary Dispute Resolution Centre (Subordinate Courts)	初级纠纷解决中心 (初级法庭)	132	2 B
Prime Minister's Office (Istana Annexe, Istana)	总理公署 (总统府附楼)	110	2 C
Professional Engineers Board (MND Complex Twr Blk)	专业工程师管理局 (国家发展部大厦 - 大厦座)	132	2 C
PS 21 Office (The Treasury)	21世纪公共服务处 (财务大厦)	132	2 A
Public Service Commission (National Library Bldg)	公共服务委员会 (国家图书馆大厦)	111	1 D
Public Service Division (The Treasury)	公共服务署 (财务大厦)	132	2 A
Public Transport Council (The Concourse #11-01)	公共交通理事会 (鸿福 #11-01)	111	1 C
Public Utilities Board (Environment Bldg)	公用事业局 (环境发展部大厦)	110	1 B
Radio & TV Licensing - MDA Customer & Licensing Services (Novena Square Twr A)	收音机及电视执照组 - 传媒发展局客户与执照组 (诺维娜广场大厦座A)	110	2 A
Reach Panel (SLF Bldg)	伸援委员会 (新加坡劳工基金大厦)	88	1 B
Registry of Co-operative Societies (MCYS Bldg)	合作社注册局 (社会发展及体育部大厦)	88	1 B
Registry of Marriages	婚姻注册局	132	2 A
Registry of Money Lenders & Pawnbrokers (URA Ctr East Wing)	贷款商及典当商注册局 (市区重建局中心,东座)	132	2 C
Registry of Muslim Marriages (Registry of Marriages)	回教婚姻注册局 (婚姻注册局)	132	2 A
Registry of Mutual Benefit Organisations (MCYS Bldg)	互助会注册局 (社会发展及体育部大厦)	88	1 B
Registry of Societies (ICA Bldg)	社团注册局 (ICA大厦)	111	2 C
Registries Of Trademarks, Patents and Designs (Plaza By The Park)	商标,专利权与设计注册局 (新苑大厦)	110	2 D
Rehabilitation, Protection and Residential Services Division (MCYS Bldg)	感化改造, 保护及留宿服务处 (社会发展及体育部大厦)	88	1 B
School Cluster Centre (Hoy Fatt Road)	学校群组中心 (开发路)	130	2 A
School Health Service Division (HPB Bldg)	学校保健服务组 (保健促进局大厦)	132	1 C
Science Centre Board (Singapore Science Centre)	科学馆管理局 (新加坡科学馆)	82	2 B
Sembawang Animal Quarantine Station	三巴旺动物检疫站	26	2 B
Sentosa Development Corporation (Sentosa Office)	圣淘沙发展局 (圣淘沙办事处)	142	2 C
Service Quality Centre (SPRING Singapore Bldg)	服务素质促进中心 (新加坡标新局大厦)	131	1 B
Sikh Advisory Board (Central Sikh Gurdwara)	锡克人咨询局 (锡克中心)	111	2 A
Singapore Academy of Law (Supreme Court)	新加坡法学院 (最高法院)	133	1 A
Singapore Air Traffic Control Ctr	新加坡航空交通控制中心	54	1 B
Singapore Anti-Narcotics Association (SANA)	新加坡肃毒协会 (新加坡肃毒协会总部)	49	1 B
Singapore Chinese Chamber of Commerce & Industry	新加坡中华工商总会	132	2 A
Singapore Civil Defence Force (Civil Defence HQ Cplx)	新加坡民防部队新总部 (民防部队新总部大厦)	91	1 B
Singapore Corporation of Rehabilitative Enterprises (Prison Hq Cplx)	新加坡复员技训企业管理局 (监狱总部大厦)	74	2 A
Singapore Dental Council (College of Medicine Bldg)	新加坡牙科理事会 (医学院大厦)	132	1 C
Singapore Environment Institute (Environment Bldg)	新加坡环境学院 (环境发展部大厦)	110	1 B
Singapore Examinations and Assessment Board (Bukit Ho Swee)	新加坡考试及鉴定局 (河水山)	131	2 A
Singapore Eye Research Institute (Eye Ctr)	新加坡眼科研究学院 (眼科中心)	132	1 C
Singapore Film Commission (MICA Bldg)	新加坡电影检查委员会 (新闻及艺术部大厦)	132	2 A
Singapore Health Services Pte Ltd (Sing Health) (Bowyer Blk C)	新加坡卫生服务私人有限公司 (新卫)(鲍尔C座)	132	1 C
Singapore Immunology Network (Biopolis-Proteos)	新加坡免疫学网络 (启奥生物医药研究园-Proteos)	107	2 C
Singapore Indian Development Association (Beatty Road)	新加坡印族发展协会 (美智路)	111	1 A
Singapore Institute for Clinical Sciences (Biopolis-Centros)	新加坡临诊学院 (启奥生物医药研究园-Centros)	107	2 C
Singapore Institute of Architects	新加坡建筑学会	132	2 C
Singapore Institute of Commerce	新加坡商学会	110	2 C
Singapore Institute of International Affairs	新加坡国际事务研究所	109	2 B

Singapore Institute of Manufacturing Technology (SIMTECH Twr Blk)	新加坡制造技术学院(SIMTECH Twr Blk)	59	1 D
Singapore Labour Foundation (One Marina Boulevard)	全国职总 (滨海林荫道一号)	133	1 B
Singapore Land Authority (8 Shenton Way)	新加坡土地管理局(珊顿大道八号)	132	2 C
Singapore Mass Rapid Transit (SMRT Hq Bldg)	新加坡地铁局(地铁局总部大厦)	133	1 A
Singapore Mediation Centre (Supreme Court)	新加坡仲裁中心(最高法院)	133	1 A
Singapore Medical Council (College of Medicine Bldg)	新加坡医药理事会(医学院大厦)	132	1 C
Singapore National Eye Centre	新加坡国立眼科中心	132	1 C
Singapore Nursing Board (College of Medicine Bldg)	新加坡护理管理局(医学院大厦)	132	1 C
Singapore Pharmacy Board (College of Medicine Bldg)	新加坡药剂管理局(医学院大厦楼)	132	1 C
Singapore Police Force (Police Hq)	新加坡警察部队(警察总部)	88	2 D
Singapore Prison Service (Prison Hq)	新加坡监狱服务(监狱总部)	74	2 A
Singapore Science Centre	新加坡科学馆	82	2 B
Singapore Sports Council (Stadium Boulevard)	新加坡体育理事会 (体育场林荫道)	112	2 C
Singapore Tourism Board (Tourism Court)	新加坡旅游局	109	2 C
Singapore Workforce Development Agency (One Marina Boulevard)	新加坡劳动力促进局(滨海林荫道一号)	133	1 B
Singapore Youth Olympics Organising Committee	新加坡青年奥运会执行委员会	109	2 C
Small Claims Tribunal (Subordinate Courts)	小额索偿庭(初级法庭)	132	2 B
Social Development Unit (Stevens Road)	社交促进组(史蒂芬路)	110	1 B
Social Service Training Institute (Ulu Pandan CC)	社会服务训练所(乌鲁班丹民众联络所)	107	2 B
South East CDC (Singapore Post Ctr)	东南社理会(新加坡邮政中心)	113	1 A
South West CDC (The JTC Summit)	西南社理会(顶峰大厦)	83	1 C
Specialists Accreditation Board (College of Medicine Bldg)	专家鉴定局(医学院大厦)	132	1 C
Sports Division (MCYS Bldg)	体育组(社会发展及体育部大厦)	88	1 B
SPRING Singapore (Standards Productivity And Innovation Board)	新加坡标准, 生产力与创新局 (生产力与标准局)	131	1 B
Sri Temasek	淡马锡楼	110	2 C
Strata Titles Board (URA Ctr- East Wing)	分层地契局(市区重建局中心-东座)	132	2 C
Street and Building Names Board (Revenue House)	街道与建筑屋名称局(税务大厦)	110	2 A
Subordinate Courts	初级法庭	132	2 B
Supreme Court	最高法院	133	1 A
Syariah Court (MCYS Bldg)	回教婚事法庭(社会发展及体育部大厦)	88	1 B
TCM Practitioners Board	中医师管理局	132	1 B
Teacher's Network (Training & Dev't Div)	教育部教师联络中心(课程规划与发展署)	109	2 D
The Cabinet & Cabinet Office (Istana Office Wing)	内阁与内阁办事处(总统府办公侧楼)	110	2 C
Tote Board (Singapore Racecourse)	新加坡赛马博彩管理局 (新加坡赛马场)	23	1 A
Tourism Academy	旅游学院	142	1 C
Traditional and Complimentary Medicine Branch (226 Outram Rd Blk A)	传统医药及义诊组 (226 欧南路大牌A)	132	1 B
Traffic Police Dept	交通警察总部	91	1 C
Travellers' Health and Vaccination Clinic (Tan Tock Seng Hospital)	旅游保健及疫苗注射诊疗所 (陈笃生医院)	88	2 D
Tribunal for Maintenance of Parents (MCYS Bldg)	赡养父母仲裁庭(社会发展及体育部大厦)	88	1 B
Urban Redevelopment Authority (URA Ctr)	市区重建局(市区重建局中心)	132	2 C
Veterinary Public Health Ctr	兽医公共卫生实验中心	7	1 D
Visitor Services Ctr (ICA Bldg)	外国游客服务中心(ICA大厦)	111	2 C
VITAL.ORG (MND Complex - Tower Blk)	机要机关(国家发展部大厦-大厦座)	132	2 C
Water Reclamation Dept (Environment Bldg)	水源开发组(环境发展大厦)	110	1 B
Weight & Measures Div (SPRING S'pore Bldg)	度量衡组(新加坡标准,生产力与创新局大厦)	131	2 B
Welfare Services (MCYS Bldg)	福利组(社会发展及体育部大厦)	88	1 B
Wills Registry (Insolvency & Public Trustee's Office - URA Ctr Eastwing)	遗嘱登记局 (负债及公共受托管理人办事处-市区重建局中心东侧楼)	132	2 C
Work Injury Compensation Department (Ministry of Manpower Bldg)	工伤赔偿局 (人力部大厦)	132	2 B
Work Pass Division (Ministry of Manpower)	工作准证组(人力部)	132	2 B
Work Pass Services Ctr (Tanjong Pagar Complex)	工作准证服务中心 (丹戎巴葛大厦)	132	2 D
Work Safety & Health Council (MND Cplx - Tower Blk)	工作安全及卫生理事会 (国家发展部大厦-大厦座)	132	2 C
Yayasan Mendaki (Wisma Mendaki)	新加坡回教社群发展理事会基金(MENDAKI大厦)	115	1 B

HDB BRANCH OFFICES / SERVICE CENTRES

Ang Mo Kio HDB Branch Office	宏茂桥建屋发展局分局	67	2 A
Balestier Service Centre	马里士他服务中心	89	1 D
Bedok HDB Branch Office	勿洛建屋发展局分局	93	1 D
Bishan HDB Branch Office	碧山建屋发展局分局	68	1 D
Bukit Batok HDB Branch Office	武吉巴督建屋发展局分局	62	2 D
Bukit Merah HDB Branch Office	红山建屋发展局分局	131	1 B
Buona Vista Service Centre	波那维斯达服务中心	107	2 B
Chin Swee Service Centre	振瑞服务中心	132	1 A
Choa Chu Kang HDB Branch Office	蔡厝港建屋发展局分局	41	1 C
Clementi HDB Branch Office	金文泰建屋发展局分局	106	1 B
Geylang HDB Branch Office	芽笼建屋发展局分局	112	2 A
Hougang HDB Branch Office	后港建屋发展局分局	70	1 A
Jurong East HDB Branch Office	裕廊东建屋发展局分局	83	1 A
Jurong West HDB Branch Office	裕廊西建屋发展局分局	82	1 A
Pasir Ris HDB Branch Office	巴西立建屋发展局分局	73	2 A
Pioneer Service Centre	先驱服务中心	73	
Queensway HDB Branch Office	女皇镇建屋发展局分局	108	1 D
Sembawang HDB Branch Office	三巴旺建屋发展局分局	13	1 A
Sengkang HDB Branch Office	盛港建屋发展局分局	49	2 C
Sims Drive HDB Branch Office	沈氏通道建屋发展局分局	112	1 A
Tampines HDB Branch Office	淡滨尼建屋发展局分局	72	1 C
Toa Payoh HDB Branch Office	大巴窑建屋发展局分局	88	2 C
Woodlands HDB Branch Office	兀兰建屋发展局分局	11	2 C
Yishun HDB Branch Office	义顺建屋发展局分局	14	1 D

HISTORICAL SITES / NATIONAL MONUMENTS

HISTORICAL SITES 历史古迹

HS of Alexandra Hospital	亚历山大医院	130	1 B
HS of Anglo Chinese School	英华学校原址	132	2 C
HS of Battle for Bukit Timah	武吉知马战役	64	1 D
HS of Battle for Pasir Panjang	巴西班让战役	129	2 B
HS of Boy's Brigade	少年旅	110	2 C
HS of Bukit Batok Memorial	武吉巴督纪念碑	63	2 D
HS of Central Sikh Gurdwara	锡克古庙	111	1 D
HS of Changi Beach Massacre Site	樟宜海滩大屠杀地点	54	1 B
HS of Chin Kang Huay Kuan	晋江会馆	132	1 C
HS of Clifford Pier	红灯码头	133	1 B
HS of Ee Hoe Hean Club	怡和轩俱乐部	132	1 C
HS of Former Labrador Battery	拉柏多古炮台	141	1 A
HS of Fuk Tak Chi	福德祠古庙	132	2 B
HS of Gan Eng Seng Sec School	颜永成学校原址	132	2 C
HS of Gate of Hope	希望之门	111	1 D
HS of Japanese Propaganda Dept Hqrs	日军宣传总部	110	2 D
HS of Jurong - Kranji Defence Line	裕廊–克兰芝防线	60	2 C
HS of Katong Park	加东公园	112	2 D
HS of Kempeitai East District Branch	前日军宪兵东区支部	110	2 D
HS of Kranji Beach Battle	克兰芝历史性海滩战役地点	8	2 B
HS of Lower Peirce Reservoir	贝雅士下段蓄水池公园	66	2 A
HS of Machine Gun Pillbox	机关枪碉堡	129	1 A
HS of MacRitchie Reservoir	麦里芝蓄水池	87	2 A
HS of Methodist Girls Sch	美以美女中	110	2 C
HS of Ministry Of Labour Bldg	劳工部大厦历史古迹	132	2 B
HS of Middle Rd Church/Christian Institute	密驼路教堂	111	1 D
HS of National Theatre	国家剧场原址	132	2 A

HS of Old Kallang Airport	旧加冷机场	112	1 B
HS of Pondok Peranakan Gelam Club	土生华人鹭鸶俱乐部原址	132	2 C
HS of Punggol Beach Massacre World War II	榜鹅海滩第二次世界大战大屠杀地点	31	1 A
HS of Queen Elizabeth Walk	伊丽莎白女皇道	133	1 A
HS of Raffles Girls Sch	莱佛士女校	110	2 D
HS of Raffles Institution	莱佛士书院	133	1 A
HS of Raffles Place (Commercial Square)	莱佛士坊(商业区)	133	1 B
HS of Saint Margaret's School	圣玛格烈学校	110	2 C
HS of Sarimbun Beach Landing	莎琳汶海滩历史性登陆战地点	7	1 B
HS of Sentosa Beach Massacre	圣海沙海滩大屠杀地点	143	1 C
HS of Silat Road Sikh Gurdwara	石叻路锡克庙	132	1 C
HS of Sime Road Camp	森路兵营	87	1 B
(WWII Commemorative Signboard)	(第二次世界大战纪念牌)		
HS of Sime Road Pillbox and Flagstaff House	森路碉堡及旗杆屋	86	2 B
HS of Singapore Badminton Hall	新加坡羽球馆	112	2 B
HS of Singapore Chinese Girls Sch	新加坡女子学校	110	1 C
HS of Sook Ching Centre	日治时期肃清检证中心	132	2 B
HS of the Indian National Army Monument	印度国民军纪念碑	133	1 A
HS of United Chinese Library	同德书报社	110	2 D
HS of United Overseas Bank	大华银行	132	2 B
HS of Upper Seletar Reservoir	实里达上段蓄水池	25	2 D
WWII Commemorative Signboard	第二次世界大战纪念牌	130	1 B
(Alexandra Hospital)	(亚历山大医院)		
WWII Commemorative Signboard (Bukit Batok)	第二次世界大战纪念牌(武吉巴督)	63	2 D
WWII Commemorative Signboard	第二次世界大战纪念牌	74	1 A
(Selarang Park)	(史拉兰公园)		
WWII Commemorative Site (Ford Factory)	第二次世界大战古迹(福特车厂)	63	2 D
WWII Commemorative Site (Sime Road)	第二次世界大战古迹(森路)	87	1 B

NATIONAL MONUMENTS 国家纪念古迹

Armenian Church	亚米尼亚教堂	132	2 A
Attorney-General's Chambers	总检察署	133	1 A
(Parliament House Blk C)	(国会大厦C座)		
Cathedral of the Good Shepherd	善牧主教大教堂	111	1 D
Cenotaph	战亡纪念碑	133	1 A
Central Fire Station	中央消防局	132	2 A
Chesed-El Synagogue	圣诺犹太教堂	110	2 D
City Hall	政府大厦	133	1 A
Clock Tower Building (Chinese High School)	华中钟楼(华侨中学)	86	1 D
College of Medicine Building	医学院大厦	132	1 C
Convent of the Holy Infant Jesus Chapel	前圣婴女修院圣堂及柯威大厦	111	1 D
and Caldwell House (CHIJMES)	(赞美广场)		
Dalhousie Monument	达豪施纪念碑	133	1 B
Empress Place Building	皇后坊大厦	133	1 B
Far East Command Building	前英军远东司令部大厦	110	2 D
(Legends)	(Legends俱乐部)		
Fullerton Building (The Grand Fullerton Hotel)	浮尔顿大厦(富来登大酒店)	133	1 B
Hong San See Temple	凤山寺	132	1 A
House of Tan Yeok Nee	陈旭年故居	110	2 D
Istana & Sri Temasek	总统府及淡马锡楼	110	2 C
Jinriksha Station	人力车站	132	2 C
Kranji War Memorial	克兰芝阵亡战士纪念碑	23	1 A
Lian Shan Shuang Lin Monastery	莲山双林寺	89	1 C
Lim Bo Seng Memorial	林谋盛纪念塔	133	1 A
Maghain Aboth Synagogue	马海阿贝犹太教堂	110	2 D
Masjid Abdul Gaffoor	阿都卡夫回教堂	111	1 C

Masjid Al-Abrar	阿尔阿布拉回教堂	132	2 C
Masjid Hajjah Fatimah	哈惹花蒂玛回教堂	111	2 C
Masjid Jamae	詹美回教堂	132	2 B
Masjid Malabar	马拉巴回教堂	111	1 C
Masjid Sultan	苏丹回教堂	111	1 C
Masjid Temenggong Daeng Ibrahim	天猛公德恩依布拉欣回教堂	142	2 A
Nagore Durgha (Shrine)	纳宫回教堂(圣祠)	132	2 C
National Museum (Singapore History Museum)	国家博物院(新加坡历史博物馆)	110	2 D
Old Hill Street Police Station (MICA Building)	旧禧街警察局(新闻及艺术部大厦)	132	2 A
Old Ministry of Labour Building	前劳工部大厦	132	2 B
Old Nanyang University Arch, The	前南大旧牌坊	80	2 B
Old Nanyang University Library & Administration Bldg (Chinese Heritage Centre), The	前南大图书馆和行政楼 (华裔馆)	80	1 A
Old Nanyang University Memorial	前南大建校纪念碑	80	1 A
Old Thong Chai Medical Institution, The	前同济医院	132	2 B
Parliament House & Annexe Building (Old Parliament House)	国会大厦及侧楼 (旧国会大厦)	133	1 A
Prinsep Street Presbyterian Church	布连士街长老会磐石堂	111	1 C
Raffles Hotel	莱佛士大酒店	111	1 D
Singapore Cricket Club	新加坡板球俱乐部	133	1 A
Siong Lim Temple (Shuang Lin Cheng Huang Temple)	双林寺 (双林城隍庙)	89	1 C
Sir Stamford Raffles Statue	莱佛士铜像	133	1 A
Sri Mariamman Temple	马里安曼兴都庙	132	2 B
Sri Srinivasa Perumal Temple	斯里尼瓦沙柏鲁马兴都庙	111	1 A
St. Andrew's Cathedral	圣安德烈教堂	133	1 A
St. George's Church (Tanglin)	圣乔治教堂(东陵)	109	1 C
St. Joseph's Institution (Singapore Art Museum)	圣约瑟书院 (新加坡美术馆)	111	1 D
Sun Yat Sen Villa (Sun Yat Sen Nanyang Memorial Hall)	晚晴园 (孙中山南洋纪念馆)	88	2 C
Supreme Court	最高法院	133	1 A
Tan Kim Seng Fountain	陈金声喷泉	133	1 A
Tan Si Chong Su (Po Chiak Keng Temple)	陈氏宗祠(保赤宫)	132	2 A
Tao Nan School (Asian Civilisations Museum)	道南学校(亚洲文明博物馆)	110	2 D
Telok Ayer Chinese Methodist Church	卫理公会直落亚逸礼拜堂	132	2 C
Telok Ayer Market (Lau Pa Sat)	直落亚逸巴刹(老巴刹)	132	2 C
The Old Ford Factory	前福特车厂	63	2 D
Thian Hock Keng Temple	天福宫	132	2 C
Tower Block (Goodwood Park Hotel)	良木塔楼(良木园大酒店)	110	1 B
Victoria Theatre & Concert Hall	维多利亚剧院及音乐会堂	133	1 A
War Memorial Park	日治时期蒙难人士纪念碑公园	133	1 A
Ying Fo Fui Kun	应和会馆	132	2 B
Yueh Hai Ching Temple	粤海清庙	132	2 B

HOMES FOR THE AGED/WELFARE HOMES / HOSPICE

Adventist Home for the Elders (Blk 195 Kim Keat Ave)	基督复临安老院 (大牌195金吉道)	89	1 C
All Saints Nursing Home	万圣疗养院	73	1 B
Apex Day Care Ctr (Blk 119 Bt. Merah View)	艾逸日间护理中心 (大牌119红山景)	131	1 B
Ayer Rajah Day Care Ctr	亚逸拉惹日间护理中心	83	2 D
Assisi Home & Hospice	雅西西晚期慈怀病院	88	1 A
Bethany Methodist Nursing Home	贝特尼卫理教堂疗养院	41	1 B
Bishan Home (For the Intellectually Disabled)	碧山智障之家	68	1 D
Blue Cross Thong Kheng Home	蓝十字同庆之家	61	2 D
Bo Tien Home for the Aged (Bo Tien Temple)	武天安老院 (武庙)	82	1 C
Boy's Town Singapore	儿童城	63	2 A
Bright Hill Evergreen Home	光明山修身院	67	1 B
Bukit Batok Boy's Hostel Teen Challenge	武吉巴督少男之家 – 少年挑战	84	2 A
Bukit Batok Home for Bt the Aged	武吉巴督安老院	62	1 B
Canossaville Childrens' Home	康诺赛维尔儿童之家	90	2 C
Catholic Welfare Centre	天主教福利中心	111	1 D
Chen Su Lan Meth Children's Home	陈树南基督教儿童教养院	68	2 A
Christalite Methodist Home	基督卫理之家	11	1 B
Darul Ihsan Orphanage (Mattar Road)	达鲁益善孤儿院 (玛达路)	90	2 D
Darul Ihsan Orphanage (Wan Tho Avenue)	达鲁益善孤儿院 (运涛道)	90	1 C
Dover Park Hospice	托福园	110	2 A
Econ Medicare Ctr (Braddell)	宜康医务中心 (布莱德)	89	2 A
Econ Medicare Ctr & Nursing Home (Buangkok)	宜康医务中心及疗养院 (万国)	48	2 C
Econ Medicare Ctr (Chai Chee)	宜康医务中心 (菜市)	92	2 C
Econ Medicare Ctr (Choa Chu Kang Rd)	宜康医务中心 (蔡厝港路)	42	1 D
Econ Medicare Ctr (Upp East Coast)	宜康医务中心 (东海岸上段)	115	2 A
Econ Nursing Home (Bt Timah Ave)	宜康疗养院 (武吉知马道)	85	1 A
Geylang East Home for the Aged (Blk 97 Aljunied Cres)	芽笼东安老院 (大牌97阿裕尼弯)	90	2 D
Gift of Love Home	爱之礼屋	49	2 B
Grace Lodge (Home of the Aged Sick)	慈恩林 (疗养院)	49	1 C
Gracehaven The Salvation Army	救世军恩典之家	69	1 A
Green Haven	绿荫所	61	1 C
Handicap Welfare Association	残疾人士福利协会	89	1 D
Highpoint Social Enterprise Hub	社会企业中心	112	2 B
Jamiyah Halfway House	沾美亚戒毒所	129	1 A
Jamiyah Home for the Aged (Changi Rd)	沾美亚老人院 (樟宜路)	113	2 A
Jamiyah Home for the Aged (Tampines)	沾美亚老人院 (淡滨尼路)	72	2 D
Ju Eng Home for Senior Citizens	聚英爱老院	48	1 A
Kheng Chiu Happy Lodge	琼州乐善居	73	1 C
Kwong Wai Shiu Hospital and Nursing Home	广惠肇留医院	111	1 A
Lee Ah Mooi Old Age Home	李亚妹安老院	88	1 C
Ling Kwang Home for Senior Citizens	灵光爱老院	68	2 A
Lions Nursing Home for the Elderly	狮子会老人之家	88	1 B
Lions Home for the Elders	狮子会乐龄之家	115	2 A
Man Fatt Lam Home for Aged	万佛林敬老院	94	1 D
Man Fut Tong Nursing Home	万佛堂护理所	11	2 B
Metta Home for the Disable	慈光乐陶居	11	1 D
Min Chong Comfort Home	民众舒适之家	112	1 A
Moonlight Home for the Aged & Handicapped	月光安老与陶养之家	69	1 B
Moral Home for Disabled Adults	德教迟钝院 (成人)	92	2 C
Moral Home for The Aged Sick	德观病老院	94	1 D
Moral Welfare Home	德教慈善院	130	2 D
Muhammadiyah Welfare Home	莫哈末迪亚福利所	112	2 D
Nightingale Nursing Home	南丁格尔护理所	89	2 A
Orange Valley Nursing Home	柑谷护理所		
(Biggin Hill Road)	(美仁山路)	54	1 B
(Clementi Ave 4)	(金文泰四道)	106	2 A
(148A Silat Avenue)	(148A 石叻道)	132	1 C
(Simei St 3)	(四美3街)	94	1 A
(Woodlands Ave 1)	(兀兰1道)	10	2 D
Our Lady of Lourdes Nursing Home for the Aged	圣母劳德丝安老院	74	2 B
Pacific Healthcare Nursing Home	太平护理疗养院	42	1 C
Paean Nursing Home	百安疗养院	114	1 A
Peacehaven Nursing Home	安乐疗养院	74	1 C

Pelangi Village (MCDS)	彩虹村 (社会发展及体育部)	48	2 C
Pertapis Children Home (Blk 4 Joo Chiat Complex)	新加坡回教神学会儿童之家 (大牌4号如切大厦)	113	2 A
Pertapis Halfway House (Kovan Rd)	新加坡回教神学会戒毒所(高文路)	69	1 C
Ramakrishna Mission Boy's Home	拉马克里斯南教会男之家	90	2 A
Red Cross Home for the Disabled	红十字会残疾人士之家	63	1 B
Rochor 'Kongsi' for the Aged (Blk 3 Rochor Rd #04-626)	梧槽公司安老院(大牌3梧槽路#04-626)	111	1 C
Singapore Baptist Convention Golden Age Home (Blk 64 Kallang Bahru)	新加坡浸信会联会乐龄之家 (大牌64加冷巴鲁)	111	2 A
Singapore Boys Home	新加坡少男感化院	60	1 D
Singapore Cheshire Home	新加坡柴郡之家	68	2 B
Singapore Children's Society (Convalescent Home)	新加坡儿童协会(疗养院)	1	2 D
Singapore Girls' Home	新加坡少女收容所	70	1 D
Society for the Aged Sick	养老病院	69	2 D
Sree Narayana Mission Home for The Aged Sick	圣那亚拉那教团养老院	14	1 D
St. John's Home for Elderly Persons	圣约翰养老院	90	1 B
St. Joseph's Home	圣若瑟之家	60	1 D
St. Theresa's Home	圣德肋撒安老院	88	1 A
Sunlove Abode for the Intellectually Infirmed	日爱弱智之家	48	2 C
Sunshine Welfare Action Mission Home (SWAMI)	阳光福利社会安老院	13	2 B
Sunnyville Home	阳光院	20	1 D
Surya Home	舍雅院	48	2 C
Tai Pei Old People's Home	大悲老人院	89	1 D
Taman Bacaan Female Halfway House	达曼巴参女子戒毒所	129	1 C
Tampines Homes (West Coast Road)	淡滨尼之家 (西海岸路)	128	2 A
Tembusu Neighbourhood Link	登布苏邻里联络中心	113	2 A
The Ashram	The Ashram安老院	3	2 D
The Helping Hand	援手之家	69	2 C
The Hiding Place	退隐居	47	2 B
The Moral Home for Disabled	残疾人士精神之家	113	2 A
The Salvation Army Balestier Corps	救世军马里士他团部	89	1 D
The Salvation Army Bedok Multiservice Ctr for the Elderly	救世军勿洛乐龄服务中心日间乐龄中心	93	2 C
The Salvation Army Pasir Panjang Corps	救世军巴西班让团部	129	1 A
The Salvation Army Peacehaven	救世军安乐之家	74	1 C
The Turning Point	转折点	3	2 C
Thong Teck Home for Senior Citizens	同德安老院	112	2 A
Thuja Home @ Pelangi Village (Pelangi Village)	彩虹村都惹之家(彩虹村)	48	2 C
United Medicare Ctr	联合医药护理中心	89	1 B
Villa Francis Home for the Aged	法兰斯养老别墅	23	1 C
Windsor Nursing Home	温莎护理所	115	1 A

HOSPITALS / MEDICAL CENTRES / POLYCLINICS / FIRST AID POINTS

HOSPITALS & MEDICAL CENTRES 医院 & 医务中心

Adam Road Medical Centre (King's Arcade)	亚当路医务中心(王雅阁)	86	2 D
Alexandra Hospital	亚历山大医院	130	1 B
Ang Mo Kio Thye Hua Kwan Hospital	宏茂桥大和观医院	46	1 C
Bright Vision Hospital	光明综合医院	69	1 A
Camden Medical Centre	康登医务中心	109	2 C
Cerebral Palsy Ctr	脑神经麻痹中心	51	2 D
Changi General Hospital	樟宜综合医院	94	1 A
Communicable Disease Centre	传染病医疗中心	110	2 A
East Coast Medicare Centre	东海岸医药中心	94	2 D
East Shore Hospital	东海岸医院	114	1 A
East Shore Medical Centre	东海岸医务中心	114	1 A
Eye Hospital	眼科医院	111	1 A
Farrer Pk Mediplex	花拉公园医药中心	111	1 B
Gleneagles Hospital	鹰阁医院	109	1 C
Gleneagles Maritime Medical Centre	鹰阁海上医疗中心	109	1 B
HMI Balestier Medical Ctr & Health Screening	HMI马里士他医药中心及健康检查中心	89	1 D
Institute of Mental Health - Woodbridge Hospital	精神健康学院 – 板桥医院	48	2 C
Johns Hopkins S'pore Int'l Medical Centre (Tan Tock Seng Hospital)	新加坡约翰霍普金斯国际医疗中心 (陈笃生医院)	88	2 D
Jurong Medical Centre	裕廊医务中心	81	1 A
Khoo Teck Phuat Hospital	邱德拔医院	27	1 A

PLACES			MAP GRID
KK Women's & Children's Hospital	竹脚妇幼医院	110	2 B
Kwong Wai Shiu Hospital	广惠肇留医院	111	1 A
Mount Alvernia Hospital	安微尼亚山医院	88	1 A
Mount Alvernia Medical Centre	安微尼亚山医务中心	88	1 A
Mount Elizabeth Hospital	伊丽莎白医院	110	1 C
Mount Elizabeth Medical Centre	伊丽莎白医务中心	110	1 C
National Cancer Centre of Singapore	新加坡癌症中心	132	1 C
National Dental Centre	全国牙科中心	132	1 C
National Heart Centre of Singapore	新加坡全国心脏中心	132	1 C
National Neuroscience Institute of Singapore	国立神经学院	88	2 D
National Skin Centre	国立皮肤诊疗中心	110	2 A
National University Hospital	国立大学医院	107	1 D
Raffles Hospital	莱佛士医院	111	1 C
Ren Ci Hospital & Medical Centre (Jalan Tan Tock Seng)	仁慈医院及医护中心(惹兰陈笃生)	88	2 D
Ren Ci Hospital & Medicare Centre (Buangkok Green)	仁慈医院及医护中心(万国埔)	48	2 C
Singapore Gamma Knife Centre	新加坡伽玛刀中心	132	1 B
Singapore General Hospital	新加坡中央医院	132	1 C
Singapore National Eye Centre	新加坡全国眼科中心	132	1 C
St. Andrew's Community Hospital	圣安德列社区医院	115	1 B
St. Andrew's Mission Hospital (U/C)	圣安德列教会医院(建造中)	94	1 A
St. Luke's Hospital for the Elderly	圣路加爱老医院	62	1 D
Tan Tock Seng Hospital	陈笃生医院	88	2 D
Thomson Medical Centre	康生医院	88	1 D
West Point Hospital	康裕医院	82	1 C

NATIONAL HEALTHCARE GROUP POLYCLINICS (NHG) 全国保健集团综合诊疗所

Ang Mo Kio Polyclinic	宏茂桥综合诊疗所	67	2 A
Bukit Batok Polyclinic & Dental Clinic	武吉巴督综合诊疗所和牙科诊疗所	62	1 C
Choa Chu Kang Polyclinic	蔡厝港综合诊疗所	41	2 C
Clementi Polyclinic	金文泰综合诊疗所	106	1 A
Hougang Polyclinic & Dental Clinic	后港综合诊疗所和牙科诊疗所	70	1 A
Jurong Polyclinic & Dental Clinic	裕廊综合诊疗所和牙科诊疗所	61	2 D
Toa Payoh Polyclinic & Dental Clinic	大巴窑综合诊疗所和牙科诊疗所	89	1 B
Woodlands Polyclinic & Dental Clinic	兀兰综合诊疗所和牙科诊疗所	11	1 D
Yishun Polyclinic	义顺综合诊疗所	27	1 A

SINGHEALTH POLYCLINICS 新健综合诊疗所

Bedok Polyclinic & Dental Clinic	勿洛综合诊疗所和牙科诊疗所	93	1 D
Bukit Merah Polyclinic	红山综合诊疗所	131	1 B
Geylang Polyclinic & Dental Clinic	芽笼综合诊疗所和牙科诊疗所	112	2 A
Marine Parade Polyclinic	马林百列综合诊疗所	113	2 C
Outram Polyclinic (HPB Bldg)	欧南园综合诊疗所 (HPB大厦)	132	1 C
Pasir Ris Polyclinic	巴西立综合诊疗所	73	2 A
Queenstown Polyclinic & Community Wellness Ctr	女皇镇综合诊疗所及社区服利中心	108	1 D
Sengkang Polyclinic	盛港综合诊疗所	49	1 B
Tampines Polyclinic & Dental Clinic	淡滨尼综合诊疗所和牙科诊疗所	73	1 C

CLINICS 诊疗所

Chung Hwa Free Clinic	中华医院	89	1 C
Kwan-In Welfare Free Clinic	观音救苦会义诊所	91	2 D
Public Free Clinic Society	大众医院	112	1 B
SATA Chinatown Clinic	新加坡防痨会牛车水诊疗所	132	2 C
SATA Jurong Clinic	新加坡防痨会裕廊诊疗所	83	1 B
SATA Uttamram Clinic	新加坡防痨会诊疗所(菜市街)	92	2 C
SATA Woodlands Clinic	新加坡防痨协会兀兰诊疗所	11	2 C

FIRST AID POINTS 急救站

Sentosa Ranger Station	圣淘沙巡逻员站	142	2 C
Macritchie Reservoir - Sime Track Ranger Station	麦里芝蓄水池 - 森道看守员站	66	1 C

HOSTELS/ DORMITORIES / STAFF ACCOMODATION

5 Star	5星宿舍	92	1 B
ACS Independent Boarding Sch	英华自主寄宿学校	107	1 C
ACS Oldham Hall	英华奥罕宿舍	110	1 A
Alliance Int'l Hostel	联盟国际宿舍	48	2 C
ame Lodging	ame宿舍	111	1 A
Amsen International Hostel	Amsen国际宿舍	110	1 A
Balestier Student Hostel	马里士他学生宿舍	88	2 D
Blue Stars Dormitory	蓝星宿舍	80	2 B
Bukit Batok Boys' Hostel Teen Challenge	武吉巴督少年之家–少年挑战	84	2 A
Bukit Batok Boys' Hostel Teen Challenge	武吉巴督少年之家–少年挑战	84	2 A
Cambridge Int'l Hostel	剑桥国际宿舍	111	1 A
Catholic Junior College Hostel	公教初院宿舍	88	1 D
Dunman High Hostel	德明政府中学宿舍	112	2 D
East Lodge Student Hostel	东舍学生宿舍	114	1 A
Eton Hall	伊登楼	130	1 B
Farmway Dormitory	农道宿舍	47	2 A
FEB College Hostel	FEB学院宿舍	110	1 A
Goodman Eduserve	良人教育服务中心	113	1 B
International Student Support Ctr (Sin Tai Hin Bldg)	国际学生支援中心 (新泰兴大厦)	111	1 C
Jurong Penjuru Dormitory 1 & 2	裕廊本莱鲁1及 2宿舍	104	2 A
Jurong View Apartments	裕廊景公寓	79	2 C
Kaki Bukit Hostel	加基武吉宿舍	91	2 B
Kallang Dormitory	加冷宿舍	111	2 B
Katong Hostel	加东学生宿舍	113	1 C
Kian Teck Dormitory	建德宿舍	80	2 C
Kian Teck Hostel	建德宿舍	80	2 B
LASALLE Residences (St. Patricks Sec Sch)	拉萨尔宿舍 (圣伯特理中学)	114	1 B
Methodist Ctr Hostel	卫理中心宿舍	88	1 B
Metro-Y Apartments (YMCA Metropolitan)	美罗Y公寓 (新加坡京华基督教青年会)	109	2 A
Nanyang Girl's Boarding School	南洋女子寄宿学校	86	1 C
Nanyang Polytechnic Apartments	南洋理工学院公寓	47	1 D
Ngee Ann Polytechnic Staff Apartments	义安理工学院教职员公寓	84	2 B
Novena Hall International Students Hostel	诺维娜国际学生宿舍	110	2 A
NTU - Accomodation for Graduate Students (NTU)	南洋理工大学–研究生宿舍	59	1 C
NTU - Nanyang Circle Staff Housing	南洋理工大学–南洋圈教职员宿舍	80	2 B
NTU - Nanyang Heights, Meadows & Terrace	南洋理工大学–南洋岭, 南洋美土 & 南洋台	59	1 D
NTU - Nanyang View	南洋理工大学–南洋景	59	1 C
"NTU Students Hostel - Halls 1, 3, 4, 5, 7"	"南洋理工大学学生宿舍–第1,3,4,5,7楼"	80	1 A
"NTU Students Hostel - Halls 2, 6, 8, 12, 13"	"南洋理工大学学生宿舍–第2,6,8,12,13楼"	59	1 D
"NTU Students Hostel - Halls 9, 10, 11, 14, 15"	"南洋理工大学学生宿舍–第9,10,11,14,15楼"	59	1 C
NUS - Eusoff Hall, Kent Ridge Hall	新加坡国立大学–尤素夫楼, 肯特岗宿舍	128	2 A
NUS - Kent Vale	新加坡国立大学–肯特谷楼	106	2 C
NUS - King Edward VII Hall	新加坡国立大学–爱德华楼	129	1 A
NUS - Prince George's Park Student Housing, Sheares Hall	新加坡国立大学–乔治太子园学生楼, 薛尔思楼	129	1 A
NUS - Temasek Hall	新加坡国立大学–淡马锡宿舍	128	2 A
NUS - Visitors Lodge, Yusof Ishak House	新加坡国立大学–外宾楼, 尤素夫宿舍	106	2 D
Pearl's Hill Hostel	珍珠山宿舍	132	2 B
Presbyterian Girl's Hostel	长老会女生宿舍	114	1 A
Raffles Institution Boarding Cplx	莱佛士书院宿舍	67	2 D
Scal Dormitory	Scal 宿舍	80	2 C
SMU Residences	新加坡管理大学宿舍	111	1 C
S'pore Boys Hostel	新加坡男生宿舍	60	1 D
S'pore Polytechnic Staff Apartments	新加坡理工学院教职员公寓	106	2 B
Soon Lee Lodge	顺利宿舍	80	2 C
Tampines Dormitory	淡滨尼宿舍	72	1 B
Temasek Polytechnic Temasek Green	淡马锡理工学院淡马锡园	72	1 D
Toh Guan Dormitory	卓源宿舍	83	2 B
The Chinese High Boarding House	华中学生宿舍	86	1 D
The Inncrowd (Dunlop Street)	The Inncrowd 宿舍 (南洛街)	111	1 C
Vita Hostel	维达宿舍	110	2 A
Waterloo Hostel (Catholic Welfare Ctr)	滑铁卢宿舍 (天主教福利中心)	111	1 D
Westlite Dormitory	伟来宿舍	83	2 A
Winfield Hall	Winfield楼宿舍	90	2 A
Woodlands Dormitory	兀兰宿舍	2	1 D
Yew Hua Boarding House	Yew Hua 宿舍	112	2 A
Yo-Ha@Ulu Pandan	乌鲁班丹Yo-Ha宿舍	85	1 D

HOTELS

PLACES		MAP	GRID
Albert Court Hotel	雅柏酒店 (雅柏广场)	110	2 C
Aliwal Park Hotel	爱丽华酒店	111	2 C
Allson Hotel S'pore	豪绅酒店	111	1 D
Amara Sanctuary Resort Singapore	新加坡安国胜地酒店	142	2 C
Amara S'pore	安国酒店	132	2 C
"Amazing Inn, The"	奇妙客栈	112	2 B
Ambassador Hotel	国宾酒店	111	1 B
Amber Hotel	安柏酒馆	113	2 C
Amrise Hotel	安来士酒店	112	1 B
Ascott Singapore Raffles Place	Ascott酒店新加坡莱佛士坊	133	1 B
Asia Star Hotel	雅星酒馆	111	1 B
Asphodel Inn	Asphodel旅店	111	1 A
"Aspinals, The"	Aspinals酒店	111	1 B
Backpacker Cozy Corner Guesthouse	背包客舒适之家	111	1 D
Balestier Hotel	马里士他旅店	88	2 D
Bayview Hotel S'pore	海湾酒店	110	2 D
Beach Hotel	美芝酒店	111	1 D
Berjaya Hotel Singapore	达腾酒店	132	2 C
Bright Star Hotel	星光大酒店	112	2 B
Broadway Hotel	大路大酒店	111	1 B
Cameron Hotel	金马仑酒店	94	2 B
Capella S'pore	新加坡吉贝拉酒店	142	2 C
Carlton Hotel	华丽大酒店	111	1 D
Champagne Hotel	香槟酒店	112	2 B
Changi Hotel	樟宜酒店	113	2 A
Changi Village Hotel	樟宜村酒店	54	1 B
Chang Ziang Hotel	长江酒店	112	1 B
Chinatown Hotel	中国城客栈	132	2 C
Citi Hub	Citi Hub旅店	111	1 B
"Claremont, The"	Claremont旅馆	111	1 B
Classique Hotel	豪华酒店	111	1 B
Conrad Centennial S'pore	港丽酒店	133	1 A
Copthorne King's Hotel Singapore	国敦统一大酒店	132	1 A
Copthorne Orchid Hotel Singapore	国敦胡姬大酒店	87	2 D
Crowne Plaza Changi Airport	皇冠广场樟宜机场	75	1 C
Darlene Hotel (Geylang)	达玲珍馆 (芽笼)	112	1 B
Deluxe Hotel	豪华酒店	112	1 B
Diamond Hotel	钻石大旅店	112	2 B
Dickson Court Hotel	亿升酒店	111	1 C
"Elizabeth, The"	伊丽莎白酒店	110	1 B
Fairmont Hotel	费尔蒙旅店	133	1 A
Farrer Park Backpackers Hostel	花拉园背包旅店	111	1 B
Fortuna City	Fortuna City 酒店	111	1 B
Four Chain View Hotel	四泉大酒店	113	1 A
Four Seasons Hotel	四季饭馆	109	2 C
Fragrance Hostel	飞龙背包客旅馆	111	1 C
"Fragrance Hotel, The"	飞龙酒店	113	2 B
Fragrance Hotel (Balestier)	飞龙酒店 (马里士他)	89	1 D
Fragrance Hotel (Classic)	飞龙酒店 (经典)	88	2 B
Fragrance Hotel (Crystal)	飞龙酒店 (水晶)	112	2 B
Fragrance Hotel (Emerald)	飞龙酒店 (绿宝)	112	1 B
Fragrance Hotel (Imperial)	飞龙酒店 (皇家)	111	2 B
Fragrance Hotel (Kovan)	飞龙酒店 (高文)	69	2 C
Fragrance Hotel (Lavender)	飞龙酒店 (劳明达)	111	2 B
Fragrance Hotel (Oasis)	飞龙酒店 (绿洲)	88	2 D
Fragrance Hotel (Pearl)	飞龙酒店 (珍珠)	112	2 B
Fragrance Hotel (Rose)	飞龙酒店 (玫瑰)	89	1 D
Fragrance Hotel (Ruby)	飞龙酒店 (红宝)	112	2 B

PLACES		MAP	GRID
Fragrance Hotel (Sapphire)	飞龙酒店 (蓝宝)	112	1 B
Fragrance Hotel (Selegie)	飞龙酒店 (实利基)	110	2 C
Fragrance Hotel (Viva)	飞龙酒店 (威华)	131	1 D
Fragrance Hotel (Waterfront)	飞龙酒店 (河畔)	128	2 A
"Fullerton Bay Hotel, The"	富来登海大酒店	133	1 B
"Fullerton Hotel, The"	富来登大酒店	133	1 B
Furama City Centre S'pore	富丽华市中心	132	2 B
Furama Riverfront S'pore	富丽华河畔	132	1 A
"Gallery Hotel, The"	佳乐丽酒店	131	1 A
Garden Hotel	国园大酒店	110	1 A
Gateway Hotel	杰威酒店	113	2 A
Gay World Hotel	繁华大旅店	112	1 B
Golden Dragon Hotel	金龙酒店	112	2 B
Golden Landmark Hotel	黄金大酒店	111	1 C
Golden Star Hotel	金星酒店	112	1 B
Goodwood Park Hotel	良木园大酒店	110	1 B
Grandmax Hotel	太元酒店	111	1 B
Grand City Lodge	大城市旅店	113	2 B
Grand Copthorne Waterfront Hotel S'pore	国敦河畔大酒店	132	1 A
Grand Hyatt S'pore	新加坡君悦酒店	110	1 C
Grand Mercure Roxy Hotel	大和星大乐斯酒店	113	2 C
Grand Plaza Hotel City Hall	华滨酒店政府大厦	132	2 A
Haising Hotel	海星酒店	111	1 C
Hangout @ Mt Emily	爱美丽山旅馆	110	2 C
Happy Hotel	快乐旅店	112	1 B
Happy Hotel Spring	快乐旅店 (春天)	112	1 B
Harbour Ville Hotel	海苑旅店	131	2 D
Hilton Singapore	新加坡希尔顿大酒店	109	2 C
Holiday Inn Atrium, S'pore	新加坡Atrium假日酒店	132	1 A
Holiday Inn Park View	园景假日酒店	110	1 C
Hoover Hotel	豪华旅店	89	1 D
Hotel 6	6旅店	112	1 B
Hotel 12	12旅店	112	1 B
Hotel 1929	1929旅店	132	2 C
Hotel 81 Balestier	81旅店 (马里士他)	89	1 D
Hotel 81 Bencoolen	81旅店 (明古连)	110	2 D
Hotel 81 Bugis	81旅店 (武吉士)	111	1 D
Hotel 81 Changi	81旅店 (樟宜)	114	1 A
Hotel 81 Cherry	81旅店 (樱桃)	112	1 B
Hotel 81 Chinatown	81旅店 (唐城坊)	132	2 B
Hotel 81 Classic	81旅店 (古典)	113	1 A
Hotel 81 Cosy	81旅店 (舒适)	132	2 C
Hotel 81 Elegance	81旅店 (优雅)	111	2 B
Hotel 81 Fuji	81旅店 (富士)	89	1 D
Hotel 81 Geylang	81旅店 (芽笼)	112	2 B
Hotel 81 Gold	81旅店 (黄金)	112	2 B
Hotel 81 Hollywood	81旅店 (好莱坞)	112	1 B
Hotel 81 Joo Chiat	81旅店 (如切路)	113	2 B
Hotel 81 Joy	81旅店 (欢乐)	112	1 B
Hotel 81 Kovan	81旅店 (高文)	69	2 C
Hotel 81 Lavender	81旅店 (薰衣草)	111	2 B
Hotel 81 Lucky	81旅店 (幸运)	112	1 B
Hotel 81 Opera	81旅店 (歌剧)	113	2 B
Hotel 81 Orchid	81旅店 (胡姬)	112	1 B
Hotel 81 Palace	81旅店 (宫殿)	112	2 B
Hotel 81 Princess	81旅店 (公主)	112	1 B
Hotel 81 Rochor	81旅店 (梧槽)	111	1 D
Hotel 81 Sakura	81旅店 (樱花)	113	2 B
Hotel 81 Selegie	81旅店 (实利基)	110	2 C
Hotel 81 Spring	81旅店 (春天)	112	1 B
Hotel 81 Star	81旅店 (星星)	112	1 B
Hotel 81 Tristar	81旅店 (鑫星)	113	1 A
Hotel 81 Violet	81旅店 (紫罗兰)	112	1 B
Hotel Ascendere	锦升酒店	112	1 B
Hotel Bencoolen	明古连酒店	110	2 D

INDEX

PLACES		MAP GRID		PLACES		MAP GRID	
Hotel Compass	康宝旅店	112	2 B	Peninsula Excelsior Hotel	半岛大酒店	132	2 A
Hotel Dragon	龙旅店	132	2 B	Penta Hotel	Penta旅店	111	1 B
Hotel Fuji	富士旅店	112	2 B	Perak Hotel	百乐楼酒店	111	1 C
Hotel Grand Central	大中酒店	110	2 C	Quality Hotel, Singapore	Quality酒店	111	1 A
Hotel Hamilton	翰蜜顿酒店	111	1 D	Quincy Hotel	Quincy旅店	110	1 B
Hotel Inter-Continental S'pore	新加坡洲际大酒店	111	1 D	Raffles Hotel (1886)	莱佛士大酒店 (1886)	111	1 D
Hotel Miramar	美丽华大酒店	132	1 A	Rasa Sentosa Resort, S'pore	圣淘沙度假村	141	2 B
Hotel Re! @ Pearls Hill	珍珠山Hotel Re!旅店	132	1 B	"Regent S'pore, The"	丽晶大酒店	109	2 C
Hotel Rendezvous	龙都大酒店	110	2 D	Regin Hotel	丽晶酒店	112	1 B
Hotel Royal	京华大酒店	110	1 A	RELC International Hotel (RELC Bldg)	区域语言中心国际旅馆	109	2 B
Hotel Royal @ Queens	皇家酒店(Queens)	111	1 D				
Hotel Sunflower	葵花酒店	112	1 B	Rider's Lodge	Rider's Lodge旅店	86	1 B
Hotel Supreme	原首大酒店	110	2 C	"Ritz-Carlton, Millenia Singapore, The"	丽嘉登酒店	133	1 A
Hotel Windsor	温莎酒店	90	1 C				
Hua Shui Hotel	华士旅店	112	2 A	River View Hotel	濠景大酒店	132	1 A
Hup Hoe Hotel	合和酒店	112	2 B	Robertson Quay Hotel	罗玻申码头酒店	132	2 A
Jade Hotel	翡翠酒店	112	2 B	Royal India Hotel	皇家印度酒店	111	1 B
Jin Dong Hotel	锦东酒店	112	1 B	"Royal Peacock, The "	孔雀皇酒店	132	2 C
Joo Chiat Hotel	如切旅店	113	2 A	Royal Plaza	皇家假日大旅馆	110	1 C
Kampong Ubin Resort	甘榜乌敏度假村	33	2 D	Santa Grand Hotel Aljunied	阿裕尼大圣达旅店	112	2 B
"Keong Saik Hotel, The"	供适客栈	132	2 C	Santa Grand Hotel West Coast	西海岸大圣达旅店	128	2 A
Kerbau Hotel	嘉宝大旅店	111	1 B				
Kim Tian Hotel	金田旅店	112	1 B	"Scarlet Hotel, The"	Scarlet旅店	132	2 C
La Mode (Sophia) Hotel	旅梦(苏菲)旅店	112	1 B	Seng Wah Hotel	新华大旅店	112	2 B
Lai Ming Hotel	丽明旅店	112	2 B	"Sentosa Resort & Spa, The"	圣淘沙度假村及Spa	142	2 D
Lai Ming Hotel Cosmoland	丽明旅店	112	2 B				
Le Meridien S'pore	新加坡美丽殿大酒店	110	2 D	"Sha Villa, The"	Sha旅舍	110	1 D
Lex Hotel	乐斯旅店	112	1 B	Shangri-La Hotel	香格里拉大酒店	109	2 B
Link Hotel	联合旅店	132	1 B	Sheraton Towers Singapore Hotel	新加坡喜来登大酒店	110	1 B
Lion City Hotel	狮城大旅店	113	1 A				
Lloyds Inn	来益饭店	110	1 D	Shing Hotel	大盛酒店	111	1 B
M Hotel Singapore	M酒店	132	2 D	Siloso Beach Resort	喜乐圣淘沙酒店	142	1 B
Madras Hotel	马德拉斯旅店	111	1 C	Simpang De Bedok Boarding House	勿洛新纳邦宿舍	94	1 C
Madras Hotel Eminence	马德拉斯旅店(卓越)	111	1 A				
Malacca Hotel	马六甲旅店	113	2 A	Sing Hoe Hotel	新和酒店	113	1 D
Mandarin Oriental, S'pore	文华东方(新加坡)	133	1 A	Singapore Marriott Hotel	万豪酒店	110	1 C
Marina Mandarin	滨华酒店	133	1 A	Sleepy Sams	Sleepy Sams旅店	111	1 C
Mayo Inn	美雅旅店	111	1 C	Sloane Court Hotel	施伦谷旅店	110	1 A
Meng Yew Hotel	民友旅店	112	2 B	South East Asia Hotel	东南亚大旅店	111	1 D
Meritus Mandarin S'pore	文华大酒店	110	1 C	St. Regis Hotel S'pore	瑞吉大酒店(新加坡)	109	2 C
Min Wah Hotel	明华旅店	112	2 B	Strand Hotel	市中大酒店	110	2 D
Namaste Hotel	Namaste旅店	111	1 B	Summer Hotel	夏日旅店	112	2 B
Naumi Hotel	诺美旅店	111	1 D	Summer Tavern	夏舍	132	2 A
New Cathay Hotel	新国泰旅店	112	2 B	Summer View Hotel	日晶酒店	111	1 C
New Majestic Hotel	新大华旅馆	132	1 C	Super 8 Hotel	超8酒店	112	1 B
New Orchid Hotel	新胡姬酒店	89	1 D	Swissotel Merchant Court, S'pore	贸商阁瑞士酒店	132	2 A
New 7th Storey Hotel	新七层楼大酒店	111	1 D				
New Queens City Hotel	女皇市酒店	112	2 B	Swissotel The Stamford, S'pore	史丹福瑞士酒店	133	1 A
Nicoll Hotel	尼诺酒店	111	1 B				
Novotel Clarke Quay, S'pore	诺富特克拉码头旅店	132	2 A	Tai Hoe Hotel	泰和旅店	111	1 B
				Tai Seng Hotel	大成旅店	111	1 C
Orchard Hotel S'pore	豪景大酒店	109	2 B	Taipei Hotel (2000)	台北旅店 (2000)	112	1 B
Orchard Parade Hotel	乌节广场酒店	109	2 C	Tekka Hotel	德卡旅店	111	1 B
Oxford Hotel	万富大酒店	111	1 D	The Inn at Temple St	登宝客栈	132	2 B
Oxley Blossom Hotel	欧思礼之花旅店	112	1 B	Traders Hotel S'pore	商贸饭店	109	2 C
Oxley Hotel	豪利酒店	112	1 B	Treasure Resort	宝地度假旅店	142	1 C
Oxley Hotel 88	豪利88酒店	112	1 B	Tropical Hotel	泰宝阁	132	2 C
"Pan Pacific Hotel S'pore, The"	泛太平洋大酒店	133	1 A	Victoria Hotel	维多利亚大酒店	111	1 D
				VIP Hotel	贵宾大旅店	110	1 A
Pan Pacific Orchard	泛太平洋乌节酒店	109	2 B	Waterloo Hostel	滑铁卢旅店	111	1 D
Paramount Hotel	百乐门酒店	113	2 C	Yes Chinatown Pt Hotel	唐城客栈	132	2 B
Park Hotel Orchard, S'pore	新加坡乌节酒店	110	1 C	Yew Lian Hotel	友联旅店	112	2 B
Parkroyal on Beach Road, S'pore	新加坡美芝路皇园酒店	111	2 D	Yong Nan Hotel	永南旅店	112	1 B
				York Hotel	约克酒店	110	1 B
Parkroyal on Kitchener Rd	新加坡吉真那路皇园酒店	111	1 B	YWCA Fort Canning Lodge	YWCA福康宁居	110	2 D
Park View Hotel	美景酒店	111	1 D				
Pasir Panjang Inn	巴西班让旅店	128	2 A				

PLACES		MAP	GRID

INDUSTRIAL PARKS / ESTATES

PLACES		MAP	GRID
AMK Tech 1	宏茂桥第1科技园	47	2 D
AMK Techplace 1	宏茂桥第1科技坊	68	1 B
AMK Techplace II	宏茂桥第2科技坊	47	2 D
Admiralty Ind Park	海军部工业园	2	1 D
Alexandra Distripark	亚历山大分销园	130	1 C
Aljunied Ind Estate	阿裕尼工业区	91	1 D
Ang Mo Kio Ind Park 2 (AMK Ave 3)	宏茂桥工业园2 (宏茂桥3道)	68	2 A
Ang Mo Kio Ind Park 2 (AMK Ave 5)	宏茂桥工业园2 (宏茂桥5道)	47	2 D
Ang Mo Kio Ind Park 3	宏茂桥工业园3	46	2 B
Ayer Rajah Ind Estate	亚逸拉惹工业区	107	2 D
Bedok Ind Estate	勿洛工业区	92	2 C
Bedok Ind Park C	勿洛工业园C	92	1 B
Bedok Ind Park E	勿洛工业园E	93	2 B
Bukit Batok Ind Estate Park A	武吉巴督 工业园A	83	2 A
Changi Business Park	樟宜商业园	95	1 B
Changi North Ind Park	樟宜北工业园	74	1 D
Changi South Ind Est	樟宜南工业区	94	1 C
Clementi West Distripark	金文泰西分销园	84	1 C
Defu Ind Estate	德福工业区	91	1 A
Depot Lane Ind Estate	德普巷工业区	130	2 B
Eunos Ind Park	友诺士工业区	91	2 D
Freight Links Express Distripark	辉联配运分销园	83	2 B
Geylang East Ind Est	芽笼东工业区	113	1 A
Henderson Ind Park	亨德申工业园	131	1 B
Int'l Business Park	国际商业园	83	2 C
JTC Serangoon North Ind Estate	裕廊集团实龙岗北工业园	48	1 D
Jurong Island	裕廊岛	125	2 A
Kaki Bukit Ind Estate	加基武吉工业区	91	2 B
Kallang Ave Ind Ctr	加冷道工业中心	111	2 B
Kallang Ave Ind Est	加冷道工业区	111	2 B
Kallang Bahru Ind Estate	加冷巴鲁工业区	111	2 A
Kallang Distripark	加冷分销园	111	2 A
Kallang Way Flatted Fty	加冷大道工厂大厦	90	1 D
Kallang Way Ind Est	加冷大道工业区	90	1 D
Kampong Ampat Ind Est	甘榜安拔工业区	90	2 B
Keppel Distripark	发巴分销园	131	2 D
Kg Ubi Ind Estate	甘榜乌美工业区	91	1 C
Kolam Ayer Ind Estate	哥南亚逸工业区	90	1 D
Kranji Ind Estate	克兰芝工业区	9	2 C
Loyang Agro Technology Pk	罗央农业科技园	51	1 D
Loyang Ind Estate	罗央工业区	74	1 A
Loyang Ind Park	罗央工业区	53	1 C
Marsiling Ind Estate	马西岭工业区	11	1 B
North Coast Ind Park	北海岸工业园	1	2 D
Pan Tech Ind Complex	Pan Tech工业大厦	105	2 B
Pasir Panjang Distripark	巴西班让分销园	129	2 C
Pasir Ris Coast Ind Pk	巴西立海岸工业园	51	1 A
Pasir Ris Wafer Fab Pk	巴西立晶片园	51	1 D
Paya Lebar Districentre	巴耶利巴分销中心	70	2 D
Paya Lebar Ind Est	巴耶利巴工业区	91	1 B

PLACES		MAP	GRID
Redhill Ind Est	红山工业区	130	2 B
Science Park I	科学园1	129	2 A
Serangoon Nth Ind Est	实龙岗北工业区	48	1 D
Shun Li Ind Pk	顺利工业园	92	1 B
Sin Ming Ind Est	新民工业区	67	1 C
Sungei Kadut Ind Est	双溪加林工业区	22	1 A
T.T. Int'l Trade Pk	T.T.国际贸易园	83	2 C
Tagore Ind Est	太戈尔工业区	45	2 B
Tai Seng Ind Est	大成工业区	91	1 B
Tampines Nth Wafer Fab Pk	淡滨尼北晶片园	72	1 A
Tanjong Pagar Distripk	丹戎巴葛分销园	132	1 D
Technopark @ Chai Chee	菜市科技园	92	2 D
Tech Park 21	科技园21	84	1 B
Telok Blangah Ind Est	直落布兰雅工业区	130	1 D
Tiong Bahru Ind Est	中巴鲁工业区	131	2 B
Toa Payoh Ind Est	大巴窑工业区	88	2 A
Toa Payoh Ind Park	大巴窑工业园	89	2 D
Toa Payoh West Ind Est	大巴窑西工业区	88	2 B
Toh Tuck Ind Est	道德工业区	84	1 B
Ubi Tech Park	乌美科技园	91	1 D
Woodlands East Ind Pk	兀兰东工业园	2	2 D
Woodlands Wafer Fab Pk	兀兰晶片园	10	1 C
Yew Tee Ind Estate	油池工业区	41	2 A
Yishun Ind Park A	义顺工业园A	14	1 B

LIBRARIES

COMMUNITY / REGIONAL 图书馆

		MAP	GRID
Ang Mo Kio Community	宏茂桥社区图书馆	46	2 D
Bedok Community	勿洛社区图书馆	93	1 D
Bishan Community	碧山社区图书馆	67	2 D
Bukit Batok Community	武吉巴督社区图书馆	62	2 D
Bukit Merah Community	红山社区图书馆	131	1 B
Bukit Panjang Community	武吉班让社区图书馆	42	1 D
Central Lending Library (National Library)	中央图书馆 (国家图书馆)	111	1 D
Cheng San Community	静山社区图书馆	70	1 A
Choa Chu Kang Community	蔡厝港社区图书馆	41	1 C
Geylang East Community	芽笼东社区图书馆	112	2 A
Jurong East Regional	裕廊东区域图书馆	83	1 B
Jurong West Community	裕廊西社区图书馆	81	1 A
Library @ Esplanade - Marine Parade Community (Marine Parade Community Bldg)	滨海湾图书馆 马林百列社区图书馆	133 114	1 A 1 C
National (Ctrl)	国家中央社区图书馆	111	1 D
Pasir Ris Community	巴西立社区图书馆	52	1 D
Queenstown Community	女皇镇社区图书馆	108	2 D
Sembawang Community	三巴旺社区图书馆	13	1 A
Sengkang Community	盛港社区图书馆	49	1 B
Tampines Regional	淡滨尼区域图书馆	72	2 C
Toa Payoh Community	大巴窑社区图书馆	89	1 B
Woodlands Regional	兀兰区域图书馆	11	2 C
Yishun Community	义顺社区图书馆	14	1 B

PLACES		MAP GRID

PLACES		MAP	GRID

COMMUNITY CHILDREN'S LIBRARIES (CCLs)
社区儿童图书馆
(Symbol not shown in maps)

Clementi	金文泰	106	2 A
(Blk 322 Clementi Ave 5)	(大牌322金文泰5道)		
Nee Soon East	义顺东	14	2 D
(Blk 356 Yishun Ring Rd)	(大牌356义顺环路)		

MRT / LRT STATIONS

EAST WEST LINE 东西地铁线

EW 1 -	Pasir Ris	巴西立		52	1 D
EW 2 -	Tampines	淡滨尼		72	2 C
EW 3 -	Simei	四美		94	1 A
EW 4 -	Tanah Merah	丹那美拉		94	1 D
	(Interchange)	(转换站)			
EW 5 -	Bedok	勿洛		93	1 D
EW 6 -	Kembangan	景万岸		92	1 D
EW 7 -	Eunos	友诺士		113	2 A
EW 8 -	Paya Lebar	巴耶利巴		113	1 A
EW 9 -	Aljunied	阿裕尼		112	2 A
EW 10 -	Kallang	加冷		112	1 B
EW 11 -	Lavender	劳明达		111	2 B
EW 12 -	Bugis	武吉士		111	1 D
EW 13 -	City Hall	政府大厦		133	1 A
	(Interchange)	(转换站)			
EW 14 -	Raffles Place	莱佛士坊		133	1 B
	(Interchange)	(转换站)			
EW 15 -	Tanjong Pagar	丹戎巴葛		132	2 C
EW 16 -	Outram Park	欧南园		132	1 C
EW 17 -	Tiong Bahru	中巴鲁		131	2 B
EW 18 -	Redhill	红山		131	1 A
EW 19 -	Queenstown	女皇镇		108	2 D
EW 20 -	Commonwealth	联邦		108	1 C
EW 21 -	Buona Vista	波那维斯达		107	2 C
EW 22 -	Dover	杜佛		107	1 B
EW 23 -	Clementi	金文泰		106	1 A
EW 24 -	Jurong East	裕廊东		83	1 B
	(Interchange)	(转换站)			
EW 25 -	Chinese Garden	裕华园		82	2 A
EW 26 -	Lakeside	湖畔		82	1 A
EW 27 -	Boon Lay	文礼		81	1 B
EW 28 -	Pioneer	先驱		80	2 B
EW 29 -	Joo Koon	裕群		79	2 C
CG 1 -	Expo	博览		94	2 B
CG 2 -	Changi Airport	樟宜机场		75	1 C

NORTH SOUTH LINE 南北地铁线

NS 1 -	Jurong East	裕廊东		83	1 B
	(Interchange)	(转换站)			
NS 2 -	Bukit Batok	武吉巴督		62	2 D
NS 3 -	Bukit Gombak	武吉甘柏		62	2 C
NS 4 -	Choa Chu Kang	蔡厝港		41	1 C
NS 5 -	Yew Tee	油池		41	2 A
NS 7 -	Kranji	克兰芝		10	1 D
NS 8 -	Marsiling	马西岭		10	2 C
NS 9 -	Woodlands	兀兰		11	2 C
NS 10 -	Admiralty	海军部		12	1 B
NS 11 -	Sembawang	三巴旺		13	1 A
NS 13 -	Yishun	义顺		14	1 D
NS 14 -	Khatib	卡迪		27	1 B
NS 15 -	Yio Chu Kang	杨厝港		46	2 C
NS 16 -	Ang Mo Kio	宏茂桥		67	2 A
NS 17 -	Bishan	碧山		67	2 D
NS 18 -	Braddell	布莱德		88	2 A
NS 19 -	Toa Payoh	大巴窑		88	2 C
NS 20 -	Novena	诺维娜		110	2 A
NS 21 -	Newton	纽顿		110	1 B
NS 22 -	Orchard	乌节		110	1 C
NS 23 -	Somerset	索美塞		110	1 D
NS 24 -	Dhoby Ghaut	多美歌		110	2 D
	(Interchange)	(转换站)			
NS 25 -	City Hall	政府大厦		133	1 A
	(Interchange)	(转换站)			
NS 26 -	Raffles Place	莱佛士坊		133	1 B
	(Interchange)	(转换站)			
NS 27 -	Marina Bay	滨海湾		133	1 C

NORTH EAST LINE 东北线

NE 1 -	Harbour Front	港湾		142	1 A
NE 3 -	Outram Park	欧南园		132	1 C
NE 4 -	Chinatown	牛车水		132	2 B
NE 5 -	Clarke Quay	克拉码头		132	2 A
NE 6 -	Dhoby Ghaut	多美歌		110	2 D
	(Interchange)	(转换站)			
NE 7 -	Little India	小印度		110	2 C
NE 8 -	Farrer Park	花拉公园		111	1 B
NE 9 -	Boon Keng	文庆		111	2 A
NE 10 -	Potong Pasir	波东巴西		90	1 C
NE 11 -	Woodleigh	兀里		90	1 B
NE 12 -	Serangoon	实龙岗		69	1 D
NE 13 -	Kovan	高文		69	2 C
NE 14 -	Hougang	后港		70	1 A
NE 15 -	Buangkok	万国		49	1 C
NE 16 -	Sengkang	盛港		49	1 B
NE 17 -	Punggol	榜鹅		30	2 D

PLACES		MAP GRID

CIRCLE LINE 市区环线 (U/C)

CC 1 -	Dhoby Ghaut	多美歌	110	2 D
CC 2 -	Bras Basah	百胜	110	2 D
CC 3 -	Esplanade	滨海中心	133	1 A
CC 4 -	Promenade	宝门廊	133	2 A
CC 5 -	Nicoll Highway	汇广大道	111	2 D
CC 6 -	Stadium	体育场	112	1 C
CC 7 -	Mountbatten	蒙巴登	112	2 C
CC 8 -	Dakota	达科达	112	2 B
CC 9 -	Paya Lebar (Int)	巴耶利巴(转换站)	113	1 A
CC 10 -	MacPherson	麦波申	91	1 D
CC 11 -	Tai Seng	大成	90	2 B
CC 12 -	Bartley	巴特礼	90	1 A
CC 13 -	Serangoon (Int)	实龙岗(转换站)	69	1 D
CC 14 -	Lorong Chuan	罗弄泉	68	2 D
CC 15 -	Bishan (Int)	碧山(转换站)	67	2 C
CC 16 -	Marymount	玛丽蒙	67	1 D
CC 17 -	Thomson	汤申	88	1 B
CC 18 -	Bt Brown(Future)	武吉布朗	87	2 B
CC 19 -	Botanic Gardens	植物园	87	1 D
CC 20 -	Farrer Road	花拉路	108	2 A
CC 21 -	Holland Village	荷兰村	108	1 B
CC 22 -	Buona Vista (Int)	波雅维斯达(转换站)	107	2 C
CC 23 -	One-North	纬壹	107	2 D
CC 24 -	Kent Ridge	肯尼岭	129	1 A
CC 25 -	West Coast(Future)	西海岸	129	1 B
CC 26 -	Pasir Panjang	巴西班让	129	2 C
CC 27 -	Labrador Park	拉柏多	130	1 D
CC 28 -	Telok Blangah	直落布兰雅	130	2 D
CC	HarbourFront (Int)	港湾(转换站)	142	1 A

SENTOSA EXPRESS LRT 圣海沙轻轨快车站

S 1 -	Waterfront	水滨	142	1 B
S 2 -	Imbiah	音庇亚	142	1 C
S 3 -	Beach	美芝	142	1 C

BUKIT PANJANG LRT 武吉班让轻轨列车站

BP 1 -	Choa Chu Kang	蔡厝港	41	1 C
BP 2 -	South View	南景	41	2 C
BP 3 -	Keat Hong	吉丰	41	2 D
BP 4 -	Teck Whye	德惠	41	2 D
BP 5 -	Phoenix	凤凰	42	1 D
BP 6 -	Bukit Panjang	武吉班让	42	1 D
BP 7 -	Petir	柏提	42	2 D
BP 8 -	Pending	秉定	42	2 D
BP 9 -	Bangkit	万吉	42	2 C
BP 10 -	Fajar	法嘉	42	2 C
BP 11 -	Segar	实加	42	2 B
BP 12 -	Jelapang	泽拉邦	42	2 B
BP 13 -	Senja	信加	42	1 C
BP 14 -	Ten Mile Junction	十里广场	42	1 C

PUNGGOL EAST LRT 榜鹅东轻轨列车站

PE 1 -	Cove	海湾	49	2 A
PE 2 -	Meridian	丽园	50	1 A
PE 3 -	Coral Edge	珊瑚	50	1 A
PE 4 -	Riviera	里维拉	50	1 A
PE 5 -	Kadaloor	卡达鲁	31	1 D

PE 6 -	Oasis	绿洲	31	1 D
PE 7 -	Damai	达迈	31	1 D

PUNGGOL WEST LRT 榜鹅西轻轨列车站 (Not in service)

PW 1 -	Sam Kee	三记	30	2 C
PW 2 -	Teck Lee	德利	30	2 B
PW 3 -	Punggol Point	榜鹅坊	30	2 B
PW 4 -	Samudera	山姆	30	2 B
PW 5 -	Nibong	尼蒙	30	2 B
PW 6 -	Sumang	苏芒	30	2 C
PW 7 -	Soo Teck	树德	30	2 D

SENGKANG EAST LRT 盛港东轻轨列车站

SE 1 -	Compassvale	康埔桦	49	2 A
SE 2 -	Rumbia	棕美站	49	2 B
SE 3 -	Bakau	峇高	49	2 B
SE 4 -	Kangkar	港脚	49	2 C
SE 5 -	Ranggung	兰岗	49	1 C

SENGKANG WEST LRT 盛港西轻轨列车站

SW 1 -	Cheng Lim	振林	49	1 A
SW 2 -	Farmway	农道	49	1 A
SW 3 -	Kupang	古邦	49	2 A
SW 4 -	Thanggam	丹甘	48	1 A
SW 5 -	Fernvale	芬微	48	1 B
SW 6 -	Layar	拉雅	48	2 B
SW 7 -	Tongkang	同港	48	2 B
SW 8 -	Renjong	仁宗	49	1 C

NKF DIALYSIS CENTRES

DIALYSIS CENTRES 洗肾中心

Aljunied Crescent	阿裕尼弯	112	2 A
Ang Mo Kio Avenue 3	宏茂桥3道	68	1 A
Ang Mo Kio Avenue 6	宏茂桥6道	46	2 C
Ang Mo Kio Avenue 9	宏茂桥9道	46	1 C
Bangkit Rd	万吉路	43	1 D
Bukit Batok Central	武吉巴督中路	62	2 D
Clementi Ave 5	金文泰5道	106	2 A
Henderson Road	亨德申路	131	1 B
Hougang	后港	70	1 D
Jurong West St 52	裕廊西52街	60	2 D
Jurong West St 73	裕廊西73街	59	2 D
Kim Keat	金吉	89	1 D
New Upper Changi Road	新樟宜路上段	93	1 D
Pasir Ris St 11	巴西立11街	73	2 B
Serangoon	实龙岗	69	1 D
Simei	四美	94	1 A
Sims Drive	沈氏通道	112	2 A
Tampines St 91	淡滨尼91街	93	2 A
Teck Whye	德惠	41	2 D
Toa Payoh	大巴窑	89	1 B
Woodlands Ave 5	兀兰5道	11	2 C
Woodlands St 81	兀兰81街	11	2 B
Yishun	义顺	14	1 D

PLACES		MAP	GRID

PARK CONNECTORS

PLACES		MAP	GRID
Ang Mo Kio	宏茂桥	67	2 A
Bedok	勿洛	94	2 D
Buangkok Green	万国埔	48	2 C
Bt Batok East	武吉巴督东	62	2 D
Bt Panjang	武吉班让	42	2 C
Changi	樟宜	53	2 B
Choa Chu Kang	蔡厝港	41	1 C
Coastal	海岸	75	2 D
Geylang	芽笼	113	1 C
Hillview	山景	63	1 D
Jurong (Jurong Lake)	裕廊(裕廊湖)	82	1 A
Jurong (Boon Lay)	裕廊(文礼)	81	1 B
Kallang (Bishan)	加冷(碧山)	68	1 D
Kallang (Boon Keng)	加冷(文庆)	112	1 A
Kallang-Geylang Link	加冷芽笼连路	90	2 C
Khatib Bongsu	卡迪逢苏	14	2 D
Loyang	罗央	74	1 A
Pasir Ris	巴西立	52	2 D
Sembawang	三巴旺	12	2 B
Serangoon	实龙岗	49	2 D
Simei	四美	94	1 C
Siglap	实乞纳	114	1 A
Simpang Kiri	新邦吉里	4	1 D
Tampines (Pasir Ris)	淡滨尼(巴西立)	52	1 D
Tampines (TPE)	淡滨尼 (淡滨尼快速公路)	73	1 A
Ulu Pandan (West Coast)	乌鲁班丹(西海岸)	105	2 A
Ulu Pandan (Sungei Pandan)	乌鲁班丹 (双溪班丹)	83	2 B
Ulu Pandan II (Bt Batok)	乌鲁班丹 II (武吉巴督)	63	1 D
Whampoa	黄埔	89	1 D

PARKS / GARDENS

Admiralty Park	海军部公园	11	1 A
Alexandra Canal Linear Park	亚历山大干拿直线公园	108	2 D
Ang Mo Kio Town Garden East	宏茂桥镇东	67	2 A
Ang Mo Kio Town Garden West	宏茂桥镇西	46	2 D
Bedok Reservoir	勿洛蓄水池	92	2 A
Bedok Town	勿洛镇	93	1 B
Bishan Park 1	碧山1	67	1 B
Bishan Park 2	碧山2	67	2 B
Bougainvillea	紫茉莉园	86	2 D
Brontosonur Park	雷龙公园	51	2 D
Bukit Batok Hillside	武吉巴督山	62	1 B
Bukit Batok Nature	武吉巴督天然公园	63	1 D
Bukit Batok Town	武吉巴督镇	62	2 B
Bukit Panjang	武吉班让	42	2 C
Bt Timah Nature Reserve	武吉知马天然保护区	63	2 D
Changi Beach	樟宜海滨	55	1 D
Changi Business Park	樟宜商业园	95	2 C
Cheng Hua Gdn	正华花园	43	1 D
Choa Chu Kang	蔡厝港	41	2 B
Clementi Woods	金文泰林	106	2 C
Duxton Plain	达士敦坪	132	2 C
East Coast	东海岸	115	2 B
Esplanade	海滨	133	1 A
Fort Canning	福康宁	110	2 D
Gardens by the Bay	海湾花园	133	2 C

PLACES		MAP	GRID
Hindhede Nature Park	海希德天然公园	64	1 D
Istana	总统府	110	2 D
Jelutong Harbour Park	日落洞海港公园	3	1 D
Jurong Hill	裕廊山	103	1 A
Jurong Lake Park	裕廊湖公园	82	1 B
Kallang Riverside	加冷河畔	111	2 C
Katong	加东	112	2 D
Kent Ridge	肯特岗	129	2 B
Kranji Reservoir	克兰芝蓄水池	8	2 B
Labrador Nature Reserve	拉博拉天然保护区	141	1 A
Limbang	林邦	41	1 B
Lower Peirce Reservoir	比雅士下段蓄水池	45	2 D
Lower Seletar Reservoir	实里达下段蓄水池	26	2 C
Macritchie Reservoir	麦里芝蓄水池	88	1 A
Mandai Tekong Pk	万里德光公园	11	2 C
Marina Promenade	滨海龙坊	133	2 A
Mount Faber	花柏山	131	2 C
Nee Soon East Park	义顺东公园	14	2 D
Pasir Ris	巴西立	52	1 C
Pasir Ris Town	巴西立镇	52	1 D
Pearl's Hill City	珍珠山	132	1 B
Punggol	榜鹅	49	2 D
Read Cres Park	李德弯公园	132	2 C
Sakra (Jurong Island)	莎克拉(裕廊岛)	139	1 A
Sembawang	三巴旺	4	1 C
Sengkang	盛港	29	2 D
Sengkang Sculpture Pk	盛港雕塑公园	49	1 A
Stagmont	史达蒙	41	2 A
Sun Plaza	太阳广场	72	2 D
Sungei Api Api Park	双溪阿比阿比公园	52	1 C
Taman Jurong Green	达曼裕廊埔	82	1 B
Tampines Central Pk	淡滨尼中心公园	72	2 D
Teck Whye Garden	德惠花园	41	2 C
Telok Blangah Hill	直落布兰雅山	130	2 C
Toa Payoh Town	大巴窑镇	88	2 C
Upper Peirce Reservoir	贝雅士上段蓄水池	44	2 D
Upper Seletar Reservoir	实里达上段蓄水池	25	2 D
Vanda Miss Joaquim	卓锦万黛兰	132	2 C
War Memorial	日治时期蒙难人士 纪念碑公园	133	1 A
West Coast	西海岸	128	2 A
Woodlands Crescent Pk	兀兰弯公园	12	1 A
Woodlands Town Garden	兀兰镇花园	10	1 B
Woodlands Town Pk East	兀兰镇公园东	11	1 C
Yew Tee	油池	41	1 A
Yishun	义顺	27	2 A
Yishun Neighbourhood	义顺邻里	14	1 C
Yishun Town Garden	义顺镇花园	27	2 A
Youth	青年公园	110	1 D
Yunnan Park	云南园广场	80	2 B
Zhenghua	正华	43	1 C

PLACES OF INTEREST / LEISURE

Air Force Museum	空军博物馆	70	2 D
Alkaff Mansion	阿尔卡大厦	130	2 C
Archery (Archery Assn)	射箭场(射箭协会)	90	1 B
(Zhenghua National Archery Range)	(正华国家射箭场)	42	2 B
Army Museum	陆军博物馆	79	2 C
ASEAN Sculpture Garden	亚细安雕塑园	110	2 D
Asian Civilisations Museum	亚洲文明博物馆	133	2 D
Boat Quay	驳船码头	132	2 D
Bt Timah Nature Reserve	武吉知马天然保护区	64	1 D

PLACES		MAP GRID		PLACES		MAP GRID	
Buddha Tooth Relic Tp and Museum	佛牙寺及博物馆	132	2 C	Pasir Panjang Hill Village	巴西班让山村	129	2 C
Burkill Hall	植物园伯尔基楼	109	1 B	Peranakan Museum	土生华人博物馆	110	2 D
Changi Village	樟宜村	54	1 B	Playground @ Big Splash	水上游乐场	113	2 D
Chinatown Heritage Ctr	牛车水原貌馆	132	2 C	Police Heritage Ctr (New Phoenix Park)	警察文物馆 (新凤凰园)	88	2 D
Chinese Garden / Japanese Garden	裕华园 / 星和园	82	2 B	Raffles Museum of Biodiversity Research	莱佛士生物 多元化研究博物馆	107	1 D
Chinese Heritage Ctr	华裔馆	80	1 A	Reflections At Bt Chandu	武吉占都缩影	129	2 B
Civil Defence Heritage Gallery	民防发展事迹陈列室	132	2 A	Robertson Quay	罗拔申码头	132	2 A
Civil Service - Aloha Loyang Resort	公务员-阿罗哈 罗央度假村	52	2 C	Royal Selangor (Selangor Pewter)	皇家雪兰莪 (白镴)	132	2 A
Civilian War Memorial	战时纪念碑	133	1 A	Sailing - National Sailing Ctr	国家帆船中心	116	2 A
Clarke Quay	克拉码头	132	2 A	Shooting-National Shooting Ctr	新加坡射击协会	38	1 D
Costa Sands Resort Pasir Ris	高士达度假村 (巴西立)	52	2 C	S'pore Art Museum	新加坡美术馆	111	1 D
Costa Sands Resort Sentosa	高士达度假村 (圣淘沙)	142	1 B	S'pore Botanic Gdns	新加坡植物园	109	1 B
Dempsey Hill	登布西山	108	2 C	S'pore City Gallery	新加坡城市文物馆	132	2 C
DHL Balloon Ride	DHL气球升空游	111	1 D	S'pore Crocodile Farm	新加坡鳄鱼园	69	2 C
Downtown East	Downtown East度假村	52	1 D	S'pore Discovery Ctr	知新馆	79	2 B
Dragon Kiln Village	龙庭	59	2 C	Spore Mint Coin Gallery	新加坡造币厂展览馆	83	1 D
EJH Corner House	植物园科纳楼	109	1 A	S'pore Navy Museum	新加坡海军博物馆	119	1 A
Escape Theme Park	休闲主题公园	52	1 C	S'pore Philatelic Museum	新加坡集邮馆	132	2 A
Eu Yan Sang Bird's Nest Gallery	余仁生燕窝馆	132	2 B	S'pore Science Ctr	新加坡科学馆	82	2 B
Fort Canning Park	福康宁公园	110	2 D	S'pore Tyler Print Institute	新加坡泰勒印刷学院	132	1 A
Fountain Of Wealth	财富之泉	133	1 A	S'pore Zoo	新加坡动物园	24	2 D
Fuk Tak Chi Museum	福德祠博物馆	132	2 B	Sungei Buloh Wetland Reserve	双溪布洛 湿地保留区	8	2 A
Gillman Village	吉门村	130	2 C	Sun Yat Sen Nanyang Memorial Hall	孙中山南洋纪念馆	88	2 C
G-Max Reverse Bungy Jump	G-Max 绑紧跳	132	2 A	Tag Paintball	漆球园	27	2 B
Haw Par Villa	虎豹别墅	129	1 B	Tanglin Village	东陵村	108	2 C
Holland Village	荷兰村	108	1 B	Tan Tock Seng Hospital Heritage Museum	陈笃生医院文物馆	88	2 D
HortPark	HortPark公园	130	1 C	The Arts House at the Old Parliament	旧国会大厦艺术馆	133	1 A
Ice Skating - Snow City	溜冰-雪城	82	2 B	The Battle Box	碉堡	110	2 D
Island Resort (East Coast)	岛屿度假村(东海岸)	114	2 C	The Changi Museum	樟宜监狱博物馆	74	2 B
Jacob Ballas Childrens Garden	雅谷巴拉士儿童乐园	109	1 A	The Jewel Box (Cable-Car)	"珠宝盒" (缆车)	131	1 D
Jalan Bahar Clay Studios	惹兰巴哈陶瓷屋	59	2 D	The Merlion - Merlion Park	鱼尾狮塔-鱼尾狮公园	133	1 A
Johor Battery (Monster Gun)	柔佛炮台(Monster Gun)	74	2 B	The Singapore Flyer	新加坡摩天轮	133	2 A
Jurong Bird Park	裕廊飞禽公园	81	1 D	The Woodbridge Museum (Woodbridge Hospital)	板桥博物馆 (板桥医院)	48	2 C
Kong Hiap Memorial Museum	广洽纪念馆	112	2 A	Tree-Top Walk (Macritchie Nature Trails)	树顶径 (麦里芝天然径)	65	2 B
Kranji Commonwealth War Cemetery	克兰芝英联邦战亡 坟场	23	1 A	West Coast Recreation Ctr	西海岸康乐中心	106	1 B
Labrador Secret Tunnels	拉拔多秘密隧道	130	1 D	Wild Wild Wet	Wild Wild Wet	52	1 D
Lilliput Indoor Mini Golf (Playground @ Big Splash)	小人国室内迷你高尔夫 球场(Big Splash游乐场)	113	2 D				
Malay Village	马来村	113	1 A	**SENTOSA 圣淘沙**			
Mandai Orchid Garden	万礼胡姬花园	24	1 C	4D Magix	4D Magix	142	1 B
Mountain Biking	越野脚车			Animal & Bird Encounters	禽兽园	142	1 C
- Bt Timah Nature Reserve	- 武吉知马天然保护区	63	2 C	Butterfly Pk & Insect Kingdom	蝴蝶园及世界昆虫馆	142	1 B
- Tampines	- 淡滨尼	72	2 A	Cineblast	电影场	142	1 B
Mt Faber Park	花柏山公园	131	1 D	Dolphin Lagoon	海豚乐园	142	2 D
National Archives of S'pore	新加坡档案馆	132	2 A	Fort Siloso Tours	西乐索炮台旅游团	141	2 B
National Museum of S'pore	新加坡国家博物馆	110	2 D	Images of S'pore	万象新加坡	142	1 C
National Orchid Garden	国家胡姬园	109	1 B	Luge & Skyride	Luge & Skyride	142	1 C
Newater Visitor Centre	新生水游客中心	94	2 D	Nature Walk - Dragon Trail	龙径自然走道	142	1 B
Night Safari	夜间野生动物园	24	2 D	Sky Tower	摩天塔	142	1 B
NUS Museums	国大博物馆	106	2 C	Sijori Wondergolf	新世纪高妙球场	142	1 B
Omni Theatre	万象馆	82	2 B	Songs of The Sea	海之颂	142	1 C
Omnimax Movies - Omni Theatre	万象电影 -万象馆	82	2 B	The Flying Trapeze	空中飞人	141	2 B
Orchid Plaza (Botanic Gdns)	胡姬坊(新加坡植物园)	109	1 B	The Merlion & Merlion Wk	鱼尾狮塔及鱼尾狮园径	142	1 C
				Underwater World	海底世界	141	2 B

INDEX

PLACES

MAP GRID

• PLACES OF WORSHIP

PLACES

MAP GRID

• PLACES OF WORSHIP 庙宇与教堂

PLACES OF WORSHIP

CHINESE / BUDDHIST TEMPLES 华人庙宇／佛寺

Aaloka Buddhist Ctr	阿乐佳佛教中心	112	1 A
Ang Chee Sia Ong Temple	安济圣王庙	106	1 B
Ban Siew San Temple	万寿山	130	2 D
Bao Gong Temple	包公庙	48	1 B
Bee Low See Temple	毗卢寺	84	2 B
Bo Tien Temple	武天	82	1 C
Boo Tong San Temple	武当山庙	2	1 D
Boo Tang San Temple	武当山	61	1 D
Buddha Tooth Relic Tp	新加坡佛牙寺	132	2 B
Buddhist Fellowship Poh Ern Shih Tp	佛友会报恩寺	129	2 C
"Buddhist Union, The"	佛教会	92	1 D
Bukit Timah Seu Teck Sean Tong Temple	武吉知马修德善堂	83	1 A
Burmese Buddhist Temple	缅甸玉佛寺	88	2 C
Chai Chee United Temple	菜市联合宫	92	2 C
Chan Chor Min Tong Tp	陈佐勉堂	88	2 D
Chee Ghee Deang Chiang Ching Meow	慈义堂将军庙	84	1 D
Chee Hoon Sun Kong Tp	慈云山宫	14	1 B
Chee Seng Temple (Choa Chu Kang Lian He Tp)	齐神宫 (蔡厝港联合庙)	41	1 B
Chee Tong Temple	慈忠坛	70	1 C
Chek Chai Long Chuen Tp	七寨龙泉庙	9	2 C
Chek Sian Tng Temple	积善堂	68	1 A
Cheng Hong Siang Tng Tp	众弘善堂	91	1 D
Cheng Hwa Cher Siah Tp	正华慈圣宫	42	2 D
Cheng Lim See Tp	清莲寺	94	1 B
Cheo Lim Chin Sun Lian Hup Keng Temple	石林晋山联合宫	94	1 B
Cheow Leng Beo Tp	昭灵庙	14	1 B
Cher Li Temple	慈礼坛	88	2 C
Cher Lian Tong Bud Tp (Cheng Hwa Cher Siah Tp)	慈莲堂 (正华慈圣宫)	42	2 D
Chi Hock Keng Temple	七福宫	42	2 C
Chia Hung Boo Temple	顺山亭	92	2 C
Chin Chwee Temple	清水庙	2	1 D
Chin Long Kong Temple (Chua Chu Kang Combined Tp)	九龙宫 (蔡厝港联合庙)	41	2 C
Choa Chu Kang Lian He Tp	蔡厝港联合庙	41	1 B
Choa Chu Kang Yew Tee Chun Lian He Miow	蔡厝港池村联合庙	41	1 B
Chong Ghee Temple	万典山崇义庙	49	2 B
Chong Pang Combined Tp	忠邦联合庙	14	1 C
Chong Yee Tp	忠义庙	47	2 A
Chu Sheng Temple	聚圣庙	46	2 C
Chu Siang Tong Temple	聚善堂	14	1 C
Chu Siang Wah Sua Tp	聚善华宫	14	1 C
Chwee Kang Beo	水工庙	112	1 A
Ci Zheng Gong Temple	赐正宫	90	2 A
Da Bogong Temple (Kusu Island)	大伯公庙 (龟岛)	149	—
Dong Shan Temple	东山庙	27	1 A
Dou Tian Gong Temple	斗天宫	60	1 D
Fa Hua Monastery	法华神寺	69	2 D
Fa Shi Lin Temple	法施林庙	92	1 D
Fang Huo Yuan Temple	风火院	91	1 C
Fo Guang Shan Bud Tp	佛光山寺	30	2 C
Foo Hai Ch'an Monastery	福海禅院	112	2 A
Fu An Temple	福安庙	85	1 D
Fu De Gong Temple	福德宫	89	1 D
Fu Xi Tang Temple	福喜堂	111	1 A
Gang Tian Da Di Temple	宫天大地寺	112	2 B
Gek Hong Temple	玉皇庙	112	2 B
Geylang United Temple	芽笼联合庙	113	1 A
Giok Hong Tian Temple	玉皇殿	132	1 A
Golden Pagoda Budh Tp	护国金塔寺	72	1 A
Gow Hong Temple	五凤庙	111	1 A
Guilin Combined Temple	桂林联合庙	62	1 D
Hai Inn Temple	海印寺	40	2 D
Hean Thuan Chong Toh Tong Tp	显传总道堂	72	1 B
Hiang Foo Siang Temple	玄夫仙庙	69	1 A
Hiang Tong Keng Temple	昱当宫	72	1 B
Hiap Tien Keng Leng Poh Tien Tp	协天宫	72	1 A
Ho Lim Kong Temple	豪林宫	132	1 B
Hock Huat Keng Temple	福发宫	14	1 B
Hock Siew Tong Temple	福修堂	111	1 A
Hock Teck See Temple	福德寺	132	2 D
Hock Thong Temple	福同庙	84	1 A
Hong Lai Sze Temple	蓬莱寺	69	2 D
Hong Leng Yien Temple	云龙院	110	2 A
Hong San See Temple	凤山寺	132	1 A
Hong San Si Temple	凤山寺	114	1 A
Hong San Tan Temple	凤山坛	12	1 A
Hong San Temple	凤山宫	91	2 A
Hong Tho Temple	凤图庙	11	1 B
Hoon Lam Tua Peh Kong Tp	云南大伯公庙	83	2 A
Hoon Sian Temple	云仙宫	113	2 A
Huang Lao Xian Si Temple	黄老仙师	90	2 C
Hwee San Temple	横山庙	14	1 B
"Jayamangal Buddh Tp, The"	惹亚曼加佛寺	69	1 C
Ji De Tang Temple	济德堂	111	1 A
Ji Huang Kok Tp	济皇阁	49	1 A
Jin Fu Gong Tp (W'lands)	金福宫(兀兰)	2	1 D
Jin Fu Gong Tp (Jurong West)	金福宫(裕廊西)	80	2 D
Jin Long Si Temple	金龙寺	90	2 A
Jiu Huang Da Di Temple	九皇大帝庙	69	2 C
Jurong Temple	裕廊总宫	61	1 C
Kai San Temple	开山庙	131	2 C
Kancanrama Budh Tp	坎�拉玛佛寺	69	2 D
Karma Kagyud Budh Ctr	迦马佳育佛教中心	112	2 B
Kiew Lee Tong Tp	九鲤洞庙	66	2 B
Kiew Sian King Temple	九仙宫	72	1 B
Kim Lan Temple	金兰庙	131	2 B
Kim San Temple	金山寺	115	1 A
Kong Hock Keng Temple	广福宫	130	2 D
Kong Leap Thiam Lim Tua Tp	天南堂显源道堂	112	2 B
Kong Meng San Phor Kark See Temple	光明山普觉寺	67	1 B
Koon Seng Ting Temple	坒成堂	130	2 D
Kuan Im Tng Temple	观音堂	88	2 C

PLACES		MAP	GRID
Kuan Yin San Temple	观音山庙	86	2 D
Kuang Chee Tng	宽济堂	110	2 A
Buddhist Association			
Kwan Im Tng Temple	观音堂	113	2 B
Kwan Im Tong	观音堂佛祖庙	111	1 D
Hood Che Tp			
Kwan Imm See Temple	观音寺	112	2 A
Kwan Siang Tng Temple	观音堂	69	2 B
Kwan Yam Theng Budh Tp	观音亭佛寺	130	2 C
Kwang Hua	广化寺	72	1 A
Buddhist Monastery			
Leang San King Temple	灵山宫庙	67	1 B
Lei Yin Temple	雷音寺	131	1 B
Leng Ern Jee Temple	灵隐寺	88	2 D
Leng Foo Prajina Tp	灵福山	92	1 D
Leng Hup San	龙合山七寨庙	41	2 C
Chee Chea Temple			
Leong Hwa Chan Si Tp	龙华禅寺	110	2 A
Leong San See Temple	龙山寺	111	1 A
Li Teck Chuan	立德传心堂	113	2 A
Cin Tang Temple			
Lian Chee Kek Temple	莲池阁寺	69	2 D
Lian Chi Jing She Tp	莲池精舍	69	2 B
Lian Shan Shuang	莲山双林寺	89	1 C
Lin Monastery			
Lin Tan Temple	林檀寺	91	2 D
Ling Hong Tong Temple	灵凤阁	83	2 A
Ling San Teng Temple	麟山亭	131	1 C
Ling Shan Temple	灵山寺	112	1 B
Liuxun Sanhemiao	三合庙	46	2 C
Long Shan Tang Temple	龙山堂	111	1 A
Loyang Tua Pek Kong Tp	洛阳大伯公宫	74	1 A
Man Fatt Lam Budh Tp	万佛林	94	1 D
Mangala Vihara BudhTp	曼加拉维哈拉庙	113	2 A
Meow Im Kok Yuen Tp	妙音觉苑	90	1 D
Mun Sun Fook	土地庙	112	1 A
Tuck Chee Temple			
Nam Ann Siang Theon Tp	南安善堂	69	2 D
Nam Hong Siang Theon Tp	南凤善堂	13	2 C
Nan Hai Fei Lai Temple	南海飞来寺	112	2 A
Nan Hai Temple	南海寺	89	1 D
Nanyang Thong Hong	南洋同奉善堂	49	1 A
Siang Thng Tp			
Pai Hai Sheng Mu Fa Miao	排海圣母母法庙	67	1 D
Palelai Buddhist Temple	巴利莱佛堂	94	1 C
Pao Kwan Foh Tang Tp	宝光佛堂	67	1 D
Phang Pheng Mei Tp	飞霞精舍	89	1 D
Phoh Teck Siang Tng Tp	普德善堂	130	1 C
Phok Kiu Siang Tng Tp	普救善堂	69	2 B
Phou Tai Kok Temple	普提阁	84	2 A
Po Chiak Keng Temple	保赤宫	132	2 A
(Tan Si Chong Su Tp)	(陈氏宗祠)		
Poh Chung Tian	普忠殿助善堂	89	1 C
Chor Sian Tong Temple			
Poh Jay Temple	普济寺	114	1 A
Poh Meng Tse Temple	普明寺	86	2 D
Poh Tiong Kiong Temple	锦江秤寺	112	2 A
Poo Thor Jee Temple	普陀寺	132	2 C
Potong Pasir Joint	波东巴西联合庙	68	1 B
Temples Association			
Pu Ti Buddhist Temple	菩提佛院	49	1 C
Puat Jit Buddhist Temple	普济佛堂	49	1 A
Qi Tian Gong Temple	齐天宫	132	1 C
Qi Tian Tan Temple	齐天坛	131	1 C
Qing De Gong Temple	清德宫	110	2 A
Qing De Tang Temple	清德堂	89	1 D
Qing Yun Combined Tp	青云联合庙	69	2 D
Sakya Muni	释加牟尼菩提迦耶寺	111	1 A
Buddha Gaya Temple			
Sakya Tenphel Ling Tp	释加寺	73	2 A
San Jiang Gong Ci Tp	三江公祠	131	1 C
San Lian Deng Tp	新莲灯庙	2	2 C
Sattha Puchaniyaram	功德林佛寺	62	1 D
Buddhist Temple			
See Thian Foh	西天佛联合庙	84	1 A
Combined Temple			
Seh Ong Charity	闽王氏宗祠	83	2 A
Sembawang God of	三巴旺财神庙	2	2 C
Wealth Tp			
Seng Ong Temple	城隍庙	91	1 D
Seng Wong Beo Temple	都城隍庙	132	2 C
Seu Teck Sean Tong	修德善堂联心社	93	1 C
Yian Sin Sia Temple			
Shan Fook Tong Temple	善福堂	112	1 B
Shang Di Miao	山帝庙济公坛	11	1 B
Chai Kong Temple			
Sheng Hong Temple	城隍庙	83	2 D
Sheng Jia Temple	圣迦庙	50	1 A
Sheng Leng Temple	圣龙庙	61	1 D
Shuang Lin	双林城隍庙	89	1 C
Cheng Huang Tp			
Shui Xian Temple	水显宫	132	1 A
Sian Keng Tong Temple	仙宫堂	113	2 A
Sian Teck Tng Temple	善德堂	110	1 C
Siang Cho Keong Temple	凤山寺	132	2 C
Sim Choon Huat Temple	沈春发庙	89	2 D
Sim Poh Seng Temple	香莲寺	113	2 B
"S'pore Budh Lodge, The"	佛教居士林	110	1 D
S'pore Budh Youth Mission	佛教青年团	84	1 D
S'pore Han Clan Tp	韩氏祠	110	2 A
Soon Leng Temple	顺龙庙	41	1 B
(Choa Chu Kang	(蔡厝港油池村联合庙)		
Yew Tee Chun Lian He Miow)			
Soon Thian Keing Temple	顺天宫	112	2 A
Swee Kwan Kuan Temple	水沟馆庙	46	2 C
Tai Kak Seah Temple	大觉寺	114	1 B
Tai Pei Yuen Temple	大悲阮	89	1 D
Tai Yeong Kon Temple	太阳宫	131	2 C
Tain Chor Temple	天祖庙	2	1 D
Tampines Chinese Tp	淡滨尼庙	73	1 C
Tan Kong Tian Temple	圆福殿	107	1 A
Tang Gah Beo Temple	东狱庙	131	2 D
Tee Kwee Hood Sia Tp	知归佛社	115	2 A
Teng San Tian Hock Tp	镇山天福宫	69	1 A
Thai Buddhist Temple		131	2 C
Thai Good News Ctr	泰人喜讯中心	111	2 C
(Golden Mile Complex)	(黄金地带购物中心)		
The Mahaprajna Buddhist	马哈布拉纳教会	112	2 A
Society			

PLACES		MAP	GRID	PLACES		MAP	GRID
Thekchen Choling (Singapore)	大乘禅寺	111	2 B	All Saints Chapel	万圣教堂	69	2 B
Thian Hock Keng Temple	天福宫	132	2 C	All Saints Church	诸圣堂	93	2 C
Thian Ling Chong Toh Tong Temple	天灵总道堂	114	1 A	Amazing Grace Presby Ch	神奇恩典堂	115	2 B
Thomson Temple	汤申庙	67	1 C	Ang Mo Kio Gospel Hall (Chinese Assembly)	宏茂桥福音堂 (Bethesda Hall AMK)	46	1 D
Thong Teck Sian Tong Lian Sin Sia Tp	同德善堂念心社	88	2 D	Ang Mo Kio Methodist Ch	宏茂桥卫理教堂	67	1 A
Tian De Temple	天德庙	70	1 B	Ang Mo Kio Presby Ch	宏茂桥长老会堂	46	2 C
Tian Gong Miao	天公庙	130	2 D	Apostolic Ch of S'pore (Guilin Bldg)	Apostolic教会 (桂林大厦)	112	2 A
Tian Kong Buddhist Tp	天降佛堂	94	1 B	Armenian Church	亚米尼亚教堂	132	2 A
Tian Kong Temple	天空庙	72	1 A	Ascension Church	圣公会荣升堂	89	2 C
Tian Leong Keng Temple	天龙宫	67	2 C	Assembly of Christians of S'pore, 'The'	新加坡基督徒聚会所	69	1 B
Tien Seng Tua Temple	天圣坛	91	1 C	Barker Rd Methodist Ch	巴克路卫理教堂	110	1 A
Tioh Hin Cho Temple	重兴祖庙	113	2 A	Bartley Christian Ch (Bartley Rd)	巴特礼基督教堂 (巴特礼路)	90	2 A
Tiong Ghee Temple	忠义庙	130	2 A	Bedok Lutheran Church	勿洛路德教堂	93	2 D
Toa Payoh Seu Teck Sean Tong Temple	大巴窑修德善堂	89	1 B	Bedok Methodist Church	勿洛卫理教堂	94	1 D
Tong Heng Kang Ah Hood Kampong Sin Huay Tp	五合庙	89	1 B	Berean Assembly of God Church (Guilin Building)	卫理神召会列利安堂 (桂林大厦)	112	2 A
Tong Tien Kung Temple	东天宫	83	2 A	Bethany Emmanuel Missions	列惠以玛内利教堂	113	2 B
Tong Whye Temple	南天门	61	2 D	Bethany Evangelical Free Church	贝特尼福音教堂	114	2 A
Tong Sian Ting Temple	同善堂	110	1 C	Bethany Independent Presbyterian Church	长老会贝特尼独立教会	90	1 D
Tse Tho Aum Temple	自度庵	67	1 B	Bethany Presbyterian Ch	长老会贝特尼堂	69	2 D
Tua Pek Kong Tp (Bukit Timah)	大伯公宫 (武吉知马)	84	2 A	Bethel Assembly of God Church S'pore	新加坡神召会 贝特利堂	90	1 D
Tua Pek Kong Tp (Pulau Ubin)	大伯公宫 (乌敏岛)	34	1 D	Bethel Presbyterian Ch	长老会伯特堂	89	2 A
Tua Pek Kong Tp (Woodlands)	大伯公宫 (兀兰)	23	1 D	Bethesda (Bedok-Tampines) Ch	勿洛-淡滨尼)	93	1 C
Tui San Temple	翠上庵	81	2 A	Bethesda (Katong) Church	贝特斯达教会(加东)	113	2 B
Uttamayanmuni Budh Tp	乌他玛雅慕尼佛庙	41	2 D	Bethesda Cathedral	优诺福音堂	92	2 C
Wan Li Lian He Dian Tp	万礼联合殿	12	1 A	Bethesda Chapel	贝特斯达堂	92	1 D
Wei Tuo Fa Gong Temple	韦陀法宫	33	2 C	Bethesda Church	贝特斯达礼堂	68	2 D
Wei Zhen Miao	威镇庙	132	1 B	Bethesda Frankel Estate Church	富兰克福音堂	114	2 A
Wu Cao Da Bo Gong Gong Temple	梧槽大伯公宫	89	1 D	Bethesda Hall (Ang Mo Kio)	贝特斯达礼堂(红茂桥)	46	1 D
Wu Lui Sien Sze Temple	五雷宫	83	2 A	Bethesda Pasir Ris Mission Church	宜道福音堂	73	2 A
Wu Tai Shan Budh Tp	五台山佛堂	106	1 C	Bethesda Serangoon Ch	贝特斯达实龙岗教堂	69	2 C
Yan Kit Village Chinese Tp	寅吉村庙	74	1 B	Bethlehem Bible Presbyterian Church	长老会贝特能圣经教堂	87	1 D
Yishun Town Combined Tp	义顺镇联合庙	14	2 C	Blessed Sacrament Church	圣体堂	108	1 D
Yu Huang Tian Combined Tp	玉皇殿联合庙	60	1 D	Breakthrough Mission	突破教会	129	2 C
Yu Huang Zhi Zun Tp	玉皇至尊庙	112	2 A	Bukit Batok Presbyterian Church	长老会武吉巴督堂	62	1 D
Yuan Ming Si Temple	圆明寺	116	1 A	Bukit Panjang Gospel Chapel	武吉班让福音堂	42	1 D
Yueh Hai Ching Temple	粤海清庙	132	2 B	Bukit Panjang Methodist Church	武吉班让卫理教堂	63	2 B
Yun Shan Temple	云山宫	86	1 D	Cairnhill Methodist Church (Cairnhill Gardens)	经禧卫理教堂 (经禧园)	110	1 D
Zeh Shing Keong Temple	七星宫	67	1 C				
Zhen Ren Gong Temple	真龙宫	131	1 B	Calvary Assembly of God Church	加略神召会	115	2 A
Zhong Yi Tian Ming Tp	忠义天明庙	48	1 D	Calvary Baptist Church	加略浸信教会	90	1 C
Zi Yun Kai Ji Kong Tp	紫云开吉宫	70	1 C	Calvary Jurong Bible Presbyterian Church	裕廊基督教哥信	82	1 B
Zu-Lin Temple	竹林庙	62	2 A	Calvary Tengah Bible Presbyterian Church	登加基督教笃信	39	2 C
Zumang Kalyud Buddhist Ctr	朱孟迦育佛教中心	112	2 B		圣经长老会加略堂		

CHURCHES 教堂

Abundant Grace Presbyterian Church	长老会恩典教堂	48	1 A				
Adam Rd Presbyterian Ctr	长老会亚当路中心	87	1 C				
Agape Baptist Church (East Asia Sch of Theology)	艾格浸信会 (东亚神学院)	110	2 B				
Aldersgate Methodist Ch	亚德阁卫理教堂	107	2 C				

PLACES		MAP GRID	
Calvary Pandan Bible Presbyterian Church	加略班丹圣经长老会教堂	83	1 D
Carmelite Monastery	卡马奈修道院	131	2 C
Cathedral of the Good Shepherd	善牧主教大教堂	111	1 D
Catholic Church of Christ the King	耶稣君王堂	68	1 B
Catholic Church of Saint Francis Xavier	圣芳济天主教堂	68	2 C
Catholic Church of Saint Ignatius	圣依纳爵堂	108	2 A
Cemetery Chapel	坟场教堂	38	2 D
Central Christian Church	中央基督教堂	31	1 D
Centre of Light Church (Tailee Building)	光明中心教会 (德利大厦)	67	2 D
Changi Baptist Church	樟宜浸信教会	74	2 B
Changi Bethany Church	樟宜伯大尼堂	94	2 A
Changi Chapel (& Museum)	樟宜教堂(及博物馆)	74	2 B
Changi Methodist Church (Association Building)	卫理公会樟宜堂 (联合大厦)	112	2 B
Chapel of Christ the King	基督君王堂	110	2 C
Chapel of Christ the Redeemer	基督救赎堂	72	2 D
Chapel of the Holy Spirit	圣灵堂教会	89	2 B
Charis Assembly of God Church	卫理神召会特利堂	89	2 A
Charis Methodist Church	卫理公会颂恩堂	113	2 B
"Charis Tabernacle Church, The"	卫理圣经教堂	113	1 B
Chen Li Presbyterian Ch	长老会基督教真理堂	112	2 B
Chen Lien Bible Seminary	金链灵修神学院	113	1 B
Chinese Seventh-Day Adventist Church	基督教复临安息日会重生堂	88	2 D
Choa Chu Kang Bible Ctr	蔡厝港圣经中心	41	1 A
Christ Methodist Church	基督卫理教堂	114	1 B
Christian Assembly	基督迦南会	110	2 C
Christian Canaan Church	基督迦南堂	89	2 D
Christian Community Chapel	基督社区教堂	131	1 D
"Church in S'pore, The"	新加坡教会	110	2 A
Church in Singapore (Christian Stewards)	新加坡教会 (基督监护会)	128	2 A
Church of Christ (Bedok)	基督教会(勿洛)	92	1 C
Church of Christ (Jurong)	基督教会(裕廊)	81	2 A
Church of Christ (Moulmein Road)	基督教会(摩绵)	110	2 A
Church of Christ (Pasir Panjang)	基督教会(巴西班让)	129	1 A
Church of Christ of Malaya	马来亚基督教会	110	2 C
Church of God	基督神召会	94	1 D
Church of God (S)	基督神召会(新)	131	1 A
"Church of Jesus Christ of Latter-Day Saints, The"	耶稣基督末世圣徒教会	110	1 A
Church of Our Lady of Lourdes	露德圣母堂	111	1 C
Church of Our Lady of Perpetual Succour	永援圣母堂	114	2 A
Church of Our Lady Queen of Peace	和平之后堂	113	1 B
Church of Our Lady Star of the Sea	海星圣母堂	14	1 C
Church of Our Saviour	救主堂	108	1 D
Church of Sacred Heart	圣心堂	110	2 D
Church of Saint Anthony of Padua	圣安东尼天主堂	11	1 D
Church of Saint Bernadette	圣伯纳德堂	109	2 D
Church of Saint Francis of Assisi	圣芳济亚西西堂	60	2 D
Church of Saint Joseph	圣若瑟教堂	63	2 A
Church of Saint Mary of the Angels	天使之后堂	63	1 D
Church of Saint Michael	圣弥额尔堂	89	2 D
Church of Saints Peter & Paul	圣伯多禄圣保禄堂	111	1 D
Church of Saint Vincent de Paul	圣文生堂	48	1 C
Church of Singapore (Bt Timah)	新加坡教会 (武吉知马)	85	1 A
Church of Singapore (Marine Parade)	新加坡教会 (马林百列)	113	2 C
Church of Singapore (Woodlands Point)	新加坡教会 (兀兰岭)	10	2 B
Church of St. Stephen	圣斯德望堂	90	2 C
Church of St. Teresa	圣德肋撒堂	131	2 D
Ch of the Assemblies of God of S'pore (Guilin Bldg)	新加坡神召总会 (桂林大厦)	112	2 A
Church of the Good Shepherd	圣公会善牧堂	111	1 D
Church of the Holy Cross	圣十字架教堂	106	2 B
Church of the Holy Family Katong	圣家堂	113	2 C
Church of the Holy Spirit	圣神堂	67	1 C
Church of the Holy Trinity	天主圣三堂	73	1 D
Church of the Messiah (Peninsula Shopping Ctr)	弥赛亚堂 (半岛购物中心)	132	2 A
Ch of the Nativity of The Blessed Virgin Mary	圣母圣诞堂	49	2 D
Church of the Resurrected Living Christ (S'pore Gospel Church)	耶稣重生堂 (新加坡福音教会)	112	1 D
Church of the Risen Christ	耶稣复活堂	89	1 B
Church of the True Light	真光堂	111	1 C
City Harvest Church	城市丰收教会	80	2 A
Clementi Bible Centre	金文泰圣经中心	106	1 C
Community of Praise Baptist Church (West Coast Recreation Ctr)	赞美浸信教会 (西海岸消闲中心)	106	2 B
Cornerstone Community Church (Odeon Katong Shopping Ctr)	基石社区教会 (奥迪安加东购物中心)	113	2 C
Coronation Baptist Church	加冕浸信教会	112	2 B
Covenant Community Baptist Church (The S'pore Baptist Ch)	圣约社区浸信教堂 (新加坡浸信教会)	110	2 B

PLACES		MAP GRID
Covenant Community Methodist Church	圣约社区卫理教会	85 1 C
Covenant Evangelical Ch	圣约播道会	42 2 B
Covenant Evangelical Ch	圣约播道会	12 1 D
"Crystal Tabernacle Church, The"	水晶教堂	129 1 A
Danish Seaman's Church	丹麦教堂	131 1 D
East Asia Sch of Theology	东亚神学院	110 2 B
Ebenezer Chapel	依本乃哲教堂	109 1 C
Elim Church	依灵教堂	89 2 D
"Emmanuel Assembly of God Church, The"	以马内利神召会	115 1 A
Emmanuel Ch of S'pore (Association Building)	新加坡以马内利教会 (联合大厦)	112 2 B
Emmanuel Evangelical Ch	以玛内利播道会	129 1 B
Emmaus Baptist Church (Selegie House)	以马斯教堂 (实利基大厦)	110 2 C
Epiphany Church	阿风尼教堂	29 1 D
Eternal Life Assembly	神召会永生堂	85 1 A
Eternal Life Baptist Ch (Kim Keat Rd)	永生浸信教会 (金吉路)	89 1 D
Evangel Family Church	福音家庭教会	14 2 D
Faith Assembly of God Ch	信召会信心堂	89 1 D
Faith Bible - Presbyterian Church	笃信圣经长老会忠心堂	68 2 A
Faith Community Baptist Church (Touch Centre)	坚信浸信教会 (触爱中心)	113 2 C
Faith Methodist Church	思珍堂	108 1 C
Faith Sanctuary	信心之殿堂	112 1 B
First Evangelical Reformed Church	第一福音悔改教会	46 1 C
"Fisherman of Christ Fellowship, The (Queenstown)"	基督教渔人团契 (女皇镇)	108 2 D
Foochow Methodist Ch	福灵堂	111 1 B
"Free Christian Church of S'pore, The"	新加坡耶稣教自立会	110 2 C
Galilee Bible Presbyterian Church	长老会加利里圣经教会	83 1 D
Geylang Chinese Methodist Church	基督教卫理公会芽笼堂	112 2 A
Glad Tidings Church	佳音礼拜堂	70 1 B
Glory Presbyterian Church	长老会荣耀堂	85 1 B
Goodnews Baptist Church (RELC Bldg)	喜讯浸信教会 (区域语言中心)	109 2 B
Gospel Light Christian Ch	福音之光基督教会	87 2 D
Grace (S'pore Chinese Christian Church)	怀恩堂 (新加坡华人基督教会)	111 1 D
Grace Assembly of God Ch	神召会恩典堂	
- (Tanglin)	东陵	109 1 D
- (Bt Batok)	武吉巴督	62 2 B
Grace Baptist Church	恩典浸信堂	90 2 D
Grace Bible Presbyterian Church	长老会恩典圣经堂	116 1 A
Grace Independent Baptist Church	恩典自主浸信教会	94 2 B
Grace Methodist Church	恩典堂	131 1 D
Grace Redeemed Church (Guilin Bldg)	恩典赎救教会 (桂林大厦)	112 2 A
Harvester Baptist Church	收割者浸信会	90 1 A
Hebron Bible - Presbyterian Church (CCK Bible Centre)	笃信圣经长老会希伯仑堂	41 1 A
Hephzibah Christian Fellowship	合喜悦基督团契	130 2 A
Herald Assembly of God (Wing Fong Bldg)	神召会禧信堂 (永丰大厦)	112 1 B
Hing Hwa Methodist Ch	兴化天道堂	111 1 B
His Sanctuary Services	神的圣殿	111 1 A
Holy Covenant Meth Ch	卫理公会盟约堂	131 1 D
Immaculate Heart of Mary Church	圣母无玷圣心堂	69 1 C
International Baptist Church (King's Rd)	国际浸信教会 (京士路)	108 2 A
International Baptist Church (Furama Hotel)	国际浸信教会 (富丽华酒店)	132 1 A
Jesus Lives Church (Bible House)	耶稣复活堂 (圣经大厦)	132 1 A
Jubilee Assembly of God (Bible House)	神召会蒙恩堂 (圣经大厦)	132 1 A
"Jubilee Presby Ch, The"	禧年堂	132 1 B
Jurong Christian Church	裕廊基督教会	82 1 B
Kampong Kapor Methodist Church	甘榜加卜卫理公会	111 1 B
Katong Presbyterian Ch	长老会加东教会	113 2 B
Kay Poh Road Baptist Ch	基博浸信教会	109 2 D
Kim Keat Christian Ch	金吉基督教会	89 2 D
Kim Tian Christian Ch	金殿基督教会	69 2 C
Korean Church in S'pore	新加坡韩国人教会	88 1 D
Kum Yan Methodist Ch	Kum Yan卫理教堂	111 1 D
Leng Kwang Bapist Ch	灵光浸信教会	109 1 A
Life Bible Presby Ch	笃信圣经长老会生命堂	110 1 A
Light of Christ City Ch	基督之光城市教会	111 1 B
Lighthouse Baptist Ch (Townshend Bldg)	灯塔浸信教会 (陶胜大厦)	111 1 B
Lighthouse Evangelism	灯塔福音会	72 1 D
Living Hope Methodist Ch	活望卫理教堂	73 2 D
Living Praise Presby Ch	赞生教堂	68 1 D
Living Sanctuary Brethren Church	圣殿福音教会	70 1 C
Lutheran Church	信义会救主堂	86 2 D
Maranatha Baptist Ch	马兰纳德浸信教会	13 2 D
Maranatha Bible Presby Ch (St. George's Chapel)	马兰纳德笃信圣经长老会教堂 (圣乔治教堂)	53 2 A
Marine Parade Chr Ctr	马林百烈基督教中心	113 2 B
Methodist Church of the Incarnation, "The"	卫理公会道生堂	41 2 C
Moriah Bible-Presby Ch	笃信圣经长老会摩利亚堂	94 2 A
Mount Calvary Baptist Ch	加略山浸信教会	112 2 B
Mount Gerizim Bible Presbyterian Church (Choa Chu Kang Bible Ctr)	基利心圣经长老会 (蔡厝港圣经中心)	41 1 A
Mount Hermon Bible- Presbyterian Church (Choa Chu Kang Bible Ctr)	西山堂 (蔡厝港圣经中心)	41 1 A
My Saviour's Church	救世主教堂	131 2 A

PLACES		MAP GRID		PLACES		MAP GRID	
Nativity Church Centre	耐迪维迪教堂中心	70	1 A	Singapore Bible	新加坡圣经浸信会	128	2 A
Nazareth Bible-	长老会那萨拉教堂	128	2 A	Baptist Church			
Presbyterian Church				Singapore Bible College	新加坡圣经堂	87	1 D
Neighbourhood	亲邻基督教会	89	2 A	Singapore Gospel Church	新加坡福音堂	112	1 D
Christian Church				Singapore Hakka	新加坡客音堂	110	1 A
New Life Bible	长老会新生圣经教堂	11	1 A	Methodist Church	卫理公会客音天恩堂		
Presbyterian Church				Singapore Life Presby Ch	长老会新加坡生命教会	111	1 C
Newlife Church	新生命堂	112	2 B	"S'pore Thomson Rd	新加坡汤申路浸信堂	110	2 A
(Association Bldg)	(联合大厦)			Baptist Church, The"			
Newton Life Church	纽顿生命堂	110	1 A	Sion Christian Church	基督教锡安堂	113	2 B
Norweigian	挪威海员基督团契	129	1 B	Sisters of the Infant	圣婴姐妹堂	60	2 D
Seamen's Mission				of Jesus Church			
Novena Church	圣葳风索堂	88	2 D	Smyrna Assembly of God	士每拿教会	14	1 D
Orchard Presbyterian Ch	长老会乌节乌节礼拜堂	110	2 D	Spiritual Grace Presby Ch	长老会恩典圣灵教堂	26	1 C
Parish of Christ Church	基督教区教堂	110	2 B	St. Andrew's Catheral	圣安德烈教堂	133	1 A
Pasir Panjang Christ Ch	巴班让基督教堂	129	1 A	St. Andrew's Chapel	圣安德烈堂	3	2 D
Pasir Panjang Hill	巴班让	129	2 B	St. Anne's Church	圣安妮堂	49	2 D
Brethren Chapel	山贝特能教堂			St. Francis Xavier	圣芳济大神学院	30	2 B
Pasir Panjang Tamil	巴班让	131	1 D	Major Seminary			
Methodist Church	淡米尔卫理教堂			St. Francis Xavier	圣芳济小神学院	49	2 D
Paya Lebar Chinese	巴耶利巴卫理公会	90	2 A	Minor Seminary			
Methodist Church				St. George's Church	圣乔治教堂	109	1 C
Paya Lebar Methodist Ch	巴耶利巴卫理教堂	69	1 D	(Tanglin)	(东陵)		
Pentecost Methodist Ch	卫理公会五旬节堂	73	2 A	St. Hilda's Church	圣公会圣希达堂	113	2 C
Pentecostal Ch of S'pore	新加坡班特彻可基督教堂	88	2 C	St. James Church	圣雅各堂	108	1 B
"People's Bible Ch, The"	人民圣经教堂	69	2 D	St. John's Chapel	圣约翰堂	108	2 A
Pilgrim Covenant Church	朝圣教堂	132	2 B	(Farrer Road)	(花拉路)		
(Int'l Factors Bldg)				St. John's Chapel	圣约翰堂	90	1 B
Praise Evangelical Church	赞美福音教堂	13	2 B	(Wan Tho Ave)	(运涛道)		
Prinsep Street Presby Ch	布连拾街长老会盘石堂	111	1 C	St. John's-Saint	圣约翰	107	1 C
Queenstown Baptist Ch	女皇镇浸信教会	108	2 D	Margaret's Church	圣玛格烈教堂		
Queenstown Lutheran Ch	女皇镇基督教信义会	108	1 C	St. Joseph's Church	圣若瑟教堂	111	1 D
Revival Centre Church	复兴中心教堂	110	2 A	(Victoria Street)	(维多利亚街)		
Riverlife Church	江河生命堂	52	2 D	St. Matthew's Church	圣马太堂	132	1 B
"Salvation Army Balestier	救世军马里士他团部	89	1 D	St. Paul's Church	圣保罗教堂	69	2 C
Corps, The"				St. Peter's Church	圣彼得教堂	68	2 A
"Salvation Army	救世军总部及	67	2 B	St. Thomas Orthodox	圣汤姆正	46	1 D
Command Headquarter	中央团部			Syrian Cathedral	统叙利亚堂		
S'pore Ctr Corps, The"				Tai Seng Christian Church	大成基督教堂	69	1 C
"Salvation Army Kallang	救世军加冷巴鲁团部	111	2 A	Tamil Methodist Church	淡米尔卫理公会教堂	110	2 C
Bahru Corps, The"				Telok Ayer	卫理公会礼拜堂	132	2 C
"Salvation Army Pasir	救世军巴西班让团部	129	1 A	Chinese Methodist Ch			
Panjang Corps, The"				Telok Ayer	直落亚逸卫理堂	131	1 D
Sembawang Baptist Ch	三巴旺浸信教堂	45	2 D	Chinese Methodist Ch	(第二圣堂)		
Sembawang Presby Ch	长老会三巴旺教堂	13	2 B	(TA2 Sanctuary)			
Sengkang Meth Church	盛港卫理教堂	48	2 B	The Bible Church S'pore	新加坡圣经教堂	106	1 C
Seventh-Day Adventist Ch	基督复临安息日会	111	1 A	(Clementi Bible Centre)	(金文泰圣经中心)		
(Balestier)	(马里士他)			The Harvest Force	收割团教会	132	2 A
Seventh-Day Adventist Ch	基督复临安息日会	83	1 B	(River Valley Rd)	(里巴巴利大厦)		
(Jurong East)	(裕廊东)			Titular Roman Catholic	帝道拉科曼天主教堂	51	1 C
Seventh-Day Adventist Ch	基督复临安息日会	113	2 B	Church			
(Maranatha)	(马兰他)			Toa Payoh Methodist Ch	大巴窑卫理公会礼拜堂	88	2 B
Shalom Bible-Presby Ch	长老会沙龙圣经教堂	52	2 D	Toong Chai Presby Ch	长老会同才教堂	113	2 C
(Loyang)	(罗央)			Trinity Christian Church	三一基督教堂	87	1 C
Shalom Baptist Chapel	沙龙浸信教会	39	2 D	Trinity Methodist Church	三一卫理公会堂	68	2 D
Shalom Church S'pore	新加坡沙龙教会	90	2 A	True Jesus Church	真耶稣教会	87	1 D
(LHK Bldg)	(LHK大厦)			(Adam Rd)	(亚当路)		
"S'pore Baptist Ch, The"	新加坡浸信教堂	110	2 B				
S'pore Baptist Convention	新加坡浸信教联会	110	2 A				
(Goldhill Plaza)	(金岭商场)						

PLACES		MAP	GRID
True Jesus Church	真耶稣教会	113	2 A
(Lorong H Telok Kurau)	(直落古楼H巷)		
True Way Presby Ch	基督长老会正道堂	130	2 A
Wesley Methodist Church	卫理公会卫斯理教堂	110	2 D
Woodlands Evangelical Free Church	基督教兀兰播道会	11	2 B
Yio Chu Kang Chapel	杨厝港教堂	69	1 A
Yishun Christian Church (Lutheran / Anglican)	义顺基督教会 (信义会 / 圣公会)	13	2 D
Zion Bible-Presby Ch (Bishan Street 13)	锡安圣经长老会教堂 (碧山13街)	68	1 D
Zion Bible-Presby Ctr (Tavistock Avenue)	笃信圣经长老会 (协恩堂(达维士道道)	68	2 A
Zion Full Gospel Church	锡安全拥福音教会	109	2 D
Zion Presbyterian Church	中华基督教 长老会锡安堂	94	1 B

HINDU TEMPLES 印度教庙宇

Arulmigu Velmurugan Gnana Muneeswarar Tp	阿鲁米古兴都都教庙	50	1 B
Arya Samaj	阿雅沙玛兴教庙	111	1 B
Holy Tree Sri Balasubramaniar Tp	圣树巴拉素巴曼尼亚庙	14	1 B
Nagore Durgha (Shrine)	纳哥德卡殿	132	2 C
Shree Lakshminarayanan Tp	拉萨米那炎米都庙	111	1 B
Sree Maha Mariamman Tp (Yishun)	义顺兴都庙	26	2 A
Sree Ramar Temple (Changi)	拉玛兴都庙	54	1 B
Sree Veeramuthu Muneeswaran Temple	维拉慕都 曼尼斯华拉庙	14	1 B
Sri Arasakesari Tp	阿拉沙克沙里西凡庙	22	2 C
Sri Arulmigu Murugan Tp	阿鲁密古慕鲁根庙	83	1 A
Sri Darma Muneeswaran Tp	达玛慕尼斯哇然庙	69	1 A
Sri Krishnan Tp	克里斯那庙	111	1 D
Sri Krishna Mandir Tp	斯里克里斯纳庙	111	1 D
Sri Layan Sithi Vinayagar Tp	莱亚西迪维纳雅加庙	132	2 C
Sri Manmatha Karuneshwarar Tp	曼玛达克鲁尼瓦拉庙	111	2 B
Sri Mariamman Temple	马里安曼庙	132	2 B
Sri Muneeswaran Temple	曼尼哇拉庙	108	1 D
Sri Murugan Hill Temple	慕鲁根山庙	42	1 D
Sri Ruthra Kaliamman Tp	鲁拉卡里曼庙	131	1 C
Sri Senpaga Vinayagar Tp	圣帕加维那雅加庙	113	2 C
Sri Sivadurga Temple	西瓦米都庙	89	2 C
Sri Siva Krishna Temple	西瓦克里斯那庙	11	1 B
Sri Sivan Temple	西瓦兴都庙	112	2 A
Sri Srinivasa Perumal Tp	实里尼维沙伯鲁玛庙	111	1 A
Sri Thendayuthapani Tp	丹达乌他帕尼庙	110	2 D
Sri Vadapathira Kaliamman Temple	维拉巴蒂拉卡拉曼庙	111	1 A
Sri Vairavimada Kaliamman Temple	维拉温马达卡拉曼庙	89	1 B
Sri Veerama Kaliamman Temple	维拉马卡卡拉曼庙	111	1 B

MOSQUES 回教堂

Masjid Abdul Aleem Sidique	阿都亚林西迪回教堂	114	1 B
Masjid Abdul Gafoor	阿都卡夫回教堂	111	1 C
Masjid Abdul Hamid	阿都哈米回教堂	110	1 A
Masjid Abdul Razak	阿都拉萨回教堂	91	2 D
Masjid Ahmad	阿末回教堂	129	2 C
Masjid Ahmad Ibrahim	阿末依布拉欣回教堂	26	1 C
Masjid Al-Abrar	阿布拉回教堂	132	2 C
Masjid Al-Amin	阿敏回教堂	131	1 C
Masjid Al-Ansar	安沙回教堂	92	2 C
Masjid Al-Falah	法拉回教堂	110	1 C
Masjid Al-Firdaus	费道斯回教堂	39	2 D
Masjid Al-Huda	胡达回教堂	86	1 B
Masjid Al-Iman	阿依曼回教堂	42	2 D
Masjid Al-Istighfar	依斯迪法回教堂	73	2 A
Masjid Alkaff (Upp Serangoon)	阿卡夫回教堂 (实龙岗上段)	90	1 B
Masjid Alkaff Kampong Melayu	马来甘榜阿卡夫 回教堂	92	1 B
Masjid Al-Khair	阿尔凯回教堂	41	2 C
Masjid Al-Istiqamah	依斯迪阿马回教堂	69	1 A
Masjid Al-Mukminin	穆敏宁回教堂	83	2 A
Masjid Al-Muttaqin	慕达金回教堂	67	2 A
Masjid Al-Taqua	阿达哇回教堂	94	1 D
Masjid Angullia	安古利亚回教堂	111	1 B
Masjid An-Nahdhah	安纳达达回教堂	68	1 C
Masjid An-Nur	安努尔回教堂	10	2 B
Masjid Ar-Raudhah	阿劳哈回教堂	62	2 D
Masjid Assyafaah	阿沙法回教堂	3	1 C
Masjid Assyakirin	亚细安吉林回教堂	82	1 B
Masjid Baalwie	阿尔维回教堂	109	1 A
Masjid Bencoolen	明古连回教堂	110	2 D
Masjid Burhani (Dawoodi Bohra)	本罕尼回教堂 (达兀迪波拉)	132	2 A
Masjid Darul Aman	达鲁阿曼回教堂	113	2 A
Masjid Darul Ghufran	达鲁法法兰回教堂	72	2 C
Masjid Darul Makmur	达鲁马慕回教堂	14	1 C
Masjid Darussalam	达鲁沙南回教堂	106	2 B
Masjid En-Naeem	那依恩回教堂	70	1 B
Masjid Haji Mohd Salleh	莫哈末沙礼回教堂	112	1 B
Masjid Haji Muhd Salleh	哈芝莫哈末礼回教堂	132	2 D
Masjid Haji Yusoff	哈芝尤索夫回教堂	69	2 C
Masjid Hajjah Fatimah	哈查花蒂玛回教堂	111	2 C
Masjid Hajjah Rahimabi	哈悉拉欣马比回教堂	89	1 C
Masjid Hang Jebat	汉杰巴回教堂	130	1 C
Masjid Hasanah	哈山纳回教堂	83	1 D
Masjid Hussein Sulaiman	胡申苏来曼回教堂	128	2 A
Masjid Jamae (Chulia)	詹美回教堂	132	2 C
Masjid Jamak (Queenstown)	詹美回教堂 (女皇镇)	131	1 A
Masjid Jamiyah Ar-Rabitah	杰米亚拉比达回教堂	131	1 A
Masjid Kampong Delta	甘榜立达回教堂	131	2 A
Masjid Kampong Holland	甘榜荷兰回教堂	107	2 B
Masjid Kampong Siglap	甘榜实乞纳回教堂	115	1 B
Masjid Kassim	卡欣回教堂	114	1 A
Masjid Khadijah	卡迪杰回教堂	112	2 A
Masjid Khalid	卡立回教堂	113	2 B

PLACES		MAP GRID
Masjid Malabar	马拉巴回教堂	111 1 C
Masjid Moulana Md Ali	莫兰那莫哈末 阿里回教堂	132 2 B
Masjid Muhajirin	穆哈芝林回教堂	89 1 A
Masjid Mujahidin	穆扎希丁回教堂	108 1 D
Masjid Mydin	迈丁回教堂	92 1 D
Masjid Omar Kampong Melaka	甘榜马六甲 回教堂	132 2 A
Masjid Omar Salmah	奥马沙马回教堂	88 1 B
Masjid Petempatan	三巴旺柏淡巴当	4 2 C
Melayu Sembawang	回教堂	
Masjid Pulau Bukom (P. Bukom)	毛广岛回教堂	148 __
Masjid Pusara Aman	布沙拉安曼回教堂	38 2 D
Masjid Sallim Mattar	沙林马达回教堂	90 2 D
Masjid Sultan	苏丹回教堂	111 1 C
Masjid Surau Pusara Aman	布沙拉安曼小回教堂	38 2 C
Masjid Tasek Utara	达西乌达拉回教堂	110 2 B
Masjid Temenggong Daeng Ibrahim (State of Johor Masjid)	天猛公德恩依布拉欣 (柔佛州回教堂)	142 2 A
Masjid Tentera Di-Raja	登德拉迪拉杰回教堂	106 2 D
Masjid Wak Tanjong	华丹绒回教堂	113 1 A

SIKH GURDWARAS 锡克庙

Central Sikh Gurdwara	中央锡克庙	111 2 A
Gurdwara Bhai Maharaj Singh	巴海马哈礼星庙	132 1 C
Gurdwara Sahib Yishun	义顺锡克庙	27 1 B
Khalsa Dharmak Sabha	卡沙达马沙哈锡克庙	110 2 C
Pardesi Khalsa Dharmak Diwan	巴德西卡沙达马迪万庙	112 2 A
Silat Road Sikh Gurdwara	石叻路锡克庙	132 1 C
Sri Guru Nanak Satsang Sabha	古鲁纳那沙胜沙哈庙	113 1 C
Sri Guru Singh Sabha	古鲁新锡克庙	110 2 C

SYNAGOGUES 犹太教堂

Chesed-El Synagogue	圣诺犹太教堂	110 2 D
Maghain Aboth Synagogue	马海阿布犹太教堂	111 1 D

PLACES		MAP GRID

POLICE ORGANISATIONS / UNITS

Airport Police Division	机场警署	95 2 A
Alexandra Hospital Police Post	亚历山大医院警岗	130 1 B
Alexandra NPP	亚历山大邻里警岗	108 1 D
Aljunied NPP	阿裕尼邻里警岗	90 2 B
Ang Mo Kio North NPC	宏茂桥北邻里警局	46 2 C
Ang Mo Kio Police Divisional Hq	宏茂桥警署	46 2 C
Ang Mo Kio South NPC	宏茂桥南邻里警局	68 1 A
Arms & Explosives Branch (Cantonment Cplx)	武器与炸药组 (广东民大厦)	132 1 C
Ayer Rajah NPP	亚逸拉惹邻里警岗	83 1 D
Bedok NPP	勿洛邻里警岗	93 1 D
Bedok Police Divisional Hq	勿洛警署	93 2 C
Bedok North NPC	勿洛北邻里警局	93 2 C
Bedok South NPC	勿洛南邻里警局	92 2 D
Bishan NPC	碧山邻里警局	67 2 C
Bishan NPP	碧山邻里警岗	68 1 A
Boon Lay NPP	文礼邻里警岗	60 2 D
Boon Teck NPP	文德邻里警岗	88 2 A
Bt Batok NPC	武吉巴督邻里警局	63 1 D
Bt Batok NPP	武吉巴督邻里警岗	62 2 D
Bt Merah East NPC	红山东邻里警局	132 1 C
Bt Merah West NPC	红山西邻里警局	131 2 B
Bt Panjang North NPP	武吉班让北邻里警岗	10 2 B
Bt Panjang NPC	武吉班让邻里警局	42 2 B
Bt Panjang South NPP	武吉班让南邻里警岗	42 2 D
Bt Timah NPC	武吉知马邻里警局	86 2 D
Bt Timah NPP	武吉知马邻里警岗	84 2 A
Buona Vista NPP	波那维斯达邻里警岗	107 2 B
Cairnhill NPP	经禧邻里警岗	111 1 A
Cantonment Cplx	广东民大厦	132 1 C
Ctrl Narcotics Bureau (Cantonment Cplx)	中央肃毒局 (广东民大厦)	132 1 C
Ctrl Police Division Hq (Cantonment Cplx Blk A)	中央警署 (广东民大厦第A座)	132 1 C
Chai Chee NPP	菜市邻里警岗	92 2 D
Changi Airport Police Cargo Pass Office	樟宜机场警察 准证处	54 2 C
Changi NPC	樟宜邻里警局	94 2 A
Changkat NPP	尚育邻里警岗	73 1 D
Choa Chu Kang NPC	蔡厝港邻里警局	41 1 A
Choa Chu Kang NPP	蔡厝港邻里警岗	41 1 D
Chong Pang NPP	忠邦邻里警岗	13 2 D
Clementi Police Div Hq	金文泰区警署	106 2 A
Clementi NPC	金文泰邻里警局	106 2 A
Clementi NPP	金文泰邻里警岗	106 1 B
Commercial Affairs Dept (Cantonment Cplx Blk D)	商业事务局 (广东民大厦第D座)	132 1 C
Commonwealth NPP	联邦邻里警岗	108 1 C
Criminal Investigation Dept (Cantonment Cplx Blk C)	刑事侦查局 (广东民大厦第C座)	132 1 C
Dover NPP	杜佛邻里警岗	107 1 C
ECP Police Post & Lifeguard Stn	东海岸公园大道警岗 与救生站	114 1 C
Eunos NPP	友诺士邻里警岗	92 1 B
Geylang NPC	芽笼邻里警局	91 1 D

PLACES		MAP	GRID
Geylang Serai NPP	芽笼士乃邻里警岗	90	2 D
Geylang West NPP	芽笼西区邻里警岗	112	2 A
Gurkha Contingent	辜加部队	90	2 B
HomeTeam Academy	内政团队学院	40	1 D
HomeTeamNS	内政团队战备人员协会		
Ah Hood Rd Club House	亚佛路俱乐部	88	2 C
Bt Batok Club House & Adventure Ctr	武吉巴督俱乐部及探险中心	62	2 B
Sembawang Resort	三巴旺度假村	3	1 C
Smith St Club House	史密斯街俱乐部	132	2 B
UE Square Club House	友乃德广场俱乐部	132	2 A
Hong Kah North NPP	丰加北邻里警岗	62	2 B
Hong Kah South NPP	丰加南邻里警岗	61	1 D
Hougang NPC	后港邻里警局	48	2 D
Hougang NPP	后港邻里警岗	49	2 D
Internal Security Dept (New Phoenix Park)	内部安全局 (新凤凰园)	88	2 D
Joo Chiat NPP	如切邻里警岗	113	2 B
Jurong East NPC	裕廊东邻里警局	83	1 A
Jurong NPP	裕廊邻里警岗	82	1 C
Jurong Police Divisional Hq	裕廊警署	60	1 D
Jurong West NPC	裕廊西邻里警局	60	2 D
Kaki Bukit NPP	加基武吉邻里警岗	93	1 B
Kallang NPP	加冷邻里警岗	89	2 D
Kampong Glam NPP	甘榜格南邻里警岗	111	2 C
Kampong Java NPC	甘榜爪哇邻里警局	110	2 B
Kampong Kembangan NPP	甘榜景万岸邻里警岗	92	1 D
Kampong Ubi NPP	甘榜乌美邻里警岗	91	2 C
Kebun Baru NPP	哥本巴鲁邻里警岗	67	1 A
Kim Keat NPP	金吉邻里警岗	89	1 B
Kim Seng NPP	金声邻里警岗	131	2 A
Kolam Ayer NPP	哥南亚逸邻里警岗	90	1 D
Kreta Ayer NPP	牛车水邻里警岗	132	2 B
Licensing Div (Cantonment Cplx)	执照组 (广东民大厦)	132	1 C
Macpherson NPP	麦波申邻里警岗	90	2 D
Marine Parade NPC	马林百列邻里警局	114	1 C
Marine Parade NPP	马林百列邻里警岗	113	2 C
Marsiling NPP	马西岭邻里警岗	11	1 B
Moulmein NPP	摩绵邻里警岗	89	1 C
Mountbatten NPP	蒙巴登邻里警岗	112	2 B
Nanyang EPP	南洋附属警岗	80	2 A
Nanyang NPC	南洋邻里警局	60	1 D
National University Hospital Police Post	国大医院警岗	129	1 A
Nee Soon South NPP	义顺南邻里警岗	27	1 A
Orchard NPC	乌节邻里警局	110	1 D
Pasir Panjang NPP	巴西班让邻里警岗	129	2 C
Pasir Ris NPC	巴西立邻里警局	73	2 A
Paya Lebar NPP	巴耶利巴邻里警岗	70	1 D
Police Coast Guard	警察海岸卫队		
- HQ (Pulau Brani)	总部(布拉尼岛)	143	1 B
- Gul Base	卡尔基地	101	2 B
- Lim Chu Kang Base	林厝港基地	7	1 A
- Loyang Base	罗央基地	53	1 B
Police Hqrs (New Phoenix Park)	警察总部 (新凤凰园)	88	2 D
Police Intelligence Dept (New Phoenix Park)	警察情报局 (新凤凰园)	88	2 D
Police K-9 Unit	警犬组	41	1 A
Police KINS Training Ctr	警察KINS训练中心	84	2 D
Police Logistics Dept (New Phoenix Park)	警察后勤局 (新凤凰园)	88	2 D
Police Nat'l Service Dept	国民服役警察局	88	1 C
Police Public Affairs Dept (New Phoenix Park)	警察公共事务局 (新凤凰园)	88	2 D
Police Radio Div (New Phoenix Park)	警察无线电署 (新凤凰园)	88	2 D
Police Security Command	警察安全指挥部	88	2 B
Police Special Operations Command	警察特别行动组	108	1 D
Police Tactical Training Camp	警察战术训练营	23	1 C
Police Training Command (HomeTeam Academy)	警察训练指挥部 (内政团队学院)	40	1 D
Police Welfare Div (Cantonment Cplx)	警察福利署 (广东民大厦)	132	1 C
Potong Pasir NPP	波东巴西邻里警岗	89	2 B
Pulau Ubin Police Post	乌敏岛警岗	34	1 D
Queenstown NPC	女皇镇邻里警局	130	1 A
Radin Mas NPP	拉丁马士邻里警岗	131	1 C
River Valley NPP	里巴巴利邻里警岗	131	2 A
Rochor NPC	梧槽邻里警局	111	1 B
Sembawang NPC	三巴旺邻里警局	13	1 A
Sengkang NPC	盛港邻里警局	49	1 A
Serangoon Gdns NPP	实龙岗花园邻里警岗	68	2 B
Serangoon North NPP	实龙岗北邻里警岗	69	1 D
Serangoon NPC	实龙岗邻里警局	69	1 D
SGH Police Post, A & E Dept (Blk 1)	新加坡中央医院警岗 (大牌1号)	132	1 C
Siglap NPP	实乞纳邻里警岗	115	1 A
Tampines East NPP	淡滨尼东邻里警岗	73	1 D
Tampines North NPP	淡滨尼北邻里警岗	73	2 C
Tampines NPC	淡滨尼邻里警局	93	2 A
Tanah Merah NPP	丹那美拉邻里警岗	93	1 D
Tanglin Police Divisional Hq	东陵警署	110	2 B
Tanjong Pagar NPP	丹戎巴葛邻里警岗	131	2 C
Teck Ghee NPP	德义邻里警岗	67	2 B
Telok Blangah NPP	直落布兰雅邻里警岗	130	1 D
Thomson NPP	汤申路邻里警岗	67	1 C
Tiong Bahru NPP	中巴鲁邻里警岗	131	2 B
Toa Payoh NPC	大巴窑邻里警局	88	2 D
Traffic Police Dept	交通警察局	91	1 C
Tuas JOC Police Stn	大士联合行动中心警局	56	2 D
Ulu Pandan NPP	乌鲁班丹邻里警岗	107	2 B
Volunteer Special Constabulary Hq (Blk C Cantonment Cplx)	志愿特警总部 (第C座广东民大厦)	132	1 C
West Coast NPP	西海岸邻里警岗	106	1 C
Whampoa NPP	黄埔邻里警岗	89	1 D
Whitley NPP	惠德礼邻里警岗	87	2 D
Woodlands NPC	兀兰邻里警局	12	1 D
Woodlands JOC Police Station (Causeway)	兀兰联合行动 (长堤)	10	2 A
Yishun North NPC	义顺北邻里警局	14	1 D
Yishun South NPC	义顺南邻里警局	27	1 B

PLACES		MAP GRID	PLACES		MAP GRID

POST OFFICES / PHILATELIC COUNTERS -MARKED WITH ★

Place	中文		
Alexandra P.O.	亚历山大	131	1 A
Ang Mo Kio Ctrl P.O	宏茂桥中路	67	2 A
Balestier Est P.O.	马里士他住宅区	89	1 D
Bedok Ctrl P.O.	勿洛中路	93	1 C
Bras Basah P.O.	勿拉士峇沙	111	1 D
Bukit Batok Ctrl P.O.	武吉巴督中路	62	2 D
Bukit Merah Ctrl P.O.	红山中路	131	1 B
Bukit Panjang P.O.	武吉班让	42	1 C
Bukit Timah P.O.	武吉知马	86	1 C
Change Alley P.O.	真者里	133	1 B
Changi Airport P.O.	樟宜机场	★ 75	1 C
Chinatown Pt P.O.	唐城坊	★ 132	2 B
Choa Chu Kang Ctrl P.O.	蔡厝港中路	41	1 C
Clementi Ctrl P.O.	金文泰中路	106	1 A
Clementi West P.O.	金文泰西	106	1 C
Covent Gdn P.O.	哥文园	132	1 A
Crawford P.O.	哥罗福	111	2 C
Geylang East P.O.	芽笼东	90	2 D
Geylang P.O.	芽笼	112	2 D
Ghim Moh Est P.O.	锦茂住宅区	107	2 B
HarbourFront Ctr P.O.	港湾中心	142	1 A
Hougang Ctrl P.O.	后港中路	70	1 A
IMM P.O.	国际商品批发中心	83	2 B
Jurong Pt P.O.	裕廊坊	★ 81	1 A
Jurong West P.O.	裕廊西	61	1 D
Katong P.O.	加东	113	1 C
Kent Ridge P.O.	肯特岗	106	2 D
Killiney Rd P.O.	基里尼路	★ 110	1 D
Kitchener Rd P.O.	吉真那路	111	1 B
Lim An Pin Rd P.O.	林业炳路	70	1 D
Lucky Plaza P.O.	幸运中心	110	1 C
Macpherson Rd P.O.	麦波申路	90	1 C
Marine Parade P.O.	马林百列	113	2 C
Newton P.O.	纽顿	110	2 B
Novena P.O.	诺维娜	110	1 D
Orchard P.O.	乌节	110	1 C
Pasir Panjang P.O.	巴西班让	128	2 A
Pasir Ris Ctrl P.O.	巴西立中路	52	1 D
Robinson Rd P.O.	罗敏申路	★ 132	2 C
Rochor P.O.	梧槽	111	1 C
Sengkang Central P.O.	盛港中路	49	1 B
Serangoon Ctrl P.O.	实龙岗中路	69	1 C
Serangoon Gdn P.O.	实龙岗花园	68	2 B
Siglap P.O.	实乞纳	115	1 B
Simpang Bedok P.O.	新邦勿洛	94	1 C
S'pore Post Ctr	新加坡邮政中心	★ 113	1 A
Sun Plaza P.O.	太阳大厦	13	1 A
Suntec City P.O.	新达城	133	1 A
Tampines Ctrl P.O.	淡滨尼中路	72	2 D
Tanglin Halt P.O.	东陵福	108	1 D
Tanglin P.O.	东陵	★ 109	2 C
Tanjong Pagar P.O.	丹戎巴葛	132	2 C
Teban Gdn P.O.	德曼花园	83	1 D
Telok Blangah East P.O.	直落布兰雅东	131	1 C
Thomson Rd P.O.	汤申路	★ 67	1 D
Tiong Bahru P.O.	中巴鲁	131	2 B
Toa Payoh Ctrl P. O.	大巴窑中路	★ 88	2 C
Toa Payoh Nth P. O.	大巴窑北	88	2 A
Towner P.O.	陶纳	111	2 A
Upper Serangoon Rd P.O	实龙岗路上段	69	2 C
Woodlands Central P.O.	兀兰中路	★ 11	2 C
Yishun Ctrl P.O.	义顺中	14	1 D

PRISONS / DRUG REHABILITATION CENTRES

Place	中文		
Admiralty West Prison	海军部西路监狱	1	1 D
Changi Prison Complex	樟宜监狱	74	1 C
Changi Women's Prison	樟宜女子监狱	74	1 B
Kaki Bukit Ctr (Prison Sch)	加基武吉中心(监狱学校)	92	1 B
Khalsa Crescent (Prison)	卡沙弯弯戒毒改造所	1	1 D
Lloyd Leas Work Release Camp	菜益园工作假释营	74	2 A
Portsdown Centre	波斯陶监狱	107	2 C
Prison Dept HQ	新加坡监狱署总部	74	2 A
Prison Digital Media Unit	监狱数字媒体组	74	2 A
Prison Link Centre	监狱联系中心	74	1 C
Prison Logistics Branch	监狱后勤组	74	2 A
Prison Transport Unit	监狱运输组	74	2 A
Prisons Staff Training Sch	监狱职员训练学院	4	1 D
Queenstown Remand Prison	女皇镇拘候监狱	108	2 D
Selarang Pk DRC	史拉兰园戒毒改造所	74	2 A
Sembawang (DRC)	三巴旺 (戒毒改造所)	3	2 C
Tanah Merah Prison	丹那美拉监狱	74	2 B

PRIVATE HOUSING / CONDOS / APARTMENTS

Place	中文		
1 Holt Road	1号贺德路	109	2 D
1 King Albert Pk	1号阿尔柏王园	85	1 B
1 Moulmein Rise	1号摩绵坡	110	2 A
2 rvg	2号rvg	110	1 D
3 Balmoral	3号百慕乐	109	2 B
6B OGR	6B OGR公寓	109	2 B
7 Claymore Rd	7号克雷摩路	109	2 B
7 Draycott Drive	7号德雷葛通道	109	2 B
8 Hullet Rd	8号合乐路	110	1 C
8 Lincoln Rd	8号林肯路	110	2 A
8 @ Mt. Sophia	8号苏菲雅山	110	2 C
8 Napier	8号纳比雅	109	1 C
8 Orange Grove	8号桔林	109	2 B
10 Leedon	10号Leedon	108	1 B
11 Amber	11号安珀	113	2 D
18 Ardmore	18号雅茂	109	2 B
19 Shelford Rd	19号赐福路	86	2 D
24 @ Newton	纽顿24号	110	2 A
28 Shelford	28号赐福	86	2 C
31 Balmoral	31号百慕乐	109	2 A
78 Gilstead	78号吉士德	110	2 A
90 Holland Road	90号荷兰路	108	1 B
Aalto	雅都	113	1 D
Abelia	艾贝利亚园	109	2 B
Acacia Lodge	艾凯萨苑	83	2 B
Accord Apartments	雅阁公寓	112	1 B
Adam Pk	雅登苑	87	1 C
Adam Pl	亚当坊	87	1 B
Adelphi Hill Gdn	亚达菲山花园	66	2 C
Adelphi Pk Est	亚达菲园住宅区	66	2 C
Advance Apt	先进公寓	112	2 A
Affluence Apt	雅美伦阁	69	2 D
Airview Twrs	风景楼	110	1 D
Aldea Blanca	雅迪邦阁	115	2 A
Alegria	爱丽格雅	88	1 D

PLACES		MAP	GRID
Alessandrea	亚历珊丽	131	2 A
Alexandra Hts	亚历山大岭	131	1 A
Allsworth Pk	奥斯华园	107	1 A
Alocassia Apts	雅罗凯萨公寓	109	2 A
Alpha	雅发公寓	113	2 B
Alwyn Pk	雅威园	69	1 B
Amaninda	雅曼丽达园	88	1 D
Amanusa	安曼娜莎	46	1 C
Amaranda Gdn	紫馨园	68	2 D
Amaryllis Ville	嘉丽苑	110	1 A
Amber Glades	安柏林园	113	2 C
Amber Glory	安柏楼	112	1 B
Amber Pk	安柏园	113	2 D
Amber Pt	安柏坊	113	2 D
Amber Residences	安柏居	113	2 C
Amber Twrs	安柏大楼	113	1 D
Ampas Apts	安柏斯公寓	89	1 D
Amsterdam Apt	阿姆斯特丹公寓	85	1 D
Anderson 18	安徒生18号	109	2 B
Anderson Grn	安徒生林	109	2 B
Angsana Pk	空中花园	64	1 D
Angullia Mans	安而乐公寓	109	2 C
Angullia View	安哥烈景	109	2 C
Apt 8	8号公寓	89	2 C
Apex Harmony Lodge	艾柏计安乐居	74	1 A
Apollo Gdn	阿波罗花园	94	2 B
Appleton View		110	2 A
Aquarine Gdns	雅桂林园	115	1 B
Aquarius By The Pk	丽泽苑	93	2 B
Aquene	雅郡	114	1 A
Ardisia Gdns	雅迪舍花园	69	1 D
Ardmore II	雅茂II	109	2 B
Ardmore Pk Luxury Apts	雅茂园	109	2 B
Ardmore Pt	雅茂峰	109	2 B
Arizona Ville	雅宗村	69	1 D
Armadale	雅美典园	110	1 A
Arthur 118	雅瑟118	112	2 D
Arthur Ct	亚瑟阁	112	2 D
Arthur Mans	亚瑟大厦	112	2 D
Arwaa Man	Arwaa Man大厦	109	1 B
Ascott (Raffles Place)	爱士阁(莱佛士坊)	133	1 B
Ashley Grn	爱诗里林	85	2 D
Asia Gdns	亚洲花园	132	1 C
Asimont Gdn	爱思梦园	110	1 A
Aspen Hts	爱诗苑	110	1 A
Aspen Loft	白杨楼	113	2 A
Aston Lodge	艾诗敦苑	112	1 B
Aston Mans	翠丽园	113	1 B
Aston Residence	艾诗敦居	52	2 C
Astor	雅林苑	92	1 C
Astor Grn	雅德林	107	1 A
Astoria Apts	埃斯托里雅公寓	110	1 B
Astoria Pk	雅士花园	92	1 D
Astrid Meadows	爱士特苑	108	1 A
Astridville	爱士特别墅	86	1 D
Atrium Residences	雅念居	112	2 B
Au-Jiang Apt	区江公寓	89	2 C
Aura Pk	奥拉园	108	2 B
Austral View	南景园	112	2 D
Ava Twr	爱雅园	89	1 D
Avalon	雅菲伦园	109	2 B
Avenue Pk	林荫道园	85	2 C
Avenue Villa	林荫道别墅	86	1 C
Avila Gdns	阿维拉花园	74	1 B

PLACES		MAP	GRID
Avila Ter	阿维拉岭	74	1 B
Avon Pk	雅丰苑	90	1 B
Axis@Siglap	威菲花园	114	2 B
Azalea Pk	雅萨列园	74	1 C
Bagnall Ct	百纳阁	116	1 A
Balestier 288	马里士他288	89	1 D
Balestier Cplx	百利购物商场	89	1 D
Balestier Ct	马里士他阁	88	2 C
Balestier Plaza	马里士他大厦	89	1 D
Balestier Pt	马里士他坊	89	1 D
Balestier Regency	马里士他丽苑	89	1 D
Balestier Twrs	马里士他楼	89	1 D
Ballota Pk	美如画花园	74	1 C
Balmeg Ct	宝美阁	129	1 B
Balmoral	百慕乐	109	2 B
Balmoral 2	百慕乐2	110	1 A
Balmoral 8	百慕乐8	110	1 A
Balmoral Condo	百慕乐共管式公寓	110	1 A
Balmoral Crest	百慕乐峰	110	1 A
Balmoral Gdns	百慕乐园	109	2 A
Balmoral Gate	百慕乐门	110	1 A
Balmoral Grove	百慕乐园林	110	1 A
Balmoral Hill	百慕乐山	109	2 A
Balmoral Hts	百慕乐岭	110	1 A
Balmoral Lodge	百慕乐苑	110	1 B
Balmoral Pl	百慕乐坊	110	1 A
Balmoral Residences	百慕乐公寓	110	1 A
Balmoral Twr	百慕乐楼	110	1 A
Balmy Ct	宝美阁	112	2 B
Bamboo Grove Pk	竹林园	63	1 C
Ban Guan Pk	万源园	85	2 D
Banyan Condo	榕林公寓	129	2 C
Banyan Pk	榕林园	129	2 C
Banyan Villas	榕林别墅	46	1 B
Baode Bldg	宝德大厦	113	1 A
Barossa Gdns	芭萝园	129	1 C
Bartley Gr Apts	百丽苑	90	1 A
Bartley Ter	巴特丽台	90	1 A
Bartley Villas	葩萝别墅	90	1 A
Bassein Ct	百幸阁	88	2 D
Bayshore Pk	碧湾园	115	2 B
Bayville Condo	柏园	129	2 B
Baywater	碧水苑	93	1 B
Beachfront Collection	海滨之珍	146	2 A
Beacon Heights	信标岭	89	2 D
Beaufort on Nassim	博福特那森	109	2 B
Beauty Gdn	美丽花园	49	2 B
Beauty World Plaza	美世界购物中心	85	1 A
Beaverton Ct	美维数阁	107	1 A
Bedok Ct	勿洛阁	93	2 D
Bedok Grove	勿洛山庄	94	1 D
Bedok Pk	勿洛园	94	1 D
Bedok Ria	勿洛丽雅	94	1 D
Bedokville	美都园	94	1 D
Beechwood Ter	碧丽林台	11	1 D
Belgravia Pk	丽雅园	47	2 C
Bella Vista	美拉景	90	1 A
Belle Vue	豪景园	110	2 A
Bellerive	贝雅莱	109	2 A
Bellezza @ Katong	加东贝拉宅	113	2 C
Belmond Green	百蒙园	110	1 A
Belmondo View	贝蒙多景	89	1 D
Belmont Gdns	贝蒙园	108	1 D
Belmont Hse	贝蒙屋	108	1 A

• PRIVATE HOUSING / CONDOS / APARTMENTS

PLACES		MAP GRID	PLACES		MAP GRID
Beta Grove	贝他林	114 1 B	Butterworth 8	家丽园8	113 1 B
Beulah	贝乐楼	113 2 A	Butterworth 33	家丽园33	113 1 B
Beverly Hill	比华丽岭	109 2 D	Butterworth View	家丽苑	113 1 B
Beverly Mai	梅园	109 2 C	Cactus Bloom	仙人掌苑	47 1 B
Beverly Pk	柏丽花园	69 2 B	Cactus Grn	仙人掌林	47 1 B
Bin Tong Pk	民东园	108 1 A	Cadence Light	凯登之光	114 1 B
Binjai Crest	明才峰	85 2 A	Cai Gdn	财园	92 1 C
Binjai Pk	明才园	85 2 A	Cairnhill Crest	经禧峰	110 1 C
Birchwood Mans	桦木园	89 1 D	Cairnhill Hts	经禧岭	110 1 B
Birmingham Mansions	柏明亨大厦	110 2 A	Cairnhill Man	经禧楼	110 1 B
Bishan 8	碧山豪园	67 2 D	Cairnhill Plaza	经禧大厦	110 1 C
Bishan Loft	碧山楼	68 1 D	Cairnhill Residences	经禧居	110 1 B
Bishan Pk Condo	碧山花园	67 1 B	Cairnhill Twrs	经禧园	110 1 B
Bishan Pt	碧山坊	67 1 C	Calarasi	嘉乐园	89 1 D
Bishops Wk	主教径	109 2 D	Caldecott Hill Est	加利谷山住宅区	88 1 B
Bleu at East Coast	东海岸蓝楼	115 2 B	Calin Mans	卡林大厦	112 2 A
Bliss Regalia	极乐丽嘉楼	111 1 A	Calisay	卡立沙	69 2 D
Bliss Residences	幸福居	114 1 A	Camay Ct	佳美阁	114 1 B
Blissful View	乐天园	108 1 B	Cambridge Village	剑桥村	110 2 B
Blossoms	富胜	89 2 B	Camden Pk	甘登园	87 1 C
Blossom Mans	富胜园	113 1 A	Camelia Lodge	敏黎苑	112 2 A
Blossom View	富胜景	112 2 B	Camellia Pk	佳丽园	47 1 B
Blue Horizon	蓝贺来胜楼	106 1 D	Camelot	佳莱丽苑	112 1 D
BLU Coral	蓝珊瑚	114 1 B	Camwood Pk	甘木园	108 2 A
Bluwaters	蓝水楼	52 2 C	Canary Pk	金丝雀园	94 1 C
Bluwaters 2	蓝水楼 2	52 2 C	Canary Ville	金丝雀山庄	114 1 A
Boon Lay Gdns	文礼园	60 2 D	Canberlin Apartments	康伯灵公寓	112 2 A
Boon Teck Apt	文德公寓	89 1 D	Canberlin Lodge	康伯灵苑	112 1 B
Boon Teck Lodge	文德苑	89 1 D	Candence Light	肯登之光	114 1 B
Boon Teck Twr	文德大厦	88 2 C	Candeville	肯德维尔	114 1 A
Boon Teck View	文德景	88 2 D	Cannaville	卡纳山庄	113 2 B
Boon View	文景楼	67 2 D	Canne Lodge	纤苑	112 1 A
Botanic Gdns Man	植物园楼	109 1 B	Canne Ville	纤居	112 1 B
Botanic Gdns View	植物园景	109 1 B	Cantiz@Rambai	兰排Cantiz公寓	113 2 B
Botanika	Botanika公寓	108 2 B	Carabelle	Carabelle公寓	105 2 A
Botannia	Botannia公寓	105 2 A	Cardiff Ct	卡迪夫阁	68 2 C
Bougainvilla Apts	蔓华阁	112 2 B	Carribean At Keppel Bay	发巴湾加拉勒比村	142 1 A
Boulevard Vue	林荫园	109 2 C	Carissa Pk	佳丽莎花园	74 1 C
Bournemouth Eight	波茂士8	113 1 C	Carlisle Ct	卡莱阁	110 2 B
Braddell Hts Est	布莱德村	68 2 D	Carlton Ter	卡尔顿排屋	108 2 B
Braddell Pk	百丽园	90 1 A	Carlyx Gdn	克丽园	110 2 B
Braddell Regalia	布莱德丽嘉园	89 1 D	Carlyx Residence	克丽居	110 2 B
Braddell Rise Est	布莱德坡村	88 2 A	Carmi Man	卡美大厦	112 2 A
Braddell View	布莱德景	88 1 A	Carpmael Lodge	佳明园	113 1 A
Breeze by the East	东风楼	115 2 B	Casa Aroma	卡莎雅乐门	113 2 B
Breezeway In Katong	加东风道	113 2 C	Casa Cairnhill	卡莎经禧	110 1 B
Breezy Man	风临门	69 1 B	Casa Contendere	卡莎肯特里	110 1 A
Brighton View	布莱顿景	69 1 B	Casa Emerald	卡莎伊玛拉	112 2 B
Brightview Apts	明景公寓	112 2 B	Casa Espania	卡莎艾斯斑雅	90 1 A
Bristol Lodge	布里斯托楼	110 2 B	Casa Esperanza	卡莎埃斯珀兰莎	85 1 B
Brizay Pk	布里赛园	85 2 C	Casa Fidelio	卡莎弗德里奥	114 2 A
Brookvale Pk	翠湖园	84 2 C	Casa Flora	卡莎佛拉	94 1 D
Buckley 18	巴克丽18号	110 1 A	Casa Irrawaddy	卡莎依拉瓦迪	88 2 D
Buckley Man	巴克丽楼	110 1 A	Casa Jervois	卡莎泽维士	109 1 D
Buckley Mews	巴克丽苑	110 1 A	Casa Melwani	卡莎美瓦尼	110 2 A
Buckley Residence	百吉利居	110 1 A	Casa Merah	卡莎美拉	94 1 C
Bukit Gdn Est	武吉园村	86 1 D	Casa Meya	卡莎美雅	89 2 C
Bukit Regency	武吉丽晶园	63 1 D	Casa Meyfort	卡莎美耀特	113 1 D
Bukit Timah Mans	武吉知马大楼	110 1 A	Casa Novacrest	卡莎诺麦宅	110 1 B
Bukit View	武吉景	85 1 A	Casa Pasir Ris	卡莎巴西立	52 2 C
Bukit Villas	骏景花园	22 2 B	Casa Perla	卡莎柏特	86 2 C
Bullion Pk	金湖山庄	46 1 B	Casa Riviera	卡莎河滨坊	69 1 C
Buona Lodge	波那苑	129 2 B	Casa Rosa Condo	卡莎罗沙公寓	90 2 A
Buona Vista Gdns	波那维丝达花园	129 2 B	Casa Sarina	卡莎沙丽娜	91 2 D
Burgundy Hill	柏雅丽山庄	84 1 B			
Burlington Residences	柏林登居	111 1 C			

PLACES		MAP GRID		PLACES		MAP GRID	
Casa Sophia	卡莎苏菲亚	110	2 C	Chapel Mans	教堂大厦	113	2 C
Casa Uno	卡莎文诺	109	2 A	Char Yong Gdns	茶阳花园	110	1 C
Casabella	卡莎贝拉	86	1 D	Charis Lodge	陈氏苑	128	2 A
Casablanca	卡沙布兰加园	11	2 D	Charisma View	彩丽景	84	2 A
Casafina	凯丰园	115	1 A	Charles Ville	查尔斯山庄	69	2 D
Cascadale	卡莎德里	94	2 A	Charleston	查尔斯顿苑	109	2 D
Cascata	凯斯卡达	92	1 C	Charlton Corner	佳登角	69	2 C
Casero @ Dunman	德阳凯胜楼	113	1 B	Charlton Ct	佳登阁	69	2 C
Cashew Gdns	凯秀花园	63	2 A	Charlton Pk	爵枫园	69	2 C
Cashew Hts	凯秀岭	42	2 D	Charlton Villas	爵敦别墅	69	2 C
Cashew Hill	凯秀山	63	2 A	Charming Gdns	嘉铭花园	108	1 A
Cashew Pk Condo	凯秀园共管式公寓	63	2 A	Chateau Eliza	伊丽莎山庄	110	1 B
Cashew Villas	凯秀别墅	63	2 A	Chateau La Salle	乐莎堡	114	2 A
Cassia View	诗雅苑	112	2 B	Chateau Le Fame	名人山庄	109	2 A
Castle Ct	嘉城阁	114	1 A	Chatelet Condo	渡假公寓	109	2 A
Castle Grn	嘉城林	46	2 B	Chelsea Gdns	彩丽园	109	2 B
Casuarina Cove Condo	家园湾	112	1 D	Chelsea Grove	乔西林	89	1 D
Cathay Gdns	国泰花园	114	2 B	Chelsea Lodge	彩丽苑	113	1 C
Cavenagh Ct	嘉文纳阁	110	2 B	Chen Jing Jue Mans	陈静觉大厦	69	1 B
Cavenagh Fortuna	福慧苑	110	1 C	Cheng Soon Gdn	正顺园	84	2 B
Cavenagh Gdns	嘉文纳大厦	110	1 C	Cherry Gdns	绮鲤苑	69	2 D
Cavenagh Hse	嘉文纳楼	110	1 B	Cherryhill	查理山	69	2 D
Cavenagh Lodge	嘉文纳苑	110	1 C	Chester Pk	策士特园	129	2 B
Cavenagh Mans	嘉文纳园	110	1 C	Chestervale	芊桦园	43	1 D
Cavendish Pk	加文迪花园	107	1 A	Chestnut Ave Apts	策士纳道公寓	64	1 A
Cedarwood Grove	雪松林	11	1 D	Chestnut Green	策士纳林	63	2 A
Celadon View	翠峰景	52	2 D	Chestnut Ville I	爵士那1园	63	2 A
Celestia	色丽胜雅	113	2 A	Chestnut Ville II	爵士那2园	63	2 A
Centennia Suites	百年盛贺	132	1 A	Chia Gdn	谢氏花园	114	1 B
Central	中央梭贺	132	2 A	Chiang's Ct	蒋阁	115	1 B
Central Grn Condo	中央绿	131	2 B	Chiku Mans	世古大厦	113	2 C
Central Grove	百裕景	112	2 A	Chiltern Pk	翠登苑	68	2 D
Central Meadows	中央美乐	112	2 B	Chin Bee Man	振美大厦	113	2 C
Central Place	百裕坊	48	2 D	Chinatown Plaza/Apts	唐城大厦 / 公寓	132	2 C
Central Square/Apts	市中广场 / 公寓	132	2 A	Chip Bee Gdns	集美苑园	108	1 B
Central View	市景园	69	2 D	Chip Hock Gdns	集福花园	87	1 D
Centrepoint Apts	先得坊公寓	110	1 C	Chiverton	Chiverton公寓	109	2 A
Centro Mans	盛中楼	112	2 B	Choon Kim Hse	春金楼	69	2 C
Centurion 12	盛都隆12	67	1 C	Choon Sing Gdn	春盛花园	67	2 D
Centurion Residences	盛都隆居	90	1 C	Chuan Loft	泉厦	68	2 D
Century Mans	世纪楼	63	1 C	Chuan Pk	春景花园	68	2 D
Century Ville	世纪园	109	2 A	Chuan Seven	春景七	68	2 B
Century Woods	世纪林	11	1 D	Chuan Ter	川台	68	2 B
Ceylon Ct	锡兰阁	113	2 B	Chuan View	春景园	68	2 C
Ceylon Crest	锡兰岭	113	2 C	Chuan Villas	嘉利园	68	2 D
Ceylon Flats	锡兰居	113	2 C	Chuan Vista	泉景苑	68	2 B
				Chuan Vista II	泉景苑II	68	2 C
Chambery Mans	香柏栎苑	110	1 B	Chun Tin Ct	春田阁	84	2 A
Chancery Corner	彰思礼角	110	1 A	Chung Chin Flats	Chung Chin大楼	114	1 B
Chancery Ct	彰思礼阁	110	1 A	Chuville	朱氏山庄	129	1 C
Chancery Esquire	彰思礼绅士苑	110	1 A	Chwee Chian View	推迁景	129	2 C
Chancery Gdn	彰思礼花园	88	1 D	City Edge	City Edge公寓	110	2 A
Chancery Grove	彰思礼公寓	88	1 D	City Gate	城门	111	1 A
Chancery Lodge	彰思礼苑	88	1 D	City Lofts	City Lofts公寓	111	2 C
Chancery Pk	彰思礼园	110	1 A	City Regency	城市丽晶	89	2 D
Chancery Ville	彰思礼山庄	110	1 A	City Square Residence	城市雅居	111	1 B
Changi Cplx	樟宜大厦	94	1 C	City State Apt	城邦大厦	132	2 B
Changi Ct	樟宜阁	94	2 A	City Twrs	城市大厦	110	1 A
Changi Gdn	樟宜花园	74	1 B	City Vale	城市谷	110	2 C
Changi Gdn Condo	樟宜花园大厦	74	1 B	City View	市景楼	111	2 A
Changi Green	樟宜林	94	2 A	Citylights	城光	111	1 B
Changi Grove	樟宜林	74	1 B	Cityvista Residences	市景居	110	1 B
Changi Hts	樟宜岭	74	1 B	Claremont	奇鹏坊	110	1 D
Changi Rise	樟宜苑	73	2 D	Classical Ter	典雅台	90	1 A
Chantilly Rise	璨�园	63	1 C	Claymore Plaza Apts	克雷摩公寓	109	2 C
Chapel Ct	教堂阁	113	2 C	Claymore Pt	克雷摩楼	109	2 B
Chapel Lodge	教堂苑	113	2 B				

PLACES		MAP	GRID	PLACES		MAP	GRID
Clemenceau Apts	克里门梭公寓	110	1 B	Dalvey Ct	纳美园	87	1 D
Clementi Grn	金文泰景	84	2 D	Dalvey Villas	大威别墅	109	1 A
Clementi Park	金文泰园	84	2 C	Darby Pk	达美园	109	2 B
Clementiwoods	金文泰林	106	2 D	Dawn Ville	映霞园	113	1 B
Cliften	克立登公寓	109	2 A	D'Banyan	迪班洋公寓	13	2 B
Cliveden at Grange	格兰芝克莱大登公寓	109	2 D	D'Cambridge	剑桥楼	110	2 A
Clover Pk	高华园	67	2 D	D'Casita	迪克适达	92	1 D
Cluny Ct	古鲁尼阁	87	1 D	D'Dalvey	第大威	87	1 D
Clydes Residence	Clydes公寓	111	1 A	D'Ecosia	逸稼轩	114	1 C
Clydescove	克莱德斯科公寓	52	2 C	De Angelo	德安格罗	88	2 C
Clydesview	克莱兹景	109	1 D	De Centurion	迪胜特隆	112	2 D
Clydeswood	克莱兹林	89	2 A	Dedap Gdns	德达花园	47	2 B
Coastal Breeze	岸边迎风楼	52	2 D	De LaSalle	迪拉莎	114	1 D
Coastal View Residences	沿海景居	52	2 C	De Lente	迪兰特苑	108	1 B
Colonnade	科伦纳柱廊	109	2 D	Delfi Orchard	德辉大厦	109	2 B
Comfort Gdn	康福花园	41	2 B	Delight Ct	喜福园	112	2 A
Compass Green	盛堡林	74	2 B	Deng Fu Ville	登富园	113	2 A
Compass Hts	盛堡	49	1 B	De Paradiso	柏兰治舍	89	1 D
Compass Pt	康堡坊	49	1 B	Derby Ct	达比阁	110	2 A
Concorde	康格楼	88	2 C	Derbyshire Hts	德比郡苑	110	2 A
Concourse Residence	鸿福居	111	2 C	Derbyshire Mans	德比莎阁	110	2 A
Coral Pk	珊瑚园	67	2 C	De Royale	富贵园	88	2 C
Corona Ct	哥伦纳阁	86	1 D	D'Evelyn	丽伊芙琳	110	1 A
Corona Ville	哥伦纳庭	86	1 D	Devonshire Apts	德文沙尔公寓	110	1 D
Coronation Gdns	加冕园	86	2 D	Devonshire Lodge	德文沙尔苑	110	1 D
Coronation Grove	加冕林	86	1 D	D Flats H Park	D Flats H Park公寓	108	2 B
Coronation Plaza	加冕大厦	86	2 D	D'Focus Apts	迪焦点公寓	113	2 B
Coronation Ville	加冕林安	86	2 D	D'Fresco	如画楼	113	2 B
Costa Del Sol	旭日湾	115	2 B	D'Gallery	D'Gallery公寓	114	1 A
Costa Este	阔达苑	114	1 B	D'Grove Villas	迪林别墅	109	2 B
Coastarina	科斯达林娜	114	2 B	D'Heritage Castle	豪丽城	92	1 C
Costa Rhu Condo	禺滨园	111	2 D	D'Hillside Loft	山边公寓	129	2 B
Cosy 23	舒适23	112	2 B	D'Kenaris	D'Kenaris公寓	48	1 C
Cosy Lodge	舒怀阁	112	2 A	Diamond Twr	宝碹大厦	88	2 C
Cosy Mansion	舒适园	94	1 D	D'Lotus	D'Lotus公寓	89	1 D
Cote D Azur	优景阁	113	2 D	DLV	DLV公寓	109	2 A
Country Esquire	城乡绅士园	67	1 B	D'Manor	绿晶庄	94	1 C
Country Grandeur	富丽乡村	67	1 B	D'Marine	丽马林	113	2 C
Country Pk	城乡园	94	1 D	D'Oasia	绿洲公寓	114	1 A
Country View	乡园景	13	2 B	Domain 21	Domain 21公寓	131	2 A
Craig Place	克力坊	132	2 C	Dong Xing Ct	东光园	115	1 B
Crane Court	克兰阁	113	2 B	Dormer Pk	多尔墨园	109	1 D
Cree Ct	克利阁	109	2 A	Dorset Mans	多实大厦	110	2 B
Crescendo Pk	顶峰园	114	2 B	Dover Parkview	多福景	107	1 C
Crown Centre	皇冠中心	86	2 D	D'Palma	巴尔马公寓	114	1 A
Crystal Ct	水晶阁	131	2 A	D'Pavilion	豪亭楼	69	2 C
Crystal De Azure	蔚蓝水晶楼	90	2 A	Dragon Man	龙门大厦	132	1 C
Crystal Dew	Crystal Dew公寓	112	2 A	Draycott 8	Draycott 8公寓	109	2 B
Crystal Heights	水晶苑	129	2 B	D'Saville	萨维尔园	114	1 C
Crystal Lodge	水晶园	112	2 B	D'Sunrise	黎明公寓	113	2 B
Crystal Mans	水晶大厦	112	1 B	Dublin Lodge	杜比铃苑	110	1 D
Crystal Rhu	景湾园	112	2 D	Dublin Rd Flats	杜比铃路公寓	110	1 D
Crystal Twr	水晶大厦	109	2 A	Duchess Crest	嘉皇阁	86	1 D
Culford Gdns	高富花园	115	1 A	Duchess Gdns	大吉花园	86	1 D
Cuscaden Residence	卡斯加登居	109	2 C	Duchess Green	嘉皇林	86	2 D
Cuscaden Royale	卡斯加登皇楼	109	2 C	Duchess Manor	公爵夫人园	86	2 D
Cuscaden Wk	卡斯加登径	109	2 C	Duchess Residences	嘉皇居	86	1 D
Dakota Residences	达高轩	112	2 C	Duchess Royale	公爵夫人殿寓	86	2 D
Dahlia Pk	黛丽雅	74	1 C	Duet	瑞悦	108	2 B
Dairy Farm Est	牡丹园	63	2 B	Duke's Gdn	公爵花园	86	2 D
Daisy Apts	丽施公寓	89	2 A	Duke's Residence	公爵居	86	2 D
Daisy Lodge	丽施苑	89	2 A	Duku Ct	仁心果阁	113	2 B
Daisy Pk	丽施园	89	2 A	Dunearn Ct	杜尼安阁	86	2 D
Daisy Terrace	丽施台	89	2 A	Dunearn Est	杜尼安村	87	2 D
Dalla Vale	达拉谷	26	2 D	Dunearn Gdns	杜尼安花园	110	1 A
				Dunearn Rd Flats	杜尼安宅	86	2 D

PLACES		MAP	GRID	PLACES		MAP	GRID
Dunman Pl	德明苑	113	1 B	Emerald Lodge	绿宝石苑	110	1 C
Dunman View	德明景	113	1 B	Emerald Man	绿宝石大厦	110	1 C
Dusun Ct	都顺阁	88	2 C	Emerald Pk	绿宝石园	131	2 A
Dusun Grove	都顺林	88	2 C	Emery Point	金玉协	113	1 B
Dynasty Garden I	御花1园	85	2 D	Emily Hill	爱美丽山	110	2 C
Dynasty Garden II	御花2园	85	2 D	Emily Residence	爱美丽公寓	110	2 C
Dynasty Lodge	御苑	85	2 D	Emmanuel Hse	以玛内利大厦	112	2 A
East 25 Apts	25东公寓	112	2 A	Emprado Suites	Emprado楼房	114	1 B
East Coast Apts	东海岸公寓	114	2 A	En Fu Mans	恩福大厦	112	2 A
East Coast Hill	东海岸岭	115	2 A	Eng Apts	英公寓	112	2 A
East Coast Pk	东海园	114	2 A	Eng Aun Pk	永安园	88	2 A
East Coast Residence	东海岸居	115	2 B	Eng Hoon Man	英云大厦	132	1 B
East Cove	东湾	114	1 A	Eng Kong Grn	永康林	84	2 B
East Ct	东阁	113	2 B	Eng Say Gdn	永舍园	114	2 A
East Elegance	东雅居	113	2 A	English Villas	英文别墅	94	1 D
East Galleria	东坊	113	2 C	Equatorial Apts	赤道公寓	112	2 D
East Grv	东林楼	114	1 B	Equity Hts	平正大厦	110	2 C
East Meadows	东景园	93	2 C	Escada View	艾斯卡达景	92	1 C
East Mews	东妙	113	1 C	Espa	Espa公寓	63	2 A
East Palm	东桐	115	1 B	Espace	开明楼	114	1 B
East Point Green	东福苑	94	1 B	Espana	埃斯伯纳	88	1 D
East Shine	东曙轩	92	1 D	Espira Residence	爱士百�之居	114	1 A
East Shore Ct	东岸阁	114	1 B	Essen Apts	怡生楼	110	2 A
East Signature	东名望楼	115	1 B	Esta Ruby	东方红宝石	113	1 B
East Treasure	东宝楼	114	1 B	Estella Gdns	艾斯特拉花园	74	1 B
East View	东景	113	2 C	Estilo	Estilo公寓	110	2 C
East View Gdn	东景花园	94	2 A	Estique	Estique公寓	113	1 B
East Ville	东苑	113	2 B	Eton Ct	Eton公寓	114	1 B
Eastern Grv	东方林	93	2 D	Eunos Green	友乐林	113	2 A
Eastern Lagoon I	东湖滨1园	115	1 B	Eunos Man	友乐大厦	91	2 C
Eastern Lagoon II	东湖滨2园	115	1 B	Eunos Pk	友乐花园	113	2 A
Eastern Lodge	东方苑	112	2 A	Euphony Gdns	优芬丽园	26	1 A
Eastern Residence	东方居	113	2 A	Euro-Asia Apt	华洋楼	89	2 D
Eastern Way Man	东道大厦	69	2 D	Euro-Asia Ct	华洋阁	110	1 D
Eastpac Bldg	东太平洋大厦	88	2 D	Euro-Asia Lodge	华洋苑	113	2 A
Eastside Loft	东雅阁	113	1 B	Euro-Asia Pk	华洋公园	89	2 B
Eastvale	东桦苑	52	1 B	Evania	益万年	69	2 D
Eastwind Mans	东风大厦	113	2 A	Evelyn Mans	艾芙林大厦	110	1 A
Eastwood Grn Condo	东林苑公寓	94	1 D	Ever Lodge	长久苑	113	1 A
Eastwood Grn Ter	东林绿台	94	2 D	Evergreen Pk	青山苑	70	2 D
Eastwood Lodge	东苑	94	2 D	Evergreen Woods	青山林	64	2 D
Eastwood Pk	东林园	94	2 D	Everitt Green	艾弗烈绿园	113	2 A
Eastwood Pl	东林坊	94	2 D	Ewart Park	友和园	85	1 D
Eastwood Ter	东林台	94	2 D	Ewe Boon Regent	友文丽苑	109	2 A
Eastwood Vale	东林谷	94	2 D	Excellence Mans	俊杰大厦	112	2 A
Eastwood Ville	东林村	94	2 D	Excelsior Gdns	艾excel瑟花园	94	1 D
Eastwood Wk Gdns	东林径花园	94	2 D	Faber Crest	花柏山庄	84	1 D
Eaton Pk	伊顿园	48	1 B	Faber Gdn	花柏花园	66	2 B
Eber Gdns	艾珀园	110	1 D	Faber Hills	花柏岭	84	1 D
Ebony Mans	艾珀尼公寓	114	1 B	Faber Ter	花柏台	83	2 D
Eco Ville	Eco Ville公寓	89	1 D	Faberhills Apts	花柏岭公寓	84	1 D
Edelweiss Park	火绒查草园	74	1 C	Fairhaven	菲海苑	110	2 C
Eden Crest	伊登峰	90	1 A	Fairlodge	美花苑	108	1 B
Eden Park	伊登园	85	2 C	Fairmount Condo	美丽山公寓	94	2 D
Eden View	伊甸景	90	1 A	Fairways	唯美园	130	2 D
Edward Lee Apts	爱德华李公寓	109	2 D	Fairwood Pk	美木园	85	1 B
Ee Wang Pk	艺苑园	114	1 A	Falkland Barracks	福克兰营	3	2 C
Ek Toh Ct	艺茂阁	69	1 C	Fame Ct	名望阁	114	2 A
el Centro	el Centro公寓	132	2 C	Familie Mans	泛美大厦	112	1 B
Elias Green	怡�园	72	2 A	Fanta Gdn	华达花园	47	2 B
Elias Ter	伊丽雅台	51	2 D	Far East Plaza	远东商业中心	110	2 C
Elizabeth Hts	伊丽莎白岭	110	1 B	Far Horizon Gdns	平远花园	46	1 C
Elizabeth Twrs	伊丽莎白大厦	110	1 C	Ferraria Park	花拉丽园	74	1 C
Elmira Hts	爱美园	110	1 A	Farrer Ct	花拉阁	108	2 A
Emerald Ct	绿宝石阁	109	2 A	Fenara Ct	芬那拉阁	114	1 A
Emerald East	绿晶苑	112	2 D	Fern Lodge	芬苑	112	1 B
Emerald Gdn	翠玉园	132	2 B				

PLACES			MAP GRID		PLACES			MAP GRID	
Fernhill Cottage	苏恩楼	109	2	B	Gilstead 38	吉士德38	110	1	A
Fernhill Ct	苏恩岭阁	109	2	A	Gilstead Apts	吉士德阁	110	1	A
Fernhill Lodge	苏恩岭苑	109	2	B	Gilstead Brooks	吉士德河楼	110	1	A
Fernwood Twrs	苏木大厦	114	2	B	Gilstead Ct	吉士德阁	110	1	A
Fifth Ave Condo	第五道共管式公寓	86	1	C	Gilstead Man	吉士德大厦	110	1	A
Finland Gdns	苏兰花园	114	2	B	Gilstead View	里斯德景	110	1	A
Fiorenza	苏伦宅	69	2	B	Gisborne Light	吉士本之光	109	2	A
Flame Tree Pk	烽树园	66	2	B	Glamour Ville	辉煌公寓	114	1	B
Flamingo Valley	祥鹤谷	114	2	A	Glasgow Grn	格拉斯哥园	69	1	B
Flora East	富罗东园	113	2	A	Glastech Residence	格乐德居	110	2	A
Florida Pk	佛罗里达园	47	1	B	Glendale Pk	金桃园	63	1	B
Floridian	佛罗里殿	85	2	C	Glenfield Apts	葛兰雅公寓	113	2	A
Florissa Pk	富临花园	46	1	B	Glentrees	葛兰特丽	107	1	A
Flynn Pk	福林园	129	2	C	Glenville	葛兰雅山庄	69	1	C
Foh Pin Gdn	和平园	69	2	C	Global Ville	环球村	88	2	C
Foh Pin Man	和平大厦	69	2	C	Globe Apt	世界大厦	112	1	B
Fontaine Parry	Fontaine Parry公寓	69	2	B	Gloria Man	辉煌大厦	129	1	B
Fontana Hts	豪岭	107	1	A	Gloucester Mans	康乐大厦	110	1	B
Forest Hills	绿林山	26	1	C	Goldcoast Condo	黄金海岸	129	1	A
Fort Gardens	炮台园	112	2	D	Golden Hill Park	金山岭	68	2	D
Fortredale	炮台谷	112	2	D	Golden Hill Est	金山岭	68	2	C
Fortuna Gdns	鸿运花园	69	2	B	Golden Hill Villas	金山景	68	2	C
Fortune Jade	运玉园	113	1	B	Golden Hts	黄金岭	68	2	D
Fortune Pk	鸿运园	70	1	B	Golden Mile Cplx	黄金地带购物中心	111	2	C
Fortune Spring	幸福园	115	1	B	Golden Rise Est	金升园	84	1	B
Fortville	炮台山庄	112	2	D	Goldhill Gdn	金岭花园	88	1	D
Four Seasons Pk	四季园	109	2	C	Goldhill Plaza	金岭大厦	110	2	A
Fragrance Ct	香阁	129	2	C	Goldhill Twrs	金岭洋楼	88	1	D
Fragrance Ctr	香中心	113	2	B	Goldleaf Mans	金叶大厦	114	1	B
Fragrant Gdns	花香花园	90	2	A	Goldlink Pk	金联园	13	2	D
Frankel Est	福兰克园	114	2	A	Goldpalm Mans	金林苑	114	1	B
Frazer Suites	花莎楼	131	2	A	Goodluck Gdn	好运园	84	2	A
Freesia Woods	斐薆西亚林	84	2	D	Goodluck View	好运景	84	2	B
Fruition	Fruition公寓	113	2	A	Goodrich Pk	嘉富园	69	2	B
Fudu Pk	富都园	46	1	B	Goodview Apt	好景公寓	112	1	B
Fulton Hill	福登岭	67	1	B	Goodwill Ct	信誉阁	115	1	B
Futura	翡翠乐大厦	110	1	D	Goodwill Man	信誉大厦	89	1	D
Fuyuen Ct	福园阁	113	1	A	Goodwood Gdns	良木园	110	1	A
G Le Wilkie	基乐伟吉	110	2	C	Goodwood Residence	良木苑	109	1	A
Gabriel Villas	格利利雅别墅	69	1	D	Govt Co-op Housing Est	政府合作社住宅区	66	2	C
Galaxy Twr	雅图大厦	113	1	A	GPL Terrace	GPL台	90	1	C
Gallery 8	Gallery 8公寓	113	2	B	Grace Apts	玉丽公寓	90	2	D
Gallery Fifteen	Gallery Fifteen公寓	88	2	C	Grace Ct	恩典阁	115	1	A
Gallop Ct	格洛阁	108	2	A	Grace Pk	玉丽园	68	2	C
Gallop Gables	居乐雅	108	2	A	Grand Chateau	宏伟花园公寓	84	2	A
Gallop Green	格洛绿苑	108	2	A	Grand City Lodge	豪城楼	113	2	C
Gallop Pk	格洛园	108	2	A	Grand Duchess	圣百帝	114	1	B
Gallop Ridge	格洛岭	108	2	A	At St. Patrick's	公爵夫人豪居			
Gallop Villas	格洛别墅	108	2	A	Grand Regalia	宏丽佳丽	69	2	C
Gambler Ct	甘必尔阁	132	1	A	Grand Regency	宏伟丽苑	84	2	A
Garden Apts	花园大厦	109	2	B	Grand Residence	豪华居	114	1	A
Garden View Est	花园景住宅	68	2	B	Grand Twr	伟大阁	110	2	A
Garden Vista	帝景园	85	1	B	Grandeur 8	宏楼 8	46	2	D
Gardenia Ct	加丁尼亚阁	13	2	D	Grande Vista	峰运园	47	1	B
Gardenville	香园景	109	2	B	Grandlink Square	金联广场	113	1	A
Garlick Ville	雅丽村	85	2	D	Grandneo Mans	伟良大厦	113	1	A
Gay Villas	家乐别墅	89	2	A	Grange 70	格兰芝70	109	2	D
Gek Lim Mans	玉林大厦	112	2	A	Grange 80	格兰芝80	109	2	D
Gemini Apts	双子星公寓	114	2	A	Grange Ct	格兰芝阁	109	2	D
Gerald Gdns	杰乐园	48	1	B	Grange Hts	格兰芝大厦	110	1	D
Gerald Pk	日乐园	48	1	B	Grange Infinite	格兰芝大楼	110	1	D
Gerald Residences	日乐居	48	1	B	Grange Residences	格兰芝居	109	2	C
Geylang Heritage	芽笼史苑	112	2	B	Grange Rd Apartment	格兰芝路公寓	109	2	D
Geylang Mans	嘉伦大厦	112	2	B	Grangefront Apt	景福阁	110	1	D
Gideon's Lodge	吉迪昂苑	113	2	B	Gray Mans	格烈大厦	113	1	B
Giffard Man	吉福大厦	88	2	D	Great World City	世界城	132	1	A
Gilman Hts Condo	吉门岭公寓	130	2	B	Great World Service Apts	大世界服务公寓	110	1	D

PLACES		MAP	GRID	PLACES		MAP	GRID
Green Bank Pk	绿岸园	64	2 D	Hillington Green	喜临登园	63	1 B
Green Ct	绿阁	112	2 B	Hills	Hills公寓	88	1 D
Green Hill Est	青山园	63	2 A	Hillside Gdns	山边花园	69	1 B
Green Lodge	翠林山庄	84	2 A	Hillside Homes	山边新村(又名豪园)	86	2 C
Green Springs	绿滨园	48	1 B	Hillside Mans	山边大厦	69	1 C
Greenridge	绿脉	84	2 B	Hilltop Grove	山景园	63	1 C
Greenwood Villas	绿林园	86	2 B	Hilltops	山岭域公寓	110	1 B
Grosvenor View	国威景	92	1 C	Hillview 128	幽美128	63	1 C
Gryphon Ter	格风台	129	1 A	Hillview Apts	幽美公寓	63	1 C
Guan Soon Ter	源顺台	94	1 B	Hillview Ct	幽美阁	63	1 B
Guilin Court	桂林阁	112	2 B	Hillview Est	幽美新村	63	1 C
Guilin Mans	桂林大厦	113	1 A	Hillview Green	幽美林	63	1 C
Guilin View	桂林景	62	2 C	Hillview Hts	幽美岭	63	1 B
Guillemard Apts	基里玛公寓	112	2 B	Hillview Park	幽美花苑	63	1 B
Guillemard View	基里玛景	112	2 B	Hillview Regency	幽美丽苑	63	1 D
H.J. Hts	HJ岭	84	1 A	Hillview Residence	山景居公寓	63	1 C
Hai Sing Pk	海星园	70	1 B	Hillview Villas	幽美别墅	63	1 C
Haig Apts	海格公寓	113	2 C	Himoko Ct	欣美阁	107	1 A
Haig Ct	海雅阁	113	2 C	Hock Kee Hse	福祺大厦	113	1 A
Haig Eleven	海格11号	113	2 B	Hock Man	福大厦	110	2 C
Haig Gdns	海格园	113	1 B	Hock Seng Gdn	福升花园	85	2 B
Haig Grove	海格林	113	2 B	Hock Seng Pk	福升园	85	2 B
Haig Mansion	海格楼	113	1 B	Hock Swee Hill	福水山	47	2 B
Haig Ten	海格大厦	113	1 B	Holland Ct	荷兰苑	108	1 B
Hammer Ct	翰美阁	108	2 B	Holland Crest	荷兰峰	108	1 B
Hampton Court	汉普顿阁	109	2 B	Holland Gems	荷兰之宝	108	2 B
Hang Tat Gdn	恒达花园大厦	89	1 D	Holland Green	荷兰绿林	85	1 D
Happy Est	百乐花园	45	2 D	Holland Grv	荷兰林	107	1 D
Happy Gdns	安乐新村	90	2 C	Holland Hts	荷兰景	108	2 B
Happy Mans	安乐大厦	90	2 C	Holland Hill	荷兰山公寓	108	1 B
Happy Pk	幸福园	46	1 D	Holland Hill Lodge	荷兰山苑	108	1 B
Harbour View Gdns	港景花园	129	1 C	Holland Hill Mans	荷兰山公寓	108	1 B
Harbour View Twrs	湾景阁	130	2 D	Holland Hill Pk	荷兰山园	108	1 B
Harbourlights	海港乐	142	1 A	Holland Man	荷兰大厦	108	1 B
Harbourside Apts	海港苑公寓	131	2 D	Holland Mews	荷兰美居	108	1 B
Harmony Man	协和大厦	113	2 B	Holland Pk	荷兰苑	108	2 B
Harvest	Harvest公寓	131	2 A	Holland Peak	荷兰碧苑	108	1 B
Harvest Mans	丰收大厦	132	1 A	Holland Residences	荷兰碧苑	108	1 B
Harvey View	哈威景	94	1 A	Holland Suites	荷兰楼	108	1 B
Hawaii Twr	夏威夷大厦	113	1 D	Holland Twr	荷兰大厦	108	1 C
Hazel Pk Condo	榛园公寓	42	1 D	Holland Vale	荷兰谷	108	2 B
Hazel Pk Terrace	嘉林园	42	1 D	Hollandia	荷兰里亚	108	1 B
HCM Residential Cplx	HCM住宅楼	109	2 D	Hollandswood Ct	荷兰林阁	108	2 A
Heeton Pk	喜登园	45	1 A	Hollywood Apts	好莱坞公寓	110	2 D
Heji Gdn	和记园	114	1 B	Hollywood Pk	好莱坞园	87	1 D
Heliconia Lodge	海莉可尼亚苑	116	1 A	Holt Residences	贺德居	131	2 A
Helios Residence	喜乐居	110	1 C	Homes At Eastwood Place	东林坊居	94	2 D
Henley Gdns	富锦花园	69	2 A	Homey Gdns	甜密园	114	1 B
Henry Park	亨利园	107	1 A	Hong Heng Gdn	丰兴园	26	1 D
Henry Park Apts	亨利园公寓	107	1 A	Hong Heng Man	洪兴大厦	26	1 D
Heritage Apts	河德堡公寓	109	2 B	Hong Heng Ter	洪兴台	26	1 D
Heritage Residence	世豪之居	114	1 B	Hong Joo Pk	丰裕园	114	1 A
Heritage View	文艺园	107	1 C	Hong Leong Gdn	丰隆花园	105	2 A
Hertford Apts	和福公寓	110	2 B	Hong Leong Gdn Condo	丰隆花园公寓	106	1 A
Hertford Man	和福大厦	110	2 B	Honolulu Twr	檀香山大厦	109	2 A
High Oak	高林园	84	2 A	Hoover Pk	豪华园	84	2 A
High Point	高峰	110	1 B	Horizon Gdns	浩然生花园	46	1 D
Highgate Condo	高门公寓	84	1 A	Horizon Green	豪丽生苑	46	1 D
Highgate Park	高门园	84	1 A	Horizon Twrs (East Twr)	浩然大厦(东座)	110	1 D
Highland Condo	高原公寓	69	2 B	Horizon Twrs (West Twr)	浩然大厦(西座)	110	1 D
Highland Cottages	高原豪舍	69	2 C	Horizon View	浩然景	110	1 B
Highland Gdn	高原花园	69	2 B	Hougang Green	豪阁林	48	2 D
Hill Court	禧阁	110	1 C	How Sun Gdn	豪山花园	90	2 A
Hill Vista	山景	63	1 B	How Sun Pk	豪山园	90	2 A
Hillbrooks	山溪苑	63	1 C	Hua Ct	华阁	69	2 D
Hillcrest Arcadia	翠乐苑	86	2 B	Hua Guan Gdn	华源阁	85	2 B
Hillcrest Villa	翠峰别墅	86	2 C				

PRIVATE HOUSING 私人住宅区 CONDOS 共管式公寓 APARTMENTS 公寓

PLACES		MAP	GRID	PLACES		MAP	GRID
Hua Mei Gdn	华美花园	42	1 D	Kai Sheng Ct	凯胜阁	89	2 C
Hua Xin Ct	华新阁	115	1 B	Kampong Tembeling	甘榜登百灵	113	2 B
Hua Yu Man	华玉大厦	92	1 C	Kang Ching Rd Apts	康情公寓	82	1 A
Hullet Ct	幽乐阁	110	1 C	Kang Choo Bin Pk	江子民园	69	2 D
Hullet Rise	幽乐坡	110	1 C	Kartar Apts	卡尔塔大厦	110	2 A
Hume Hts	幽乐岭	63	1 C	Kasturina Lodge	佳玉苑	109	2 D
Hume Pk I	幽乐园1	63	2 C	Katong Apts	加东大厦	113	2 B
Hume Pk II	幽乐园2	63	2 C	Katong Gdns	加东花园	113	2 B
Icon	海天大厦	132	2 C	Katong Man	加东公寓	114	1 B
Idyllic East	东方宜园	116	1 A	Katong Omega Apt	东佳园	114	1 B
Idyllic Residences	宜园居	114	1 B	Katong Park Twrs	加东园大厦	112	1 D
Imperial Heights	皇岭	113	1 B	Katong Ville	加东邨	113	1 B
Indonesia Embassy Residential Units	印尼大使馆住宅	109	2 D	Kay Siang Rd Est	继祥路住宅区	108	2 D
Inova	英�华	114	1 B	Kechubong Ter	克朱蒙台	48	1 B
International Plaza	凯联大厦	132	2 C	Kellett Ct	可乐阁	86	2 C
Intero	Intero公寓	89	2 C	Kellock Lodge	家乐园	109	2 D
iR	iR公寓	88	2 C	Kelulut Hill	克鲁葛岭	48	1 C
Iridium	Iridium公寓	110	2 A	Kemaman Pt	可曼曼岭	89	1 D
Island Country Villas	岛屿别墅	45	2 D	Kemaman View	可曼景景	89	1 D
Island Gardens	岛屿园	66	2 B	Kembangan Ct	景万岸阁	114	1 A
Island Pk	岛屿园	66	2 B	Kembangan Villas	景万岸别墅	92	1 D
Island View	岛屿山庄	129	2 C	Keng Lee Ct	景丽阁	110	2 B
Ivory	象牙	113	2 B	Keng Lee View	景丽景	110	2 A
Ivory Apts	象牙山庄	114	1 B	Keng Yee Gdn	庆宜园	114	1 A
Ivory Heights	Ivory Heights公寓	83	1 B	Kensington Pk	景星园	68	2 A
J Court	J阁	113	2 B	Kentish Ct	锦爵阁	111	1 A
Jade Gdn	翠玉园	109	2 A	Kentish Green	锦爵园	111	1 A
Jade Gdns	翠玉花园	110	1 A	Kentish Lodge	锦爵苑	111	1 A
Jade Twr	碧玉楼	69	1 D	Kentview Pk	肯特景园	129	2 A
Jade Ville	翡翠园	69	2 B	Kerrisdale	克丽丝谷园	111	1 B
Jade Vine Gdns	玉安园	69	2 B	Kew Cottage	邱舍	94	1 D
Jansen 28	佳胜28	69	1 B	Kew Gate	邱门	94	1 D
Jansen Lodge	詹森苑	69	1 C	Kew Green	邱园公寓	116	1 A
Jansen Man	詹森大厦	69	1 B	Kew Green Townhouse	翠涛园	116	1 A
Jansen Spring	詹森泉	69	1 C	Kew Lodge	黎山庄	87	1 C
Jardin	渣甸公寓	85	1 B	Kew Pl	邱坊公寓	94	1 D
Jasmine Ct	捷士阁园	66	2 C	Kew Residencia	翠景园	116	1 A
Jaya Twr	洁雅大厦	109	2 A	Kew Vale Collection	邱园	94	1 D
JC Ct	JC阁	113	2 B	Kew Valley	邱苑	94	1 D
JC Draycott	爵士阁	109	2 B	Kheam Hock Gdn	谦福花园	87	1 C
JC Residence	爵士居	113	2 B	Killiney Apts	几里年花苑公寓大厦	110	1 D
Jersey Lodge	泽西苑	114	1 A	Kim Court	金阁	112	1 B
Jervois Gdns	泽维士花园	131	2 A	Kim Keat Gdn	金吉园	89	1 D
Jervois Green	泽维士林	109	1 D	Kim Keat Hse	金吉楼	89	1 D
Jervois Grove	泽维士苑	109	1 D	Kim Keat Lodge	金吉苑	89	1 D
Jervois Jade	致富士公寓	131	2 A	Kim Lin Pk	金陵园	109	2 C
Jervois Lodge	致富园	109	2 D	Kim Wee Man	金辉楼	113	2 C
Jervois Mans	泽维士大厦	131	2 A	Kimnan Pk	金南园	92	1 D
Jervois Regency	泽维士皇园	109	1 D	Kimsia Ct	金城大厦	110	1 C
Jervois View	泽维士景	109	2 D	King Albert Park	阿尔柏王苑	85	1 D
Jewel of Balmoral	巴慕乐之宝	109	2 A	King's 8	京士8号	86	2 D
JIa	JIa公寓	110	2 C	King's Apt	皇寓	113	2 B
Ji Xiang Ct	吉祥阁	114	1 B	King's Ct	皇阁	110	2 A
JLB Residence	JLB居	52	1 B	King's Gdn	德泉园	108	2 A
Joo Chiat Apts	如切公寓	113	2 C	King's Man	统一大厦	113	2 B
Joo Chiat Ct	如切阁	113	2 B	Kingsgrove Condo	锦福园	68	1 C
Joo Chiat Lodge	如切乐苑	113	2 B	Kingsley Man	锦树大厦	88	2 C
Joo Chiat Man	如切大厦	113	2 A	Kingston Ter	锦顿台	114	1 A
Joy Court	欢喜阁	113	2 A	Kingsville	御花名园	108	2 A
Joyful Mans	喜悦大厦	113	2 C	Kintyre Pk Est	金泰园村	108	1 D
Jubilee Residence	禧年之居	129	1 A	Kismis Ct	吉米斯阁	84	2 B
Juluca	Juluca公寓	128	2 A	Kismis Lodge	吉士米苑	84	2 B
Juniper at Ardmore	杜松山庄	109	2 B	Kismis View	卡斯米景	84	2 B
Jupiter Court	朱比德阁	113	2 A	KJ Mansion	KJ大楼	69	1 B
Jurong View Apts	裕廊景公寓	79	2 C	Klassic Ct	典雅阁	113	2 B
				Knox View	诺士景	114	1 B

PLACES		MAP	GRID	PLACES		MAP	GRID
Koon Seng Hse	坤成楼	113	2 B	Legenda at Joo Chiat	如切之乡公寓	113	2 B
Kovan Apts	高文公寓	69	2 C	Leicester Lodge	李斯特苑	89	2 C
Kovan Ct	高文阁	69	2 C	Leighwoods	利木园	107	1 A
Kovan Crest	高文弯	69	2 C	Leith Grv	李斯林	69	1 B
Kovan Esquire	高文绅士苑	69	2 C	Leith Pk	利达园	69	1 B
Kovan Gdn	高文花园	69	2 B	Lenik Service Apts	丽乐尼服务公寓	111	1 D
Kovan Lodge	高文苑	69	2 C	Lentor Views	伦多景	46	1 B
Kovan Melody	高文岭	69	2 B	Lentor Villas	伦多别墅	46	1 B
Kovan Primera	高文Primera公寓	69	1 C	Leong Bee Ct	隆美阁	89	2 C
Kovan Residences	高文居	69	2 B	Leonie Condotel	利安岭	110	1 D
Kovana	高文乐Kovana公寓	69	2 C	Leonie Gdns	罗尼花园	110	1 D
Kum Hing Ct	锦兴大厦	109	2 C	Leonie Hill Residences	罗尼山居	110	1 D
Kurau Ct	古楼阁	114	1 B	Leonie Parcview	利安宁园景	110	1 D
La Belle	乐美丽公寓	69	1 D	Leonie Studio	罗尼公寓	110	1 D
La Casa	拉卡莎公寓	12	1 C	Leonie Twrs (A)	乐怡大厦(A)	110	1 D
La Crystal	水晶园	110	1 D	Leonie Twrs (B)	乐怡大厦(B)	110	1 D
La Maison (Moulmein Rd)	乐美胜园(摩绵坡)	110	2 A	Leonie View	罗尼景	110	1 D
La Meyer	美乐园	113	1 D	Lermit Lodge	勒密苑	109	1 B
La Novelle	诺维丽公寓	110	2 A	Les Jardins De Hollande	荷兰花景	108	1 B
La Quinta Pk	乐郅达园	68	2 C	Leshan Gdns	乐善大楼	112	2 B
La Suisse 1	美山园1	64	2 D	Lew Lian Vale	榴桂谷	69	1 D
La Suisse 2	美山园2	85	2 A	Lew Man	刘莲大厦	109	2 A
La Ventura	乐温多拉公寓	109	2 D	Lewis Lodge	路易士苑	109	1 A
La Ville	威拉园	112	2 D	Liang Apts	良寓	113	2 A
Ladyhill Pk	淑女山园	109	2 B	Lien Twrs	连阁	108	1 D
Ladyvale	淑女谷	109	1 B	Lien Villa	连剧墅	108	2 B
Lagoon View	湖阁	115	1 B	Lilac Pk	紫丁香园	47	2 C
Laguna 88 Condo	礁湖88公寓	94	2 D	Lilydale	Lilydale公寓	27	2 A
Laguna Green	礁湖绿苑	115	1 B	Lim Tai See Walk	林太师径	85	2 D
Laguna Pk	礁湖园	115	1 B	Limau Pk	柠檬园	94	1 D
Lake Holmz	翠湖园	81	2 A	Limau Villas	茂华苑	94	1 D
Lake View Est	湖景园	67	1 D	Lincoln	林肯	110	2 A
Lakepoint Condo	湖聚园共管式公寓	81	2 A	Lincoln Lodge	林肯苑	110	2 A
Lakeside Apt	湖畔公寓	82	1 B	Lincoln Regal	林肯园	110	2 B
Lakeside Grv	湖畔林	81	2 A	Lion Twrs	狮城大楼	110	2 A
Lakeside Twrs	湖畔大厦	82	1 B	Liria Ter	丽日台	74	1 B
Lakeview Gdns	湖景花园	88	1 B	Livia	丽维亚	51	2 D
Landbay	兰景公寓	115	1 B	Livingston Mans	利文斯顿阁	114	1 B
Landmark Twr	名胜大厦	132	1 B	Lloyd Ct	来益阁	110	1 D
Landridge Condo	兰特岗公寓	129	2 C	Lloyd Man	来益大厦	110	1 D
Langston Ville	兰斯顿景	110	1 D	Llyn Gdns	林园	69	2 D
Lan's Place	兰氏大厦	109	1 B	Lodge 77	77居屋	115	1 B
Lanson Place	兰盛坊	110	1 D	Long Hua Yuan	龙花园	92	1 C
Larshimi Villa	拉丝米别墅	69	1 C	Long Nian Ct	龙年阁	113	2 A
Latitude	Latitude纬度公寓	109	2 D	Longbeach	长滩园	128	2 A
Laurel Pk	月桂园	68	2 C	Long's Ct	龙阁	109	2 A
Lau's Arcadia	刘公寓	113	2 B	Lornie 18	罗尼18公寓	87	1 B
Lauw & Son's Gdn	刘氏父子花园	67	2 D	Lornie Gdns	罗尼园	87	2 B
Le Arc	乐弧	112	2 B	Lotus at Barker	巴克莲花	110	1 A
Le Conney Pk	康妮园	114	1 B	Lotus at Jervois	泽维士莲花	131	2 A
Le Crescendo	乐馨苑	91	1 C	Lotus at Joo Chiat	如切莲花	113	2 B
Le Gambir	甘蜜园	90	1 A	Lotus at Mt Rosie	露西山莲花园	88	1 D
Le Grove Service Apts	小林服务公寓	109	2 B	Loyang	洛阳	52	2 C
Le Hill Condo	乐山公寓	129	1 B	Loyang Ct	洛阳阁	52	2 D
Le Loyang	洛阳楼	52	2 D	Loyang Gdns	乐洋花园	52	2 D
Le M Residence	Le M居	114	1 B	Loyang Green	洛阳林	52	2 C
Le Marque	特许园	109	2 A	Loyang Man	洛阳大厦	52	2 D
Le Merritt	乐麦丽	114	1 B	Loyang Valley	乐洋村	74	1 A
Le Reve	Le Reve公寓	113	2 A	Loyang Villas	洛阳山庄	74	1 B
Le Shantier	丽之坊	88	2 D	Lucida	露西达公寓	110	2 A
Le Wood	绿林园	64	1 D	Lucky Ct	幸运阁	115	2 A
Leck Teck Ct	立德阁	113	2 C	Lucky Hill	幸运岭	94	1 D
Leedon	礼敦园	108	1 B	Lucky Pk	幸运园	86	1 C
Leedon Hts	礼敦岭	108	1 A	Lucky Plaza Apts	幸运商业中心	110	1 C
Leedon Pk	礼敦园	108	1 A	Lucky Twr	幸运大厦	109	2 D
Legenda	如切之乡	113	2 B				

PLACES		MAP	GRID	PLACES		MAP	GRID
Luma	Luma公寓	110	1 D	Mellow Mans	美伦大厦	114	1 B
Lumiere	林美丽公寓	132	2 A	Melody Villas	马罗迪花园	46	1 B
Lushan Gdn	卢山园	90	2 A	Melrose	美罗苑	68	2 D
Lutheran Twrs	路德楼	86	2 D	Melrose Ct	美罗阁	89	1 D
Lynnsville 331	林思维儿331	129	1 B	Melrose Pk	金御苑	131	2 A
M21	M21号	88	2 D	Melville Pk	美景园	73	2 D
Mabelle	美宝公寓	114	1 B	Mendon Spring	明登泉	129	2 C
Mackenzie	麦肯西	110	2 C	Meng Garden Apts	明园	110	1 D
Mackenzie 138	麦肯西138	110	2 C	Mera East	嵋雅东	114	1 A
Mackenzie Man	麦肯西大厦	110	2 C	Mera Gdns	嵋雅园	63	2 A
Mackenzie Regency	麦肯西楼	110	2 C	Meralodge	嵋雅苑	63	1 C
Macpherson Gdn Est	麦波申花园	90	2 B	Mera Prime	嵋雅首苑	131	2 B
Macpherson Green	麦波申园	90	2 C	Mera Springs	美拉泉	110	2 A
Madeira Ct	马德拉阁	114	1 B	Mera Ter	嵋雅台	94	2 A
Maison Royale	皇家公寓	110	2 A	Merawoods	嵋雅林	63	1 C
Makeway View	马克维景	110	2 B	Mergui Ct	麦桂阁	111	1 A
Malcolm Pk	马康园	87	2 D	Mergui Lodge	麦桂苑	111	1 A
Malvern Spring	茂温泉公寓	113	2 C	Mergui Mans	麦桂大厦	111	1 A
Mandalay Ct	万阁大厦	88	2 D	Merlin Man	美伦楼	113	2 B
Mandalay Man	曼德里大厦	88	2 D	Merlot Ville	美乐邨	114	1 B
Mandalay Twrs	万德大厦	88	2 D	Metro-Y Apts (YMCA)	美罗Y公寓(YMCA)	109	2 A
Mandale Hts	万阁岭	88	2 D	Meya Lodge	美雅舍	89	2 C
Mandarin Gdns	文华园	114	2 C	Meyer Pk	美雅园	113	1 D
Mandarin Pk	文华大厦	84	2 A	Meyer Residences	美雅居	112	2 D
Mangis Pk	吉士园	113	2 B	Mia Place	玫园	112	2 D
Manhattan Mans	万豪登楼	109	2 D	Milford Villas	美福公寓	90	1 A
Manila Gdns	马尼拉园	114	2 A	Millcreek	Millcreek公寓	114	1 A
Mansion 28	大厦 28	112	2 A	Millpoint	美尔坊	131	2 A
Maplewoods	嘉枫园	85	2 B	Mimosa Ct	明露山阁	47	2 C
Mar Thoma Man	翠华阁	89	2 D	Mimosa Pk	明露山园	47	2 C
Margate Mans	玛格大厦	112	2 D	Mimosa Ter	美慕莎台	47	2 C
Margate Point	玛格坊	112	2 D	Mimosa Villas	美蒙莎花园	47	2 C
Marina Bay Residences	滨海湾居	133	1 C	Min Yuan	明园	111	1 A
Marina Bay Suites	滨海湾公寓	133	1 C	Minbu Ct	明埔阁	88	2 D
Marina Collection	滨海之珍	147	1 A	Minbu Villa	明埔园	88	2 D
Marine Gdn	玛玲花园	114	2 B	Ming Teck Pk	明德园	107	2 A
Marine Mans	马林楼	113	2 C	Minton Ct	民登阁	69	2 D
Marine Meadows	马林坊	113	2 C	Mint Residences @ Jansen	詹森敏居	69	1 B
Marine Point	马林坊公寓	113	2 C	Mirage Twr	美乐景	132	1 A
Marine View Mans	海景大厦	113	2 C	Mistral Pk	美风园	94	2 B
Marlene Ville	玛琳村	69	1 C	Modena	摩特纳	94	2 A
Marshall Lodge	玛士苑	113	2 C	Monarchy Apts	君主公寓	88	2 D
Marsiling Apts	马西岭公寓	10	2 C	Mondo Bldg	曼都大厦	69	1 D
Martaban Ct	玛达门阁	89	1 D	Monk's Hill Apts	蒙克山公寓	110	1 B
Martia 8	玛达八号	114	1 C	Montebleu	蓝山公寓	88	2 D
Martin 38	马丁38公寓	132	1 A	Monterey Park	满特丽园	105	2 A
Martin Edge	马丁缘	132	1 A	Montrosa	满乐山庄	63	1 C
Martin Place	马丁坊	110	1 D	Monville Man	曼维拉大厦	88	2 C
Martina Mans	玛亭那大厦	110	1 A	Moonstone Apt	月石公寓	89	2 C
Marymount View	马里蒙景	67	2 D	Moonstone Mans	月石大厦	89	2 C
Maya	美雅公寓	113	2 B	Moonstone Residences	月石豪邸	89	2 C
Maybelle Lodge	美贝拉苑	114	1 B	Moonstone Royale	蒙士顿豪邸	89	2 C
Mayfair Gdns	美华园	85	1 B	Moonstone View	月石景	89	2 C
Mayfair Pk	玫事园	85	1 A	Morimasa Gdns	茉莉马沙园	110	1 A
Mayflower Gdns	美花园	46	1 D	Moro Mans	摩洛大厦	113	1 A
Mayflower Ville	美花村	67	1 A	Moulmein Ct	摩绵阁	110	2 A
Maysprings	美馨园	42	1 D	Moulmein Green	摩绵林	110	2 A
Mayview Townhouse	美景华宅	67	2 A	Mountbatten Lodge	蒙巴登宅	113	1 C
Meadow Lodge	名林园	84	2 A	Mountbatten Regency	蒙巴登豪宅	113	1 C
Meadow @ Pierce	贝雅士之居	45	2 C	Mountbatten Suites	蒙巴登公寓	113	2 C
Medallion	奖章公寓	89	2 A	Mount Echo Pk	玉高峰	109	1 D
Medge	Medge公寓	89	1 D	Mount Faber Lodge	花柏山苑	131	2 D
Medway Pk	麦威园	106	2 B	Mount Rosie Gdn	玫瑰山园	88	1 D
Mei Hwan View	美环景	68	2 D	Mount Sophia Apts	苏菲雅山公寓	110	2 C
Meihe Gdns	美柏花园	89	2 A	Mount Sophia Suites	苏菲雅山楼	110	2 C
Melina Ct	美林阁	114	1 B	Mugliston Hill	吉利登岭	48	2 B

• PRIVATE HOUSING / CONDOS / APARTMENTS

PLACES		MAP	GRID
Mun Wah Gdn	文华苑	46	1 C
Murano	慕兰诺	129	1 A
Mutiara Crest	翠峰弯	109	2 D
Mutiara View	翠峰景	109	2 D
Nadia Man	娜雅大厦	88	2 C
Naga Ct	纳佳阁	109	2 A
Namly Ct	南利阁	86	1 C
Namly Pk	南利园	86	1 D
Nanak Mans	纳朗大厦	113	1 D
Nanyang Pk	南洋园	69	1 B
Nassim	那森公寓	109	2 B
Nassim Gdns	那森花园	109	1 B
Nassim Jade	那森玉	109	2 B
Nassim Man	那森大厦	109	1 B
Nassim Pk Residences	兰馨园居	109	2 B
Nassim Regency	那森丽苑	109	1 B
Nassim Ville	那森苑	109	2 B
Nassim Woods	那森林	109	1 C
Nathan Place	乐福苑	109	2 D
Nathan Residences	纳丹之居	109	2 D
Naturalis	纳春丽	114	1 B
Nature Mans	天然大厦	114	1 B
Naung Ct	南国花园	70	1 A
Nepal Pk	尼泊尔园	107	2 C
Neptune Ct	海皇阁	114	2 C
New Ct	新阁	88	2 C
New Gdns	新园	69	1 C
Newton 18	纽顿18	110	1 A
Newton Euro Asia	华绅纽顿大厦	110	1 A
Newton Gems	纽顿之宝	110	2 A
Newton Lodge	纽顿居	110	2 A
Newton Meadows	纽顿园	110	1 A
Newton One	Newton壹号公寓	110	1 A
Newton Pt	纽顿坊	110	1 A
Newton Suites	纽顿楼	110	2 A
Newton View	纽顿景	110	2 A
Nexus	Nexus苑	85	2 B
Nicole Green	景苑	112	2 B
Nicon Gdns	黎光园	42	1 D
Nim Gdns	林姆花园	47	2 C
Nim Pk	林姆公园	47	2 C
Niven Loft	尼文公寓	110	2 C
NOB Hill	NOB岭	109	2 A
Nomu	诺慕公寓	110	2 D
Norfolk Ct	纳福阁	111	1 A
Normanton Est	诺曼顿花园	130	1 B
Normanton Pk	诺曼顿园	129	2 B
North Vale	北谷	41	1 B
Northoaks	北林园	12	2 A
Northshore Bungalows	北岸洋房	30	2 B
Nouvelle Pk	金微园	69	1 B
Novelis	诺维丽	110	2 A
Novena Ct	诺维那阁	88	2 D
Novena Gdns	诺维那园	88	2 D
Novena Hill	诺维那山	88	2 D
Novena Lodge	诺维那苑	88	1 D
Novena Suites	诺维那楼	110	2 A
Novena Ville	诺维那宇	88	1 D
Nuovo	诺尔福	46	2 C
Oakswood Hts	逸林阁	132	1 C
Oasis @ Mulberry	慕百树绿洲	90	1 C
Oasis Gdns	绿洲园	90	2 B
Ocean Apts	海洋大厦	114	1 B
Ocean Pk	海洋花园	114	2 B
Octaville	渥大园	113	2 B
Oei Tiong Ham Pk	黄仲涵园	107	2 A
OLA Residences @ Mountbatten	蒙巴登奥乐之居	113	2 C
Oleanas Residence	欧伦纳斯之居	132	1 A
Oleander Twrs	夹竹桃大厦	88	2 B
Olina Lodge	奥丽娜大厦	108	1 B
Onan Ct	奥南阁	113	2 B
One @ Pulasan	布拉山路壹号	113	2 B
One Akyab	一号亚凯苑	88	2 D
One Amber	安珀壹号公寓	113	1 C
One Balmoral	巴莫乐一号	109	2 B
One Chatsworth	采士华壹号	109	2 D
One Devonshire	One Devonshire公寓	110	1 D
One Fort	福涛苑	112	2 D
One Jervois	泽维士壹号	131	2 A
One K Green Lane	绿垦One K公寓	113	1 B
One Leicester	李斯特壹号	89	2 C
One Lynwood	灵兀林壹号	89	1 B
One North Residences	纬壹居	107	2 C
One Oxley Rise	欧思礼坡一号公寓	110	2 D
One Rochester	One Rochester公寓	107	2 A
One Shenton	珊顿壹号公寓	132	2 C
One St. Michael's	圣迈克壹号	89	2 D
One Tree Hill Gdns	独木山园	109	2 B
One Tree Hill Mans	独木岗大厦	109	2 D
One Tree Hill Residence	独木岗居	109	2 D
Ong's Man	王氏大厦	115	1 B
Opera Est	奥匹庭园	115	1 A
Orange Grove Residences	柑林居	109	2 A
Orange Regency	柑丽苑	109	2 B
Orchard Bel Air	乌节大厦	109	2 C
Orchard Ct	乌节花园洋楼	110	2 D
Orchard Grand Ct	乌节豪阁	110	1 D
Orchard Parksuites	乌节怡楼	110	1 C
Orchard Residences	豪杰居	109	2 C
Orchard Scotts	乌节史各士园	110	1 B
Orchard Twrs	豪杰大厦	109	2 C
Orchard View	豪杰景	109	2 C
Orchid Apts	胡姬楼	86	1 B
Orchid Pk	胡姬园共管公寓	27	1 B
Orion	奥利安公寓	109	2 B
Ovada	Ovada公寓	113	2 B
Oxford Suites	牛津公寓	111	1 A
Oxley Apt	欧思礼公寓	110	2 D
Oxley Gdn	欧思礼花园	110	2 D
Oxley Mansion	欧思礼大厦	110	1 D
Pacific Mansion	太平洋大厦	110	1 D
Paddy Green	巴提林	112	1 B
Palace Mansions	皇宫大厦	112	2 B
Palazetto	巴拉泽多	112	2 D
Palisades	峭壁园	129	1 B
Palm Beach Gdn	棕滨园	115	1 B
Palm Galleria	佳乐丽棕林	114	1 B
Palm Gardens	柏安园	41	2 D
Palm Green	棕绿园	128	2 A
Palm Grove Condo	棕林苑	69	2 B
Palm Grove Regency	棕林豪宅	69	1 B
Palm Grove Ter	棕林台	69	2 B
Palm Haven	棕乐园	69	2 B
Palm Lodge	棕庄	113	1 A
Palm Loft	棕林楼	113	2 A
Palm Mansions	棕厦	129	1 A

PLACES		MAP GRID		PLACES		MAP GRID	
Palm Oasis	棕缘洲	114	1 A	Peach Garden	桃园	113	1 D
Palm Residence	棕林居	84	2 A	Peak Ct Condo	碧松阁	88	1 D
Palm Spring	嘉棕	109	2 B	Peakview Est	峰景园	93	2 C
Palm Vista	棕林景	114	1 A	Peakville &	登峰园及	93	2 B
Palm Woods	棕林园	94	1 C	Peakview Mansion	登峰大厦		
Palmville	棕园	69	1 B	Peakville Mansion	登峰园	93	2 C
Pandan Valley	槟兰谷	107	1 A	Pearl Bank Apts	珍珠苑	132	1 B
Papillion	巴比伦公寓	88	2 D	Pebble Bay	石丽湾	111	2 D
Paradise Palms	文瑜园	113	1 B	Pebble Gardens	石丽园	113	1 B
Parbury Hill	百发丽园	115	2 A	Peily Court	佩丽阁	114	1 B
Parc Centennial	柏年园	110	2 D	Peirce Vale	贝雅士谷	45	2 C
Parc Emily	爱美丽园	110	2 C	Peirce View	贝雅士景	45	2 D
Parc Haven	阳明山庄	89	1 D	Pelikat Court	细德别墅	70	1 C
Parc Mackenzie	麦肯兰园	110	2 C	Pender Court	秉德阁	131	1 C
Parc Mondrian	蒙联园	89	2 B	Peng's Court	彭氏阁	113	2 B
Parc Oasis	柏奥花园	82	2 A	Peony Mansion	牡丹大厦	110	2 D
Parc Palais	富丽山庄	63	1 C	People's Mansions	人民大厦	112	2 A
Parc Regency	丽珍西园	129	1 B	People's Park Ctr	珍珠大厦	132	2 B
Parc Sea Breeze	海风园	113	2 C	People's Park Cplx	珍珠坊	132	2 B
Parc Sophia	苏菲亚园	110	2 C	Peppermint Grove	白柏鸣林	110	2 A
Parc Stevens	史帝芬园	109	2 A	Pepys Hill Condo	必比山公寓	129	2 C
Parc Vista	湖滨园	81	2 A	Permai Court	贝尔迈阁	131	2 D
Park Ave Residences	柏道雅居	132	1 A	Petain Court	贝当阁	111	1 B
Park Ave Suite	柏道楼	132	2 A	Philips Residence	斐立居	69	1 B
Park Court	园阁	113	2 A	Phoenix Court	凤凰楼	110	1 D
Park East	东园	114	2 A	Phoenix Height Est	凤凰仑花园	42	1 D
Park Green	绿苑	49	2 C	Phoenix Heights	凤凰岭	42	1 D
Park House	柏园	109	2 C	Picardy Gardens	百家丽花园	94	1 B
Park Infinia	英然尼亚园	110	2 A	Pinacle 16	Pinacle 16公寓	88	2 D
Park Natura	天然乐园	84	1 A	Pin Mansions	彬大厦	69	2 B
Park Shore	海湾园	111	2 D	Pin Tjoe Court	彬珠阁	109	2 B
Park Villas	园景别墅	69	2 B	Pine Court	松阁	114	1 B
Park West	伟诗园	106	1 A	Pine Grove	松林	106	2 A
Park Wing (UE Sq)	园楼(友乃德广场)	132	2 A	Pine Springs	松木春林	109	2 A
Parkview Apts	柏景公寓	84	1 A	Pine Villas	松木别墅	23	1 B
Parkview Eclat	园景村	109	2 D	Pinehurst Condo	松屋公寓	114	1 B
Parkview Est	园景园	93	2 C	Pinetree Condo	松林苑	109	2 A
Parkview Mansions	园景大厦	82	1 B	Pinevale	松霏园	72	1 C
Parkway Apts (Amber Rd)	海岸花园公寓(安珀路)	113	2 D	Pinewood Gardens	松木花园	109	2 A
Parkway Mansion	柏威大厦	113	2 D	Pinewood Terrace	松木台	11	1 D
Parkway View	百丽景	113	2 C	Platina Gdns	百帝纳园	13	2 D
Parry Court	培立阁	69	2 B	Platinum Edge	白金园	89	2 C
Parry Gardens	培立园	69	2 B	Plaza Pacific Service Apts	文雅服务公寓	111	2 D
Parry Green	松柏景	69	2 A	Poh Heng Court	宝兴阁	115	1 B
Parry Park	培立苑	69	1 B	Poh Huat Gardens	宝发园	69	2 A
Parry View	培立景	69	2 B	Point Loma	乐满园	86	2 C
Pasadena	白沙德娜园	110	2 A	Pomex Court	柏美斯阁	113	2 A
Pasir Panjang Apts	巴西班让公寓	130	1 D	Popular Estate	众乐园	63	1 B
(Workers Qtrs)				Portofino	波都滨诺	110	1 A
Pasir Panjang Ct	巴西班让阁	128	2 A	Poshgrove East	豪秋东	114	1 B
Pasir Panjang Gdns	巴西班让园	106	1 B	President Gardens	总统园	46	1 C
Pasir Panjang Lodge	巴西班让苑	128	2 A	Prestige Residence	威望居	114	1 A
Pasir Ris Beach Pk	白沙海滨别墅	51	2 C	Princess of Wales Pk	威尔斯公主园	86	2 D
Pasir View Pk	白沙景园	129	2 C	Princeton Vale	宝发公园	69	1 B
Pastoral View	大雅花园	88	2 D	Pristine Hts	碧丽登岭	111	1 A
Patent Place	碧鎏园	84	1 A	Promises Gardens	信园	85	2 D
Paterson Lodge	巴德申园	109	2 C	Prospect Court	辉煌阁	94	1 D
Paterson Tower	巴德申大厦	109	2 D	Prospero Ville	百思乐邨	114	1 A
Paterson Residence	巴德申居	109	2 D	Proximo	Proximo公寓	109	2 A
Paterson Suites	巴德申公寓	109	2 D	Public Mansion	大众大厦	88	2 D
Pavilion II at Novena	诺维娜Pavilion II公寓	88	2 D	Pumpkin Garden	南瓜花园	113	2 C
Pavillion Park	百比林园	41	2 D	Punggol Park	榜鹅园	30	2 B
Paya Lebar Gdns	巴耶利巴花园	90	2 A	Queen Astrid Gdns	爱士特女皇花园	107	2 A
Peace Mansion	建安公寓	110	2 C	Queen Astrid Park	爱士特女皇园	107	2 A
				Queens	皇后楼	130	2 A

PLACES		MAP GRID		PLACES		MAP GRID	
Queensberry Lodge	奎恩斯伯里园	109	2 D	River Wing (UE Square)	河畔楼(友乃德广场)	132	2 A
Queensway Twr	女皇道公寓	130	1 A	Riverdale Residence	河谷雅居	110	1 D
Quemoy Park	金门园	90	2 A	Riveredge	河畔公寓	112	2 D
Quinterra	Quinterra公寓	107	1 A	Rivergate	利发门	132	1 A
R66	R66公寓	111	1 A	Riveria Gdns	里维拉花园	110	1 D
Race Course Man	赛马埔楼	111	1 B	Riveria Point	里维拉楼	110	1 D
Radix	丽蒂思	114	1 A	Rivershire	河郡园	110	1 D
Rafflesia Condo	碧山莱福西亚园	67	2 D	Riverside 48	河滨 48	132	1 A
Rainbow Gardens	彩虹园	84	2 A	Riverside Point	河滨峰	132	2 A
Rainbow Mansion	彩虹大厦	109	2 D	Rivervale Crest	河谷峰	49	2 B
Raintree Valley	雨林谷	45	2 C	Riviera Residences	里维拉居	115	2 A
Rajah Tower	皇阁	88	2 C	Riz Haven	丽芝乐园	52	2 C
Rambai Court	兰排阁	113	2 B	Robertson 100	罗拔申100	132	1 A
Rambutan Mansions	红毛丹大厦	113	2 B	Robertson Blue	罗柏申蓝景	132	1 A
Rangoon Ct	仰光阁	111	1 A	Robertson Edge	罗拔申之滨	132	1 A
Raya Garden	拉亚花园	69	2 D	Robin Court	罗彬阁	109	1 A
Rebecca Park	利百加园	86	1 D	Robin Regalia	罗彬爵士	109	2 A
Red Swastica	红卍字慈善基金会	110	2 B	Robin Star	罗彬星园	109	2 A
Redwood West	红木山庄	129	1 C	Rocca Balestier	乐家马里士他	89	1 D
Reflections at Keppel Bay	吉宝湾之影	131	1 D	Rochester Hill	罗彻斯德园	107	2 C
Regal 35	丽格35公寓	112	2 A	Rodyk	Rodyk公寓	132	1 A
Regal Court	皇邸阁	89	1 D	Rosalia Park	罗斯列园	69	2 D
Regal Ville	豪华苑	92	1 D	Rose Garden	玫瑰园	113	2 C
Regency House	丽城大厦	110	2 D	Rose Lane Court	玫阁	113	1 B
Regency Lodge	丽晶苑	109	2 D	Rose Maison	玫瑰楼	113	2 C
Regency Park	旺家园	109	2 D	Rose Mansion	玫瑰大厦	113	1 B
Regency Suites	丽晶居	131	2 B	Rose Meadows	春福园	84	2 A
Regent Court	贵爵阁	89	2 D	Rose Ville	玫瑰苑	113	1 B
Regent Garden	丽景华园公寓	106	2 D	Rosedale	玫瑰谷	85	1 C
Regent Grove	丽晶林	22	2 D	Rosevale	玫瑰苑	110	2 A
Regent Heights	丽晶峰	62	2 D	Rosewood	青龙木园	11	2 D
Regent Park	丽晶园	106	1 A	Rosyth Lodge	梅景苑	69	1 B
Regent Villa	丽晶别墅	85	2 D	Rosyth Residence	乐赛之居	69	2 B
Regent Ville	丽晶山庄	48	1 D	Rosyth Ville	乐赛园	69	1 B
Regina Hill	青峰园	84	1 A	Royal Court	皇家阁	84	2 A
Regis Mansions	灵芝楼	84	2 A	Royal Palm Mansions	棕林大厦	129	1 A
Reservoir Villas	蓄水池别墅	91	2 C	Royal Ville	富贵园	85	2 C
Residence 8	第8居	109	2 C	Royale Mansions	富贵大厦	113	2 B
Residence 118	118雅居	114	1 B	Ruby Apartments	宝石公寓	89	1 D
Residences At 338A	338A公寓	110	1 D	Ruby Plaza	宝石中心	89	1 D
Residences @ Evelyn	伊芙琳居	110	1 A	Rumah Malaysia	马来西亚楼	108	2 A
Residences @ Jansen	詹森之居	69	1 B	RV Residences	RV居	131	2 A
Residences @ Limau	利茂之居	94	1 D	Sallim Lodge	莎琳苑	90	2 D
Residences @ Novena	诺维娜之居	88	2 D	Sam Kiang Mansion	三江大厦	110	1 D
Residences @ Somme	松美之居	111	1 B	Sam Leong Mansion	三龙大厦	111	1 B
Rhapsody on Mt Elizabeth	伊丽莎白山诗园	110	1 C	Sanctuary Green	怡嘉苑	112	1 D
Rich East Garden	福东园	115	2 A	Sandal Wood	仙台林	113	2 B
Rich Mansions	富豪大厦	110	1 A	Sandy Palm	沙棕楼	52	2 C
Richards Park	丽郡园	69	2 B	Sanford Park	三福园	69	1 C
Richmond Park	富门园	110	1 C	Santa Fe Mansions	圣达大厦	113	1 D
Richmond Ville	绿萌苑	94	1 D	Sanny Pk	珊尼园	87	2 D
Richmore Ct	利至茂阁	114	1 B	Sapphire 99	蓝宝石99	110	2 C
Ridge Court	佳乐园	89	2 C	Sapphire Court	蓝宝石阁	114	1 B
Ridgevale Gardens	翠峰山庄	63	2 D	Saraca Gardens	莎拉卡园	47	2 B
Ridgewood Condo	高山青住宅区	107	1 A	Sarhad Ville	莎荷苑	129	2 C
Rindu Terrace	林都台	90	1 A	Sarkies Court	沙奇士阁	110	1 B
Rio Gardens	丽河景	89	2 D	Sarkies Mansions	沙奇士大厦	110	1 B
Rio Vista	愉景湾	49	2 D	Savannah	莎旺那	73	2 D
Ris Grandeur	丽士豪园	51	2 D	Savoy Park	翠华园	84	2 B
Rising Suites	日升楼	110	1 A	Sayang Villa	沙央别墅	113	1 C
Ritz Mansions	丽士大厦	89	1 D	Scenic @ Braddell	布莱德之景	89	2 A
Ritz Residences	丽士居	110	1 D	Scenic Heights	美岭	89	1 D
Riva Lodge	河苑	110	1 D	SCK Ville	SCK苑	113	2 C
Rivage	利伟楼	112	2 D	Scotts 28	史各士28	110	1 B
River Place	翠河坊	132	1 A	Scotts High Park	史各士高园	110	1 B
River Valley Court	里巴巴利公寓	110	1 D				

PLACES		MAP	GRID	PLACES		MAP	GRID
Scotts Square	史各士广场	110	1 C	Siglap Lodge	实乞纳苑	115	1 A
Sea Avenue Mansions	海滨公寓	113	2 C	Siglap Hill 33	实乞纳山33号	114	2 A
Sea Avenue Residences	海洋道之居	113	2 C	Siglap Park	实乞纳园	114	2 A
Sea Breeze Ter	海凤楼	94	1 B	Signature At Lewis	路易士名望园	109	2 A
Sea View Park	海景园	113	1 D	Signature Crest	名望顶	113	1 B
Seaside Park	海滨园	114	2 B	Signature Park	名望园	84	2 A
Seasons Park	季景园	46	1 B	Signature Residence	名望居	113	1 B
Seasons View	佳季园	67	2 D	Silahis Apartments	实拉希公寓	114	1 B
Seaview Point	海景岭	113	2 D	Silver Hill	银景岭	70	1 A
Second Avenue Junction	第2道交界住宅	86	1 C	Silversea	银海楼	113	2 D
Selanting Green	适兰亭绿苑	84	2 A	Simei Gdns	四美园	94	1 B
Seletar Flats	实里达公寓	48	1 A	Simei Green	四美苑	94	2 A
Seletar Garden	实里达花园	47	1 B	Simon Court	西门阁	69	2 B
Seletar Hill Estate	实里达山住宅区	48	1 C	Simon Ville	西门园	69	2 B
Seletar Spring Condo	实里达春公寓	48	2 B	Sims Dorado	Sims Dorado公寓	113	1 A
Seletaris	丽泉	13	2 C	Sims Green	沈氏园	112	2 A
Sembawang Cottage	三巴旺小屋	13	2 D	Sims Meadows	森园	112	2 A
Sembawang Gdns Arcade	三巴旺雅吉住宅区	13	2 D	Sims Point	森坊	112	2 B
Sembawang Hill Est	三巴旺山住宅区	45	2 D	Sims Residences	沈氏公寓	113	1 A
Sembawang Springs Est	三巴旺春泉住宅区	13	2 B	Simsville	沈氏景	113	1 A
Sembawang Straits	三巴旺海峡楼	4	1 D	Sin Chuan Garden	新川园	92	2 D
Seng Mansion	成氏大厦	109	2 A	Sin Ming Plaza	新明大厦	67	1 D
Seng Yong Villas	成荣村	92	2 D	Singa Court	新狮阁	92	1 C
Sennett Estate	信立新村	90	1 C	Sixth Avenue Ville	第6道景	86	1 C
Sentosa Cove	升涛湾	143	2 D	SKT Mansions	SKT大厦	112	2 A
Seran Court	实然阁	69	1 D	Sky @ Eleven	天一阁	88	2 C
Serangoon Garden Est	实龙岗花园住宅区	68	2 B	Skyline Angullia	安哥烈天景园	109	2 C
Serangoon Mansion	实龙岗大厦	111	1 B	SkyPark	天际园	110	1 D
Serangoon Park	实龙岗园	68	2 D	Soho 188	苏荷188	111	1 B
Seraya Court	实拉阁	113	2 C	Soho @ Farrer	花拉素荷	111	1 B
Seraya Lodge	实拉雅苑	113	2 C	Soleil @ Sinaran	Soleil @ Sinaran公寓	110	2 A
Seraya Ville	实拉雅	113	2 C	Somerset Bencoolen	索美塞明古连	110	2 D
Serenade Gardens	西利那德花园	46	1 C	Somerset Compass	索美塞康堡	110	1 C
Serene House	实宁楼	87	1 D	Somerset Grand Cairnhill	索美塞豪华经禧	110	1 C
Serene Park	顺利园	47	2 B	Somerset Orchard	索美塞乌节	110	1 C
Serene View Mansion	实木景大厦	89	2 A	Sommerville Court	索美维阁	89	2 A
Serenity Park	春锦园	47	1 B	Sommerville Estate	索美维村	108	2 B
Serenity Terrace	丽景阁	114	1 A	Sommerville Grandeur	索美维豪苑	108	2 A
Setia Residences	实迪雅居	110	1 A	Sommerville Loft	索美维居	90	1 A
Seven Holt Road	七号贺德路公寓	131	2 A	Sommerville Park	索美维园	108	2 A
Seven Nassim	七号那森	109	2 B	Sommerville Regency	索美维皇园	89	2 A
Seven Oaks	七栎园	85	2 C	Soo Chow Garden	苏州园	66	2 D
Shamrock Park	新乐园	86	1 D	Sophia 98	苏菲亚98	110	2 C
Shan Court	祥阁	88	2 D	Sophia Court	淑雅阁	110	2 C
Shan Gate Apartment	祥门公寓	88	2 D	Sophia Crest	索菲亚岭	110	2 C
Shan He Garden	祥和花园	90	2 A	Sophia Flats	索菲亚阁	110	2 C
Shanghai One	上海壹号公寓	109	2 B	Sophia Lodge	索菲亚苑	110	2 C
Shangri-La Apts	香格里拉阁	109	2 B	Sophia Mansions	索菲亚大厦	110	2 C
Shangri-La Park	香格里拉花园	67	1 A	Sophia Service Apts	索菲亚服务公寓	110	2 C
Shangri-La Residences	香格丽阁	109	2 B	Sophia View	淑雅景	110	2 C
Shaw Corner	邵氏一角	88	2 D	Sophia Ville	苏菲雅村	110	2 C
Sheares Ville	薛尔思山庄	131	2 A	South Lake Villa	南湖别墅	69	2 A
Sheda Lodge	雪柏苑	113	1 B	Southaven I	南源山庄(1)	63	2 D
Shelford Court	赐福阁	86	2 C	Southaven II	南源山庄(2)	63	2 D
Shelford Green	世福山庄	86	2 D	Southbank	南岸	111	2 C
Shelford Man	世福大厦	86	2 C	Spanish Villa	西班牙山庄	87	1 B
Shelford Regency	赐福丽苑	86	2 D	Spanish Village	西班牙村庄	108	2 A
Shelford Residences	赐福居	86	2 C	Spottiswoode Apts	史波蒂斯兀公寓	132	1 C
Shelford Suites	世福楼	87	1 C	Springbrook Ter	滨溪园	74	1 B
Shelford Vale	赐福谷	87	1 C	Spring @ Katong	加东之泉	113	2 C
Shelford View	赐福景	86	2 C	Spring Grove	春林	109	2 D
Shepherd's Hill Estate	薛柏斯山村	130	2 A	Springdale	春源峰	63	2 D
Sherwood Condo	谢尔武公寓	84	2 A	Springdew Ter	春露台	129	2 C
Sherwood Towers	谢尔武大厦	85	1 A	Springhill	春岭	13	2 B
Siew Lim Park	秀林园	94	1 C	Springleaf Garden	春叶园	26	2 B
Siglap Court	实乞纳阁	114	2 B	Springleaf Villas	春叶邻	26	2 D

PLACES		MAP GRID		PLACES		MAP GRID	
Springvale	春谷	114	2 B	Sunny Palms	阳光棕园	114	1 A
Springwell Mans	春井楼	94	1 D	Sunny Park	阳光园	87	2 D
Springwood	春林园	129	2 B	Sunnyvale	阳光谷	114	1 A
St. Anne's Wood	圣安尼林	49	2 B	Sunrise Gardens	阳升园	47	1 B
St. Francis Court	欢久阁	89	2 D	Sunrise Townhouse	朝阳豪楼	113	2 A
St. Francis Lodge	圣法兰西苑	89	2 D	Sunrise Villa Estate	阳光别墅	47	1 B
St. Martin's Apts	圣马丁公寓	109	2 C	Sunset Lodge	斜阳苑	84	2 D
St. Martin's Lodge	圣明苑	109	2 C	Sunshine Grove	阳光林	90	1 A
St. Martin's Residence	圣明居	109	2 C	Sunshine Lodge	日光苑	90	1 A
St. Michael's Condo	圣明公寓	89	2 D	Sunshine Loft	阳光楼	113	2 B
St. Michael's Place	圣迈克坊	89	2 D	Sunshine Grandeur	阳光豪宅	114	1 B
St. Michael Regency	圣迈克园	89	2 C	Sunshine Mans	阳光公寓	113	2 A
St. Nicholas View	圣尼格拉景	46	1 D	Sunshine Plaza	阳光坊	110	2 D
St. Patrick's Court	圣巴特力阁	114	1 B	Sunshine Residence	阳光居	114	1 B
St. Patrick's Garden	圣巴特力花园	114	1 B	Sunshine Regency	阳光园	113	2 B
St. Patrick's Green	圣柏特绿苑	114	1 B	Sunville	太阳山庄	89	2 D
St. Patrick's Loft	圣巴特力阁楼	114	1 B	Surrey Court	怡景阁	110	2 A
St. Patrick's Row	圣柏特排屋	114	1 C	Surrey Point	怡景大厦	110	2 A
St. Patrick's View	圣伯景	114	1 B	Swann Court	瑞安阁	112	1 B
St. Patrick's Villa	圣巴特力山庄	114	1 B	Swiss Club Park	瑞士俱乐部园	85	2 B
St. Regis Residences	圣丽奇雅居	109	2 C	Swiss Club Villas	瑞士俱乐部别墅	85	2 B
St. Thomas Court	圣汤姆士阁	110	1 D	Sylvan Lodge	赛温楼	108	1 B
St. Thomas Lodge	圣汤姆士苑	110	1 D	Symphony Heights	雅韵岭	63	2 C
St. Thomas Suites	圣多马公寓	110	1 D	Tai Hwan Garden	大苑花园	68	2 C
St. Thomas View	圣汤姆景	110	1 D	Tai Hwan Pk	大苑园	68	2 C
St. Thomas Ville	圣汤姆士村	110	1 D	Tai Keng Court	大庆阁	90	2 A
Star Mansions	星厦	110	2 A	Tai Keng Garden	大庆花园	69	2 D
Starpoint	星园	129	1 A	Tai Keng Villas	大庆别墅	69	2 D
Starville	星园	92	1 C	Taipan Grand	大班皇园	115	2 B
Stevens Court	史蒂芬阁	109	2 A	Taipan Jade	大班玉园	113	1 B
Stevens Loft	史蒂芬楼	109	2 A	Taipan Regency	夏日园	113	2 C
Straits Garden	海峡园	4	1 C	Tai Pei Apt	大悲公寓	89	1 D
Strata	实丽达	110	2 A	Tai Peng Gardens	太平花园	70	1 B
Stratford Court	乐福阁	94	1 C	Tai Yuan Garden	泰园	69	2 C
Stratton Grn	斯特拉顿景	47	2 C	Tampines Ct	淡滨尼阁	94	1 A
Stratton Park	斯特拉顿园	47	2 C	Tampines Vista	淡滨尼景	72	1 C
Studio 3	Studio 3公寓	109	2 D	Tan Chin Tuan Man	陈振传大楼	110	1 C
Studio @ Marne	玛安公寓	111	1 B	Tan Tong Meng Tower	陈中明大厦	88	2 C
Sturdee View	史德蒂景	111	1 A	Tanah Merah Green	丹那美拉苑	93	2 C
Suffolk Premier	萨福优楼	110	2 A	Tanah Merah Mansions	丹美园	94	1 D
Sui Generis	Sui Generis公寓	110	1 A	Tanamera Crest	红山峰	93	2 C
Suites @ Amber	安柏雅居	113	2 D	Tandeville	丹德景	114	1 B
Suites @ Cairnhill	经禧公寓	110	1 B	Tangerine Grove	锦绣苑	69	2 D
Summer Gardens	夏园	94	1 C	Tanglin Hill Condo	东陵岭公寓	109	1 C
Summer Green	夏日绿苑	88	2 D	Tanglin Hill Meadows	东陵山苑	109	1 C
Summer Grove	夏日林	69	1 D	Tanglin Park	东林园	109	1 D
Summer Place	夏日坊	68	2 C	Tanglin Regency	东陵丽晶园	131	1 A
Summer View	夏日景	112	1 B	Tanglin Residence	东林雅居	109	2 C
Summer Villas	夏日花园	48	1 B	Tanglin View	东陵景	131	1 A
Summerdale	善美园	81	2 A	Tanjong Ria Condo	丹戎丽雅公寓	112	1 D
Summerhill	夏日山庄	63	1 B	Teachers Housing Est	教师园	45	2 C
Summerlea Green	夏苑林	84	2 B	Teck Guan Ville	德光山庄	115	2 A
Summit Ville	顶峰苑	63	1 D	Telok Indah	直落英达	114	1 A
Sun Court	太阳阁	84	2 A	Telok Kurau Court	德乐阁	114	1 A
Sun Glade	明媚景	69	1 D	Telok Kurau Lodge	德乐苑	114	1 A
Sun Rosier	豪山村	90	2 A	Telok Kurau Mansion	德乐楼	114	1 B
Sunbird View	桑柏景	94	2 A	Telok Kurau View	德乐景	114	1 B
Sunflower Court	葵花阁	112	1 B	Telok Mansion	德乐大厦	114	1 B
Sunflower Lodge	葵花村	112	2 B	Tembeling Grove	登百岭苑	113	2 D
Sunflower Mansions	升阳楼	112	2 B	Tembeling Mans	登百岭村	113	2 B
Sunflower Regency	葵花苑	112	2 B	Ten Suffolk	珠福之十	110	2 A
Sunflower Residences	葵花居	112	2 B	Teresa 8	特丽莎8号	131	2 C
Sunflower View	升阳景	112	2 B	Teresa Ville	新祥苑	131	2 C
Sungrove	太阳林	105	2 B	Terrace View	台景楼	113	2 C
Sunhaven	向阳楼	73	2 D	Tessa Lodge	蒂莎村	113	2 C
Sunnidora	善宁多拉	114	1 A	TG Mansion	TG大厦	114	1 A
Sunniflora	朝花楼	114	1 A				

• PRIVATE HOUSING 私人住宅区 CONDOS 共管式公寓 APARTMENTS 公寓

• PRIVATE HOUSING / CONDOS / APARTMENTS

PLACES		MAP GRID		PLACES		MAP GRID	
The Aberdeen	雅柏苑	89	2 D	The Compass at Chancery	彰思礼之罗盘	88	1 D
The Abode At Devonshire	雅博楼	110	1 D	The Cornwall	康华楼	108	1 B
The Acacias	阿卡西亚园	90	1 A	The Cosmopolitan	世界景观	110	1 D
The Adara	The Adara公寓	113	2 C	The Countryside	长青乡园	46	1 B
The Albracca	爱尔巴塞园	112	2 D	The Courtyard	高雅园	69	2 B
The Alcove	雅科夫园	112	2 A	The Daffodil	得富园	115	2 A
The Ambience	舒适楼	30	2 B	The Dew	绿亭	83	2 B
The Ambra	The Ambra公寓	114	1 A	The Draycott	德雷葛花园	109	2 B
The Ambrosia	The Ambrosia公寓	114	1 B	The East Side	东域公寓	113	2 C
The Amery	The Amery公寓	114	1 B	The Eden	伊甸园	73	2 C
The Amston	安舒村	63	1 C	The Edge on Cairnhill	经禧缘	110	1 B
The Anchorage	金锭园	130	2 A	The Edgewater	The Edgewater公寓	52	1 B
The Ansley	诺云峰	88	2 D	The Elegance @ Changi	樟宜雅居	113	2 A
The Arcadia	雅卡迪雅	86	2 B	The Elements	Elements公寓	109	2 A
The Arc at Draycott	德雷葛拱廊	109	2 B	The Elysia	爱丽厦	89	2 A
The Ardmore	雅茂公寓	109	2 B	The Equatorial	贵都楼	109	2 A
The Areca	雅利佳园	90	2 B	The ES Paris	ES巴黎园	73	2 A
The Aristo	The Aristo公寓	113	2 D	The Esquire	绅士园	110	1 C
The Armadale	雅玛达公寓	110	1 A	The Espira	The Espira公寓	114	1 B
The Arris	艾瑞斯	132	2 C	The Esta	爱丝达	113	2 C
The Arte	The Arte公寓	88	2 C	The Estiva	绿竹园	129	1 B
The Aspine	雅松园	109	2 A	The Estoril	埃斯多里园	108	1 B
The Aston	凯轩	109	2 D	The Fernhill	苏禧	109	2 B
The Atria at Meyer	爱思佳楼	113	1 D	The Floravale	花景轩	59	2 D
The Axis	中轴大厦	88	2 D	The Florentine	佛罗伦萨雅居	69	2 B
The Azure	安舒丽公寓	143	2 C	The Florida	富乐园	49	2 D
The Azzuro	青天楼	114	1 A	The Foliage	西滨园	128	2 A
The Balé	百丽公寓	113	2 A	The Ford	The Ford公寓	107	2 A
The Balmoral	百慕乐	109	2 A	The Fortune View	丰运豪	90	1 A
The Balmoral Spring	百慕乐春楼	110	1 A	The Gale	微风楼	74	1 C
The Baycourt	碧海苑	115	2 A	The Gardens at Bishan	碧山之园	67	1 B
The Bayron	碧龙园	110	1 D	The Gardens at Gerald	杰乐园	48	1 C
The Bayshore	翠湾园	115	2 B	The Geranium	天竺葵公寓	113	2 B
The Beacon	灯塔	132	1 C	The Gilstead	吉斯德景	110	1 A
The Beaumont	华邸阁	110	1 D	The Glacier	冰川园	113	2 B
The Beccagayle	贝卡盖雅	114	1 B	The Glencaird Residences	葛瑟居	109	1 A
The Bellaforte	百乐福	88	2 C	The Grandhill	Grandhill公寓	129	1 B
The Belmont	贝蒙楼	108	1 B	The Grandiflora	格兰富丽苑	114	1 B
The Belvedere	The Belvedere公寓	112	2 D	The Grange	格兰芝公寓	109	2 C
The Berth by The Cove	小湾轩	143	2 C	The Greenwood	绿林	86	2 B
The Berthside	泊宁轩	143	2 C	The Habitat 1	Habitat 1公寓	109	2 B
The Biltmore	尔特摩园	109	2 C	The Hacienda	丽园	115	1 B
The Blossomvale	繁花园	85	1 B	The Hamilton	翰密顿园	110	1 B
The Botanic on Lloyd	来益园	110	1 D	The Heliconia	海莉可尼亚苑	92	1 D
The Bougainville Msn Apts	波甘维共管公寓	113	2 A	The Hermitage	和美德苑	110	1 A
The Boulevard Residences	宝露华居	109	2 C	The Hill Park	山园公寓	87	2 C
The Cairnhill	经禧	110	1 C	The Hillside	峰嵌	63	2 D
The Callista	卡丽达园	89	2 D	The Horizon	The Horizon公寓	109	2 D
The Calrose	Calrose公寓	46	1 C	The Huntington	含丁登苑	110	2 A
The Calypso	卡立素公寓	115	2 A	The Imperial	帝国公寓	110	2 D
The Capri	嘉碧苑	109	2 A	The Infiniti	Infiniti公寓	105	2 A
The Carpmaelina	卡美丽娜	113	2 B	The Inglewood	英格林	66	2 B
The Cascadia	The Cascadia 公寓	85	2 B	The Inspira	运必乐公寓	132	1 A
The Cassandra	佳善达园	129	2 C	The Jade	玉楼公寓	62	2 D
The Cathay Residences	国泰豪居	110	2 D	The Ladyhill	淑女山楼	109	2 B
The Centrio	The Centrio公寓	88	2 D	The Lake Shore	湖滨园	82	1 A
The Centris	Centris公寓	81	1 A	The Legacy	礼畴	87	1 D
The Champagne	祥彬园	114	1 A	The Legend	丽晶园	109	2 A
The Chancery Residence	彰思礼居	88	1 D	The Lentor Residence	伦多居	46	1 B
The Chuan	川轩	68	2 D	The Level Z	The Level Z 公寓	108	2 B
The Citrine	西特灵	88	2 C	The Lincoln Modern	新林肯公寓	110	2 A
The Claymore	启茂阁	109	2 B	The Light	光穿公寓	110	1 C
The Clayton	启登楼	109	2 A	The Lighthouse	灯塔公寓	52	2 D
The Clearwater	清景园	93	1 B	The Linc	盈双阁	110	2 A
The Clementvale	金文苑	106	1 B	The Linear	里岭	42	1 D
The Clift	The Clift 公寓	132	2 C	The Loft	阁楼	109	2 C
The Coast At Sentosa Cove	升涛湾之滨	143	2 D				

• PRIVATE HOUSING / CONDOS / APARTMENTS

PLACES		MAP GRID
The Lumos	Lumos公寓	110 1 D
The Madeira	马德拉公寓	62 2 C
The Makena	麦肯那	113 1 D
The Marbella Ct	美乐园	107 1 A
The Marq Paterson Hill	巴德申山大厦	109 2 D
The Marque @ Irrawaddy	依拉瓦底标记	88 2 D
The Mayfair	玫芳园	82 2 A
The Maylea	媚丽公寓	129 2 C
The Medge	麦奇公寓	88 2 D
The Medley	The Medley公寓	114 1 A
The Mera Saga	嵋池苑	108 1 B
The Mergui	美贵园	111 1 A
The Merlot	美乐楼	110 2 B
The Metropolitan	大都会	131 1 A
The Metz	梅斯坊	110 1 D
The Meyer Place	美港坊	112 2 D
The Midas	美达公寓	112 2 B
The Mint Residences	The Mint雅居	113 2 A
The Modules	模式公寓	113 2 B
The Mondrian	蒙德里安园	64 1 D
The Montana	观潮阁	109 2 D
The Montage	蒙太奇公寓	114 1 D
The Morning Dew	晨露园	48 1 A
The Morning Glory	晨辉楼	69 1 C
The Morningside	曙光大厦	110 1 D
The Mornington	莫宁敦公寓	89 2 D
The Navigators	导航园	114 1 A
The Nclave	The Nclave公寓	114 1 B
The Oceanfront	濒洋公寓	143 2 D
The Orange Gr	橘林	109 2 B
The Palladium	帕拉典阁	113 2 C
The Parc	The Parc公寓	106 1 B
The Parisian	巴黎园	109 2 C
The Park Central	The Park Central公寓	68 1 A
The Park Vale	乐园谷	86 2 C
The Paterson	巴德申楼	109 2 D
The Paterson Edge	巴德申边园	109 2 C
The Peak	峰园	129 2 B
The Pearl	山亭	131 2 D
The Petals	百特花园	63 1 C
The Pier	天滨轩	132 1 A
The Pinnacle @ Duxton	达士岭	132 1 C
The Primero	滨美罗	112 2 B
The Princeton	滨盛楼	110 1 A
The Prominence	卓越公寓	113 1 B
The Quartz	Quartz公寓	49 1 C
The Quayside	码头苑	132 1 A
The Quintet	冠庭园	22 2 D
The Raintree	雨林	63 2 D
The Regalia	爵士大厦	110 1 D
The Regency at Tiong Bahru	中巴鲁雅居	131 2 B
The Residences at Baker	巴克雅居	88 1 D
The Richmond	富梦园	89 2 D
The Ritz Carlton Residences, S'pore Cairnhill	新加坡经禧丽嘉登雅居	110 1 B
The Riverina	丽河苑	51 2 C
The Riverine	河滨公寓	111 2 B
The Riverside Piazza/Apts	河滨坊楼 (公寓与商业大厦)	132 2 A
The Rivervale	鲤河园	49 2 C
The Riverwalk Apts	河畔公寓	132 2 A
The Sail @ Marina Bay	滨海舫	133 1 C
The Seafront on Meyer	麦雅滨海楼	112 2 D
The Seaview	海景公寓	113 2 C
The Sensoria	Sensoria公寓	13 2 C
The Sentinel	立克	110 2 A
The Serenade	小夜曲公寓	107 1 A
The Shaugnessy	肖纳思公寓	27 2 B
The Shelford	赐福公寓	86 2 D
The Sierra	金峰苑	107 1 A
The Silver Spurz	The Silver Spurz公寓	69 1 B
The Silverston	银村	113 2 B
The Solitaire	矗立公寓	109 2 A
The Sovereign	君元公寓	113 1 D
The Spectrum	宏景公寓	128 2 A
The Spinnaker	顺风楼	110 2 A
The Springbloom	春盛苑	68 2 D
The Springfield	春园	94 1 C
The Springs	春槐	110 2 A
The Springside	水乡	26 1 D
The Stellar	史特拉公寓	128 2 A
The Sterling	银树园	85 1 B
The Summit	顶峰园	115 2 A
The Sunflower	升阳园	112 2 B
The Sunniflora	向阳花楼	114 1 A
The Sunny Legend	昇阳晶公寓	114 1 A
The Sunny Spring	丽春园	113 1 B
The Sunnydale	丽春谷	68 2 D
The Sunshine	阳光公寓	90 1 A
The Taipan	大宾楼	115 1 B
The Tanamera	丹那美拉	93 2 D
The Tate Residences	塔特居	109 2 B
The Teneriffe	恬丽村	85 2 C
The Tessarina	嘉鸿花园	85 2 C
The Tiara	冠冕公寓	109 2 D
The Tomlinson	汤林生公寓	109 2 C
The Treeline	The Treeline公寓	114 1 A
The Tresor	The Tresor公寓	86 2 D
The Trevose	特富苑	87 2 D
The Trillium	特联大厦	110 1 D
The Tropic Gardens	东宝园	115 2 A
The Tropica	濠景园	72 1 D
The Trumps	王牌楼	114 1 A
The Twins	双凼楼	110 1 A
The Vantage	富利园	109 2 B
The Vermillion	凡尔美伦	114 1 A
The Vermont	凡尔门	110 1 B
The Verte	The Verte公寓	114 1 A
The Verve	The Verve公寓	88 2 C
The Vesta	The Vesta公寓	114 1 B
The View @ Meyer	麦雅美景楼	112 2 D
The Village	村园	128 2 A
The Villas @ Sentosa Cove	升涛湾别墅	143 2 C
The Vines	葡萄苑	114 1 A
The Warren	华伦	41 1 A
The Waterdale	丽水山庄	85 2 C
The Waterina	The Waterina公寓	113 1 B
The Waterside	听涛阁	112 2 D
The Wilshire	威瑟园	108 2 B
The Windmill	风车园	108 1 B
The Windsor	温莎园	66 2 C
The Woodgrove	木林苑	11 1 D
The Yardley	雅丽苑	69 1 D
Thomson 800 Condo	彤轩	88 1 A
Thomson Euro-Asia	华洋汤申	110 2 A
Thomson Garden Est	汤申花园住宅区	67 1 C
Thomson Grove	汤申林木	46 1 C
Thomson Hills	汤申山	46 1 D
Thomson Park	汤申园	67 1 C
Thomson Ridge Est	汤申岭村	67 1 D
Thomson Rise Est	汤申坡村	67 2 C
Thomson V	汤申坡村	67 2 C
Thomson View Condo	汤申景花园	66 2 C
Three Buckley	巴克里叁号	110 1 A
Three Three Robin	Three Three Robin公寓	109 2 A
Tian Court	天阁	113 2 B

PLACES		MAP GRID	PLACES		MAP GRID
Tian So Heights	恬舒岭	110 1 A	Verdun House	维顿大厦	111 1 B
Tiara	帝乐公寓	110 1 D	Versailles Condo	凡尔塞园	113 1 B
Tiara Vista	冠冕景	114 1 B	Versilia on Haig	海格华西丽亚公寓	113 1 B
Tierra Vue	Tierra Vue 公寓	114 1 B	Vertis	Vertis公寓	113 2 C
Tilton	狄尔登	108 2 A	Vetro	Vetro公寓	89 2 D
Tivoli Gardens	华丽园	90 2 A	Vicenta Lodge	云生公居	92 1 D
Tivoli Lodge	蒂沃里楼	112 2 A	Victoria Park	维多利亚园	108 1 A
Toa Payoh Rise Apts	大巴窑坡公寓	88 1 B	Victory Heights	胜利岭	89 1 D
Toh Heights	卓岭	74 1 B	Vida	伟达园	110 1 B
Toh Tuck Garden	道德花园	84 2 B	View Point Mansion	景远大厦	88 2 C
Toh Tuck Hill Estate	道德岭园	84 2 B	Villa Azura	翠蓝别墅	85 2 C
Toh Tuck Villa	道德山庄	84 2 A	Villa Begonia	秋海棠别墅	47 2 C
Toh Yi Court	道义阁	84 2 B	Villa Chancerita	钱榭里达别墅	88 1 D
Toho Garden	东丰花园	69 1 A	Villa Chancery	彰思礼别墅	88 1 D
Toho Green	东丰苑	69 1 B	Villa De West	西方别墅	128 2 A
Toho Mansion	东丰大厦	108 1 B	Villa Delle	幽谷别墅	69 1 B
Tong Kong Gardens	东光花园	90 2 B	Villa Delle Rose	玫瑰山庄	108 2 B
Tong Watt Mansion	东发大厦	132 1 C	Villa Des Flores	百花山庄	88 1 D
Top Ten Apartment	顶登公寓	110 1 C	Villa D'Este	西部山庄	109 2 A
Topaz Mansions	荣柏大厦	89 2 C	Villa Laguna	礁湖之居	115 2 A
Torie Mansions	托里大厦	113 2 B	Villa Madeleine	麦德林别墅	110 1 D
Torieview Mansions	托里景大厦	112 2 A	Villa Margaux	根高别墅	109 2 A
Torrie Ville	托里谷	112 1 B	Villa Marina	碧涛园	115 1 B
Towner Ville	陶纳园	111 1 A	Villa Marine	美林公寓	114 2 B
Townhouse Apartments	陶豪斯楼	110 2 B	Villa Martia	马西雅别墅	114 1 C
Treasure Gdns	财宝园	69 2 B	Villa Verde	丰涛别墅	41 2 B
Treasure Loft	财宝阁楼	110 2 A	Village Tower	绿村楼	107 1 A
Treasure Mansions	珍宝大厦	69 1 B	Villas at Kew	邱氏别墅	94 1 D
Treasure Place	聚宝坊	129 2 C	Villas Holland	荷兰山庄	107 2 A
Treetops Executive	树顶高级住宅	109 2 B	Villas Laguna	河畔山庄	115 2 A
Residences Service Apts	服务公寓		Ville Royale	皇家山庄	110 2 D
Trellis Towers	瑞丽大厦	88 2 C	Vina Lodge	温娜村	69 1 C
Trendale Tower	迎运园	110 1 B	Visin Apartment	威信公寓	110 2 A
Trevose 12	Trevose 12号公寓	87 2 D	Vision Crest	伟景峰	110 2 D
Trevose Park	特雷沃斯园	87 2 D	Vista Garden	伟大花园	84 1 B
Tribeca	特丽贝卡	132 1 A	Vista Park	伟大园	129 2 B
Trivoli Lodge Mansion	迪华丽园楼	112 2 A	Vistaya View	伟大雅景	113 1 A
Tropical Spring	澎涛苑	94 2 A	Vitra	伟特拉公寓	113 2 B
Tropicana Condo	热带公寓	94 2 A	Viz Holland	Viz Holland公寓	108 1 C
Trussville	Trussville园	69 2 D	Vogx	Vogx公寓	111 1 A
Tuan Sing Park	传倩园	47 2 B	Vutton	沃登公寓	88 2 D
Tudor Ten	杜德十	87 1 D	Waldorf Mansions	志远大厦	89 1 B
Tulip Garden	金香园	108 1 B	Wan Tho Lodge	运涛苑	90 1 B
Turquoise	绿松石公寓	147 1 A	Wang Lodge	王氏苑	112 1 B
Twin Hts (Shaw Plaza)	双岭楼(邵氏商业大厦)	89 1 D	Warner Court	温拿阁	108 1 B
Twin Regency	双皇楼	131 2 B	Watercrest	水田芹公寓	52 2 D
Tyrwhitt 139	德威139公寓	111 1 B	Water Place	海涛苑	112 1 D
Ultra Mansion	极豪大厦	110 2 A	Water Scape @ Cavenagh	加文纳水景楼	110 1 C
Unique Hill Est	友力园	84 2 B	Waterfall Gardens	瀑布花园	108 2 B
Unit 8	第8单位公寓	108 2 B	Waterford Res	华德福居	132 1 A
United Mansion	联合大厦	114 2 B	Waterford Terrace	海洋园	129 1 A
University Park	大学苑	87 1 D	Waterfront Collection	滨水之珍	147 1 A
Upper Serangoon	实龙岗上段	69 2 C	Waterfront View	水滨景	93 1 B
Shopping Ctr	购物中心		Waterfront Waves	滨海涛	93 1 B
Urban Edge	Urban Edge公寓	107 2 A	Waterloo Apartments	滑铁卢公寓	111 1 D
Urban Resort	市区胜楼	110 1 C	Waterloo View	伦敦楼景	111 1 D
Urbana	城市之光	110 1 D	Watten Estate	华登岭	86 2 C
Valencia	维柏西亚楼	69 2 D	Watten Estate Condo	华登岭公寓	86 2 C
Valley House	华丽屋	110 1 D	Watten Hill Condo	华登岭园	86 2 C
Valley Lodge	华丽苑	110 1 D	Wedgewood Mansions	维治兀大厦	114 1 B
Valley Mansion	巴利洋楼	110 1 D	Wei Ming Garden	玮敏花园	94 1 D
Valley Park	华丽园	131 2 A	Welkin Mansion	惠景大厦	132 1 A
Vanadium	万钠登	110 2 B	Wellington Garden	威灵顿花园	67 1 A
Varsity Park	大学园	106 2 D	Wessex Estate	威硕斯村	108 1 D
Vaughan Garden	富利园	69 1 D	West Bay	西湾	106 2 D
Venezio	温利吉公寓	115 2 A	West Coast Court	西岸阁	106 2 B
Ventana	温达娜	129 1 B	Westcove	西海湾渡假公寓	106 2 D
Ventuno Balmoral	温敦诺百慕乐	110 1 A	Western Grove	西海景园	129 1 C
Veranda	华兰达楼	114 1 B	Westlake Gardens	西湖花园	88 1 B

PLACES		MAP GRID
Westmere	蔚湄园	82 2 B
Westmont	威士蒙	128 2 A
West-N	West-N公寓	129 1 C
Westpark	西园	129 1 A
Westpark Regency	西园丽晶	129 1 A
Westpoint Condo	西林公寓	129 2 C
Westvale	西谷	129 1 A
Westville	西景山庄	59 2 C
Westwood Apartments	良园	109 2 C
Westwood Park	西林园	60 1 D
Wharton Vale	华�谷	110 2 C
White House Pk Apts	白宫园	109 2 A
White Water	清水园	51 1 C
Whitfield Garden	威菲花园	114 2 B
Whitley Heights Condo	威利岭公寓	88 1 D
Wilby Bt Timah	威美武吉知马	85 2 C
Wilby Central	威美中心	111 1 D
Wilkie 48	威基48	110 2 C
Wilkie Apartment	威基公寓	110 2 C
Wilkie Court	威基阁	110 2 C
Wilkie Grove	威基林	110 2 C
Wilkie Regency	威基皇庄	110 2 C
Wilkie Studio	威基小楼	110 2 C
Willyn Ville	维林园	108 1 B
Wilmer House	威尔玛楼	110 1 D
Wimborne Villa	温波纳别墅	112 2 C
Windermere	泫湄园	41 2 A
Windsor Park Estate	温莎园村	66 2 D
Windy Heights	永丽园	92 1 D
Winfield Mans	温装楼	112 2 B
Wing Fong Court	永丰阁	112 1 B
Wing Fong Mansions	永丰楼	112 1 B
Wing on Life Gardens	永安人寿花园	109 2 A
Winsome Apartments	永胜公寓	112 1 B
Wonder Grove	蓬莱花园	69 1 D
Woodgrove Condo	木林共管公寓	11 1 D
Woodgrove Estate	木林住宅	11 1 D
Woodlands Park	兀兰花园	23 1 B
Woodleigh Park	兀里园	89 2 A
Woodsvale	竹翠园	12 2 B
Woodsville 28	兀兰维28公寓	89 2 C
Woodsville Mansion	兀兰维大厦	89 2 C
Woollerton Park	武勒登园	108 2 A
Woollerton Park Apts	武勒登园公寓	108 2 A
Woo Man Chew Ct	胡文剑阁	115 1 A
Worthington	华丁登	113 1 B
Xie Rong Court	协融阁	89 2 C
Xiu Lan Court	秀兰阁	88 2 D
Yew Lian Park	友联园	67 1 D
Yew Mei Green	悠美苑	41 1 A
YewTee Residences	油池居	41 1 A
Yi Kai Court	毅凯阁	69 2 D
Yi Li Apartment	怡利大厦	115 1 B
Yi Mei Garden	怡美园	70 1 B
Ying Mansions	英氏大厦	109 2 A
Yishun Emerald	义顺绿宝石	13 2 B
Yishun Sapphire	义顺蓝宝石楼	13 2 B
Yong An Park	永安苑	110 1 D
Yong Siak Lodge	永瑞庭	113 2 B
Yong Siak Court	永锡阁	131 2 B
York Apartments	和丰公寓	85 1 D
Yu Li Yuan	玉丽园	85 1 B
Yuan Ching Road Apts	园景路公寓	82 1 A
Yugi Garden	友谊花园	94 1 C
Zenith	顶级楼	131 2 A
Zephyr Park	和风园	94 1 B
Zion Mansion	锡安大厦	107 2 A

PLACES		MAP GRID
PUBLIC / COMMERCIAL BLDGS / INDUSTRIAL BLDGS		
1 Philip Street	菲立士街一号	132 2 B
3M - Upper Thomson	3M - 汤申上段	45 2 C
3M - Woodlands	3M - 兀兰	12 2 A
6th Avenue Ctr	第六道中心	86 1 C
8 Shenton Way	珊顿大道八号	132 2 C
8 @ Trade Hub 21	8 @ Trade Hub 21贸易大厦	83 2 C
30 Hill Street	30禧街	132 2 A
50 Collyer Quay	50哥烈码头	133 1 B
76 Shenton Way	76 珊顿大道	132 2 D
79 Anson Rd	安顺路79号	132 2 C
80 Robinson Road	80罗敏申路	132 2 C
268 Orchard Road	268乌节路	110 1 C
600 @ TP	600 @ 大巴窑	89 1 B
888 Plaza	发发发商业中心	12 1 C
AA Singapore	新加坡汽车公会中心	
- River Valley Road	- 里巴巴利路	110 1 D
- Kung Chong Road	- 工厂路	130 2 A
Abacus Plaza	环宝大厦	72 2 D
ABV Ind Ctr	ABV工业大厦	95 1 C
Accord Famous Distri Ctr	雅阁驰名分销中心	94 1 B
Ace Bldg	亿志大厦	91 1 C
Acer Computer	宏基电脑	83 1 C
Adam FC	亚当食阁	87 1 D
Admiralty Place	海军部坊	12 1 C
Advance Bldg	益元大厦	90 2 B
Aero Space Training Ctr	宇航训练中心	74 1 D
Afro Asia Bldg	亚非大厦	132 2 C
Agility	Agility大厦	74 1 D
AIA Bldg	美国友邦保险大厦	130 1 B
AIA Changi	美国友邦保险(樟宜)	113 2 A
AIA Tampines	美国友邦保险(淡滨尼)	72 2 C
AIA Tower	美国友邦保险大楼	133 1 B
AIG Bldg	AIG大厦	132 1 A
Airline House	航空公司大厦	54 2 D
Airview Bldg	风景大厦	132 2 C
AIS Ind Bldg	AIS工业大厦	111 1 C
Albert Complex	雅柏商业大厦	111 1 C
Albert Court	雅柏广场	111 1 C
Albert Ctr	雅柏坊	111 1 C
Albert Ind Bldg	雅柏工业大厦	14 1 B
Alexandra Ctr	亚历山大中心	130 2 A
Alexandra Point	亚历山大大厦	130 1 C
Alexandra Technopark	亚历山大科技园	130 1 C
Alfa Ctr	爱华中心	110 2 C
Alfa Romeo Bldg	爱法罗密欧大厦	83 1 D
Aljunied Ind Complex	阿裕尼工业大厦	90 2 D
Alkaff Mansion	阿尔卡夫大厦	130 2 C
Allenby House	爱伦比大厦	111 1 B
Alpha Bldg	爱华工业大厦	90 2 C
ALPS Ctr 2	机场后勤园中心2	54 2 D
Alteon	Alteon大厦	74 1 D
Alumni Medical Ctr	医学院校友会	132 1 B
Atron Bldg	爱特丝大厦	91 2 D
Amar Raj House	阿玛拉吉大厦	132 2 A
Amitabha Bldg	净宗学会大厦	112 2 A
AMK Hub	宏茂桥中心	67 2 A
AMK Tech Link	宏茂桥科技链	48 1 D
Amoy Canning	淘化大同	81 2 C
Amtech Bldg	安德大厦	67 1 C
Anchor Point	安格坊	130 2 A

PRIVATE HOUSING 私人住宅 CONDOS 共管式公寓 APARTMENTS 公寓 • PUBLIC 公共 COMMERCIAL BLDGS 商业建筑物 INDUSTRIAL BLDGS 工业大厦

PLACES		MAP GRID
Ang Mo Kio Autopoint	宏茂桥汽车坊	47 2 D
Ang Mo Kio Tech 1&2	宏茂桥第一和第二科技园	47 2 D
Ann Chuan Complex	安川大厦	111 2 B
Ann Siang 47	安祥47	132 2 C
Anson Ctr	安顺大厦	132 2 D
Anson House	安盛大厦	132 2 D
AOS Bldg	AOS大厦	107 2 D
AOS Ind Bldg	AOS工业大厦	22 1 C
Apex Tower	艾柏士大厦	132 2 D
APG Bldg	APG大厦	132 2 A
Apico Ind Bldg	阿笔克工业大厦	95 1 C
Apollo Ctr	阿波罗中心	132 2 B
Apple Computers	苹果电脑	46 2 B
APS Bldg	APS大厦	132 1 A
APS Ind Bldg	APS工业大厦	67 2 D
Aqua Terra	Aqua Terra大厦	80 1 D
Armorcoat Intl Bldg	亚摩科国际大厦	91 1 B
Armorcoat Technologies Bldg	亚摩科技大厦	91 1 B
Asia Insurance Bldg (A.I. Bldg)	亚洲保险大厦	133 1 B
Asia Pacific Polyolefin Tech Ctr	陶氏亚太区聚烯烃技术中心	99 1 C
Asia Radio Bldg	亚洲无线电大厦	90 2 B
Asian Civilisation Museum	亚洲文明博物馆	133 1 B
Asiawide Ind Bldg	泛亚工业大厦	90 2 B
Association Bldg	联合大厦	112 2 B
ATD Ctr	ATD中心	90 2 B
Atland House	爱特兰屋	110 2 B
Automobile Megamart	汽车城	91 2 C
Avari Ctr	爱法利中心	113 1 A
Aviva	Aviva大厦	132 2 C
AW Transport Warehouse	AW运输货仓	99 1 B
Ayer Rajah Telecommunication Cplx	亚逸拉惹电信大厦	107 1 B
A-Z Bldg	裕集大厦	91 1 C
Aztech Bldg	爱捷特大厦	91 1 C
Balestier Complex	百利购物商场	89 1 D
Balestier Ctr	马里士他中心	88 2 D
Balestier Hill Shopping Ctr	马里士他山购物中心	88 2 D
Balestier Plaza	马里士他商场	89 1 D
Balestier Warehouse	马里士他货仓	89 1 D
Balmoral Plaza	百慕乐商场	110 1 A
Ban Hong Leong Bldg	万丰隆大厦	111 1 C
Ban Teck Han Bldg	万得行大厦	48 1 D
Banchong Bldg	万中大厦	111 2 B
Bangkok Bank Bldg	曼谷银行大厦	132 2 C
Bank of China	中国银行	133 1 B
Bank of East Asia Bldg	东亚银行大厦	132 2 B
Barry Callebout Ind Chocolate Fty	巴里加乐布商用巧克力工厂	2 1 D
BAS Bldg	盛总大厦	112 1 B
Bauer Equipment Bldg	宝峨大厦	2 1 C
Baxter Health Care Pte Ltd	白特医疗有限公司	10 1 D
BBC Far Eastern Relay Stn (Merlin Communication)	英国广播公司远播站 (梅林传播站)	21 2 A
BBR	BBR	95 1 B
Beach Ctr	美芝中心	111 1 D
Beach Junction	美芝汇集楼	111 1 D
Beauty World Ctr	美世界中心	85 1 A
Beauty World Plaza	美世界商场	85 1 A
Bedok Market Place	勿洛坊	94 1 C
Bedok Shopping Ctr	勿洛购物中心	94 1 C
Bencoolen House	明古连大厦	110 2 D
Bendemeer Shopping Mall	明地迷亚购物中心	111 2 A
Bestway Bldg	伟新大厦	132 2 D
Bethesda Ctr	贝特达中心	68 2 D
Betime Bldg	美泰大厦	90 1 C
BH Bldg	BH大厦	111 2 B
Bharat Bldg	巴拉大厦	132 2 B
BHL Tech Factories	BHL科技工厂	23 1 C
Bible House	圣经大厦	132 2 A
Big Box	Big Box大厦	83 1 C
Big Mac Ctr	宏大中心	67 2 A
Bishan Nth Shopping Mall	碧山北购物中心	67 2 C
Biz Link Ctr	商联中心	91 1 D
Biztech Ctr	Biztech中心	90 2 D
BOC Plaza	中行大厦	111 1 D
Bodynits Bldg	波帝尼斯大厦	94 1 C
Boon Bldg	文厦	132 2 B
Boon Lay Place Market & FC	文礼坊巴刹及食阁	81 2 A
Boon Lay Shopping Ctr	文礼购物中心	60 2 D
Boon Liew Bldg	文流大厦	110 2 B
Boon Siew Bldg	文秀大厦	110 2 C
Boon Teck House	文德大厦	91 2 C
Boon Thong Bldg	文忠大厦	112 2 B
Borneo/Champion Motors	婆罗洲/冠军汽车公司	106 1 C
Bottle Tree Village	红千层树村	4 2 C
Boustead House	慕安德大厦	91 1 D
Bowmont Ctr	包满中心	114 2 A
Boy's Brigade Hq	少年旅总部	131 2 A
Braddell Tech	布莱德科技大厦	89 1 A
Brani Terminal Building	布拉尼终站大厦	142 2 D
Bras Basah Complex	百胜楼	111 1 D
Bright Bldg	光明大厦	88 2 D
Bright Chambers	光明阁	111 1 D
Bright Ctr	宏明中心	114 1 B
Bright Jade Bldg	光钰大厦	111 1 B
Brightway Bldg	光玉大厦	90 1 C
British Council	英国文化协会	109 1 C
BTC Bldg	BTC大厦	90 2 B
BTH Global Bldg	BTH环球大厦	14 1 B
Buddhist Heritage Ctr	佛教文物中心	92 1 D
Budget Terminal	廉价航空终站	96 1 D
Budi Ctr	Budi中心	112 1 B
Bugis Junction	白沙浮广场	111 1 D
Bugis Junction Towers	白沙浮商业城大厦	111 1 D
Bugis Village	武吉士村	111 1 D
Builders Ctr	武吉士中心	95 1 C
Bt Batok East Point	武吉巴督东坊	63 1 D
Bt Batok West Shopping Ctr	武吉巴督西购物中心	62 1 D
Bt Panjang LRT Depot (Ten Mile Junction)	武吉班让轻轨列车总站(十里广场)	42 1 C
Bukit Panjang Plaza	武吉班让大厦	42 1 C
Bukit Pasoh Terrace	武吉巴梳台	132 1 C
Bukit Timah Plaza	武吉知马大厦	85 1 B
Bt Timah Railway Stn	武吉知马火车站	85 1 C
Bt Timah Shopping Ctr	武吉知马购物中心	85 1 A
Burkill Hall	伯基尔楼	109 1 C
Burlington Square	柏龄顿广场	111 1 C
Bylands Bldg	培元大厦	111 1 D
C&C Service Ctr	合发服务中心	132 1 A
C&P Logistics Hub 1 & 2	C&P物流中心1和2	104 2 B
C&P Vehicle Export Processing Zone	C&P车辆出口处理区	83 2 C

Place	Chinese	Grid
Cairnhill Place	金禧大厦	110 1 C
Caldecott Broadcast Ctr	加利谷广播中心	87 2 B
Cantonment Ctr	广东民中心	132 2 B
Capital Square	首都广场	132 2 B
Capital Square Three	首都广场3	132 2 B
Capital Square Two	首都广场2	132 2 B
Capital Tower	资金大厦	132 2 C
Capitol Bldg	首都大厦	133 1 B
Capitol Ctr	首都中心	133 1 A
Cargo Agents Bldgs	货物代理大厦	54 2 C
Carlton	卡尔登楼	74 1 D
Castrol House	加实多公司	104 1 D
Cathay Cineleisure Orchard	国泰乌节电影院	110 1 C
Catholic Welfare Ctr	天主教福利中心	111 1 D
Causeway Point	长堤大厦	11 2 C
CDAC Bldg	华社自助理事会大厦	113 1 B
CE Bldg	CE大厦	14 1 B
Cecil Court	丝丝阁	132 2 C
Cecil House	丝丝大厦	132 2 C
CEH Ind Bldg	CEH工业大厦	90 2 C
Cemtex Ind Bldg	申德斯工业大厦	90 2 B
Cencon Bldg	胜光大厦	90 1 C
Cendex	善德大厦	131 2 C
Centennial Tower	盛年大厦	133 2 A
Central	中央梭贺	132 2 A
Central Mall	中央广场	132 2 A
Central Plaza	中央大广场	131 2 B
Central S'pore Joint Social Service Ctr	新加坡中区联合社会福利中心	88 2 A
Central Square	市中广场	132 2 A
Centros (Biopolis)	Centros (启奥生物医药研究园)	107 2 C
Century Ind Bldg	世纪工业大厦	90 2 A
Century Square	世纪广场	72 2 D
Century Technology Bldg	世纪科技大厦	112 2 A
Century Warehouse	世纪货仓	130 1 C
CES Bldg	CES大厦	91 2 C
CGH Bldg	庄锦发大厦	110 1 D
Champagnat House	香槟那大厦	69 2 B
Chancerlodge Complex	增顺大厦	112 1 A
Change Alley Aerial Plaza	真者里空中购物长廊	133 1 B
Change Alley Aerial Tower	真者里空中购物大厦	133 1 B
Changi Airport	樟宜机场	75 1 B
Terminal 1 Bldg	第一搭客大厦	75 1 B
Terminal 2 Bldg	第二搭客大厦	75 1 B
Terminal 3 Bldg	第三搭客大厦	75 1 B
Budget Teminal	廉价航空终站	96 1 B
Changi Ferry Teminal	樟宜渡轮码头	76 1 A
Changi Logistic Ctr	樟宜后勤中心	53 1 D
Changi Sth Amenity Ctr	樟宜南便利中心	95 1 B
Changi Village	樟宜村	54 1 B
Charme Ind Bldg	光如意工业大厦	90 2 C
Chartered Semiconductor Manufacturing Ltd	特许半导体制造有限公司	10 1 C
Cheng Chwee Huat Ind Bldg	钟水发工业大厦	91 1 D
Cheng Meng Bldg	承民大厦	90 1 C
Cheng Yan Court	清渊阁	111 1 D
Chenn Leonn Bldg	金旺大厦	111 2 C
Chestnut Ave Water Works	策士纳水务站	64 1 A
Chevalier House	其士大厦	90 1 C
Chevron House	吉夫隆大厦	133 1 B
Chiat Hong Bldg	泽丰大厦	111 1 D
CHIJMES	赞美	111 1 D
Children Aid Society (Melrose)	儿童援助协会 (美乐士)	85 1 C
Chin Hin Hang Bldg	振兴行大厦	112 2 A
China Court	中国阁	132 2 B
China Square Food Ctr	中国广场美食中心	132 2 B
China Square Central	中国广场中心	132 2 B
Chinatown Complex	牛车水大厦	132 2 B
Chinatown Heritage Ctr	牛车水原貌馆	132 2 B
Chinatown Plaza	唐城大厦	132 2 C
Chinatown Point	唐城坊	132 2 B
Ching Shine Ind Bldg	正新工业大厦	90 1 B
Chinsim Ind Ctr	振森工业中心	80 1 C
Chiyoda Singapore	千代田	83 2 D
Choa Chu Kang Education Ctr	蔡厝港教育中心	41 2 C
Chomp Chomp	Chomp Chomp 食阁	68 2 B
Chong Boon Ctr	崇文中心	68 1 A
Chong Hua Tong Tou Teck Hwee Bldg	崇华堂道德会	131 1 B
Chow House	周氏大厦	132 2 C
Chromos (Biopolis)	Chromos (启奥生物医药研究园)	107 2 C
Chuan Seng Bldg	泉成大厦	111 1 B
Chung Hwa Free Clinic	中华医院	89 1 C
Chutex Bldg	骏达大厦	111 2 A
Chye Sing Bldg	再新大厦	111 1 D
CIAS Cargo Ctr	樟宜国际机场服务公司货运中心	54 2 D
Cideco Ind Complex	实业工业大厦	90 1 C
Cintech 1	新达1	129 2 A
Cintech 2	新达2	129 2 A
Cintech 3	新达3	129 2 A
CISCO Ctr	工商保安机构中心	91 1 D
CISCO Recall Ctr	工商保安信息管理中心	82 1 D
Citilink Warehouse Cplx	城联货仓大厦	130 1 C
Citimac Ind Complex	美市工业大厦	90 2 B
Citipoint Ind Bldg	中央工业中心	91 1 C
Citiport Ctr	城港中心	142 2 A
Citiraya Ctr	大城市中心	112 2 A
Cititech Ind Bldg	城市工业大厦	90 2 D
City Hall	政府大厦	133 1 A
City House	城市大厦	132 2 C
City Ind Bldg	城市工业大厦	90 2 C
City Plaza	城市购物中心	113 1 A
City Square Mall	城市广场	111 1 B
City Warehouse	城市仓库大厦	91 2 B
Citycab	城市德士	67 2 B
Citylink Mall	城联广场	133 1 A
Cityneon Design Ctr	城市霓虹灯设计中心	90 1 D
Civic Ter Warehouse	城市货仓	91 1 B
Clementi Arcade	金文泰购物廊	84 2 D
Clementi Ave 2 Shopping Ctr	金文泰2道购物中心	106 2 A
Clifford Ctr	吉利福中心	133 1 B
Clifford Pier	红灯码头	133 1 B
CMO	CMO大厦	132 2 B
Cold Storage Jelita	芝里达冷藏公司	107 2 A
Comcentre	电信中心	110 1 D

PLACES		MAP GRID		PLACES		MAP GRID	
Comcentre II	电信中心2	110	1 D	Defence Technology Twr B	国防科技大厦B	131	1 C
Comcentre III	电信中心3	110	1 D	Delfi Orchard	乌节达尔果大厦	109	2 B
Comfort Automotive Svcs	康福汽车维修服务			Delta House	立达大厦	131	1 C
- (Loyang Dr)	(罗央通道)	74	1 A	Depot Heights Shopping Ctr	德普岭购物中心	130	2 C
- (Senoko Dr)	(圣诺哥通道)	2	1 C	Devonshire Bldg	德文莎大厦	110	1 D
- (Ubi Rd 4)	(乌美4路)	91	2 C	DF Bldg	DF大厦	45	2 C
Comfort Delgro	康福德高企业	89	1 A	Dhoby Xchange	多美歌转换站	110	2 D
Comfort Transportation	康福运输	67	1 B	DHL	DHL大厦	91	1 B
Command House	司令楼	87	1 D	Diamond Ind Bldg	钻工业大厦	91	1 B
Commerce Point	鸿业大厦	132	2 B	DNV Technology Ctr	挪威船舶协会科技中心	129	2 A
Compaq Ctr	康柏中心	72	2 D	Dou Yee Bldg	道义大厦	92	1 B
Tampines Plaza	淡滨尼大厦			DP Computers Bldg	DP电脑大厦	90	2 B
Compass Point	勘宝坊	49	1 B	Dragon Land Bldg	龙置地大厦	90	1 C
Connection One	第壹联系大厦	131	1 B	DSO Nat'l Laboratories	DSO国家化验室	129	2 B
Construction House	建筑商公会	130	2 B	DSTA Bldg	DSTA大厦	129	2 B
Copytron	复印通	91	2 D	Dynasty Ind Bldg	皇朝工业大厦	130	2 B
Corex Bldg	高力大厦	90	1 C	East Coast Seafood Ctr	八鲜海味中心	115	1 C
Coronation Arcade	加冕商场	86	2 D	Eastgate	东度	113	2 C
Coronation Plaza	加冕购物中心	86	2 D	Eastlink	东联大厦	94	1 B
Corporation Place	企业大厦	82	1 D	Eastpac Bldg	东太平洋大厦	88	2 D
Cosmic Insurance Ctr	全球保险大厦	111	1 D	Eastpoint Mall	东福坊	94	1 A
Costa Sands Resort	高士达度假村	114	2 C	Eastech	东方科技大厦	94	1 B
East Coast	(东海岸)			Eastwood Ctr	东林中心	94	2 D
Courtaulds House	可得大厦	84	2 A	E-Central @ Redhill	红山中心大厦	130	2 B
Courts Tampines	Courts淡滨尼	51	1 D	ECO - SWM Complex	预科废料中心	121	2 A
CPA House	特许会计师大厦	112	2 A	ECO Resource	预科资源收复中心	77	2 C
CPF Bldg	中央公积金局大厦			Recovery Complex			
- Bishan	- 碧山	67	2 D	Econ Ind Bldg	益坚工业大厦	46	2 B
- Jurong	- 裕廊	83	1 B	Eightrium	Eightrium大厦	95	1 B
- Robinson Rd	- 罗敏申路	132	2 C	Elias Mall	伊莱雅购物中心	51	2 D
- Tampines	- 淡滨尼	72	2 D	Elite Ind Bldg I & II	益力工业大厦	90	1 C
CPG Airport Devt. Div	CPG机场发展组	74	2 A	Eminent Plaza	明辉大厦	111	1 B
Craig Place	克力坊	132	2 C	Empire Techno Ctr	帝国科技中心	91	2 B
Crawford Court	哥罗福阁	111	2 C	Empress Place Bldg	皇后坊大厦	133	1 B
Creative House	启迪大厦	111	1 D	Enterprise Ctr	企业中心	84	1 B
Creative Technology	创新科技	83	1 C	Enterprise Ind Bldg	企业工业大厦	112	1 A
Crescendo Bldg	顶峰大厦	114	2 B	Enterprise One	第一企业	91	2 C
Crescent Bldg	克礼申大厦	89	1 D	Entrepreneur Business Ctr	企业家商业中心	91	2 B
Crocodile House	鳄鱼大厦	91	1 C	Environment Building	环境发展部大厦	110	1 B
Crown Ctr	Crown中心	86	1 D	Equity Plaza	益贵地广场	132	2 B
Crystal Time Bldg	晶时大厦	90	1 C	Ericson Pet Farm	伊立逊宠物场	51	1 C
CSTK Bldg	CSTK大厦	112	2 A	Esmart Ctr	益市中心	111	2 A
Cuppage Mall	卡佩芝广场	110	1 C	Esplanade Theatres	滨海湾艺术中心	133	1 A
Cuppage Plaza	卡佩芝大厦	110	1 C	On The Bay			
Cuppage Terrace	卡佩芝台	110	1 C	EtonHouse	伊登大厦	91	1 D
Currency House	货币大厦	129	2 C	Eunos Technolink	友诺科技园	91	2 B
Custom House	海关大厦	133	1 B	Eunos Techpark	友诺士工贸园	91	2 B
Customs Operations Ctr	关口事务中心	132	2 D	Eunos Warehouse Cplx	佺禄货仓	91	2 B
CWT Distripark	CWT分销园	103	2 A	Eurasian Community House	欧亚人联络中心	113	2 B
CWT S'pore Commodities	CWT新加坡商业中心	104	2 A	Euro Chem	Euro Chem大厦	83	2 C
Hub				Europa	Europa大厦	93	2 B
Cyber Ctr	赛柏中心	130	2 B	Evan Lim Warehouse	益民货仓大厦	91	1 B
Cyber Hub	电脑企业中心	111	2 A	Ever Tech Bldg	永恒科技大厦	48	1 D
Cyber Hub IBP	IBP电脑企业中心	83	2 D	Evergreen Ind Bldg	长青工业大厦	90	2 B
Cycle & Carriage	合发集团中心	130	2 A	Everich Ind Bldg	保丰工业大厦	90	1 C
Dadlani Ind Bldg	达兰尼大厦	130	2 B	Evershine & Century Cplx	永亮世纪广场	111	1 D
Datapulse Ind Bldg	胜达科技	91	1 B	Excalibur Ctr	瑞兴大厦中心	91	2 C
David Elias Bldg	大卫伊莱雅大厦	110	2 C	Excelsior Shopping Ctr	怡东购物中心	132	2 A
Dawson Place	杜生坊	130	2 A	Exclusive Ctr	卓越中心	91	2 B
DBS Bldg Tower One	新加坡发展银行大厦1座	132	2 C	Expression Technology Ctr	立胜科技大厦	74	1 D
DBS Bldg Tower Two	新加坡发展银行大厦2座	132	2 C				
Defence Technology Twr A	国防科技大厦A	131	1 C				

PLACES		MAP GRID
Faber House	华峰大厦	110 1 C
Fajar N'hood Shopping Ctr	法嘉邻里购物中心	42 2 C
Fansida Bldg	泛思达大厦	112 2 A
Far East Febrigration Bldg	远东Febrigration大厦	111 2 B
Far East Finance Bldg	远东金融大厦	132 2 B
Far East Plaza	远东广场	110 1 B
Far East Shopping Ctr	远东购物中心	109 2 C
Far East Square	远东广场	132 2 B
Far Eastern Bank Bldg	远东银行大厦	132 2 C
Farmart	Farmart大厦	40 1 C
Federal Express	联邦快递	94 2 C
Fernvale Point Shopping Ctr	芬微尔坊购物中心	48 1 B
Ficus Point	Ficus Point大厦	142 2 C
Finger Pier Bldg	指码头大厦	133 1 D
First Engineering Techno Ctr	第一工程科技中心	12 2 A
FJ B	FJ B大厦	109 2 B
Focus One	壹号焦点	91 1 C
Foh Foh Bldg	和和大厦	105 2 C
Foo Ann Bldg	阜安大厦	111 1 D
Foo Chow Bldg	福州大厦	111 1 B
Foo Wah Ind Bldg	富华工业大厦	67 2 D
Food Xchange @ Admiralty	海军部区食品工业大厦	3 1 C
Fook Hai Bldg	福海大厦	132 2 B
Fook Tong Nam Bldg	福东南大厦	11 1 A
Foong Shoon Fui Kuan Bldg	丰顺会馆	112 2 B
Fort Canning Ctr	福康宁中心	110 2 D
Fortune Ctr	金隆大厦	111 1 D
Forum The Shopping Mall	福临购物中心	109 2 C
Four Star Bldg	四星大厦	111 2 B
Franklin	福兰克林大厦	129 2 A
Fraser & Neave	花莎尼	78 1 B
Freight Links Express Districentre	辉联配运分销中心	95 1 C
Fremason Hall	菲美胜堂	132 2 A
French Business Ctr	法国商业中心	132 2 C
Frontech Ctr	Frontech中心	130 2 B
FTMS House	FTMS大厦	110 2 D
Fu Lu Shou Complex	福禄寿大厦	111 1 C
Fu Tsu Bldg	Fu Tsu大厦	89 1 D
Fu Yuen Bldg	富源大厦	111 1 D
Fujifilm	富士软片工业大厦	90 2 A
Fuji Xerox Towers	富士施乐大厦	132 2 D
Fullfex	福利士	78 2 B
Funan The DigitaLife Mall	福南电脑中心	132 2 A
Furama	富丽华	132 2 B
Fusion Polis	启汇园	107 2 D
Futsing Bldg	福清大厦	111 1 B
Gainurin Bldg	仰恩大厦	110 2 D
Galen	Galen大厦	129 1 B
Ganges Ctr	格兰芝中心	131 2 A
Gani Bldg	Gani大厦	90 1 C
GB Bldg	源美大厦	132 2 C
GE Tower	美国通用电器大厦	132 2 D
Gek Lim Bldg	玉林大厦	112 1 B
Gek Poh Shopping Ctr	玉宝邨里购物中心	59 2 D
Genome (Biopolis)	基因科技 (启奥生物医药研究园)	107 2 C
Genova	热那亚	111 2 A
Genting Bldg	仁定大厦	90 1 D
Genting Warehouse Cplx	仁定货仓大厦	90 1 C
Geo-Tele Ctr	Geo-Tele中心	91 1 B
German Ctr	德国中心	83 2 D
GES Bldg	GES中心	11 1 A
Geylang Ctr	芽笼中心	112 1 B
Giambologna House	刚柏罗纳	70 1 D
Giant (Tampines)	Giant(淡滨尼)	72 1 A
Gillman Village	吉门村	130 2 C
Gimmill Bldg	锦美大厦	93 2 B
GlaxoSmithKline Biologicals	葛兰素史克生物产品大厦	99 1 D
Gleason	捷申	90 1 C
GMG Bldg	GMG大厦	132 2 C
GMTI Bldg	GMTI大厦	108 1 C
Goh & Goh Bldg	吴大厦	85 1 A
Goldbell Tower	蔡金钟大厦	110 1 B
Golden Landmark	黄金广场	111 1 C
Golden Mile Complex	黄金地带购物中心	111 2 C
Golden Mile Tower	黄金大厦	111 2 C
Golden Shoe Car Park	金鞋停车场	132 2 B
Golden Village	黄金村	81 1 A
Golden Wall Ctr	金城中心	111 1 C
Golden Wall Flatted Fty	金城多层工厂	88 1 D
Golden Wheel Bldg	金轮大厦	90 2 C
Golden Wheel Ind Bldg	金轮工业大厦	90 1 C
Goldhill Centre	金岭中心	110 2 A
Goldhill Plaza	金岭商场	110 2 A
Goldlion Bldg	金利来大厦	90 2 B
Goldpine Ind Bldg	金松工业大厦	90 2 B
Goodrich	国立大厦	94 1 C
Goodvine	固得万	93 2 A
Gordon Ind Bldg	高登工业大厦	113 1 A
Gordon Warehouse Bldg	高登仓库大厦	91 2 B
Gourmet East Kitchen	东厨大厦	94 1 B
Grand Bldg	繁荣大厦	132 2 B
Grandlink Square	环宇广场	113 1 A
Great Eastern Ctr	大东方保险中心	132 2 B
Great Eastern House	大东方保险大厦	111 1 D
Great Eastern Life Changi Ctr	大东方人寿樟宜中心	113 2 A
Great Pacific Warehouse	太平货库	91 2 B
Great World City	世界城	132 1 A
Greatwood	伟木	132 2 B
Greenridge Shopping Ctr	翠绿岗购物中心	42 2 C
GRP Ind Bldg	GRP工业大厦	83 2 A
GS Bldg	GS大厦	89 1 D
GSM Bldg	山湫大厦	111 1 D
GTW Ind Bldg	GTW工业大厦	91 1 B
Guan Hua Warehouse Bldg	源华货仓	90 1 D
Guide House	女童军会所	68 1 C
Guilin Bldg	桂林大厦	112 2 A
Gulab	玫瑰大厦	90 1 C
Guthrie Bldg	牙直利大厦	113 2 A
Guthrie House	牙直利大厦	86 1 C
H & H Bldg	H&H大厦	90 1 D
Habitat Warehouse	聚集货仓	45 2 B
Hai Sun Hup House	海山合大厦	130 1 C
Hainan Ind Bldg	海南工业大厦	89 1 D
Hainanese Village Ctr	海南村中心	70 1 C
Halcon Primo Logistics	Halcon Primo物流大厦	83 2 B
Halicon Bldg	Halicon大厦	67 1 D

PLACES		MAP GRID	PLACES		MAP GRID
Hamilton Sundstrand	Hamilton Sundstrand 大厦	74 1 D	Hong Joo Ind Bldg	丰裕工业大厦	45 2 B
HarbourFront Ctr	港湾中心	142 1 A	Hong Leong Bldg	丰隆大厦	132 2 C
(Former World Trade Ctr)	(前世界贸易中心)		Hong Leong Shopping Ctr	丰隆购物中心	106 1 A
HarbourFront Tower One	第1海港办公楼	142 1 A	Hong Lim Complex	芳林大厦	132 2 B
HarbourFront Tower 2	第2海港办公楼	142 1 A	Hougang Green	豪阁林购物廊	48 2 D
(Cable Car Tower)	(缆车大厦)		Shopping Mall		
Harbour Link Warehouse	港联货仓总栈	130 1 C	Hougang Mall	后港广场	70 1 A
Harbourside Ind Bldg	海港工业大厦1	130 1 C	Hougang Plaza	后港大厦	70 1 A
Harbourside Ind Bldg 2	海港工业大厦2	130 1 C	Hougang Point	后港中心	48 2 D
Harrison Ind Bldg	哈里逊工业大厦	90 2 B	House of Tan Yeok Nee	陈旭年故居	110 2 D
Hart	哈特	111 1 B	HPL House	旅店置业有限公司大厦	109 2 C
Haw Par Ctr	虎豹中心	110 2 D	HSBC Bldg	香港汇丰银行大厦	133 1 B
Haw Par Glass Tower	虎豹玻璃大厦	110 2 D	HSBC House	HSBC大厦	84 2 A
Haw Par Technocentre	虎豹科技中心	108 1 C	Hua Kok Ind Bldg	华国工业大厦	22 2 C
Haw Par Tiger Balm Bldg	虎豹万金油大厦	82 1 C	Hudson Techno Ctr	Hudson科技中心	90 2 A
HB Bldg	HB大厦	90 1 C	Hudson Ind Bldg	Hudson工业大厦	90 2 A
HB Robinson	HB罗敏申楼	132 2 C	Hui Seng	惠成	132 2 A
HDB Hub	建屋局新总部	88 2 C	Hup Huat Food Ind Bldg	合发食品工业大厦	90 2 B
HDB Prefab	建屋局预制	2 1 D	Hup Seng Warehouse	合胜货仓大厦	105 2 B
Technology Ctr	科技中心		Hwa Yew Ind Bldg	华友工业大厦	23 1 C
Heap Seng House	协城大厦	111 1 D	Hyflux Bldg	凯发大厦	111 2 A
Heartland Mall	协城大厦	69 2 C	i Axil @ S'pore Science	新加坡科学园i Axil	129 1 A
Heidehnn Bldg	海登大厦	112 2 A	Park (The Aquarius)	(宝瓶大厦)	
Helios (Biopolis)	Helios	107 2 C	IBM	国际商业机器(IBM)	95 1 B
	(启奥生物医药研究园)		ICA Air Cargo Branch	ICA空运货物组	54 2 C
Henderson Bldg	亨德申大厦	131 1 C	ICA Bldg	ICA大厦(移民关卡局)	111 2 C
Henley Bldg	鸿利大厦	90 2 A	(formerly SIR Bldg)	(前称SIR大厦)	
Heritage Place	桂兰坊	111 1 D	ICB Enterprise House	ICB企业大厦	111 1 D
Hersing Hub	Hersing Hub大厦	89 1 C	ICB Shopping Ctr	工商银行购物中心	69 1 C
Hewlett Packard	惠普	130 1 C	Icon IBP	Icon IBP大厦	83 2 C
(Alexandra Rd)	(亚历山大路)		IDS Logistics	IDS Logistics 大厦	83 1 B
Hewlett Packard	惠普	130 2 B	iHub	iHub 大厦	83 1 C
(Depot Rd)	(德普路)		Ikea	宜家	
Hiang Kie Complex	香记大厦	90 1 C	- Alexandra	- 亚历山大	130 2 A
High Street Ctr	水仙门中心	132 2 A	- Tampines	- 淡滨尼	51 1 D
High Street Plaza	谐街大厦	132 2 A	Iluma at Bugis	武吉士Iluma大厦	111 1 D
Highland Ctr	高原中心	69 1 C	IMM Bldg	国际商品批发中心大厦	83 2 B
Highpoint Social	高点社会企业大厦	112 2 B	Immunos (Biopolis)	Immunos(启奥生物医药园)	107 2 C
Enterprises Ark			Imperial House	帝国大厦	110 2 D
Hillview Bldg	山景楼	63 1 D	Inchcape Marketing Bldg	英吉大厦	132 1 D
Hillview House	山景大厦	63 1 C	Infineon	Infineon大厦	90 1 D
Hillview Warehouse	山景货仓	63 1 D	Ingolstadt Ctr	英谷斯特中心	90 1 C
Hin Fah House	兴华大厦	111 2 B	Ingram Micro	Ingram Micro大厦	74 2 D
HI-P Singapore	HI-P新加坡	83 2 D	Innovation Place	创新工业中心	23 1 D
HIS Sanctuary Services	HIS礼再堂	111 1 A	International Building	国际大厦	109 2 C
Hitachi Chemical	日立化学	53 1 D	International Factors Bldg	国际工商财务大厦	132 2 B
Hitachi Tower	日立大厦	133 1 B	International Plaza	凯联大厦	132 2 C
HNI Bldg	HNI大厦	90 2 B	International Press	合众Softcom大厦	111 2 B
Ho Printing	昌明印刷公司	95 2 B	Softcom		
Ho Seng Lee Flatted	和成利货仓大厦	89 1 D	Intervet Norbio	英特维纳比奥	7 1 D
Warehouse			Intrepid Warehouse Cplx	应德利货仓大厦	91 1 B
Hoa Nam Bldg	浩南大厦	111 1 B	IOB Bldg	印侨银行大厦	132 2 B
Hock Giap Warehouse	福业货仓大厦	132 1 A	IOI Plaza	IOI商业中心	111 1 C
Hock Seng Bldg	福成大厦	111 2 B	Ion Orchard	乌节Ion大厦	109 2 C
Hoe Huat Ind Bldg	和发工业大厦	90 2 A	IPC Bldg II	IPC大厦2	91 1 B
Holland Rd Shopping Ctr	荷兰路购物中心	108 1 B	iQuest	iQuest大厦	83 2 D
Holland Village	荷兰村	108 1 B	Irving Ind Bldg	艾文工业大厦	90 2 B
Holiday Inn Shopping Ctr	凯煌大酒店购物中心	132 1 A	Isetan Office Bldg	伊势丹办事处大厦	132 1 A
Honeywell	霍尼韦	95 1 B	Islamic Ctr of S'pore	新加坡回教中心	89 1 B
Hong Aik Ind Bldg	丰益工业大厦	111 2 B	(MUIS) (Temporary)	(MUIS) (临时)	
Hong Guan Bldg	丰源大厦	111 1 C	Istana	总统府	110 2 C
			Istana Kampung Glam	甘榜格南苏丹宫	111 2 C

PLACES		MAP GRID		PLACES		MAP GRID	
ITE Electronic Bldg	电艺大厦	90	2 B	Kapo Factory Bldg	加宝工厂大厦	90	2 B
ITS Ctr	ITS中心	132	2 A	Kar Yeng Five Districts Gen. Assn. Bldg	嘉应五属公会大厦	85	1 A
Jack's Place Bldg	杰克屋大厦	70	1 C				
Jackson Ctr	杰逊中心	90	1 C	Karma Kagyud Buddhist Ctr	加玛加育佛教中心	112	2 B
Jacob Ballas Ctr	雅各巴拉士中心	110	2 D				
Jalan Besar Plaza	惹兰勿刹大厦	111	1 B	Katong Junction	加东商场	113	2 C
Jalan Buroh Warehouse Complex	惹兰布罗货仓	103	2 A	Katong Mall	加东广场	113	2 C
				Katong Plaza	加东商业中心	113	2 C
Jay Gee House	嘉义大厦	90	1 C	Katong Shopping Ctr	加东购物中心	113	2 C
JIC Inspection Services	JIC检查服务	46	2 B	Katong Village	加东村	113	2 C
Jinriksha Station	人力车站	132	2 C	KB-1	KB-1	91	2 B
Jit Poh Bldg	日报大厦	132	2 D	KC Dat	KC Dat大厦	80	2 D
JK Bldg	JK大厦	84	2 A	Keat Hong Shopping Ctr	吉丰购物中心	41	1 D
John Wesley Ctr	约翰维思礼中心	63	2 B	Kebun Baru Mall	哥本哥鲁广场	67	1 A
Joo Chiat Complex	如切大厦	113	2 A	Keck Seng Tower	激成大厦	132	2 C
Joo Seng Warehouse	裕盛货仓	90	2 B	Kembangan Plaza	金敦大厦	114	1 A
JTA Motors	JTA汽车	91	2 C	Keng Hua Bldg	勤华大厦	90	1 C
JTC Factories (Clementi Loop)	裕廊集团工厂 (金文泰环道)	84	1 D	Keng Soon	景顺	111	1 C
				Kenwood Bldg	健伍大厦	90	1 C
JTC Food Factory (Tuas)	裕廊集团食品工厂	99	1 A	Keppel Bay Tower	吉宝湾大厦	142	1 A
JTC Food Factory (K.A. Foodlink)	裕廊集团食品工厂 (K.A. Foodlink)	90	2 B	Keppel Logistics	吉宝后勤	101	2 B
				Keppel Shipyard	吉宝船厂	101	2 D
"JTC Summit" The	顶峰大厦	83	1 C	Keppel T & T Benoi Districentre	吉宝讯通贵耐分销园	102	2 A
JTS Bldg	JTS大厦	80	2 C				
Jubilee Ctr	钻禧中心	67	2 A	Keppel Towers	吉宝中心	132	2 D
Jubilee Ind Bldg	光华工业大厦	90	1 C	Keppel Wharves Bldg	吉宝码头大厦	131	2 C
Jun Jie Ind Bldg	俊杰工业大厦	90	2 B	Keppel Workshop	发巴码头大厦	132	1 D
Jun Xin Bldg	俊新大厦	111	1 D	Kewalram Hillview	克华兰山景	63	1 C
Junction 8 Bishan Shopping Ctr	碧山第8站 购物中心	67	2 D	Kewalram House	克华兰大厦	130	2 B
				Keypoint	吉功	111	2 C
Jurong Cement	裕廊洋灰	105	2 D	KH Kea Bldg	郭国兴大厦	111	1 D
Jurong Distri Ctr	裕廊分销中心	101	1 C	Khatib Central	卡迪中心	27	1 B
Jurong Entertainment Ctr	裕廊娱乐中心	83	1 B	Kheng Chiu Bldg	琼州大厦	111	1 D
Jurong Fishing Port (AVA)	裕廊鱼港 (农业食品与兽医局)	104	1 B	Kheng Seng Bldg	庆胜大厦	90	1 C
				KHL Ind Bldg	金合利工业大厦	90	2 A
Jurong Flatted Factory	裕廊工厂大厦	82	1 C	KHL Printing	KHL印刷公司	74	1 A
Jurong Ind Services Ctr	裕廊工业服务中心	104	1 A	Khong Guan Biscuits Fty	康源饼干厂	90	2 B
Jurong Inspection Ctr	裕廊车辆检查中心	100	2 B	Khong Guan Ind Bldg	康源工业大厦	90	2 B
Jurong Point	裕廊坊	81	1 A	Kian Ann Bldg	建安大厦	94	1 C
Jurong Power Station	裕廊发电厂	103	2 B	Kilat Court	吉利阁	84	2 A
Jurong Shipyard	裕廊船厂	102	2 C	Kilat Ctr	吉利中心	84	2 A
Jurong Shipyard Limited	裕廊船厂	103	1 C	Kim Chuan Water Reclamation Plant	金泉水源开发厂	91	2 A
Jurong Logistics Hub	裕廊后勤中枢	104	1 B				
Jurong Water Reclamation Plant	裕廊污水处理厂	102	1 A	Kim Heng	金兴	106	1 C
				Kim Thye Ind Bldg	金泰工业大厦	22	1 B
JVC Logistics Ctr	JVC后勤大厦	99	1 B	Kimetal Bldg	金美德大厦	111	1 D
K.B. Warehouse Cplx	K.B.货仓大厦	91	2 B	Kimly Bldg	金利大厦	90	2 A
KA Ctr	KA中心	90	2 B	Kin Bldg	Kin大厦	90	2 B
K Box Plaza	K Box大厦	67	2 A	King George's Bldg	乔治王大厦	111	2 B
Kai Lim Bldg	奎林建材	114	1 A	King Wan Ind Bldg	庆源工业大厦	104	1 A
Kaki Bukit Amenity Ctr	加基武吉便利中心	91	2 C	Kingly Bldg	金利大厦	132	2 A
Kaki Bukit Car Mart	加基武吉汽车展销市场	91	2 B	Kings Arcade	王雅阁	86	2 D
Kaki Bukit Tech Park I	加基武吉科技园1	91	2 B	King's Ctr	京士中心	132	1 A
Kaki Bukit Tech Park II	加基武吉科技园2	92	1 B	Kingsmen Creative Ctr	金明创意中心	94	1 C
Kallang Auto Ctr	加冷汽车中心	112	1 C	Kitchener Complex	吉真那大厦	111	2 B
Kallang Bahru Complex	加冷巴鲁大厦	111	2 B	Kong Beng Ind Bldg	光明工业大厦	67	2 D
Kallang Ctr	加冷中心	90	2 D	Kovan Ctr	高文中心	69	1 C
Kallang Sector Amenity Ctr	加冷段便利中心	90	1 D	Kranji Ter Workshops	克兰芝台厂房	9	1 C
				Kranji Transmitting Stn (Sim Communication)	克兰芝传播站	21	1 A
Kallang Way Flatted Fty	加冷道多层工厂	90	1 D				
Kampong Java	甘榜爪哇	110	2 B				

PLACES		MAP	GRID	PLACES		MAP	GRID
Kranji Water Reclamation Plant	克兰芝水源开发厂	10	1 D	Logis Tech	Logis科技大厦	74	1 D
Krislite Bldg	克亮大厦	74	1 A	Lot One Shopper's Mall	第一乐广场	41	1 C
KTL Distribution Ctr	KTL分销中心	95	1 C	Lot 18	第十八地段	111	2 C
Kuie Pong Bldg	贵邦楼	109	2 A	Loyang Amenity Ctr	洛阳便利中心	74	1 A
Kwang Yeow Heng Coldroom Warehouse	广耀兴冷房货仓	130	1 C	Loyang Point	罗央峰	74	1 A
Kwek Sum Chuan	郭三川大厦	105	2 B	LTH Bldg	LTH 大厦	130	2 B
Kwong Wai Siew Peck San Theng Bldg	广惠�碧山亭公所	88	2 A	Lucky Chinatown	幸运牛车水	132	2 B
				Lucky Plaza	幸运坊	110	1 C
L&Y Bldg	L&Y大厦	67	2 D	"Lux Bldg, The"	力士大厦	91	1 D
Labone	Labone大厦	83	2 D	Luxasia Bldg	力士亚洲大厦	91	1 B
Lam Ann Bldg	南安大厦	132	1 A	Luzerne	Luzerne大厦	111	2 A
Lam Leong Bldg	南良大厦	112	1 A	LW Techno Ctr	LW科技中心	83	2 B
Lam Soon Ind Bldg	南顺工业大厦	63	1 C	MacAlister Flats	麦克里斯特公寓	132	1 C
Landbase Ind Bldg	地基工业大厦	99	1 C	MacAlister Terrace	麦克里斯特台	132	1 C
Landex House	陆氏大厦	90	2 B	MacDonald House	麦当劳大厦	110	2 D
Lau Pa Sat	老巴刹	132	2 C	MacNels	MacNels大厦	132	2 C
Lau's Arcadia	刘氏大厦	113	2 B	Macpherson Ind Complex	麦波申工业大厦	90	1 C
Lavender Food Square	劳明达食阁	111	1 B	Mactaggart Ind Bldg	麦达卡工业大厦	90	2 B
Le Mercier House	乐美赛大厦	132	1 A	Mactech Ind Bldg	麦特工业大厦	90	1 C
Le Meridien S'pore	美丽殿购物中心	110	2 D	MAE Ind Bldg	MAE 工业大厦	90	2 B
Learning Ladder, "The"	学习阶梯	84	2 A	Malacca Ctr	马六甲中心	132	2 B
Lee Hwa Ind Bldg	丽华工业大厦	90	2 B	Malay Village	马来村	113	1 A
Lee Kai House	利佳大厦	111	1 D	Malayan Railway Tanjong Pagar Stn	马来亚铁道局 丹戎巴葛火车站	132	1 D
Leisure Park Kallang	加冷娱乐广场	112	1 C	Mandai Ind Bldg	万礼工业大厦	23	1 C
Leong Hin Bldg	隆兴大厦	88	2 D	Mandarin Auto Bldg	文华汽车大厦	45	2 B
Leong Huat Bldg	隆发大厦	90	2 B	"Mandarin Shopping Arcade, The"	文华购物商场	110	1 C
Leong Jin	隆英大厦	80	2 D				
Leong On Bldg	隆安大厦	88	2 D	Manhattan House	万豪登大厦	132	1 B
Leow Sin Assn Bldg	廖氏公会大厦	112	2 A	Maresei Ind Bldg	玛日萨工业大厦	22	1 B
Leung Kai Fook Bldg	梁介福大厦	132	2 B	Marina Bay Sands	滨海湾Sands大厦	133	1 B
LHK 2 Bldg	LHK 2大厦	90	2 B	Marina House	海通大厦	132	2 D
LHK 3 Bldg	LHK 3大厦	90	2 A	Marina Leisure Plex	滨海电影院	133	1 A
LHK Bldg	LHK 大厦	112	1 A	Marina Square	滨海广场	133	1 A
Lian Cheong Ind Bldg	联昌工业大厦	90	2 B	Marine Cove	马林湾	114	1 C
Lian Huat Bldg	联发大厦	132	2 C	Marine Parade Christian Ctr	马林百列基督教中心	113	2 B
Lian Soon Bldg	联顺大厦	111	2 B	Marine Parade Comm Bldg	马林百列社区大厦	114	1 C
Lian Tong Bldg	联同大厦	90	1 C	Maritime House	航运大厦	132	1 C
Liang Court	亮阁	132	2 A	Market Place	市场坊	74	1 A
Liang Huat	联发	79	2 D	Market Street Car Park	马吉街停车场	132	2 B
Liang Seah Court	连城阁	111	1 D	Markono	马可诺	45	2 D
Liat Towers	烈士楼	109	2 C	Marsh & McLenan Ctr	Marsh & McLenan大厦	132	2 B
Liberty House	利宝楼	132	2 B	Marvell Asia	Marvell大厦	91	1 B
Liberty Warehouse	利柏迪货仓	45	2 B	MAS Bldg	金融管理局大厦	132	2 D
Lim Kim Hai Bldg	林金海大厦	111	2 A	Matrix (Biopolis)	Matrix (启奥生物医药研究园)	107	2 C
Limbang Shopping Centre (Blk 533)	林邦购物中心 (533座)	41	1 B				
Lin Ho Bldg	仁和大厦	90	2 B	Maxindo House	麦欣都大厦	90	2 B
Lingjack Ind Bldg	林杰工业大厦	2	2 D	Maxwell House	麦士威大厦	132	2 C
Linkpoint Place	林点坊	99	1 C	Maxwell Road Food Ctr	麦士威路熟食中心	132	2 C
Lion Bldg	狮子大厦	111	2 A	Maybank	马来亚银行	46	2 D
Lion Ind Bldg	狮城工业大厦	91	1 D	Maybank Towers	马来亚银行大厦	133	1 B
Lip Hing Ind Bldg	立兴大厦	67	2 D	Mayfair Ind Bldg	美辉大厦	67	2 D
Lipo Bldg	利宝大厦	90	2 D	McDonald's Place	麦当劳坊	85	1 D
Lippo Centre	立宝中心	132	2 D	MCYS Bldg	社会发展与体育部大厦	88	1 B
Lita Bldg	利达大厦	100	1 A	Medal House	Medal大厦	14	1 B
Little India Arcade	小印度中心	111	1 C	Mehson's Bldg	麦逊大厦	111	2 B
LKN Bldg	林甲岩大厦	132	2 C	Meiban Ind Bldg	美班工业大厦	91	1 D
LKS Bldg	LKS 大厦	90	2 B	Menicon	Menicon大厦	83	2 D
Lock+Store Chai Chee	菜市货仓大厦	92	2 C	Merchant Court	马真阁	132	2 A
LogisHub @ Clementi	金文泰后勤中心	84	1 C	Merchant Square	商贸坊	132	2 A
				Merrill Lynch Harbourfront	Merrill Lynch 滨海大厦	142	1 A

PLACES		MAP GRID		PLACES		MAP GRID	
Metal House	美置大厦	90	1 C	Ng Teow Yhee	黄朝员大厦	132	1 C
Metropolitan YMCA	京华基督教青年会	109	2 A	NGB Bldg	国家电脑局大厦	112	1 A
Mewah	Mewah大厦	83	2 D	(Sims Drive)	(沈氏通道)		
MICA Bldg	新闻及艺术部大厦	132	2 A	Ngee Ann City	义安城	110	1 C
Micron Bldg	美光大厦	111	2 A	Nico Bldg	Nico钢铁中心	95	1 B
Midland House	中原大厦	111	1 D	Nin Jiom Bldg	念慈庵大厦	2	2 B
Midlink Plaza	中环大厦	111	1 D	Nissan Showroom	日产陈列室	89	1 A
Midpoint Orchard	乌节中心坊	110	1 C	NKF Ctr	全国肾脏基金会中心	89	1 D
Midview	中景	84	1 B	NNB Ind Bldg	NNB工业大厦	12	1 D
Millenia Tower	美年大厦	133	2 A	No. 1 Bldg	第一大厦	91	1 D
Millenia Walk	美年广场	133	1 A	Noble Warehouse	贵雅大厦	90	1 C
Ming Arcade	明苑	109	2 C	Noel Bldg	隆辉大厦	90	2 B
Mintwell Bldg	铭威大厦	91	1 B	Noel Corporate Bldg	隆辉集团大厦	111	2 B
Minwu Ind Bldg	民武工业大厦	90	1 C	NOL Bldg	海皇大厦	130	1 C
Mirage Tower	美乐居	132	1 A	Nordic European Ctr	北欧中心	83	2 C
Mitsubishi Electric	三菱电器大厦	130	2 A	Nordix	Nordix大厦	12	1 A
Mitutoyo Bldg	三丰大厦	111	2 B	North Bridge Ctr	桥北中心	111	1 D
MK Distripark	MK区域园	82	1 D	North Bridge Commercial	桥北路商业大厦	111	1 D
MNB Bldg	MNB大厦	132	2 C	Cplx			
MND Complex	国家发展部大厦	132	2 C	North Tech	北科	2	1 C
Mobile One	第一通	83	2 D	Northland Ind Bldg 1	北原工业大厦1	2	1 D
MOE Language Ctr	教育部语言中心	68	1 C	Northland Ind Bldg 3	北原工业大厦3	2	1 D
Morning Star Ctr	晨星中心	90	2 A	Northlink Industrial	北联工业	2	2 C
Motorola	摩托罗拉	46	2 B	Northpoint Shopping Ctr	纳福坊购物中心	14	1 D
Motorway Bldg	摩托威大厦	131	1 B	Novena Square	诺维娜广场	110	2 A
Mountbatten Square	蒙巴登广场	112	2 C	NTUC Ctr	职总中心	133	1 B
MSL Bldg	MSL大厦	91	2 C	NTUC Fairprice Ctr	职总平价合作社中心	45	2 C
Multi Wide Ind Bldg	多广工业大厦	23	1 C	NTUC Hougang Mall	职总后港购物坊	70	1 A
Multicolour Bldg	七彩大厦	130	1 C	NTUC Income Ctr	职总英康	111	1 D
Mun Hean Bldg	文轩大厦	89	1 D	NTUC Income	职总英康	72	2 D
Murray Ter Food Alley	慕理台食街	132	2 C	Tampines Point	淡滨尼中心		
Mustafa Ctr	慕达发	111	1 B	NTUC Lifestyle Ctr	职总生活情趣中心	82	1 C
Nam Peng Bldg	南平大厦	111	1 D	NTUC Lifestyle World	职总娱乐中心	52	1 C
Nam Wah Bldg	南华大厦	94	1 C	Downtown East			
Nan Yuan Yin Fong	南源永芳工业大厦	90	2 B	NTUC Trade Union Hse	职总大厦	111	1 D
Ind Bldg				NTWU Bldg	NTWU大厦	113	1 D
Nankin Row	Nankin Row大厦	132	2 B	Nutzcentre	Nutz中心	22	1 C
Nanos (Biopolis)	Nanos	107	2 C	Nylect Ind Bldg	乃德工业大厦	2	2 D
	(启奥生物医药研究园)			OAC Bldg	OAC大厦	132	2 D
Nanyang Ctr	南洋大厦	90	2 A	Oasis @ Sakra	沙克拉之绿洲	139	1 A
Nanyang Pho Leng Bldg	南洋普宁大厦	110	2 A	Oasis Bldg	海京楼	112	1 D
National Computer	国家电脑服务中心	46	2 B	OCBC Ctr	华厦中心	132	2 B
Services Hub (NCS)	(NCS)			OCBC Ctr East	华厦中心东楼	132	2 B
National Gas Control Ctr	国家煤气控制中心	2	2 B	OCBC Ctr South	华厦中心南楼	132	2 B
National Heritage	国家文物保存中心	103	2 B	OCBC Tampines Ctr 1	华侨银行淡滨尼中心1	72	2 C
Conservation Centre				OCBC Tampines Ctr 2	华侨银行淡滨尼中心2	72	2 C
National Youth Ctr	全国青年中心	110	1 D	Ocean Bldg	海洋大厦	133	1 B
Natsteel Ind Bldg	大众钢铁工业大厦	90	1 C	Ocean Sky	Ocean Sky大厦	93	2 A
Nehsons' Bldg	立山大厦	132	2 C	Ocean Towers	海洋大楼	133	1 B
Neo Ind Bldg	梁工业大厦	90	2 B	O'Connor House	奥康诺大厦	130	1 C
Nestle R&D Ctr	雀巢研发中心	81	2 C	Odeon Katong	奥迪安加东	113	2 C
Neuros (Biopolis)	Neuros	107	2 C	Shopping Cplx	购物中心		
	(启奥生物医药研究园)			Odeon Towers	奥迪安大厦	111	1 D
New Bridge Ctr	新桥中心	132	2 B	OG Bldg	奥奇大厦	132	2 B
New Optometry & Occular	新视力测定护理中心	108	2 D	OG Factory	奥奇工厂	130	2 B
Care Ctr (NOOCC)	(NOOCC)			Old School	老校	110	2 D
New Tech Park	新科技园	68	2 D	Olivine Bldg	立铭大厦	90	1 B
New World Ctr	新世界中心	111	1 B	Olympia Ind Bldg	奥林比亚工业大厦	91	2 C
News Ctr	报业中心	88	2 A	OMF International	OMF国际	109	1 B
(S'pore Press Holdings)	(新加坡报业控股)			One Fullerton	浮尔顿一号	133	1 B
Newton 200	纽顿200号	110	2 A	One George Street	乔治街一号	132	2 B
Newton Hawker Ctr	纽顿熟食中心	110	1 B				

PLACES		MAP GRID		PLACES		MAP GRID	
One Marina Boulevard	滨海林荫道一号	133	1 B	People's Park Complex	珍珠坊大厦	132	2 B
One Raffles Link	莱佛士连路一号	133	1 A	People's Park Ctr	珍珠坊	132	2 B
One Raffles Quay	莱佛士码头一号	133	1 B	Perak Court	霹雳阁	111	1 C
Onn Wah Bldg	安华大厦	94	1 C	Peranakan Place	土生坊	110	1 C
Orchard Bldg	国华大厦	110	1 C	Perfect Ind Bldg	百达工业大厦	90	1 C
Orchard Central	乌节中央城	110	1 D	Performance Ctr	宝马中心	130	2 A
Orchard Credit	乌节信贷	130	2 A	Petro Ctr	Petro中心	130	2 B
Orchard Emerald	乌节翡翠	110	1 C	Phase Z Ro	纬壹科技园第Z期	107	2 C
Orchard Plaza	乌节商业中心	110	1 C	@ One - North			
Orchard Point	乌节坊	110	1 C	Philips Districentre	飞利浦分销中心	79	2 D
Orchard Shopping Ctr	乌节购物中心	110	1 C	Pickering Opr.Cplx	必麒麟运作大厦	132	2 B
Orchard Towers	豪杰大厦	109	2 C	(Singtel)	(新电)		
Oriental Plaza	东方大厦	132	2 B	Pico Creative Ctr	笔克创意中心	111	2 B
Oriental Venture Bldg	东方投资大厦	113	1 A	Pioneer Mall	先驱广场	80	2 A
Orion Ind Bldg	澳利工业大厦	91	1 C	PIL Bldg	太平大厦	132	2 C
Osim (Ubi)	傲胜(乌美)	91	1 D	Pines Ind Bldg	松工业大厦	90	1 C
Ossia Bldg	奥西娅大厦	94	1 C	Pixel	Pixel大厦	107	2 C
OUB Bldg	华联银行大厦	132	2 C	Planet Marina	环球滨海	133	1 B
OUB Ctr	华联银行中心	132	2 B	Plaza By the Park	新苑大厦	110	2 D
OUM Bldg	OUM 大厦	113	1 B	Plaza Singapura	狮城大厦	110	2 D
Outram Ctr	欧南中心	132	1 B	PM Ind Bldg	PM工业大厦	90	2 B
Pacific Bldg	太平洋大厦	90	2 D	Poh Leng Bldg	宝龙大厦	89	2 D
Pacific Plaza	太平洋广场	110	1 C	Poh Lian Bldg 1	宝联大厦1	70	1 D
Pacific Tech Ctr	太平洋科技中心	130	2 B	Poh Lian Bldg 2	宝联大厦2	69	1 C
Pak Chong Bldg	百昌大厦	90	2 B	Poly Credit Bldg	宝利信用大厦	111	1 B
Palais Renaissance	文艺复兴广场	109	2 C	Polycore Optical	保利多光学	90	1 D
Palmer House	荣辉大厦	132	2 D	Pomo Paradiz	Pomo Paradiz大厦	110	2 D
Pan Tech Ind Complex	万能工业大厦	105	2 B	Popular Holdings Bldg	大众控股大厦	84	1 C
Panasonic	松下电器	93	1 D	PPL Shipyard (Promet)	PPL船厂(Promet)	105	2 D
Pan-I Bldg	泛一大厦	112	1 A	Premier Ctr	首轮中心	111	1 D
Pan Pacific Serviced Suites	泛太平洋服务公寓	110	1 D	Prestige Ctr	Prestige中心	83	2 B
Parakou Bldg	Parakou大厦	132	2 C	Prime Bldg	百美大厦	67	1 D
Paramount Shopping Ctr	百乐门购物中心	113	2 C	Prime Ctr	首要中心	111	1 C
Park Mall	柏南中心	110	2 D	Primero Place	必马罗坊	111	1 D
Parklane Shopping Mall	百灵购物广场	110	2 C	Princess House	公主大厦	130	2 A
Parkview Square	百威广场	111	1 D	Prinsep House	布连士大厦	110	2 D
Parkway Ctr	百汇建筑中心	113	2 C	Progen Ind Bldg	宝励进工业大厦	12	2 A
Parkway Laboratory	百汇化验公司	107	2 D	Prospaq Ind Bldg	宝柏工业大厦	22	1 C
Parkway Parade	百汇广场	113	2 C	Prosper House	荣辉大厦	112	2 A
Parpia Bldg	帕比亚大厦	90	1 C	Prosperity Bldg	幸运大厦	132	2 B
Pasir Panjang Hill Village	巴西班让山村	129	2 C	Proteos (Biopolis)	Proteos	107	2 C
Pasir Panjang	巴西班让终站大厦	128	2 B		(启奥生物医药研究园)		
Terminal Bldg				Prudential Tower	保诚大厦	132	2 B
Pasir Panjang	巴西班让码头大厦	129	1 C	PSA Bldg	港务集团大厦	130	1 D
Wharves Bldg				PSA Empire Cplx	港务局Empire大厦	132	1 D
Pasir Panjang	巴西班让批发中心	129	1 B	PSA Vista	港务集团景	129	1 B
Wholesale Ctr				PSB Bldg (Spring Spore)	PSB 大厦	131	1 B
Pasir Ris West Plaza	巴西立西厦	51	2 C	PSB Science Pk Bldg	PSB科学园大厦	129	2 A
Patech		2	2 D	PSC Bldg	PSC 大厦	81	1 C
Paya Lebar Used Car Ctr	巴耶利巴二手车中心	90	1 D	PSL Ind Bldg	PSL工业大厦	90	1 C
Paya Ubi Ind Park	巴耶乌美工业大厦	91	2 D	Punggol Plaza	榜鹅大厦	50	1 A
Peace Ctr	建安大厦	110	2 C	Punggol Point	榜鹅坊	31	1 A
Pearl's Ctr	珠光大厦	132	1 C	PWC Bldg	PWC 大厦	132	2 B
Peck Chuan Bldg	百泉大厦	111	2 B	Qinan Bldg	启南大厦	111	2 B
Peck San Theng Bldg	碧山亭大厦	88	2 A	Quartz Ind Bldg	实英工业大厦	90	2 B
Pei Fu Bldg	百福工业大厦	90	1 C	Queensway Shopping Ctr	女皇镇购物中心	130	1 C
Pemimpin Ind Bldg	柏民宾工业大厦	67	2 D	Raffles City	莱佛士城	133	1 A
Peng Nam Ctr	平南中心	69	2 C	Raffles City Tower	莱佛士城大厦	133	1 A
Peninsula Plaza	柏龄大厦	133	1 A	Raffles Place	莱佛士坊	133	1 B
Peninsula Shopping Ctr	半岛购物中心	132	2 A	Raffles Xchange	莱佛士Xchange大厦	133	1 B
Penjuru Tech Hub	本茱鲁科技中心	104	2 A	Raycom	丽康大厦	74	1 D
People's Insurance Bldg	人民保险大厦	132	2 A	RBM Ctr	罗拔多中心	91	1 B

PLACES		MAP GRID	
RCL Ctr	RCL 中心	132	2 D
Realty Ctr	海德大厦	132	2 D
Red Cross House	红十字会大厦	110	2 D
Red Dot Traffic	红点交通	132	2 C
Redhill Forum	红山广场	130	2 B
Regent	Regent大厦	130	2 A
Regent Ctr	摄政中心	91	2 B
Rehau Bldg	瑞好大厦	111	1 B
RELC Building	区语语言中心大厦	109	2 B
Reliance Bldg	信义大厦	111	1 B
Republic Plaza	共和大厦	132	2 B
Reuters	路透社	129	2 A
Revenue House	税务大厦	110	2 A
Rex House	同南大厦	110	2 C
Rhode Schwarz	Rhode Schwarz大厦	95	1 B
Richfield Ind Ctr	利辉工业中心	91	1 D
River Valley Bldg	里巴巴利大厦	132	2 A
Riverside 48	河滨48	132	1 A
Riverside Piazza	河滨大厦	132	1 A
Riverside Point	河滨楼	132	2 A
Rivervale Mall	鲤河广场	49	2 B
Rivervale Plaza	鲤河大厦	49	2 C
RJ Paper Ind Bldg	富林纸业大厦	70	1 C
Robert Bosch	罗拔布斯	67	2 D
Robertson Walk	罗逊申廊	132	1 A
Robinson Ctr	罗敏申中心	132	2 C
Robinson Point	罗敏申大楼	132	2 C
Robinson Tower	罗敏申大厦	132	2 B
Roche Bldg	罗氏大厦	90	2 B
Rochor Ctr	梧槽中心	111	1 C
Roxy Square	乐斯广场	113	2 C
Royal Brothers Bldg	皇家兄弟大厦	132	2 B
Ruby Ind Complex	红宝石工业中心	90	1 D
Ruby Warehouse Cplx	宝石货仓大厦	91	2 B
Ryobi Ind Bldg	力又比工业大厦	22	1 C
Safekeep Bldg	安藏大厦	90	1 D
SAFRA Tampines	战备军协(淡滨尼)	93	2 A
SAFRA Town Club (Carpenter St)	战备军协市区俱乐部 (嘉宾达街)	132	2 A
Sai Ho Bldg	西河大厦	69	2 C
Saint John Hqr	圣约翰救伤队总部	111	2 C
Saint Michael's Flatted Fty	圣迈克多层工厂	89	1 C
Salvation Army Command HQ S'pore Ctrl Corps	救世军总部	67	2 B
Samsung Hub	三星中心	132	2 B
Sam Tat Bldg	三达大厦	111	2 C
San Ctr	山实业大厦	132	1 B
San Teh Ind Bldg	三德工业大厦	91	2 D
Sanming SCI	Sanming SCI大厦	130	2 B
Sanwa Ind Bldg	三哇工业大厦	12	2 A
Sasco	新科学航	74	1 D
Satnam House	莎南大楼	132	2 A
SATS Express & Courier Ctr	新加坡机场终站速递中心	54	2 D
SATS Inflight Catering Ctr 1	新加坡机场终站机舱膳食中心1	96	1 A
SATS Inflight Catering Ctr 2	新加坡机场终站机舱膳食中心2	95	1 A
SATS Maintenance Ctr 2	新加坡机场终站维修中心2	74	1 D
Scandinavia Warehouse	北欧货仓	84	1 C
Schaar & Niemeyer FE	Schaar & Niemeyer FE	80	2 B
Science Arts Bldg	科艺大厦	90	1 C
Science Hub	科学中心	129	2 B
Scotts Spazio	Scotts Spazio大厦	110	1 B
Scotts Square	史格士广场	110	1 C
Scott's Walk	史格士径	110	1 B
Seacare Bldg	实佳大厦	132	1 A
Sea Town Ind Ctr	海城工业中心	99	1 A
Seagate	希捷		
- Woodlands	- 兀兰	12	2 A
- Ang Mo Kio	- 宏茂桥	48	1 D
Second Ave Junction	第2道中心	86	1 C
Seiko Instruments Singapore	精工精密(新)私人有限公司	11	1 B
Selegie Arts Ctr	实利基艺术中心	110	2 D
Selegie Ctr	实利基中心	110	2 C
Selegie House	实利基大厦	110	2 C
Seletar Airport PassengerTerminal	实利达机场搭客楼	28	2 A
Sembawang Mart	三巴旺市场	3	1 D
Sembawang Shopping Ctr	三巴旺购物中心	13	1 B
SembCorp Ind	胜科企业大厦	3	2 C
Sembwaste Senoko Depot	胜科废料圣诺哥站	2	1 C
Seng Kee Bldg	成基大厦	132	1 A
Senja Grand	信佳大厦	42	1 C
Senoko Fishing Port	圣诺哥钓鱼港口	1	2 C
Senoko Gas Works / City Gas	圣诺哥煤气厂/城市煤气	2	2 B
Sentosa Ferry Terminal	圣淘沙渡轮码头	142	1 C
Serangoon Bldg	实龙岗大厦	111	1 B
Serangoon Plaza	实龙岗商业大厦	111	1 B
Serene Ctr	实宁中心	87	1 D
SFI (S'pore Food Inds)	新食品工业	105	2 A
SGX Ctr 1 & 2	新加坡证券交易所中心1与2	132	2 C
Sharely Warehouse Bldg	莎利货仓大厦	90	1 C
Shaw Ctr	邵氏大厦	109	2 C
Shaw House	邵氏楼	109	2 C
Shaw Plaza	邵氏商业大厦	89	1 D
Shaw Towers	邵氏豪华大厦	111	1 D
Shell House	蚬壳大厦	132	2 A
Shenton House	珊顿大厦	132	2 C
Shimei East Kitchen	食美东厨	94	1 B
Shin Chin	Shin Chin大厦	111	2 B
Shriro House	石利蓉大厦	130	2 A
Shun Li Ind Complex	顺利工业中心	112	1 A
SIA Bldg	新加坡航空公司大厦	132	2 C
SIA Computer Ctr	新航电脑中心	95	1 A
SIA Training Ctr	新航训练中心	95	1 A
Siakson Bldg	锡顺大厦	111	1 D
Siau Lim Bldg	少林大厦	111	1 B
Siemens Ctr	西门子中心	90	1 C
SIF Bldg	星金融大厦	132	2 C
Siglap Ctr	实乞纳中心	114	2 B
Siglap New Market	实乞纳新巴刹	114	2 B
Siix Bldg	Siix 大厦	91	1 B
Sikh Ctr	锡克教中心	132	1 C
Silk Village Handicraft Ctr	丝绸村手工艺中心	131	1 D
Sim Lim Square	森林商业中心	111	1 C
Sim Lim Tower	森林大厦	111	1 C
SIM Management Hse	新加坡管理学院大厦	86	1 C
Sim Siang Choon Bldg	新祥骏大厦	95	1 C
Sime Darby Ctr	森那美中心	85	1 B

PLACES			MAP GRID	PLACES			MAP GRID
Simon Plaza	西门大厦	69	2 B	Soon Aik Ind Bldg	顺益工业大厦	90	1 C
Sims Avenue Ctr	沈氏道2中心	113	1 A	Soon Bee Huat	顺美发大厦	83	2 B
Sin Cheong Bldg	新昌大厦	67	2 D	Soon Seng Bldg	顺成大厦	90	1 C
Sin Loong Seng	新隆成大厦	99	1 D	Soon Wing Ind Bldg	顺荣工业大厦	90	2 C
Sin Ming Autocare	新民汽车维修	67	1 C	Sops Admin Bldg	Sops 行政大厦	53	1 D
Sin Ming Ctr	新明中心	67	1 C	South Bridge Ctr	桥南中心	132	2 B
Sin Ming Plaza	新明大厦	67	1 C	South Point	南坊大厦	132	1 D
Sin Tai Hin Bldg	新泰兴大厦	111	1 C	SPA Bldg	SPA大厦	111	1 B
Sindo Bldg	森都大厦	90	1 D	Spanners Bldg	Spanners大厦	74	1 D
Sing Ind Complex	星工大厦	47	2 D	SPCA	新加坡防止虐待动物协会	90	2 A
Sing Lun Bldg	星纶大厦	11	1 A				
SingTel Cplx (Tai Seng)	新电大厦 (大成)	91	1 B	SP Corner	SP Corner大厦	111	1 B
S'pore Airlines Superhub 1 & 2	新航枢纽1 & 2	54	2 C	SPC Tower	SPC大厦	11	1 B
				SPD Ability Ctr	SPD 技能中心	131	2 B
S'pore Airshow Exhibition Ctr	新加坡空展中心	76	2 B	Specialist Shopping Ctr	专业购物中心	110	1 C
				SPH (Media Ctr)	报业控股(传媒中心)	90	1 D
S'pore Conference Hall	新加坡大会堂	132	2 C	SPH Print Ctr	报业控股印刷中心	81	2 D
S'pore Cruise Ctr	新加坡游轮中心	142	1 A	SPI Bldg	SPI 大厦	142	1 A
S'pore Discovery Ctr	知新馆	79	2 B	SPRING S'pore Bldg	新加坡标新局大厦	131	1 D
S'pore Exchange Ctr (SGX)	新加坡交易中心 (SGX)	132	2 B	Springleaf Tower	春叶大厦	132	2 C
S'pore Expo	新加坡博览中心	94	2 B	Springlife Bldg	春笙大厦	111	1 C
S'pore Federation of Chinese Clan Assns Bldg	新加坡宗乡会馆联合总会	88	2 B	Square 2	Square 2购物大厦	88	2 D
				SRI Bldg	斯里大厦	45	2 B
S'pore Gems Bldg	新加坡宝石大厦	130	2 A	Sri Temasek	淡马锡楼	110	2 C
S'pore Godown	新加坡货仓	45	2 A	SSA Youth Ctr	SSA青年中心	129	2 C
S'pore Handicrafts	新加坡手工艺中心	91	2 D	St. Andrews Ctr	圣安德烈中心	132	2 D
S'pore Hokkien Huay Kuan	新加坡福建会馆	132	2 C	ST Automotive Inspection Ctr (Ayer Rajah Ave)	新科汽车检测中心 (亚逸拉惹道)	107	2 D
S'pore Int'l Convention & Exhibition Ctr	新加坡国际会议及展览中心	133	1 A				
				ST Automotive Vehicle Inspection Ctr	新科车辆检测中心	67	1 B
S'pore Johore Factories Bldg	新柔工厂大厦	111	1 C				
				ST Electronics	新科电子	46	2 B
S'pore Land Tower	新加坡置地大厦	133	1 B	ST Logistics	新科后勤	9	2 D
S'pore Post Delivery Base	新加坡邮政递送基地			STA Autocentre	STA汽车检验中心	91	2 B
- (Jurong)	- (裕廊)	80	2 B	Stamford Arts Ctr	史丹福艺术中心	111	1 D
- (Loyang)	- (罗央)	53	1 D	Stamford Court	史丹福阁	110	2 D
- (Woodlands)	- (兀兰)	2	2 D	Stamford Ctr	史丹福中心	132	2 A
S'pore Power Bldg	新加坡能源大厦	110	1 D	Stamford Hse	史丹福大厦	132	2 A
S'pore Press Holdings	新加坡报业控股	88	2 A	Stamford Press Ctr	史丹福印务馆	111	2 A
S'pore Rowing Ctr	新加坡划船中心	105	2 B	Standard Form	Standard Form大厦	93	2 B
S'pore Shopping Ctr	新加坡购物中心	110	2 D	Star Bldg	事达大厦	22	2 C
S'pore Storage & Warehouse	新加坡货仓	91	2 B	Starhub Ctr	星和中心	110	1 C
				St. Michael's Flatted Fty	圣迈克多层工厂	89	1 C
S'pore Technologies	新加坡科技	83	1 B	Straits Trading Bldg	海峡贸易大厦	133	1 B
S'pore Technologies Kinetics	新加坡科技动力大厦	81	2 A	Subaru	Subaru大厦	89	1 A
				Sultan Gate Place	苏丹门坊	111	1 D
S'pore Technologies Bldg	新加坡科技大厦	132	2 D	Sultan Plaza	金皇商业大厦	111	2 C
S'pore Tyler Print Institute	新加坡泰勒版画院	132	1 A	Sumitomo	住友大厦	111	2 A
S'pore Warehouse	新加坡货仓	91	1 D	Sumitomo Warehouse	住友仓库	77	2 C
Sinsov Bldg	星苏大厦	132	2 B	Summit Bldg	声美大厦	91	1 C
SIS Bldg	新龙大厦	131	1 A	Sun Plaza	太阳大厦	13	1 A
Six Battery Road	百得利经路	133	1 B	Sunny Ind Bldg	山尼工业大厦	95	1 C
Sixth Avenue Ctr	第六道中心	86	1 C	Sunshine Place	金光坊	41	1 D
SK Bldg	叁强大厦	112	2 A	Sunshine Plaza	金光大厦	110	2 C
SKP Ind Bldg I	绍钦工业大厦	53	1 D	Suntec City	新达城	111	1 D
SKP Ind Bldg II	SKP工业大厦2	53	1 D	Suntec City Mall	新达城广场	111	1 D
Skyline Bldg	天际大厦	111	1 D	Suntec Tower 1	新达大厦1	111	1 D
Skywaves Ind Bldg	天浪工业大厦	89	1 D	Suntec Tower 2	新达大厦2	111	1 D
SL Bldg	SL大厦	14	1 B	Suntec Tower 3	新达大厦3	111	1 D
SLF Bldg	新加坡劳工基金大厦	88	1 B	Suntec Tower 4	新达大厦4	111	1 D
SMRT Hq Bldg	新加坡地铁局总部	133	1 A	Suntec Tower 5	新达大厦5	133	1 A
Soka Culture Ctr	新加坡创价学会	60	1 D	Super Bowl Complex	贵族保龄球场	82	1 D
Somerset Central	索美塞中心	110	1 C	Super Continental	超级大陆	77	2 A
Song Lin Bldg	松林大厦	111	1 C	Super Coffeemix	超级咖啡	2	2 C

PLACES		MAP GRID	PLACES		MAP GRID
Superior Ind Bldg	优越工业大厦	112 1 A	Teck Heng Long Ind Bldg	德兴隆工业大厦	111 1 B
Superpet Plastic	宝特塑胶	100 1 A	Teck Whye Shopping Ctr	德惠购物中心	41 2 C
Surbana One	Surbana壹号大厦	131 1 B	Tee Hai Bldg	四海大厦	77 2 B
SUTL House	SUTL大厦	130 1 C	Tekka Ctr	德卡中心	111 1 C
Suzue - PSA Cold Storage	Suzue -港务局冷藏仓库	132 1 D	Tekka Mall (The Verge)	德卡廊(The Verge大厦)	111 1 C
Swee Hin Bldg	瑞兴大厦	70 1 D	Telepark	淡滨尼电讯园	72 1 D
Swee Hong Ind Bldg	瑞虹工业大厦	91 1 D	Telephone House Cplx	电话大厦	132 2 A
Sweebi House	瑞美大厦	84 2 A	Teletech Park	电信科技园	129 1 B
SYH Logistics Bldg	SYH后勤大厦	90 2 C	Telok Blangah House	直落布兰雅大厦	142 2 A
Tac Plas House	特巴斯大厦	112 2 B	Tembeling Ctr	登百灵中心	113 2 C
Tagore 23 Warehouse	泰享23仓库	45 2 C	Tempco Technominium	多特机械工程生产大厦	107 2 D
Tagore Ind Bldg	太戈尔工业大厦	45 2 B	Ten Mile Junction	十里广场	42 1 C
Tai Pei Buddist Ctr	大悲佛教中心	111 2 B	Teo Ind Bldg	张氏工业大厦	90 2 B
Tai Sun Bldg	大山大厦	132 1 C	Teochew Bldg	潮州大厦	110 2 D
Tai Thong Hung Bldg	大通行大厦	112 2 A	TET Bldg	TET 大厦	132 2 B
Tai Wah Bldg	大华大厦	110 1 D	Textile Ctr	布业中心	111 2 C
Tailee Bldg	大利大厦	67 2 D	TG Bldg	TG大厦	45 2 B
Takashimaya Shopping Ctr	高岛屋购物中心	110 1 C	The Acceleration	The Acceleration大厦	107 2 C
Talib Ctr	达里中心	111 1 D	The Adelphi	雅达辉购物中心	133 1 A
Taman Jurong Shop. Ctr	达曼裕廊购物中心	82 1 B	The Alexcier	The Alexcier大厦	131 1 A
Tampines 1	淡滨尼1号	72 2 C	The Alpha	艾法大厦	129 1 A
Tampines Junction	淡滨尼购物中心	72 2 D	The Amara	安国大厦	132 2 C
Tampines Mall	淡滨尼广场	72 2 D	The Aquarius	宝瓶大厦	129 1 A
Tampines Mart	淡滨尼坊	73 2 C	The Arcade	雅古拱廊	133 1 B
Tampines N2 Shopping St	淡滨尼N2购物街	73 1 D	The Aries	白羊大厦	129 2 A
Tampines Plaza	淡滨尼大厦	72 2 D	The Atrium (IBP)	爱特岭大厦	83 2 C
Tampines Retail Park	淡滨尼零售园	72 1 A	The Atrium @ Orchard	乌节The Atrium大厦	111 1 C
Tampines Soka Ctr	淡滨尼创价会馆	93 2 A	The Bencoolen	明古连大楼	111 1 C
Tan Boon Liat Bldg	陈文烈大厦	132 1 B	The Besco Bldg	百事乐广场	91 2 C
Tan Chong Motor Ctr	陈唱汽车中心	85 2 B	The Blue Bldg	蓝厦	90 1 C
Tan Chong Tower	陈唱大厦	111 1 D	The Buddhist Union	佛教会	92 1 D
Tan Ean Khiam Bldg (TEK)	陈延谦大厦(TEK)	132 2 B	The Cage	The Cage大厦	112 2 C
Tan Jin Chwee Ind Bldg	陈仁水工业大厦	90 1 C	The Cannery	The Cannery大厦	132 2 A
Tan Kong Tien Bldg	陈光耀大厦	110 2 C	The Cavendish	嘉文迪大厦	129 2 A
Tan Quee Swee Bldg	陈桂水大厦	84 2 A	The Capricorn	山羊大厦	129 1 A
Tanglin Mall	东陵坊	109 2 C	The Cathay	国泰大厦	110 2 D
Tanglin Place	东陵大厦	109 2 C	The CentrePoint	先得大厦	110 1 C
Tanglin Shopping Ctr	东陵购物中心	109 2 C	The Chadwick	哲伟大厦	129 2 A
Tang Plaza	董厦	110 1 C	The Comtech	电信科技大厦	130 1 C
Tanjong Katong Cplx	丹戎加东大厦	113 1 A	The Concourse	鸿福	111 2 C
Tanjong Pagar Cplx	丹戎巴葛大厦	132 2 D	The Connection	The Connection大厦	107 2 C
Tanjong Pagar Plaza	丹戎巴葛坊	132 2 C	The Corporate Bldg	企业大厦	132 2 C
Tanjong Pagar Workshop	丹戎巴葛工场	132 2 D	The Corporate Office	企业办公楼	132 2 C
Tannery Bldg	登那利大厦	90 2 C	The Crimson	克林逊大厦	129 1 A
Tannery Hse	登那利大厦	90 1 C	The Curie	居里大厦	129 2 A
Tat Ann Bldg	达安大厦	67 2 D	The Domain	多美中心	114 2 B
Tat Hong Ind Bldg	达丰工业大厦	90 2 B	The Enterprise @ Jurong East	企业大厦	83 1 C
Technopark @ Chai Chee	菜市科技园	92 2 D	The Faraday	法拉地大厦	129 2 A
Tech Place	科技坊	68 1 B	The Fleming	菲敏大厦	129 2 A
Tech Point	科技坊	46 2 B	The Foundry	The Foundry大厦	132 2 A
Tech Semiconductor Singapore	新加坡科技半导体	10 1 D	The Frontier Community Place	边境联络坊	81 1 A
Techlink	科技岭	91 2 B	The Fullerton Waterboat House	浮尔顿水艇屋	133 1 B
Techniques Bldg	技术大厦	91 2 C	The Furniture Mall	家具广场	111 2 D
Technopreneur Ctr	科技企业中心	131 1 B	The Galaxy	光彩大厦	113 1 A
Technopreneur Centre @ Ayer Rajah	亚逸拉惹科技进企业中心	107 2 D	The Gateway	新门广场	111 1 D
Technopreneur Park	企业家园	107 2 C	The Gemini	双子大厦	129 1 A
Techview	科技景	92 1 B	The Genesis Bldg	创源大厦	110 2 B
Teck Chiang Bldg	德昌大厦	91 1 D	The Glass House	玻璃大厦	110 2 D
Teck Chiang Realty Bldg	德昌实业大厦	91 1 D	The Globe	地球大厦	132 2 C
Teck Ghee Square	德义广场	68 1 B	The Heeren	麒麟大厦	110 1 C

PLACES		MAP GRID		PLACES		MAP GRID	
The Hindu Ctr	兴都教中心	111	1 A	Tristar Complex	Tristar 大厦	113	1 A
The JTC Summit	裕廊峰	83	1 C	Tropical Ind Bldg	阳光工业大厦	90	2 B
The Majestic	大华	132	2 B	T.T. Int'l Tradepark	T.T.国际贸易园	83	2 C
The Max Pavilion	The Max Pavilion大厦	94	2 B	Tuas Amenity Ctr	大士便利中心	100	2 A
The Maxwell	麦士威	129	2 A	Tuas Bay Ind Cplx	大士湾工业大厦	99	1 A
The Mendel	孟德大厦	129	2 A	Tuas Incineration Plant	大士垃圾焚化厂	77	2 D
The Octagon	建春大厦	132	2 C	Tuas Marine Transfer Stn	大士船运转运站	98	2 D
The Office Chambers	公益大厦	111	1 B	Tuas Power Station	大士发电厂	121	2 A
The Oglivy Ctr	欧格威中心	132	2 C	Tuas Rd Ter Fty	大士路邮连工厂	100	2 A
The Oxley	欧思礼园	110	2 D	Tuas South	大士南垃圾焚化场	98	2 D
The Paragon	百丽宫	110	1 C	Incineration Plant			
The Pascal	帕斯卡大厦	129	2 A	Tuas Techpark	大士村科技园	99	1 B
The Pasteur	巴斯德大厦	129	2 A	Tudor Ct Shopping Gallery	杜德阁	109	2 C
The Pet Hotel	宠物旅店	51	1 C	Tung Ann Assn Bldg	同安会馆大厦	132	2 C
The Plaza	文雅大厦	111	1 D	Tung Ctr	汤大厦	133	1 D
The Plaza (Office)	文雅大厦(办公楼)	111	1 D	Turf City	马城	85	2 A
The Quayside	码头区	132	1 A	Tye Soon Bldg	大顺大厦	83	2 B
The Rail Mall	铁道广场	63	2 B	Ubi 55	乌美55	91	1 D
The Riverwalk	河畔廊	132	1 A	Ubi Automart	乌美汽车市场	91	2 C
The Rutherford	卢瑟福大厦	129	2 A	Ubi Car Mall	乌美汽车广场	91	2 C
The Signature	留名楼	95	1 B	Ubi Ctr	乌美中心	91	1 D
The Singapore Mint	新加坡造币厂	83	1 D	Ubi Techpark	裕ုৰ工业大厦	91	1 D
The Spazio	The Spazio大厦	132	2 A	UE Media Hub	UE传媒中心	90	2 B
The Spire	鼎锋科技大厦	84	1 B	UE Tech Park	友乃科技园	106	1 C
The Strategy	The Strategy大厦	83	2 C	UE Shopping Mall	友乃德购物广场	132	2 A
The Substation	电力站	110	2 D	UE Square	友乃德广场	132	2 A
The Sunniflora	向阳花楼	114	1 A	UIC Bldg	联合工业大厦	132	2 C
The Synergy	协同大厦	83	2 C	Ulu Pandan Refuse	乌鲁班丹	84	1 C
The Treasury	财务大厦	132	2 A	Incineration Plant	垃圾焚化厂		
The Verge (Tekka Mall)	The Verge大厦(德卡路)	111	1 C	Ulu Pandan Water	乌鲁班丹水源开发厂	83	2 C
The Village Ctr	乡村中心	129	2 C	Reclamation Plant			
The Woodgrove	木林苑	11	1 D	UNI Bldg	全合大厦	114	1 B
THK Ind Bldg	THK 工业大厦	112	2 A	Union Bldg	联厦	132	2 D
Thomson Imperial Court	汤申皇阁	67	1 D	Union Ind Bldg	友利大厦	67	2 D
Thomson Plaza	汤申大厦	66	2 B	United Agencies Bldg	联合代理大厦	45	2 B
Thong Chai Bldg	同济大厦	132	1 A	United House	华业大厦	110	2 C
Thong Sia Bldg	通城大厦	110	1 C	United Square	大华广场	110	2 A
Thong Teck Building	同德大厦	110	1 B	Unity Ctr	友力德中心	84	1 B
Thye Hong Ctr	太丰中心	131	1 A	University Town	大学城	106	2 C
TIC Tech Ctr	德怡科技中心	106	1 C	UOB Ctr	大华银行中心	85	1 A
Times Ctr	时报中心	90	2 A	UOB Jurong Warehouse	大华银行裕廊货仓	100	2 C
Tiong Aik Bldg	长益大厦	22	2 C	UOB Plaza	大华银行大厦	132	2 B
Tiong Aik Ind Bldg	长益工业大厦	22	1 C	UOB Tampines Ctr 2	大华银行淡滨尼中心2	72	2 D
Tiong Bahru Plaza	中巴鲁广场	131	2 B	Upp Serangoon Shop. Ctr	实龙岗上段购物中心	69	2 D
Toa Payoh Entertainment Ctr	大巴窑娱乐中心	88	2 C	UPS House	UPS大厦	95	1 C
Toh Guan Ctr	卓源中心	83	2 B	URA Centre	市区重建局中心	132	2 C
Toll Asia	Toll亚洲大厦	84	1 D	Used Car Mart	二手汽车场	110	2 C
Tong Bldg	董大厦	110	1 C	(Mackenzie Rd)	(麦肯西路)		
Tong Eng Bldg	同荣大厦	132	2 C	Valiant Ind Bldg	美奂工业大厦	90	1 C
Tong Fong Bldg	东方新厦	110	2 D	Valley Point	华丽岭公寓	131	2 A
Tong Lee Bldg (Blk A & B)	同利大厦(A与B座)	90	2 C	Vanguard Bldg	Vanguard大厦	110	2 D
Tong Xing Warehouse	同兴仓库	91	1 B	Verdun House	维登大厦	111	1 B
Tong Yuan Bldg	东园大厦	90	2 B	Veterinary Public	兽医公共卫生中心	7	1 D
Toshiba Data Dynamics Bldg	东芝数据动态大厦	90	1 D	Health Centre			
Touchcentre	触爱中心	113	2 C	Vertex	Vertex大厦	91	1 B
Tourism Court	旅游厅	109	2 C	Vicom Vehicle Insp Ctr	维康汽车检验中心		
Tower Fifteen	十五大楼	132	2 D	- Bukit Batok	- 武吉巴督	83	2 A
Townshend Bldg	陶胜大厦	111	1 B	- Changi	- 樟宜	74	1 D
TPI Bldg	太平保险大厦	132	2 B	- Kaki Bukit	- 加基武吉	92	1 B
Tractors S'pore	新加坡拖拉机大厦	102	1 A	- Sin Ming	- 新民	67	1 B
Traders Market Car Park	商家市场停车场	132	2 A	- Yishun	- 义顺	14	1 B
Trident Districentre	海锚分销中心	83	2 B	Victoria St Wholesale Ctr	维多利亚街批发中心	111	1 C

PLACES		MAP	GRID
Victory Bldg	胜利大厦	70	1 C
Victory Family Ctr	凯旋家庭中心		
- Choa Chu Kang	- 蔡厝港	41	1 D
- Jurong West	- 裕廊西	59	2 D
- Sembawang	- 三巴旺	3	1 D
- Tampines	- 淡滨尼	73	1 B
Vista Point	维斯达坊	12	1 D
Vivo City	怡丰城	142	1 A
Wah Yang (Food Ind) Bldg	华洋食品工业大厦	112	2 A
Wai Wing Ctr	怀永中心	88	2 D
Wallich Bldg	华利大厦	132	2 C
Wangi Ind Bldg	万宜工业大厦	91	2 C
Water Hub	水务中心	84	1 B
Waterfront Plaza	水边广场	132	1 A
Waterloo Ctr	华德楼	111	1 D
WCEGA Plaza	WCEGA大楼	84	1 B
WCEGA Tower	WCEGA 大厦	84	1 B
Wealsoft Bldg	伟福大厦	89	2 D
Wearnes Bldg	温氏大厦	89	1 B
Wedge Mt Ind Bldg	伟奇山工业大厦	67	2 D
Wellington Bldg	威灵顿大厦	110	1 C
Weltech Ind Bldg	伟特工业大厦	91	2 C
West Coast Car Mart	西海岸汽车市场	129	1 B
West Coast Plaza	西海岸广场	106	1 C
West Mall	威城	62	2 D
Westlink Techpark	西岭科技园	99	1 C
Whampoa Ice House	黄埔冰厂	132	2 A
Wheelock Place	伟乐坊	109	2 C
White House	白楼	132	2 C
White Sands	白沙购物中心	52	1 D
Widefield Ind Bldg	怀德菲工业大厦	11	1 B
Wiedson House	伟登大厦	112	2 A
Wilkie Edge	威基一隅	110	2 C
Wincor Nixdorf	温克利多	90	1 D
Winchester Place	温彻斯得坊	129	2 B
Wing Fong Bldg	永丰大厦	112	1 B
Wing Tai Bldg	永泰大厦	70	1 B
Wing Tai Warehouse	永泰货仓	70	1 B
Winsland House I	温斯兰大厦1	110	1 D
Winsland House II	温斯兰大厦2	110	1 D
Wintech Ctr	Wintech中心	91	1 D
Wisdom Ind Bldg	智慧工业大厦	67	2 D
Wisma Alsagoff	阿沙戈夫大厦	111	1 D
Wisma Atria Shopping Ctr	威士马广场	110	1 C
Wisma AUPE	AUPE 大厦	90	2 A
Wisma Mendaki	猛达基楼	115	1 B
Wisma Sugnomal	瑟诺马大厦	132	2 A
Wong Shee Fun Bldg	黄树芬大厦	132	2 B
Woodlands Civic Ctr	兀兰民事中心	11	2 C
Woodlands Market Place	兀兰市场坊	11	2 B
Woodlands Mart	兀兰坊	12	1 A
Woodlands North Plaza	兀兰北大厦	11	2 B
Woodlands Point	兀兰岭	10	2 B
Woodlands Spectrum	兀兰飞腾	2	2 D
World Pub Bldg	世界出版大厦	91	1 C
World Scientific Publishing Ctr	醒农大厦	84	1 C
World Trade Ctr (now HarbourFront Ctr)	世界贸易中心 (现新港湾中心)	142	1 A
Wu De Bldg	武德大厦	111	1 A
Wui Guang Bldg	伟光大厦	91	2 C
Wywy House	威威大厦	130	2 A

PLACES		MAP	GRID
Xilin Districentre	西林分销中心	95	1 C
Xing Bldg	兴厦	90	2 B
Yangtze Bldg	长江大厦	132	1 B
Yao Nan Bldg	耀南大厦	115	2 B
YCH Distripark	YCH分销园	100	2 A
Yeley Bldg	业利大厦	69	2 D
Yellow Pages Singapore	新加坡黄页大厦	88	2 A
Yen Ind Bldg	达富工业大厦	2	1 D
Yenom Ind Bldg	耶南工业大厦	90	2 D
Yeo's Bldg	杨氏大厦	130	2 D
Yess Ctr	Yess中心	129	1 B
Yess Leisure	Yess休闲坊	132	2 C
Yew Lee Bldg	友利大厦	91	1 B
Yew Tee Shopping Ctr	油池购物中心	41	2 A
Yi Guang Factory Bldg	艺光工业大厦	91	1 C
Yi Xiu Factory Bldg	艺秀大厦	112	1 A
Yin Lie Bldg	英烈大厦	112	1 A
Ying Fo Fui Kun	应和会馆	132	2 B
Yio Chu Kang Amenity Ctr	杨厝港便利中心	48	1 D
YMCA Int'l Hse	基督教青年会国际大厦	110	2 D
YMCA (Metropolitan)	京华基督教青年会	109	2 A
YMS Arts Ctr	YMS艺术中心	111	1 D
Yong Da Bldg	荣达大厦	112	2 A
Yong Heng Bldg	永兴大厦	74	1 A
Yong Lee Bldg	Yong Lee 大厦	91	1 D
York Intl Ind Bldg	约克国际工业大厦	90	2 B
Youth Community Village (NIE-NTU)	青奥运动村(国立教育学院 -南洋理工大学)	58	2 C
YS One (Yishun St. 23)	YS One大厦 (义顺23街)	14	2 B
YTC Bldg	远东大厦	111	1 B
Yuan Ji	Yuan Ji大厦	80	2 C
Yu Li Ind Bldg	有利工业大厦	112	2 A
Yue Hwa Bldg	裕华大厦	132	2 B
Yun Chee Bldg	云集大厦	90	2 B
YWCA Outram Ctr	基督教女青年会 欧南中心	132	1 B
Zaman Ctr	Zaman中心	111	1 B

RESERVOIRS

		MAP	GRID
Bedok	勿洛	92	2 A
Fort Canning Service	福康宁水务池	132	2 A
Jalan Eunos Service	惹兰友诺士水务池	92	1 A
Jurong Hill 65 Service	裕廊山65水务池	79	2 D
Kallang Service	加冷水务池	66	1 C
Kranji	克兰芝	21	2 B
Lower Peirce	贝雅士下段	66	2 A
Lower Seletar	实里达下段	27	1 C
MacRitchie	麦里芝	88	1 A
Marina Bay	滨海湾	133	2 B
Mt. Faber II Service	花柏山II水务池	130	2 C
Murai	慕莱	18	2 D
Murnane Service	慕南水务池	64	2 D
Pandan	班丹	105	1 A
Pearl's Hill	珍珠山	132	1 B
Poyan	波扬	36	2 D
Punggol	榜鹅实龙岗	30	1 B
Sarimbun	莎琳汶	19	1 A
Serangoon	实龙岗	50	2 A
South End	南端	95	2 A
Tengeh	登格	78	1 A
Upper Peirce	贝雅士上段	64	2 A
Upper Seletar	实里达上段	44	1 A

PLACES		MAP GRID

SAF CAMPS & FACILITIES

PLACES		MAP GRID	
Air Force Museum	空军博物馆	70	2 D
Air Force School	空军学校	70	2 D
Amoy Quee Camp	亚莫 Queee 兵营	47	1 C
Army Logistics Base	陆军后勤基地	40	1 D
Ayer Rajah Camp	亚逸拉惹兵营	129	2 A
BCTC	BCTC中心	79	1 C
Bedok Camp	勿洛兵营	116	2 A
Bukit Gombak Camp	武吉甘柏兵营	63	1 A
Bukit Panjang Camp	武吉班让兵营	63	1 A
Bukit Timah Range	武吉知马射击场	64	1 D
CMPB	中央人力局	131	2 C
Changi Air Base East	樟宜东部空军基地	97	1 C
Changi Air Base West	樟宜西部空军基地	53	2 D
Changi Camp	樟宜兵营	53	2 C
Changi Naval Base	樟宜海军基地	119	2 A
Chong Pang Camp	忠邦兵营	13	2 D
Clementi Camp	金文泰兵营	84	1 C
Defence Technology Towers A & B	国防科技楼A及B	131	1 C
Dieppe Barracks	Dieppe兵营	26	2 A
Gloucester Camp	Gloucester兵营	129	2 A
Gombak Base	甘柏基地	63	1 A
Hendon Camp	Hendon兵营	53	2 B
Hillview Camp	山景兵营	63	1 A
Jurong Camp	裕廊兵营	80	1 B
Kaki Bukit Camp	加基武吉兵营	92	1 A
Kallang Camp	加冷兵营	112	1 C
Keat Hong Camp	吉丰兵营	39	2 D
Khatib Camp	卡迪兵营	26	2 A
Kranji Camp	克兰芝兵营	41	1 A
Lim Chu Kang Camp I	林厝港兵营I	39	1 C
Lim Chu Kang Camp II	林厝港兵营II	38	2 D
Maju Camp	马裕兵营	84	2 C
Mandai Hill Camp	万礼山营	23	2 C
Mandai Camp II	万礼兵营II	23	2 C
Mandai Range	万礼射击场	24	1 D
Mowbray Camp	万礼兵营	41	1 A
Murai Camp	慕莱兵营	39	1 B
Navy Museum	海军博物馆	119	1 A
National Service Resort & Country Club	国民服务度假俱乐部	117	1 A
Nee Soon Camp	义顺兵营	26	1 C
Nee Soon Range	义顺射击场	44	2 A
NSRCC Golf Course	国民服役战备人员乡村俱乐部高尔夫球场	117	1 A
NSRCC Sea Sports Centre	国民服役战备人员乡村俱乐部海上运动中心	117	2 A
Pasir Laba Camp	巴西拉巴兵营	79	2 B
Pasir Ris Camp	巴西立兵营	51	1 B
Paya Lebar Air Base	巴耶利峇空军基地	91	2 A
Pulau Tekong Camp	德光岛兵营	35A	2 C
Rifle Range Road Camp I	射靶场路兵营I	64	2 C
Rifle Range Road Camp II	射靶场路兵营II	64	2 C
SAF Driving Circuit	武装部队驾驶练习场	92	1 A
SAF Education Centre	武装部队教育中心	26	2 A
SAF Ferry Terminal & Jetty	武装部队渡轮码头	54	2 B
SAF Holiday Chalets	武装部队度假屋	53	2 B
SAF Yacht Club	武装部队游艇俱乐部		
- (Admiralty)	- (海军部)	3	1 B
- (Changi)	- (樟宜)	119	1 B
SAFRA Mt Faber Club	战备军队花柏山俱乐部	131	1 C
SAFRA Tampines Clubhouse	战备军队淡滨尼会所	93	2 A
SAFRA Toa Payoh Clubhouse	战备军队大巴窑会所	89	1 C
SAFRA Town Club	战备军队市俱乐部	132	2 A
SAFRA Yishun Country Club	战备军队义顺乡村俱乐部	27	2 A
SAFTI 100M Range I & II	武装部队100M射击场I及II	79	1 B
SAFTI 25M Range	武装部队25M射击场	79	1 B
SAFTI 300M Range I & II	武装部队300M射击场	79	1 B
SAFTI Military Institute	武装部队军事学院	80	1 C
Sarimbun Camp	莎琳漫兵营	7	1 A
Selarang Camp	史拉兰兵营	74	2 A
Seletar Camp	实里达兵营	29	1 D
Seletar Range	实里达射击场	45	1 B
Sembawang Air Base	三巴旺空军基地	26	1 B
Sembawang Camp	三巴旺兵营	3	1 B
Stagmont Camp	史达蒙兵营	41	2 C
Sungei Gedong Camp	双溪格当兵营	19	2 A
Tanjong Gul Camp	丹戎卡尔兵营	100	2 C
Temasek Club	淡马锡俱乐部	130	1 A
Tengah Air Base	登加空军基地	39	2 D
The Chevrons	军章俱乐部	83	1 C
Tuas Naval Base	大士海军基地	101	1 D

SCDF (CIVIL DEFENCE) CAMPS & FACILITIES

PLACES		MAP GRID	
Bt Panjang Civil Defence Ctr	武吉班让民防中心	10	2 B
Civil Defence Academy	民防学院	59	2 A
HomeTeamNS	内政团队战备人员协会		
Ah Hood Rd Club House	亚佛路俱乐部	88	2 C
Bt Batok Club House & Adventure Ctr	武吉巴督俱乐部及探险中心	62	2 B
Sembawang Resort	三巴旺度假村	3	1 C
Smith St Club House	史密斯街俱乐部	132	2 B
UE Square Club House	友乃德广场俱乐部	132	2 A
HQ 1st CD Division Queensway	民防第一分区女皇大道	130	1 A
HQ 2nd CD Division Tampines Camp	民防第二分区总部淡滨尼营地	72	1 C
HQ 3rd CD Division Yishun Ind Pk A	民防第三分区总部义顺A工业园	14	1 A
HQ 4th CD Division Bukit Batok Road	民防第四分区总部武吉巴督路	41	2 D
HQ Singapore Civil Defence Force	新加坡民防部队总部	91	1 B
National Civil Defence Cadet Corps (HomeTeam Academy)	全国民防学生团(内政团学院)	40	1 D

PLACES		MAP GRID		PLACES		MAP GRID	

STADIA / SPORTS COMPLEXES / FIELDS / GOLF DRIVING RANGES

STADIA 体育场

Bedok Stadium	勿洛体育场	93	2 D
Bishan Stadium	碧山体育场	68	1 C
Bukit Gombak Stadium	武吉甘柏体育场	62	2 C
Choa Chu Kang Stadium	蔡厝港体育场	41	2 B
Clementi Stadium	金文泰体育场	106	1 B
Hougang Stadium	后港体育场	69	2 A
Jalan Besar Stadium	惹兰勿刹体育场	111	2 B
Jurong East Stadium	裕廊东体育场	61	2 D
Jurong Stadium	裕廊体育场	82	1 B
Jurong West Stadium	裕廊西体育场	80	2 B
Queenstown Stadium	女皇镇体育场	108	1 D
Serangoon Stadium	实龙岗体育场	69	1 C
Singapore Indoor Stadium	新加坡室内体育馆	112	1 D
SPE Stadium	SPE体育场	109	1 A
Tampines Stadium	淡滨尼体育场	72	2 D
Toa Payoh Stadium	大巴窑体育场	89	1 C
Woodlands Stadium	兀兰体育场	11	1 C
Yio Chu Kang Stadium	杨厝港体育场	46	2 C
Yishun Stadium	义顺体育场	27	1 B

SPORT COMPLEXES/ FIELDS 体育中心 /草场

Bedok Sports & Recreation Centre	勿洛体育及康乐中心	93	2 D
Bedok Sports Hall	勿洛室内体育馆	93	2 D
Bedok Tennis Centre	勿洛网球中心	93	2 D
Bishan Sports Hall	碧山室内体育馆	68	1 C
Bt Gombak Sports Hall	武吉甘柏室内体育馆	62	2 B
Bt Timah Field	武吉知马草场	85	2 B
BRTC Sports Cplx	BRTC体育中心	93	2 A
Burghley Squash & Tennis Centre	柏格礼壁球及网球中心	68	2 C
CBC Sports Complex	CBC 体育中心	53	2 B
Choa Chu Kang Sports Hall	蔡厝港室内体育馆	41	2 B
Choa Chu Kang Tennis Ctr	蔡厝港室内网球中心	41	2 B
Clementi Sports Hall	金文泰室内体育馆	106	1 B
Delta Hockey Pitch	立达钩球场	131	1 A
Delta Sports Hall	立达室内体育馆	131	1 A
Farrer Park Fields	花拉公园草场	110	2 B
Farrer Park Tennis Ctr	花拉公园网球中心	110	2 B
Fitness Park (ECP)	健身公园 (东海岸公园)	114	2 C
Geylang Field	芽笼草场	112	1 B
Hougang Sports Hall	后港室内体育馆	69	2 A
Jurong East Sports Hall	裕廊东室内体育馆	61	2 D
Jurong West Sports Cplx	裕廊西体育中心	80	2 B
Jurong West Tennis Ctr	裕廊西网球中心	80	2 B
Kallang Netball Centre	加冷英式篮球中心	112	2 C
Kallang Squash & Tennis Centre	加冷壁球及网球中心	112	1 C
Kallang Water Sports Ctr	加冷水上运动中心	112	1 C
National Sailing Centre	国家帆船中心	116	2 A
NSRCC Sea Sports Ctr	战备人员度假乡村俱乐部海上运动中心	117	2 A
SCA - Kallang Cricket Grounds	SCA – 加冷板球场	112	1 C
Sengkang Sports Complex	盛港体育中心	48	2 A

Singapore Badminton Hall	新加坡羽球馆	112	2 B
Singapore Sports Hub	新加坡体育中心	112	1 C
Singapore Turf Club Race Course	新加坡赛马公会赛马场	23	1 A
SPE Sports Hall / Tennis / Hockey Pitch	体育馆/网球/钩球场	109	1 A
St. Wilfred Squash & Tennis Ctr	圣威菲立壁球及网球中心	89	2 D
Tampines Sports Hall	淡滨尼室内体育馆	72	2 C
Tanglin Fields	东陵草场	109	1 C
Toa Payoh Sports Hall	大巴窑室内体育馆	89	1 C
West Coast Recreation Ctr	西海岸康乐中心	106	1 B
Woodlands Sports Hall	兀兰室内体育馆	11	1 C
Yio Chu Kang Sports Hall	杨厝港室内体育馆	46	2 C
Yio Chu Kang Squash & Tennis Centre	杨厝港壁球及网球中心	46	2 C
Yishun Sports Hall	义顺室内体育馆	27	1 B

GOLF DRIVING RANGES 高尔夫球练习场

Arena Country Club	阿连纳乡村俱乐部	80	1 C
Asian Golf Academy	亚洲高尔夫学院	67	2 B
Bukit Batok Golf Range	武吉巴督高尔夫球练习场	62	2 B
Executive Golf Course	执行员高尔夫球练习场	25	2 D
Fairway Club	花威俱乐部	82	1 C
Green Fairways	格林花威高尔夫球场	86	1 A
Jurong Country Club	裕廊乡村俱乐部	83	1 C
Keppel Driving Range	发巴高尔夫球练习场	141	2 A
Laguna National Golf & Country Club	礁湖国家高尔夫球及乡村俱乐部	94	2 D
NSRCC Golf Course	战备人员度假乡村俱乐部高尔夫球场	117	1 A
Orchid Country Club	胡姬乡村俱乐部	27	2 C
Parkland Golf Driving Range	百龄高尔夫球练习场	113	2 C
Queens Townclub	女皇市镇俱乐部	108	2 D
Raffles Country Club	莱佛士乡村俱乐部	78	2 B
Seletar Country Club	实里达乡村俱乐部	28	1 C
Sembawang Country Club	三巴旺乡村俱乐部	26	1 B
Tanglin Golf Course Country Club	东陵高尔夫球练习场乡村俱乐部	109	1 C
Transview Golf & Country Club (Night Only)	泛景高尔夫球及乡村俱乐部 (只限晚上)	106	2 B
Volkswagen Golf Centre	福士伟根高尔夫球中心	89	2 B

PLACES		MAP GRID	PLACES		MAP GRID

SWIMMING COMPLEXES

Ang Mo Kio	宏茂桥	67	2 B
Bedok	勿洛	93	2 D
Bishan	碧山	68	1 C
Bukit Batok	武吉巴督	83	2 A
Buona Vista	波那维斯达	107	2 C
Choa Chu Kang	蔡厝港	41	2 B
Clementi	金文泰	106	1 B
Delta	立达	131	1 A
Geylang East	芽笼东	90	2 D
Hougang	后港	69	2 A
Jalan Besar	惹兰勿刹	111	1 B
Jurong East	裕廊东	61	2 D
Jurong West	裕廊西	80	2 B
Kallang Basin	加冷盆地	90	1 D
Katong	加东	112	2 C
Queenstown	女皇镇	108	1 D
Sengkang	盛港	48	2 A
Serangoon	实笼岗	69	1 C
SPE	SPE	109	1 A
Tampines	淡滨尼	72	2 C
Toa Payoh	大巴窑	89	1 C
Woodlands	兀兰	11	1 C
Yio Chu Kang	杨厝港	46	2 C
Yishun	义顺	27	1 A

THEATRES / CINEMAS

THEATRES 剧场

Alliance Francaise	联合特许剧场	110	1 A
Cairnhill Arts Centre	经禧艺术中心	110	1 B
Dance Ensemble S'pore	聚舞坊	111	1 D
Drama Centre	戏剧中心	111	1 D
(National Library Bldg)	(国家图书馆大厦)		
Esplanade Theatres	滨海剧场中心	133	1 A
on the Bay			
Eton Hall	伊顿会堂	130	1 B
Goethe-Institut	歌德学院	110	1 D
(Winsland House II)	(温斯兰大厦2)		
Kreta Ayer	牛车水人民剧场	132	2 C
People's Theatre			
Lee Foundation Theatre	李氏基金剧场	110	2 D
(Nanyang Academy of	(南洋艺术学院		
Fine Arts Campus 3)	第三校园)		
Selegie Arts Centre	实利基艺术中心	110	2 D
Singapore Art Museum	新加坡美术馆	111	1 D
S'pore Conference Hall	新加坡大会堂	132	2 C
S'pore Repertory Theatre	新加坡专业艺术剧场	132	2 A
Stamford Arts Centre	史丹福艺术中心	111	1 D
Telok Ayer Performing	直落亚逸表演	132	2 C
Arts Centre	艺术中心		
The Arts House @ The	旧国会大楼艺术之家	133	1 A
Old Parliament House			
The Necessary Stage	必备舞台	114	1 C
(Marine Parade	(马林百列社区大厦)		
Community Bldg)			

The Substation	电力站	110	2 D
Touch Community Theatre	触爱社区剧场	131	1 B
Toy Factory	玩具厂制作有限公司	132	2 D
Productions Ltd			
University Cultural Centre	大学文化中心	106	2 C
Victoria Concert Hall	维多利亚音乐厅	133	1 A
Victoria Theatre	维多利亚剧院	133	1 A
Winfield Hall	温菲会堂	90	1 A
YMS Arts Centre	YMS 艺术中心	111	1 D

CINEMAS 戏院

Cathay Cineplexes	国泰电影院		
- The Cathay	国泰大厦	110	2 D
- Cineleisure Orchard	乌节电影娱乐城	110	1 C
- AMK Hub	宏茂桥中心	67	2 A
- Downtown East	职总娱乐中心	52	2 D
- Causeway Pt	长堤坊	11	2 C
Eng Wah Cinemas	荣华电影院		
- Jubilee Ctr	钻禧中心	67	2 A
- Sun Plaza	太阳大厦	13	1 A
- Suntec Twr 3	新达大厦3	111	1 D
- Toa Payoh	大巴窑娱乐中心	88	2 C
Entertainment Ctr			
- West Mall	威城	62	2 D
Golden Village Cinemas	黄金村戏院		
- Bishan (Junction 8)	碧山(第8站购物中心)	67	2 D
- Grand	华丽(世界城)	131	2 A
(Great World City)			
- Jurong Point	裕廊坊	81	1 A
- Marina	滨海(滨海电影院)	133	1 A
(Marina Leisureplex)			
- Plaza Singapura	狮城大厦	110	2 D
- Tampines Mall	淡滨尼广场	72	2 D
- Tiong Bahru Plaza	中巴鲁广场	131	2 A
- Vivo City	怡丰城	142	1 A
- Yishun	义顺	14	1 D
(51 Yishun Ctrl 1)	(51义顺中1路)		
Shaw Theatres	邵氏戏院		
- Balestier (Shaw Plaza)	马里士他	89	1 D
	(邵氏商业大厦)		
- Bugis Junction	白沙浮广场	111	1 D
- Choa Chu Kang	蔡厝港(第一乐广场)	41	1 C
(Lot 1 Shopper's Mall)			
- Jurong	裕廊(裕廊东中路)	83	1 B
(Jurong East Ctrl)			
- Lido (Shaw House)	丽都(邵氏楼)	109	2 C
- Prince	太子(邵氏休闲廊)	111	1 D
(Shaw Leisure Gallery)			
- Century Square	世纪广场	72	2 D
Golden Theatre	黄金电影院	111	2 C
(Golden Mile Twr)	(黄金大厦)		
Filmgarde	Filmgarde	112	1 C
(Leisure Park Kallang)	(加冷娱乐广场)		
Jade Cinema	翡翠戏院	111	1 D
(Shaw Twr)	(邵氏豪华大厦)		
Princess - Overseas Movie	公主-外国电影	91	1 D
(Bedok Central)	(勿洛中路)		

TOWN COUNCILS

Aljunied TC (Head Ofc)	阿裕尼市理会 (总办事处)	70	1 A
Aljunied TC (Bedok Reservoir Rd)	阿裕尼市理会 (勿洛水池路)	92	1 C
Aljunied TC (Serangoon North Ofc)	阿裕尼市理会 (实龙岗北办事处)	69	1 A
Ang Mo Kio - Yio Chu Kang TC (Head Ofc)	宏茂桥-蔡厝港市理会 (总办事处)	67	2 B
Ang Mo Kio - Yio Chu Kang TC (Collection Ofc)	宏茂桥-蔡厝港市理会 (收费站)	46	1 D
Ang Mo Kio - Yio Chu Kang TC (Yishun Ofc)	宏茂桥-蔡厝港市理会 (义顺办事处)	27	1 B
Ang Mo Kio - Yio Chu Kang TC (Ang Mo Kio Ave 10 Ofc)	宏茂桥-蔡厝港市理会 (宏茂桥10道办事处)	68	1 A
Bishan - Toa Payoh TC (Head Ofc)	碧山 - 大巴窑市理会 (总办事处)	88	2 B
Bishan - Toa Payoh TC (Bishan Ofc)	碧山 - 大巴窑市理会 (碧山办事处)	68	1 D
East Coast TC (Head Ofc)	东海岸市理会 (总办事处)	93	1 D
Holland - Bt Panjang TC (Head Ofc)	荷兰－武吉班让市理会 (总办事处)	42	2 C
Holland - Bt Panjang TC (Ulu Pandan Ofc)	荷兰－武吉班让市理会 (乌鲁班让办事处)	107	2 B
Hong Kah TC (Head Ofc)	丰嘉市理会 (总办事处)	41	1 C
Hong Kah TC (Nanyang Br. Ofc)	丰嘉市理会 (南洋分处)	80	2 A
Hong Kah TC (Bukit Gombak Br. Ofc)	丰嘉市理会 (武吉甘柏分处)	62	2 C
Hougang TC	后港市理会	70	1 B
Jalan Besar TC (Head Ofc)	惹兰勿刹市理会 (总办事处)	90	1 D
Jalan Besar TC (Ganges Ave Br.)	惹兰勿刹市理会 (恒河道分处)	131	2 A
Jurong TC (Head Ofc)	裕廊市理会 (总办事处)	83	1 A
Jurong TC (Bukit Batok Br.)	裕廊市理会 (武吉巴督分处)	62	2 D
Jurong TC (Taman Jurong Br.)	裕廊市理会 (达曼裕廊分处)	82	1 B
Marine Parade TC (Head Ofc)	马林百列市理会 (总办事处)	114	1 C
Marine Parade TC (Serangoon Ofc)	马林百列市理会 (实龙岗办事处)	69	1 D
Pasir Ris - Punggol TC (Head Ofc)	巴西立榜鹅市理会 (总办事处)	52	1 D
Pasir Ris Punggol TC (Sengkang Br.)	巴西立榜鹅市理会 (盛港分处)	49	2 B
Potong Pasir TC	波东巴西市理会	89	2 B
Sembawang TC (Head Office)	三巴旺市理会 (总办事处)	10	2 D
Sembawang TC (Nee Soon Central Br.)	三巴旺市理会 (义顺分处)	14	1 D
Sembawang TC (Yishun Br)	三巴旺市理会 (义顺分处)	14	1 C
Tampines TC	淡滨尼市理会	93	2 A
Tanjong Pagar TC	丹戎巴葛市理会	131	1 B
West Coast TC (Head Ofc)	西海岸市理会 (总办事处)	106	1 A
West Coast TC (Boon Lay Ofc)	西海岸市理会 (裕廊西办事处)	61	1 D

VETERINARY CENTRES / CLINICS

Animal & Plant Health Ctr	动植物卫生中心	7	1 D
Animal & Plant Quarantine Unit (Changi Airfreight Ctr)	动植物检疫组 (樟宜机场)	54	2 D
Aquaculture Services Ctr (AVA Research Ctr)	水产养殖服务中心 (农粮兽医局研究中心)	26	2 B
Central Veterinary Laboratory	中央兽医实验所	7	1 D
Centre for Animal Welfare & Control	动物福利与控制中心	130	1 D
Marine Aquaculture Ctr (St. John's Island)	海产养殖中心 (圣约翰岛)	149	— —
Marine Fishery Research Dept	海上渔业研究组	7	1 D
Mount Pleasant Animal Hospital	快乐山动物医院	87	2 D
NUS Care	国大护理中心	7	1 D
NUS Lab Animal Ctr	国大实验动物中心	26	2 B
Singapore Equine Quarantine Station	新加坡马类检疫站	8	2 B
Society for Prevention of Cruelty to Animals	防止虐待动物协会	90	2 A
Veterinary Public Health Ctr	兽医公共卫生中心	7	1 D

VISITORS INFORMATION CENTRES

Singapore Visitors Centre @ Changi - Changi Airport Arrival Halls	新加坡旅客咨询中心 (樟宜) - 樟宜机场入境大厅		
• Terminal 1	• 第一搭客大厦	75	1 B
• Terminal 2	• 第二搭客大厦	75	1 C
• Terminal 3	• 第三搭客大厦	75	1 C
Singapore Visitors Centre @ Little India (The Inncrowd Hostel- Dunlop Street)	新加坡旅客咨询中心 (小印度) (The Inncrowd宿舍 - 南洛街)	111	1 C
Singapore Visitors Centre @ Orchard Tel: 1800 736 2000	新加坡旅客咨询中心 (乌节) 电话: 1800 736 2000	110	1 C
Singapore Visitors Ctr @ Suntec City Mall	新加坡旅客咨询中心 (新达城)	133	1 A

MAP 1

Scale @ 1 : 18,382

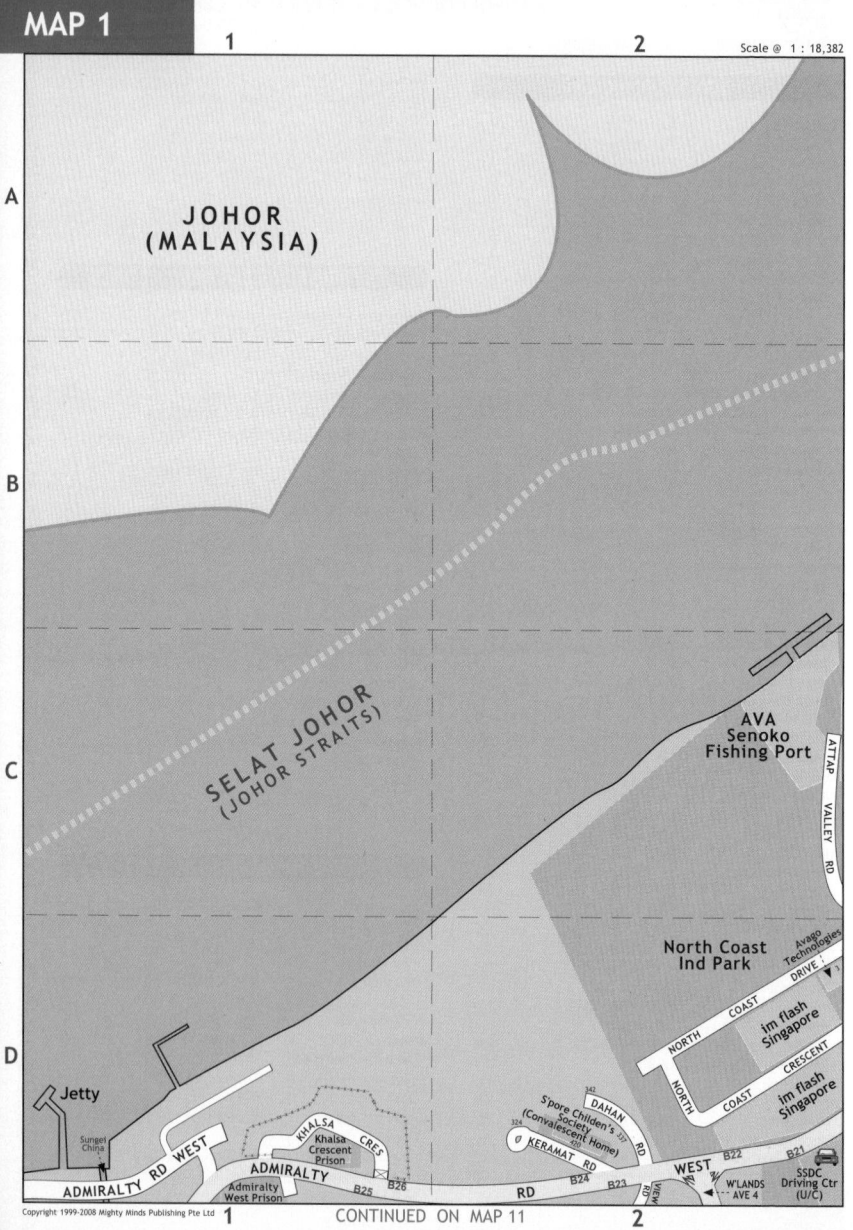

JOHOR
(MALAYSIA)

SELAT JOHOR
(JOHOR STRAITS)

AVA
Senoko
Fishing Port

ATTAP VALLEY RD

North Coast
Ind Park

Avago Technologies

NORTH COAST DRIVE

im flash
Singapore

NORTH COAST CRESCENT

im flash
Singapore

Jetty

Sungei China

ADMIRALTY RD WEST

KHALSA CRES

Khalsa
Crescent
Prison

ADMIRALTY

Admiralty
West Prison

B25

B26

S'pore Childen's
Society
(Convalescent Home)

DAHAN RD

KERAMAT RD

RD

B24

B23

WEST

B22

B21

W'LANDS AVE 4

SSDC
Driving Ctr
(U/C)

MAP 2

Scale @ 1 : 18,382

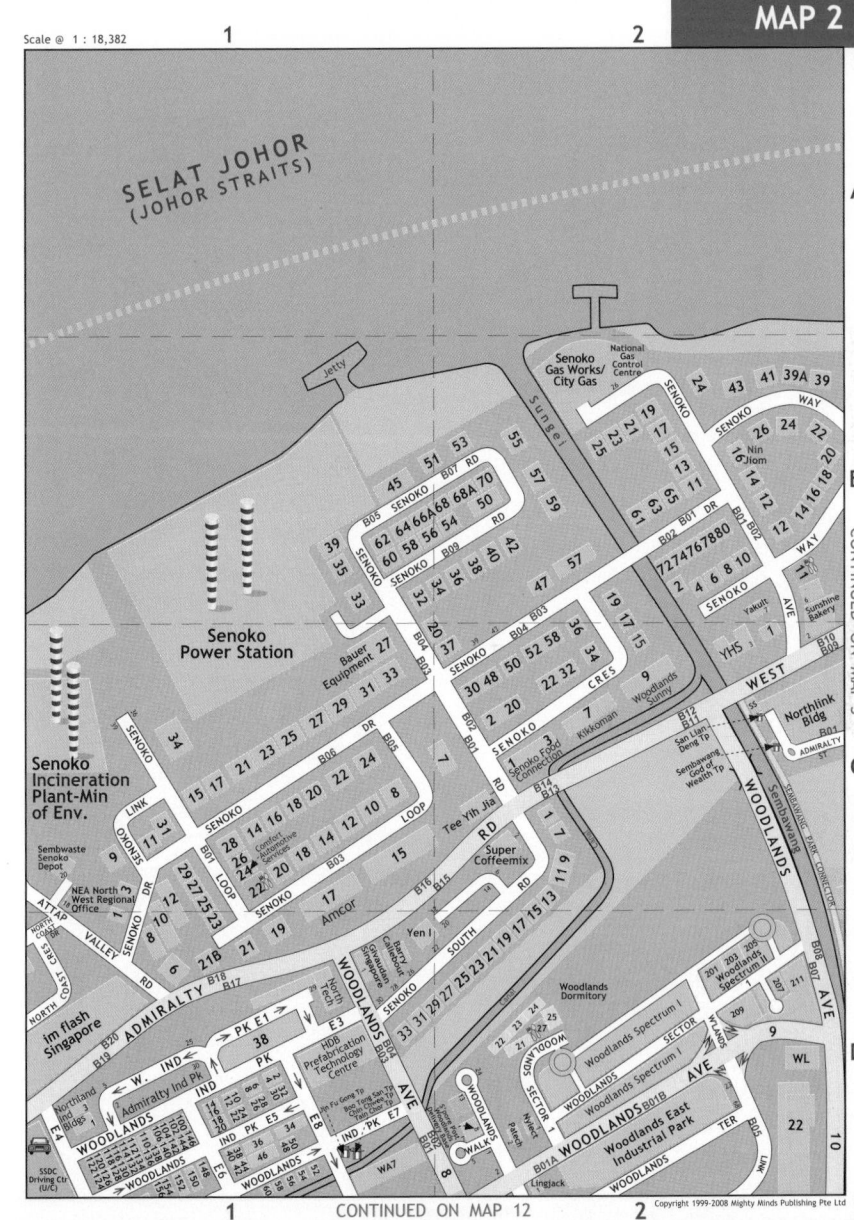

CONTINUED ON MAP 12

CONTINUED ON MAP 3

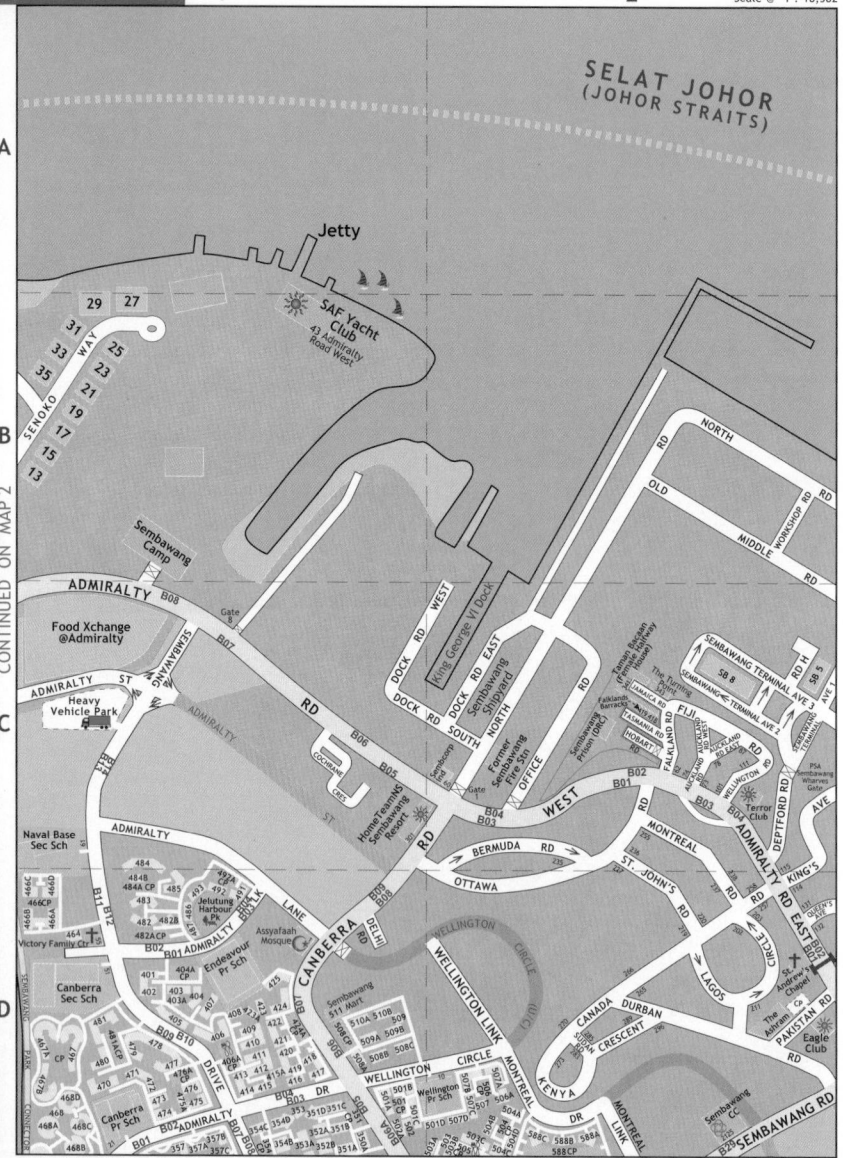

MAP 3

Scale @ 1 : 18,382

SELAT JOHOR
(JOHOR STRAITS)

Jetty

SAF Yacht Club
43 Admiralty Road West

SENOKO WAY
29 27
31 25
33 23
35 21
19
17
15
13

Sembawang Camp

ADMIRALTY

Food Xchange @Admiralty

ADMIRALTY ST

Heavy Vehicle Park

Naval Base Sec Sch

ADMIRALTY

Victory Family Ctr

Canberra Sec Sch

Endeavour Pr Sch

Assyafaah Mosque

Canberra Pr Sch

Gate 8

DOCK RD WEST
King George VI Dock
DOCK RD EAST
Sembawang Shipyard
DOCK RD SOUTH
DOCK RD NORTH
Sembawang Rd
Gate

HomeTeamNS Sembawang Resort

Former Sembawang Fire Stn

Former Sembawang Fire Stn
OFFICE

Sembawang Prison (DP)

ADMIRALTY RD

NORTH RD
OLD RD
MIDDLE RD
WORKSHOP RD

SEMBAWANG TERMINAL RD H
SB 8   SB 5
SEMBAWANG TERMINAL AVE 3
Taman Rasean (Private Housing Estate)
The Turning Point
JAMAICA RD
FIJI
Falklands Barracks
TASMANIA RD
HOBART
FALKLAND RD
WELLINGTON RD
B02   B01
B03   B04
Terror Club
DEPTFORD RD
PSA Sembawang Wharves Gate
KING'S AVE

WEST RD

BERMUDA RD
OTTAWA
ST. JOHN'S RD
MONTREAL RD
ADMIRALTY RD EAST
CIRCLE
KING'S RD
QUEEN'S CL
St. Andrew's Chapel
The Ashram Ca
Eagle Club
PAKISTAN RD

484
484B
484A CP 485
483
482 482B
482A CP
4898
Jelutong Harbour Pk
BLOCK
LANE
466C 466D
466B
466CP
464
B11 B12
401 404A
402 403 404
481
480 479 478
470
477
465 CP
468 468A
468B 468C
468D
475
Canberra Pr Sch
CANBERRA DR
DELHI RD
CANBERRA DRIVE
ADMIRALTY
DRIVE

Sembawang 511 Mart
501B 510B
509A 509B
508C
508A 508B
B01
B02
B03
WELLINGTON LINK
WELLINGTON CIRCLE
Sembawang Pri Sch
501A
501 CP
507B 507A
504A
504B
CRESCENT
MONTREAL
CANADA DURBAN
LAGOS
KENYA
DR
MONTREAL LINK
Sembawang CC
SEMBAWANG RD

Copyright 1999-2008 Mighty Minds Publishing Pte Ltd

MAP 4

Scale @ 1 : 18,382

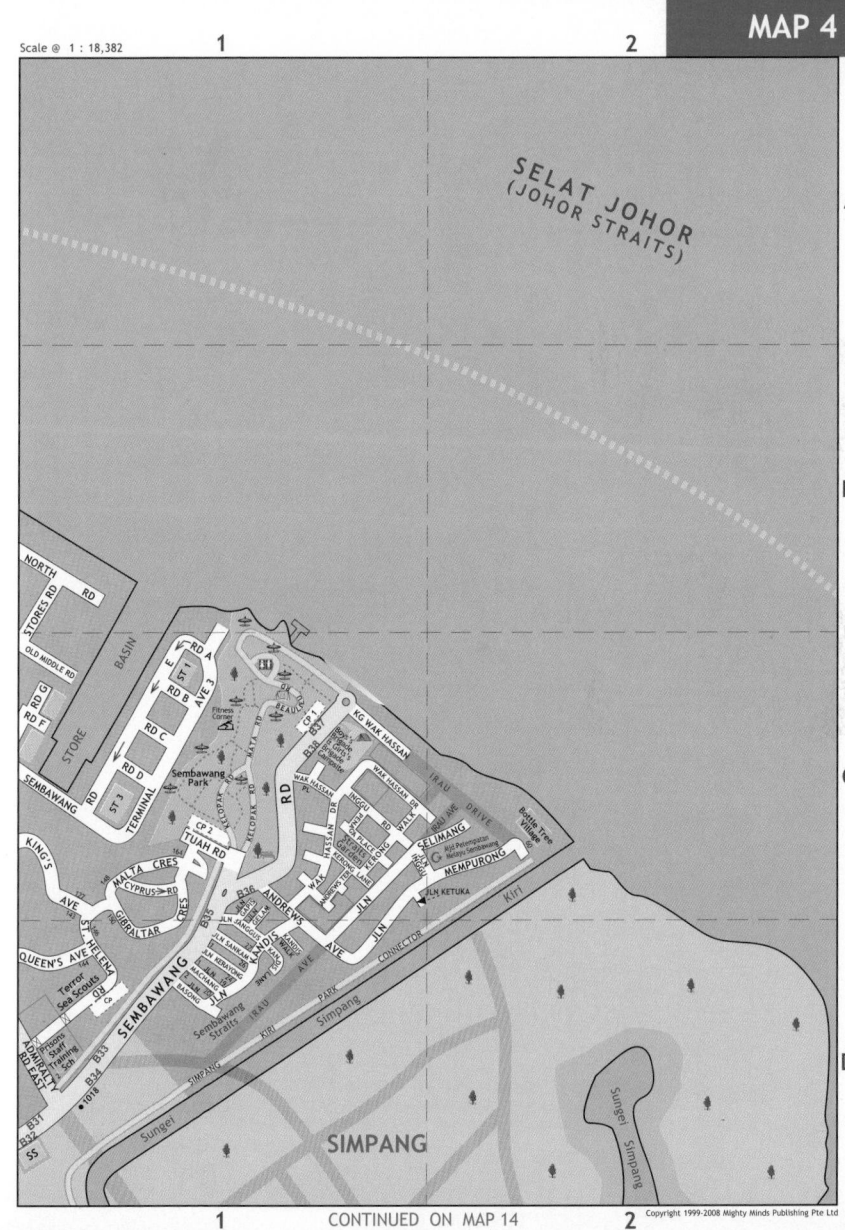

SELAT JOHOR
(JOHOR STRAITS)

SIMPANG

CONTINUED ON MAP 14

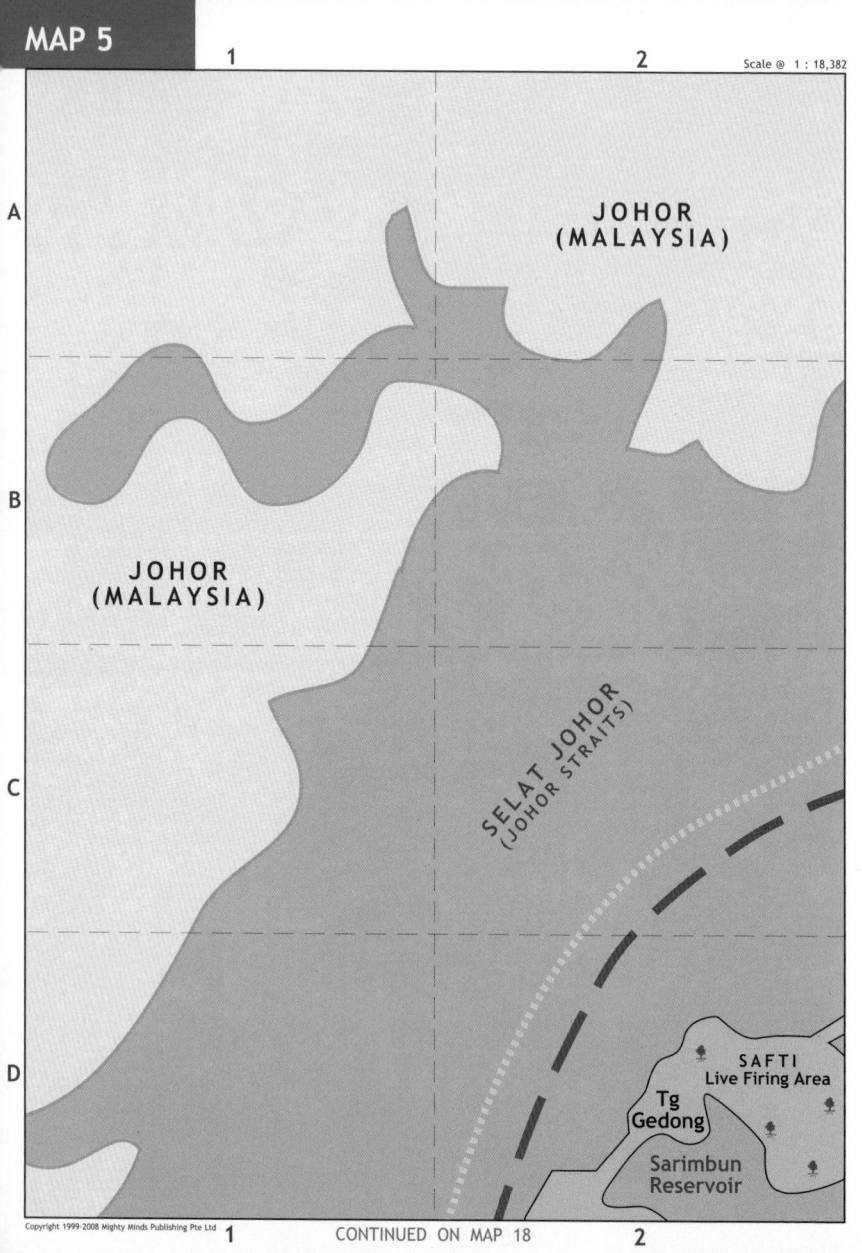

MAP 5

Scale @ 1 : 18,382

JOHOR
(MALAYSIA)

JOHOR
(MALAYSIA)

SELAT JOHOR
(JOHOR STRAITS)

SAFTI
Live Firing Area

Tg
Gedong

Sarimbun
Reservoir

CONTINUED ON MAP 18

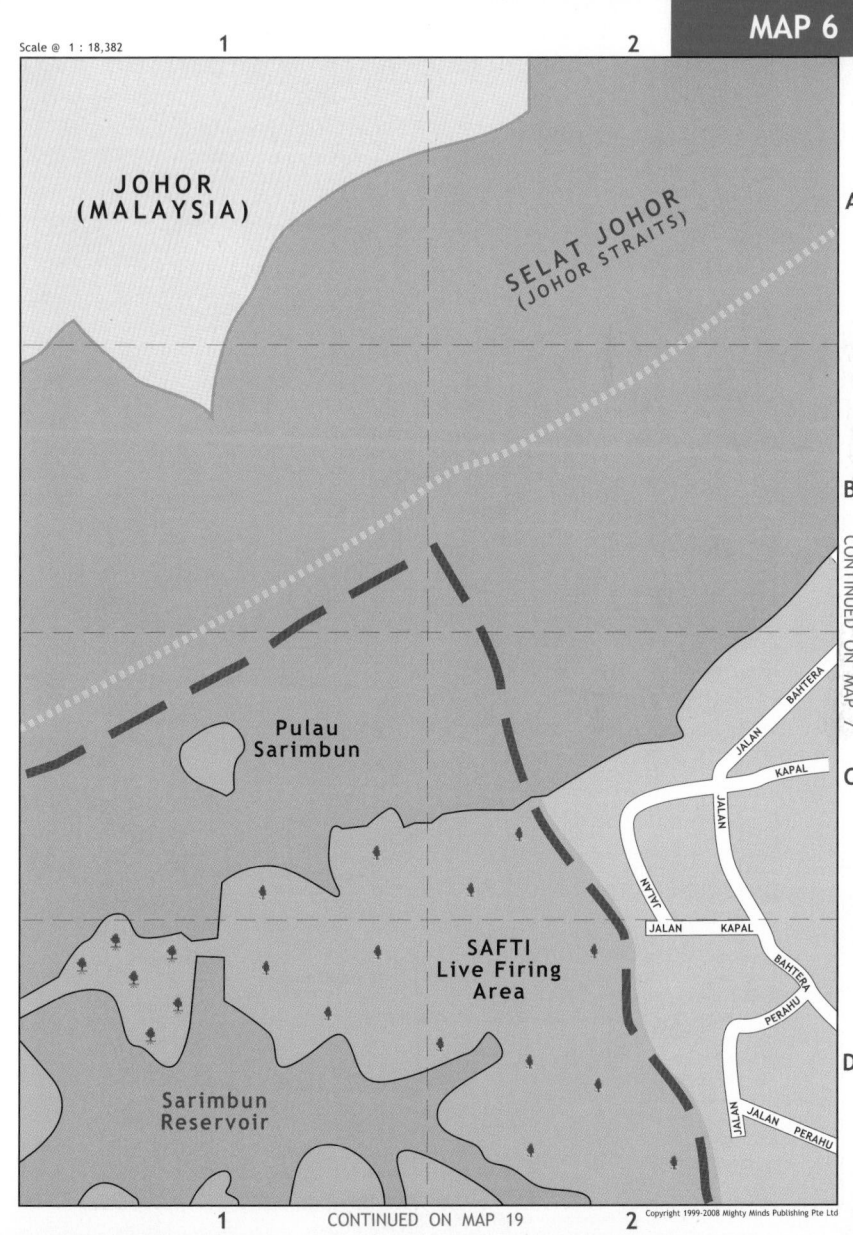

MAP 6

Scale @ 1 : 18,382

JOHOR
(MALAYSIA)

SELAT JOHOR
(JOHOR STRAITS)

CONTINUED ON MAP 7

Pulau
Sarimbun

JALAN BAHTERA

KAPAL

JALAN

JALAN

JALAN KAPAL

SAFTI
Live Firing
Area

BAHTERA

PERAHU

Sarimbun
Reservoir

JALAN JALAN PERAHU

CONTINUED ON MAP 19

MAP 7

Scale @ 1 : 18,382

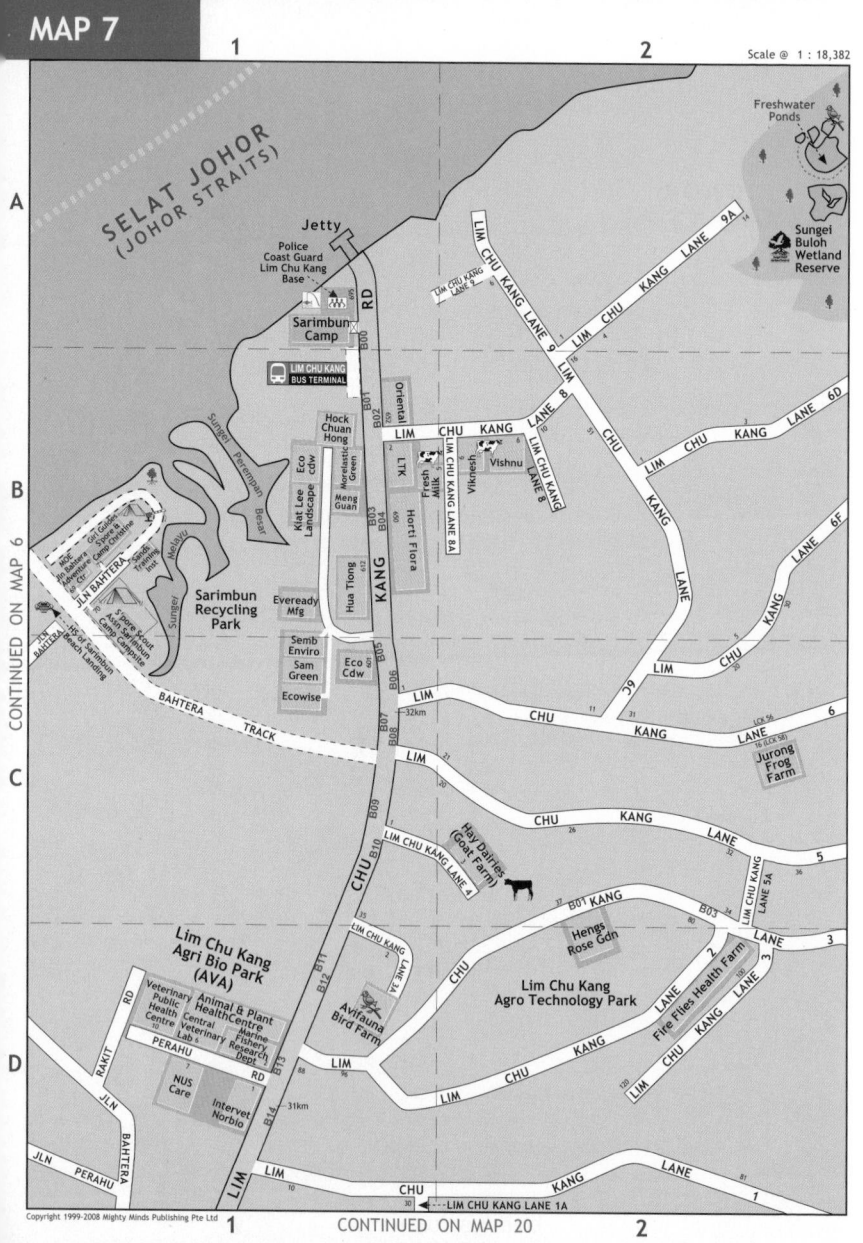

CONTINUED ON MAP 6

CONTINUED ON MAP 20

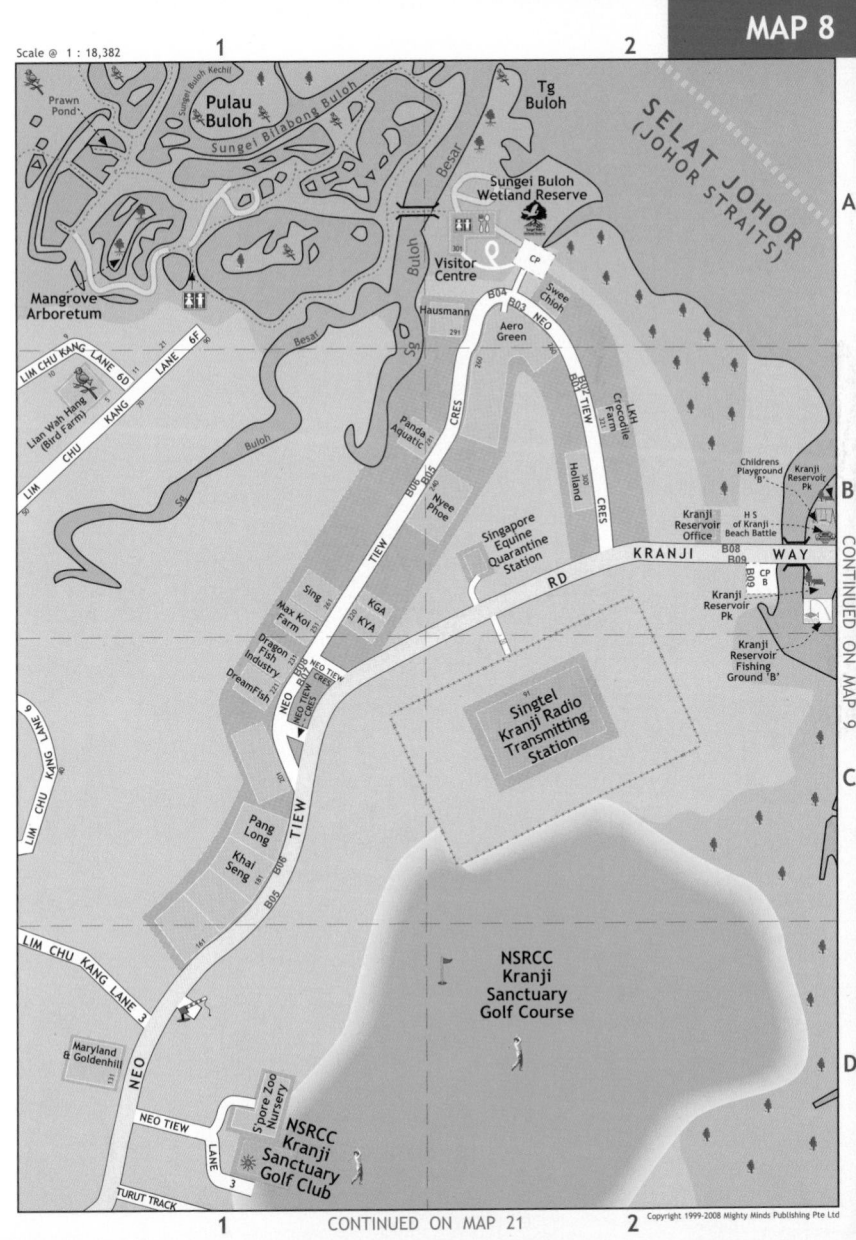

MAP 8

Scale @ 1 : 18,382

CONTINUED ON MAP 9

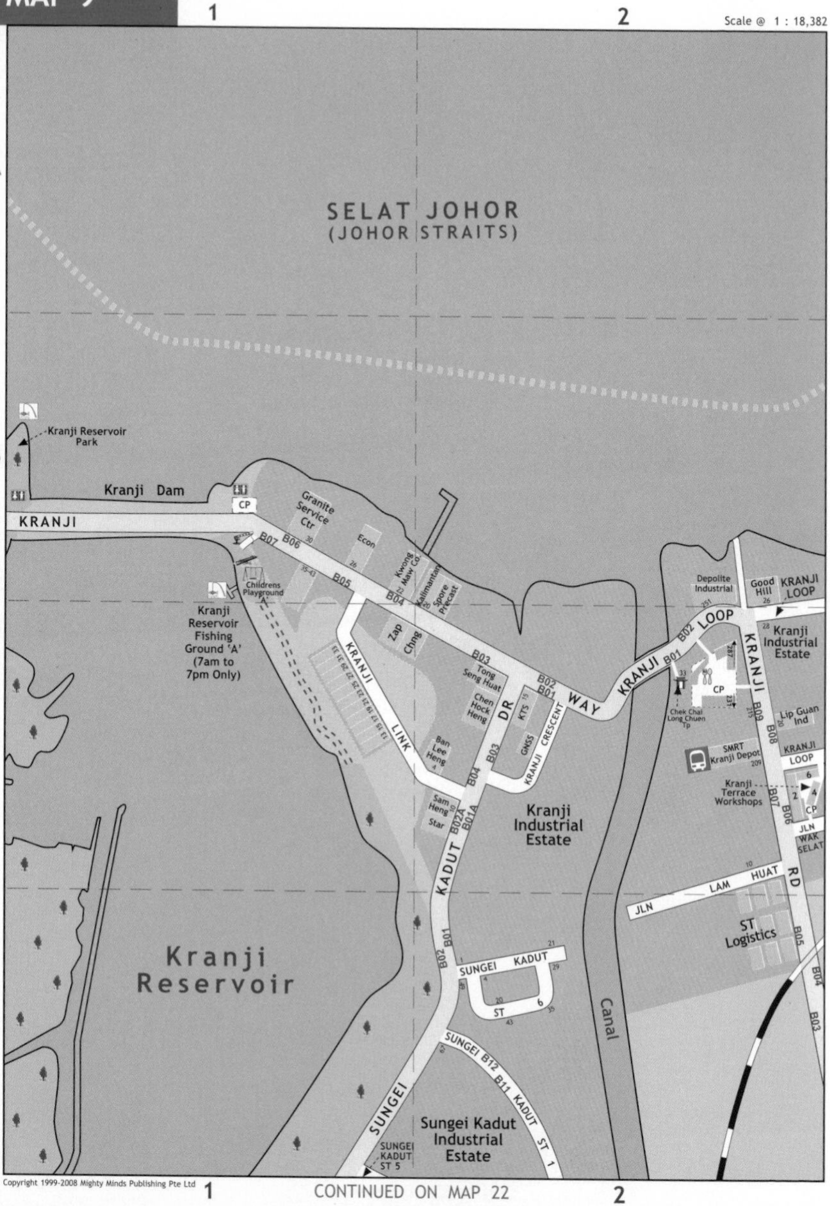

MAP 9

1   2

Scale @ 1 : 18,382

A

SELAT JOHOR
(JOHOR STRAITS)

B

Kranji Reservoir Park

Kranji Dam

CP

Granite Service Ctr

KRANJI

CONTINUED ON MAP 8

Econ

B07 B06

B05

Kwong Maw Cd

Depolite Industrial

Good Hill

KRANJI LOOP

B04

Stone PreCast

KRANJI LOOP

Kranji Industrial Estate

Childrens Playground

Kranji Reservoir Fishing Ground 'A' (7am to 7pm Only)

C

Zap

Ching

B03

Tong Seng Huat

B03 B01

B02

KRANJI WAY

B01

KRANJI LOOP

Chek Chai Long Chuen Tp

B09

Lip Guan Ind

KRANJI LINK

Chen Hock Heng

KT5

KRANJI CRESCENT

SMRT Kranji Depot

KRANJI LOOP

KADUT

B04

B03

GMS

Ban Lee Heng

Kranji Terrace Workshops

6

2 4

CP

JLN WAK SELAT

Sam Heng

Star

B01A

Kranji Industrial Estate

B07

B06

Kranji Reservoir

JLN   LAM   HUAT

JLN

RD

B01

B02

SUNGEI   KADUT

ST Logistics

B05

B04

D

ST

SUNGEI KADUT ST

Canal

B03

SUNGEI   B12 B11 KADUT   ST 1

SUNGEI

SUNGEI KADUT ST 5

Sungei Kadut Industrial Estate

1

CONTINUED ON MAP 22

2

MAP 10

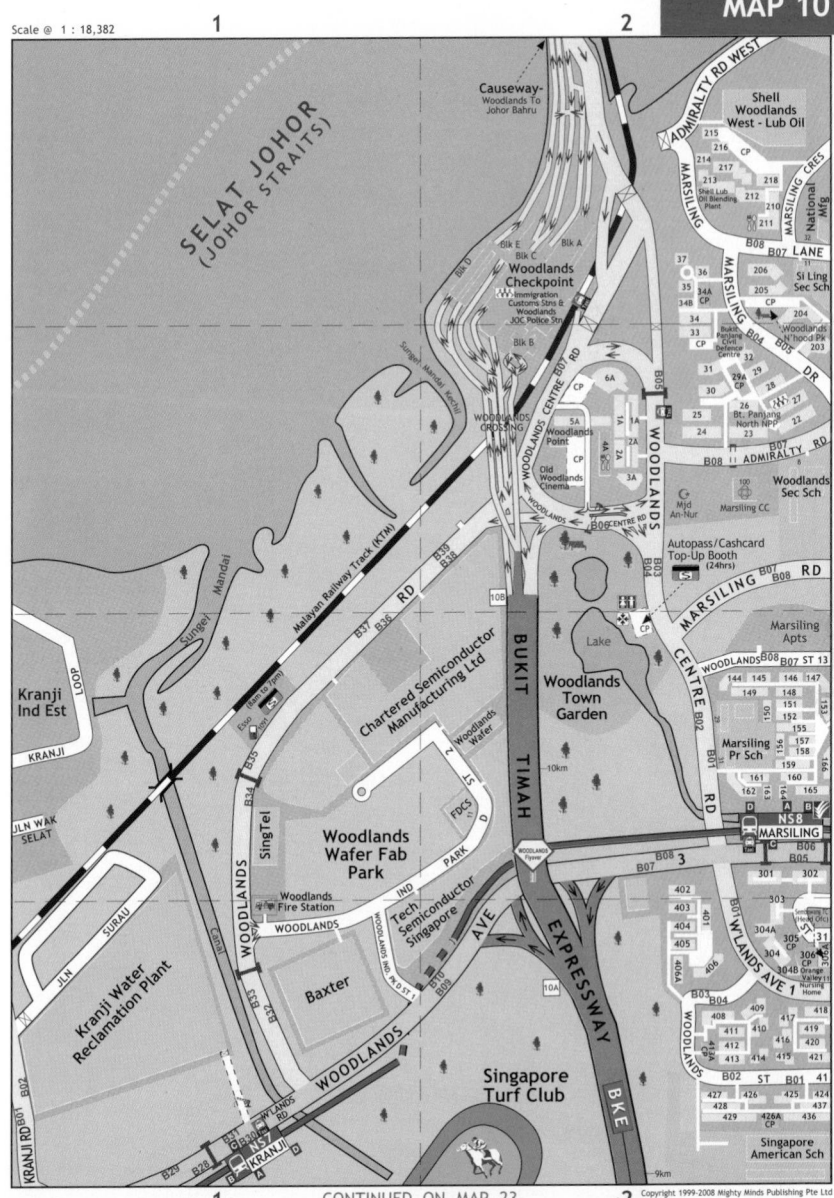

Scale @ 1 : 18,382

SELAT JOHOR
(JOHOR STRAITS)

Causeway-
Woodlands To Johor Bahru

Woodlands Checkpoint
Immigration Customs Stns & Woodlands JOC Police Stn

Kranji Ind Est

Chartered Semiconductor Manufacturing Ltd

Woodlands Wafer Fab Park

SingTel

Woodlands Fire Station

Tech Semiconductor Singapore

Baxter

Kranji Water Reclamation Plant

Woodlands Town Garden

Singapore Turf Club

Singapore American Sch

Shell Woodlands West - Lub Oil

Si Ling Sec Sch

Woodlands Sec Sch

Marsiling CC

Marsiling Apts

Marsiling Pr Sch

NS8 MARSILING

Autopass/Cashcard Top-Up Booth (24hrs)

CONTINUED ON MAP 11

Copyright 1999-2008 Mighty Minds Publishing Pte Ltd

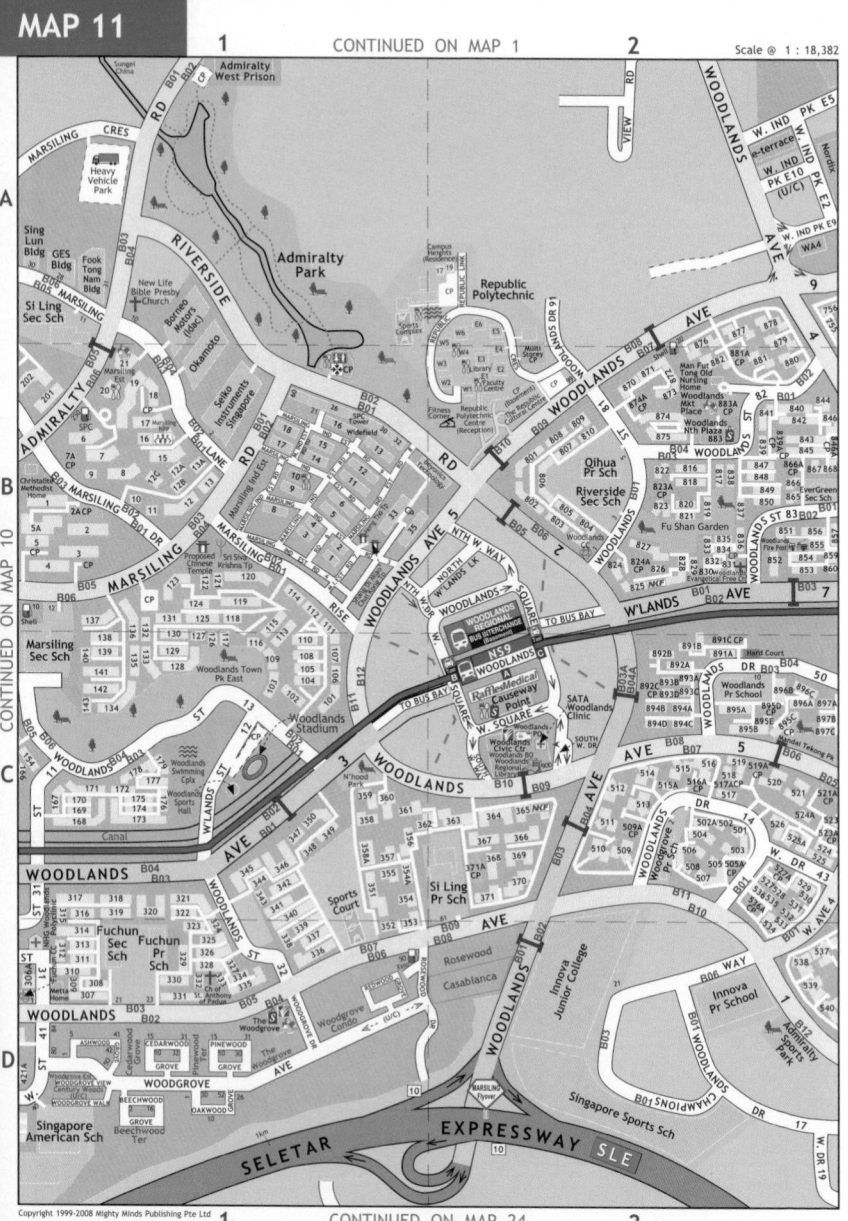

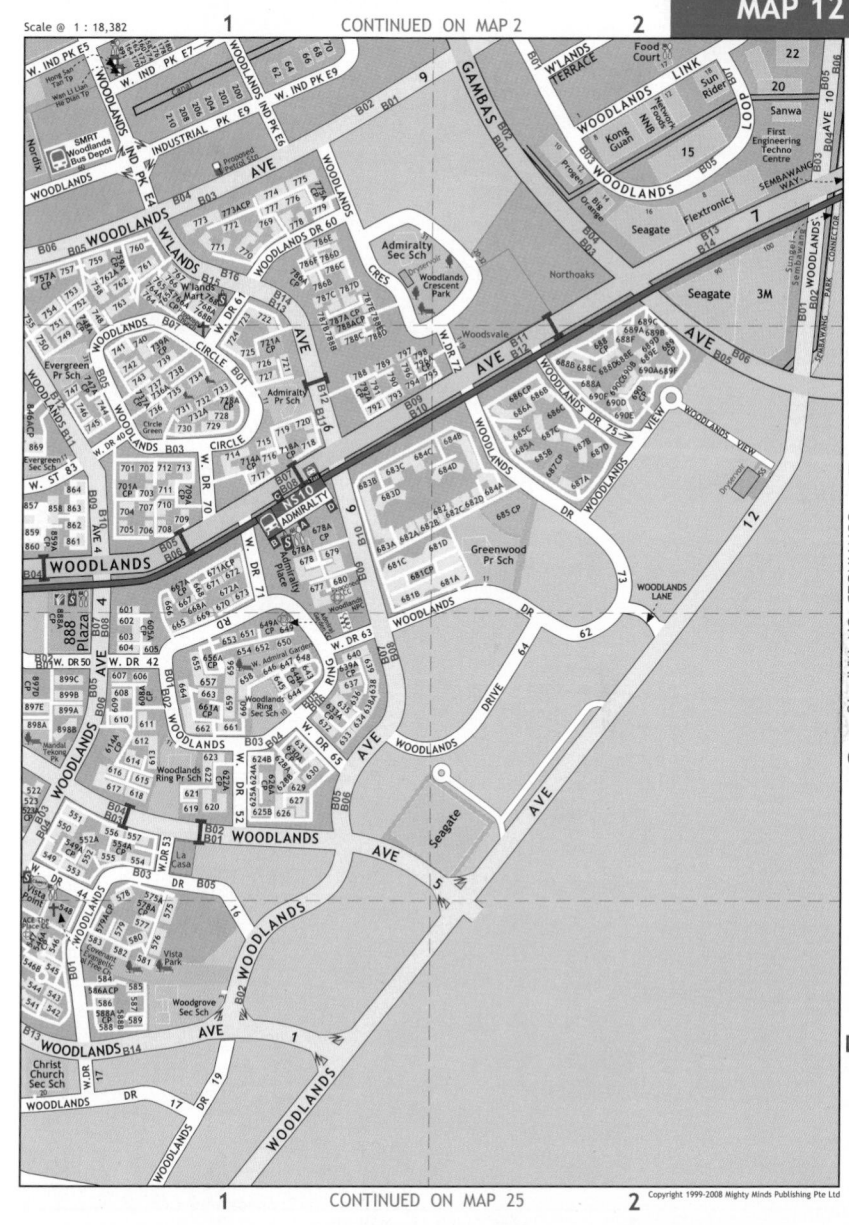

MAP 12

Scale @ 1 : 18,382

CONTINUED ON MAP 2

CONTINUED ON MAP 13

Copyright 1999-2008 Mighty Minds Publishing Pte Ltd

MAP 13

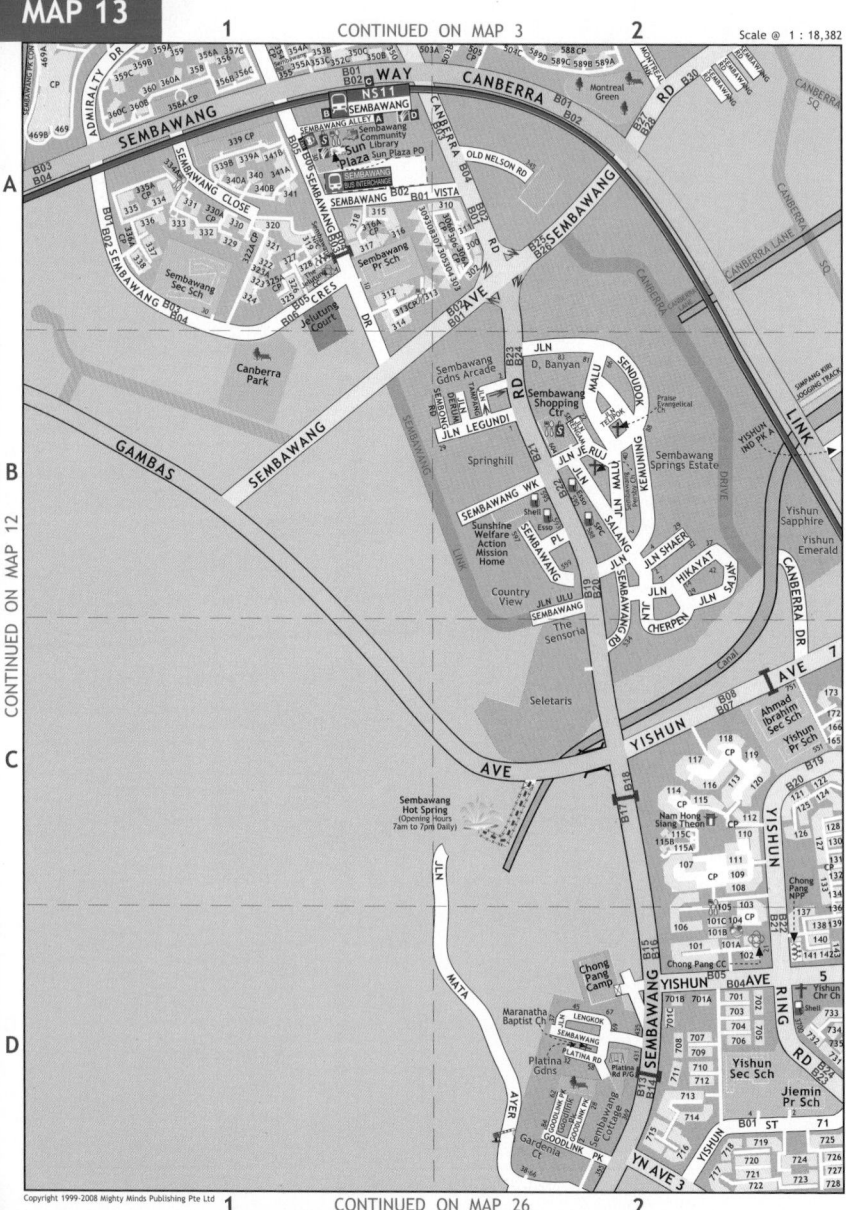

CONTINUED ON MAP 12

MAP 14

Scale @ 1 : 18,382

CONTINUED ON MAP 4

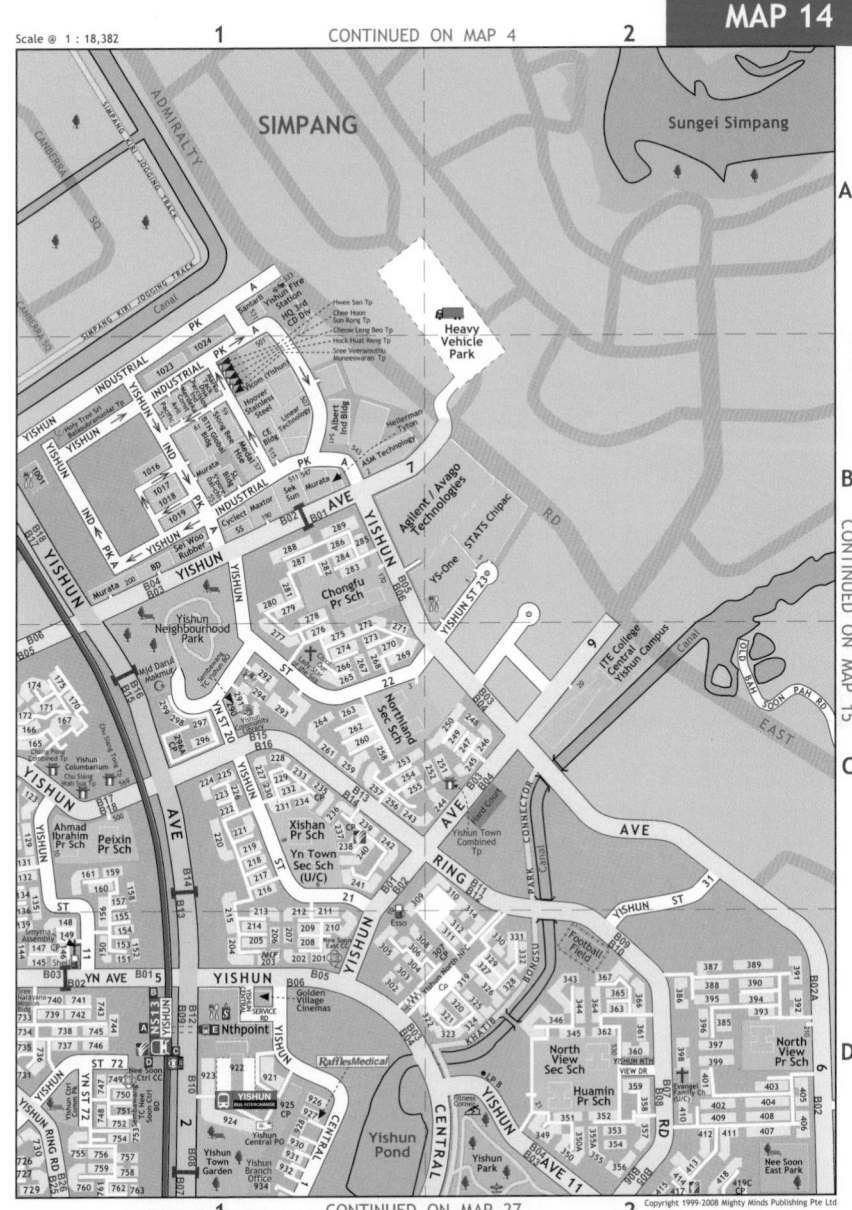

SIMPANG

Sungei Simpang

Heavy Vehicle Park

Agilent / Avago Technologies

STATS ChipPAC

YS-One

ITE College Central Yishun Campus

Chongfu Pr Sch

Yishun Neighbourhood Park

Northland Sec Sch

Xishan Pr Sch

Yn Town Sec Sch (U/C)

Ahmad Ibrahim Pr Sch

Peixin Pr Sch

Yishun Columbarium

Golden Village Cinemas

Nthpoint

RafflesMedical

North View Sec Sch

Huamin Pr Sch

North View Pr Sch

Nee Soon East Park

YISHUN BUS INTERCHANGE

Yishun Central PO

Yishun Town Garden

Yishun Branch Office

Yishun Pond

Yishun Park

CONTINUED ON MAP 27

CONTINUED ON MAP 15

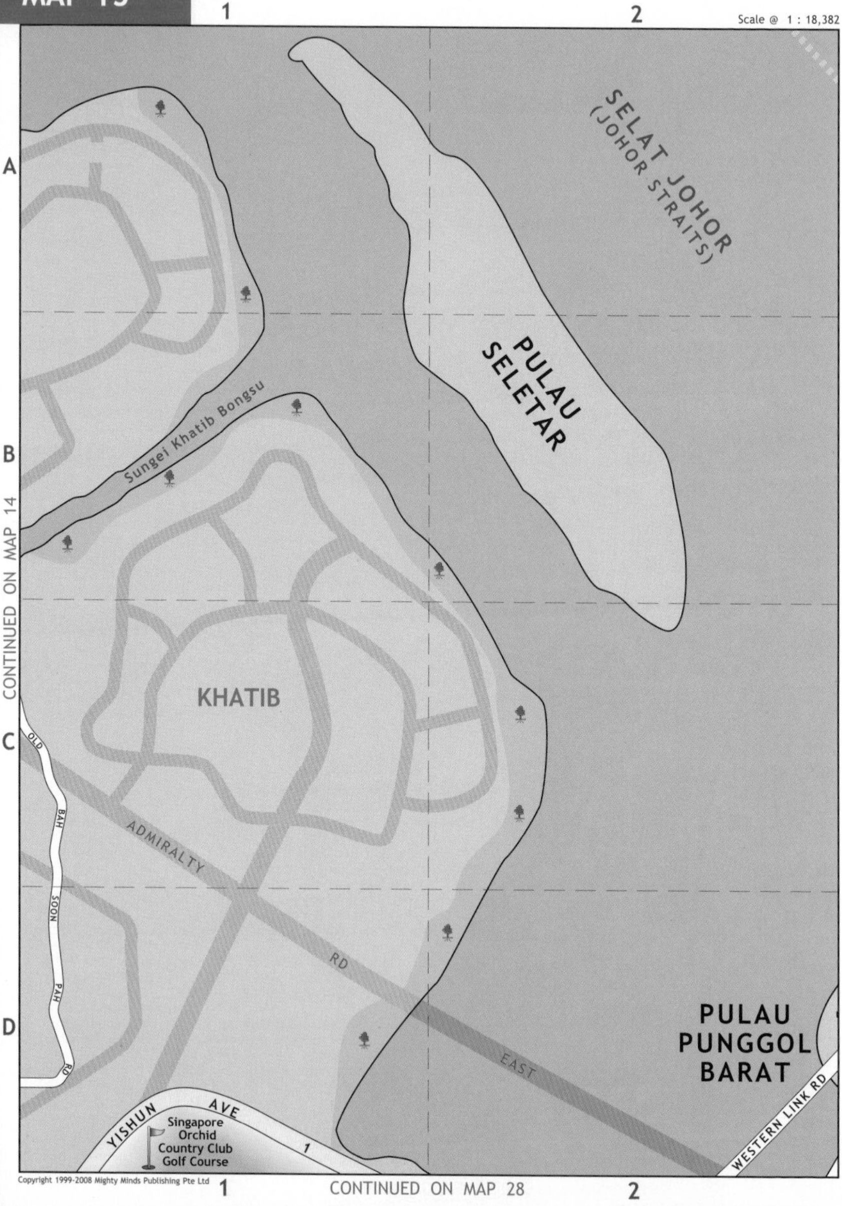

MAP 15

Scale @ 1 : 18,382

CONTINUED ON MAP 14

SELAT JOHOR
(JOHOR STRAITS)

PULAU SELETAR

Sungei Khatib Bongsu

KHATIB

ADMIRALTY

RD

EAST

PULAU PUNGGOL BARAT

OLD NELSON RD

YISHUN AVE 1

Singapore Orchid Country Club Golf Course

WESTERN LINK RD

CONTINUED ON MAP 28

MAP 16

Scale @ 1 : 18,382

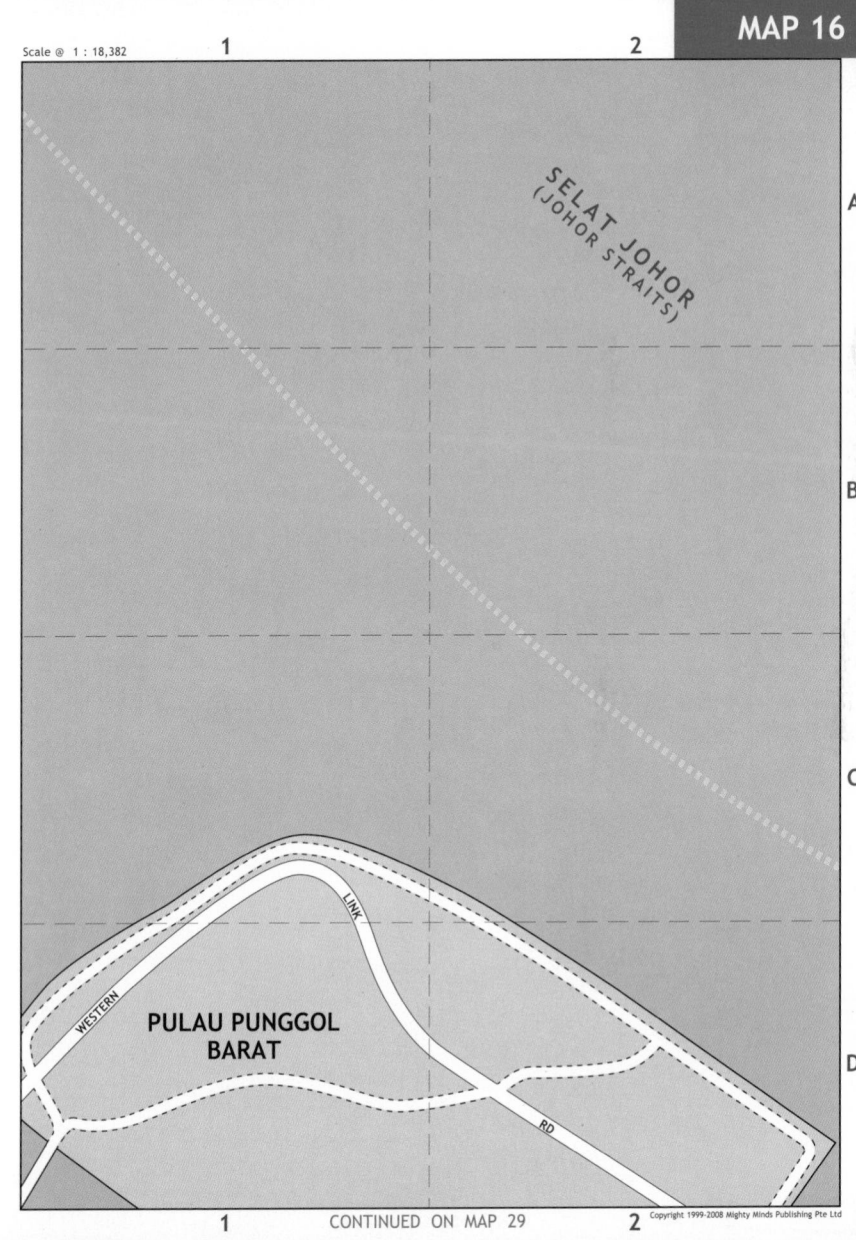

SELAT JOHOR
(JOHOR STRAITS)

WESTERN

LINK

**PULAU PUNGGOL
BARAT**

RD

CONTINUED ON MAP 29

MAP 17

Scale @ 1 : 18,382

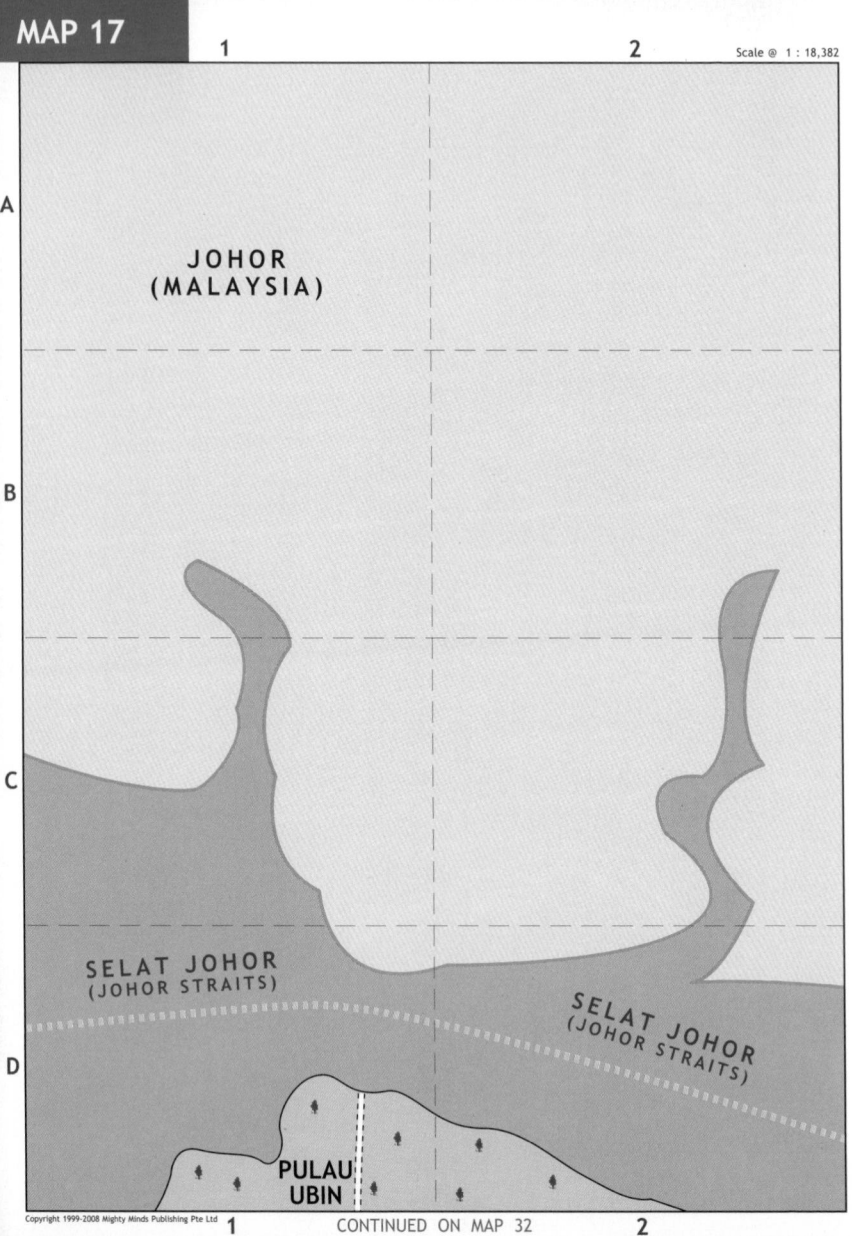

JOHOR
(MALAYSIA)

SELAT JOHOR
(JOHOR STRAITS)

SELAT JOHOR
(JOHOR STRAITS)

PULAU
UBIN

CONTINUED ON MAP 32

LOOK OUT
for us

Pal, 61

Taqi, 5

Alysha, 10

Audrey, 7

Shahid, 22

Lea, 23

Look out.
Stay safe.

**Not all road-users have the chance to warn you of their intentions early.
Be alert and look out for them. Or, you risk losing lives.**

TRAFFIC POLICE

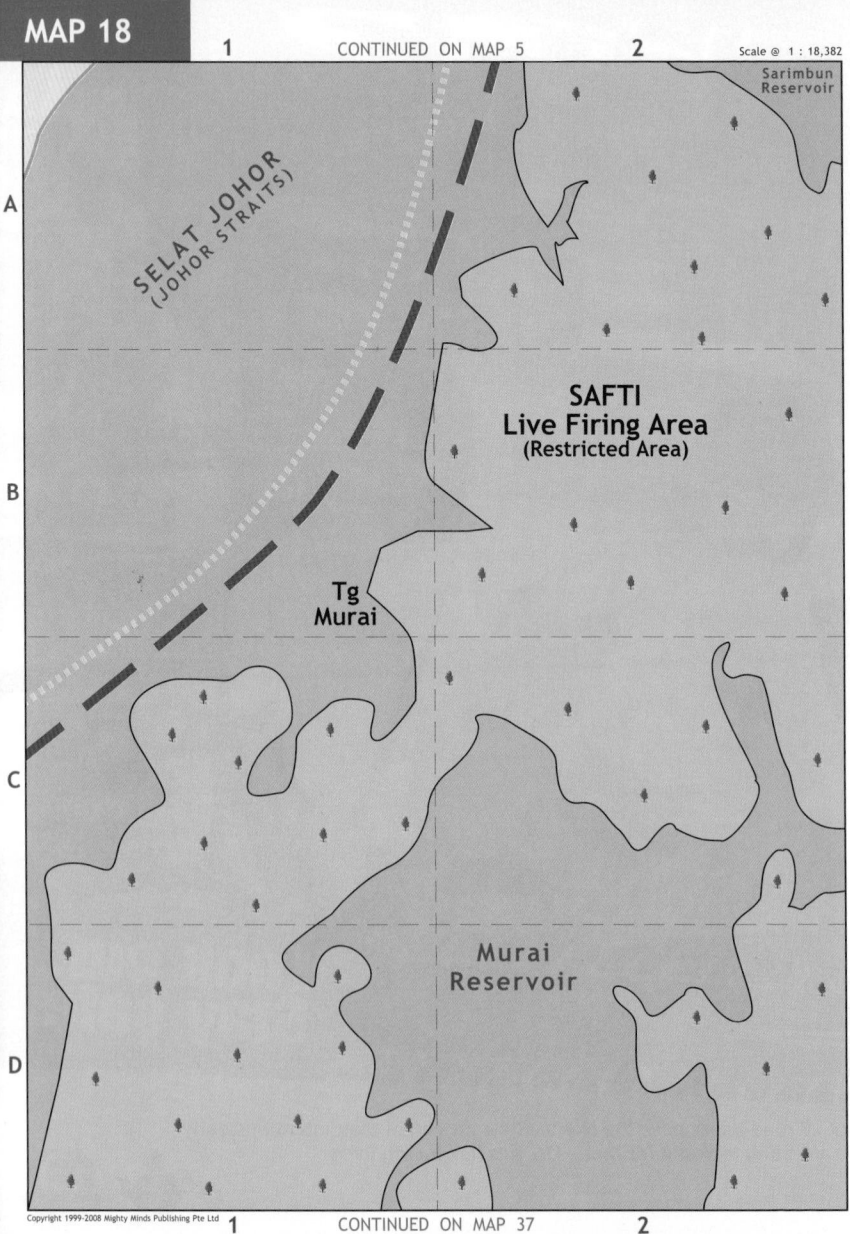

Sarimbun Reservoir

SELAT JOHOR (JOHOR STRAITS)

SAFTI Live Firing Area (Restricted Area)

Tg Murai

Murai Reservoir

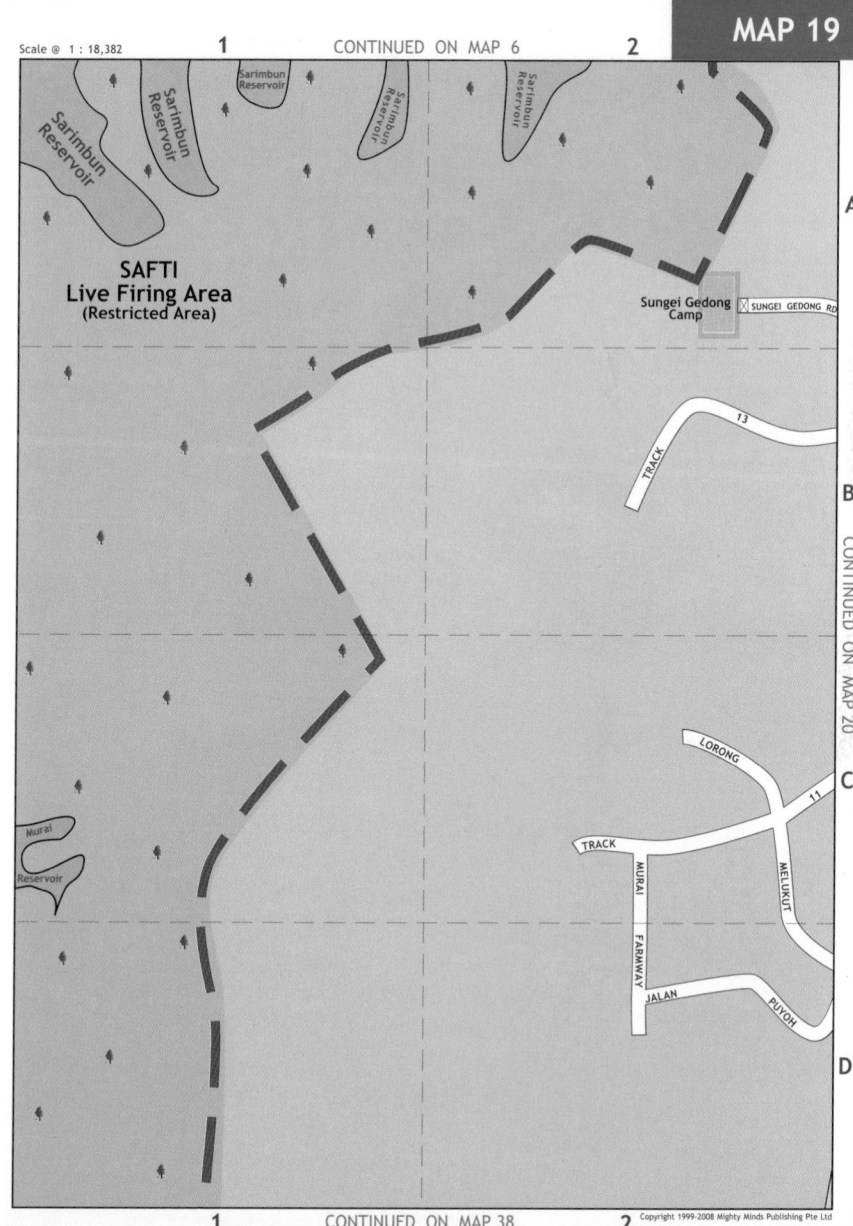

Sarimbun Reservoir

SAFTI
Live Firing Area
(Restricted Area)

Murai
Reservoir

Sungei Gedong Camp

SUNGEI GEDONG RD

TRACK 13

LORONG 11

TRACK

MURAI FARMWAY

MELUKUT

JALAN PUYOH

MAP 20

1　　CONTINUED ON MAP 7　　2

Scale @ 1 : 18,382

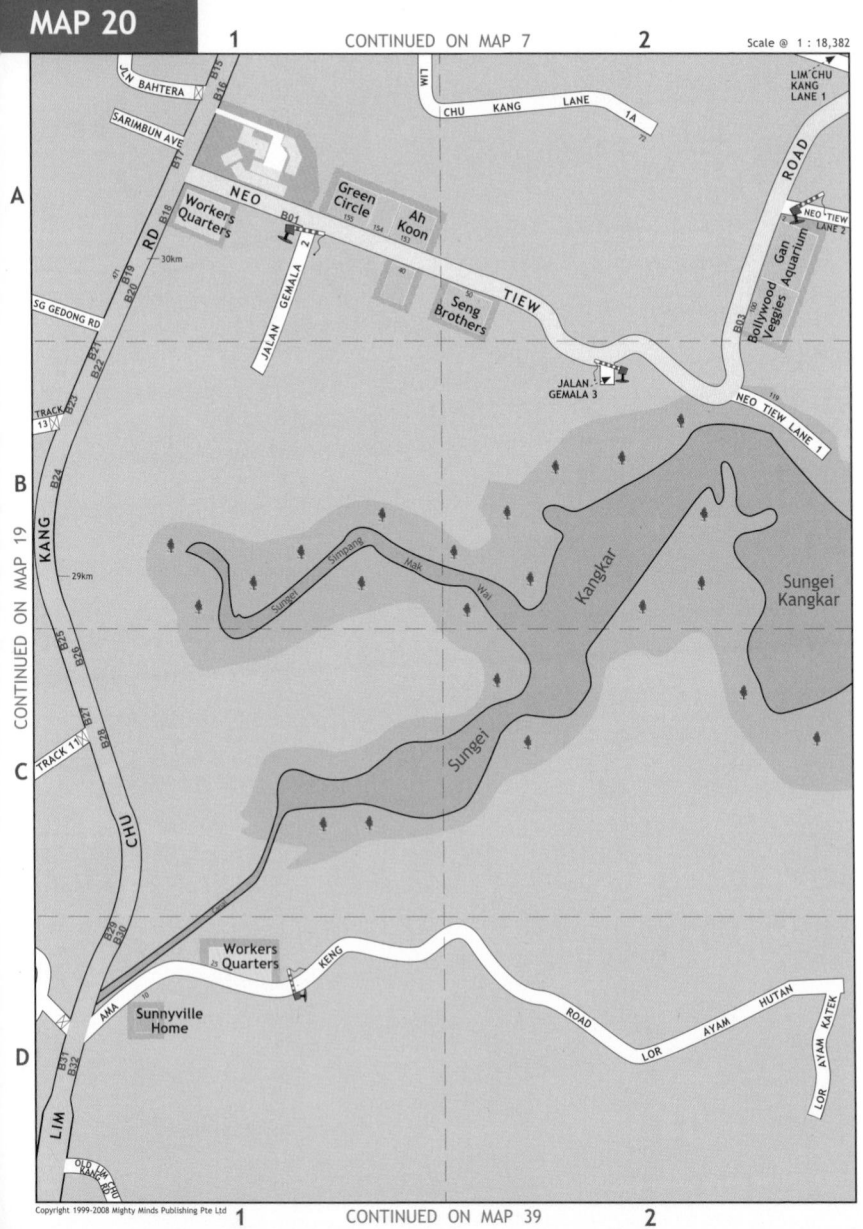

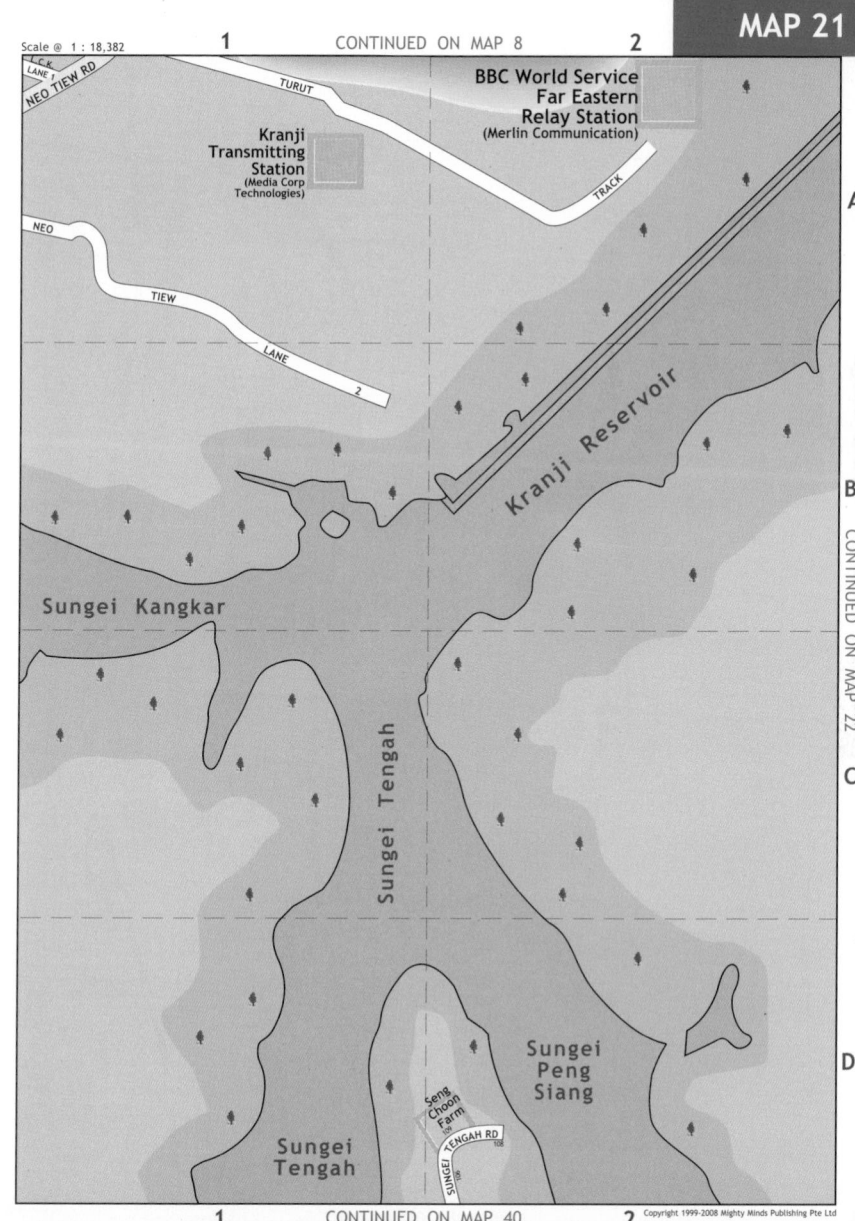

MAP 21

CONTINUED ON MAP 8

Scale @ 1 : 18,382

L.C.K.
LANE 1
NEO TIEW RD

TURUT

BBC World Service
Far Eastern
Relay Station
(Merlin Communication)

Kranji
Transmitting
Station
(Media Corp
Technologies)

TRACK

NEO

TIEW

LANE 2

Kranji Reservoir

A

B

Sungei Kangkar

Sungei Tengah

C

D

Sungei
Peng
Siang

Seng
Choon
Farm

SUNGEI TENGAH RD

Sungei
Tengah

Copyright 1999-2008 Mighty Minds Publishing Pte Ltd

MAP 22

CONTINUED ON MAP 9

Scale @ 1 : 18,382

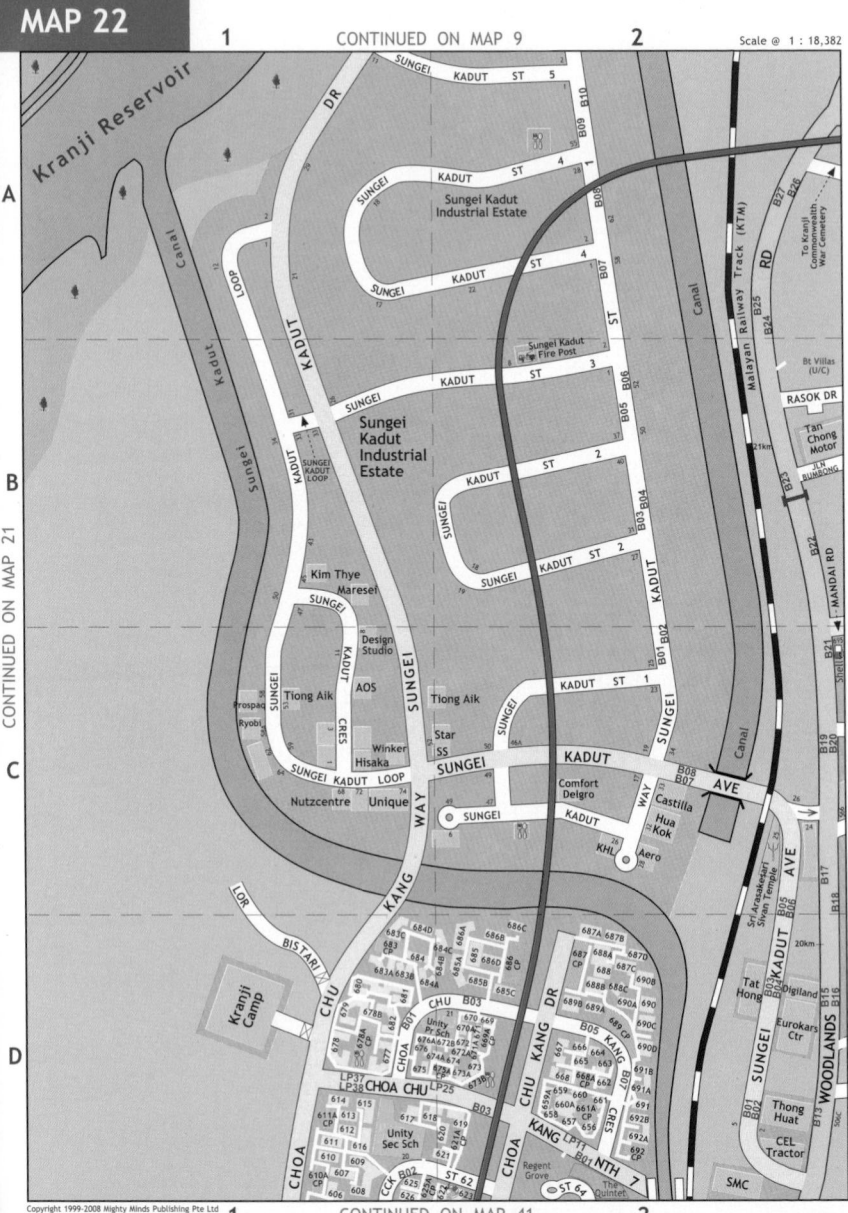

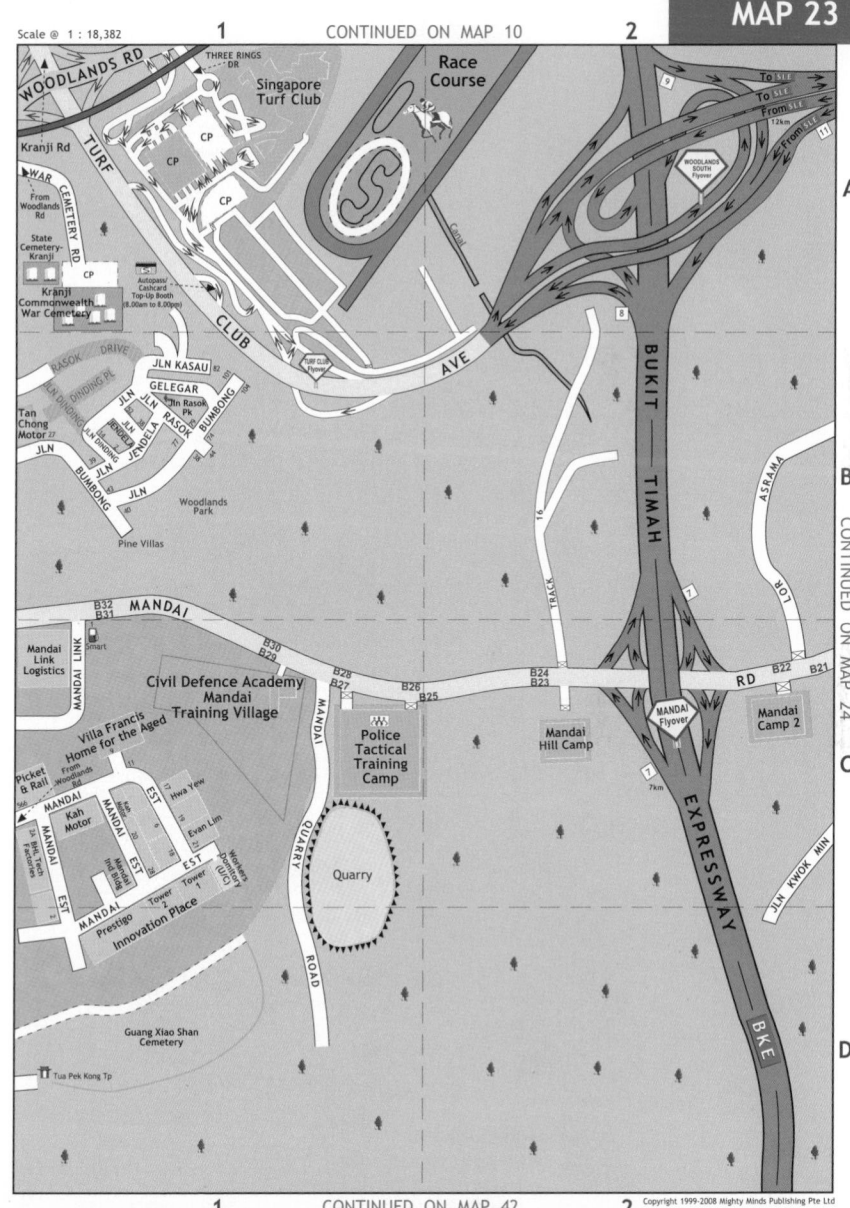

CONTINUED ON MAP 10
CONTINUED ON MAP 24

WOODLANDS RD
THREE RINGS DR
Singapore Turf Club
Race Course
Kranji Rd
TURF
WAR
From Woodlands Rd
State Cemetery-Kranji
CEMETERY RD
Kranji Commonwealth War Cemetery
Autopass/Cashcard Top-Up Booth (8.00am to 8.00pm)
CP
CLUB
AVE
Woodlands South Flyover
To SLE
To SLE
From SLE 1.2km
From SLE
Canal
BUKIT TIMAH
JLN KASAU
RASOK DRIVE
GELEGAR
Jln Rasok Pk
JLN RASOK
JUMBONG
JLN JENDELA
Tan Chong Motor
JLN BUMBONG
JLN
Woodlands Park
Pine Villas
ASRAMA
LOR
TRACK
MANDAI
B32 B31
B30 B29
B28
B27
B26 B25
B24 B23
B22 B21
RD
Mandai Link Logistics
Smart
Civil Defence Academy Mandai Training Village
MANDAI LINK
Villa Francis Home for the Aged
Police Tactical Training Camp
Mandai Hill Camp
Mandai Flyover
Mandai Camp 2
JLN KWOK MIN
EXPRESSWAY
Picket & Rail
From Woodlands Rd
Kah Motor
MANDAI EST
Hwa Yew
Evan Lim
Workers' Dormitory (UIC)
7km
MANDAI
Prestigo
Tower
Tower
Innovation Place
QUARRY
Quarry
ROAD
Guang Xiao Shan Cemetery
Tua Pek Kong Tp
BKE

MAP 24

CONTINUED ON MAP 11

Scale @ 1 : 18,382

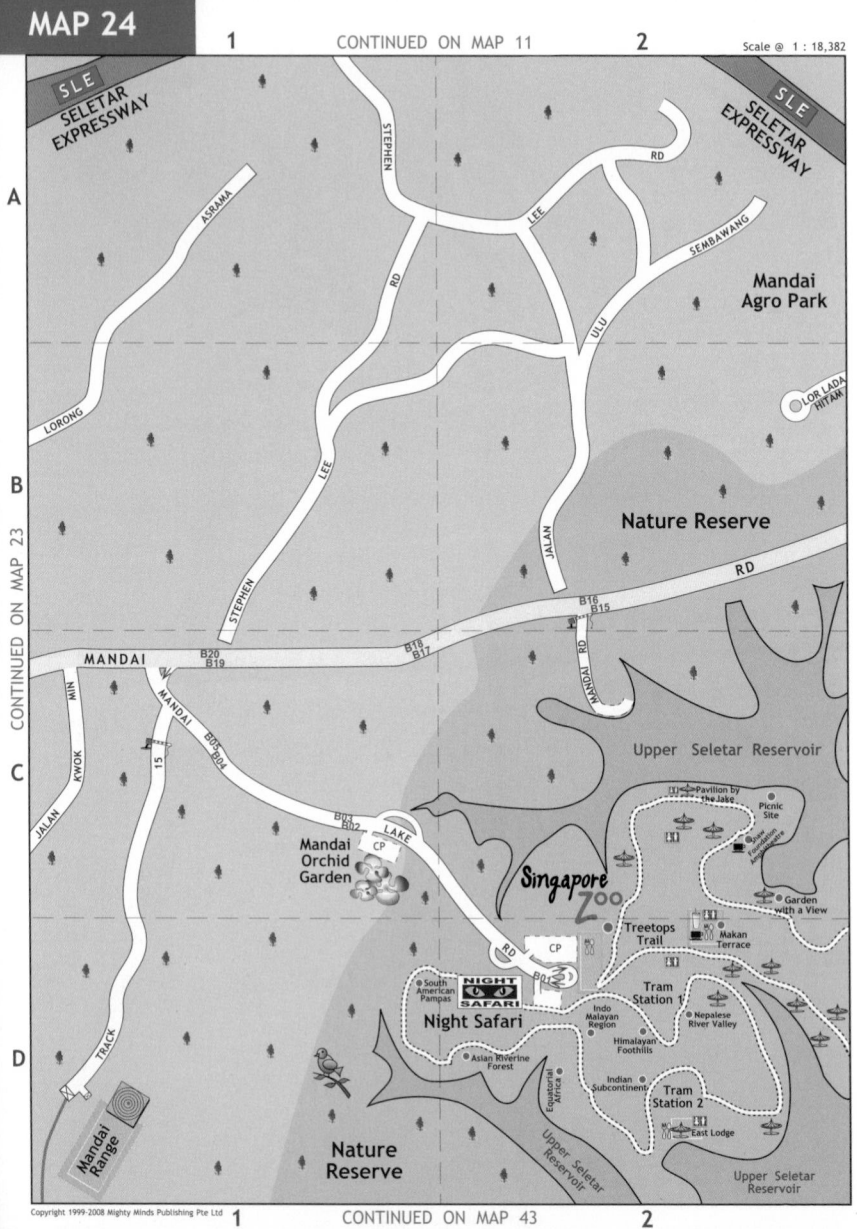

SLE
SELETAR EXPRESSWAY

SLE
SELETAR EXPRESSWAY

STEPHEN

RD

LEE

SEMBAWANG

ULU

Mandai
Agro Park

ASRAMA

RD

LORONG

LOR LADA
HITAM

LEE

JALAN

Nature Reserve

STEPHEN

RD

MANDAI
RD

B16
B15

MANDAI

B20
B19

B18
B17

Upper Seletar Reservoir

MIN
KWOK

JALAN

MANDAI

15

B04

B01
B02

LAKE

CP

Mandai
Orchid
Garden

Singapore
Zoo

Pavilion by
the Lake

Picnic
Site

Garden
with a View

Treetops
Trail

Makan
Terrace

RD

CP

B01
B02

Tram
Station

NIGHT
SAFARI

South
American
Pampas

Night Safari

Indo
Malayan
Region

Nepalese
River Valley

TRACK

Asian Riverine
Forest

Himalayan
Foothills

Indian
Subcontinent

Tram
Station 2

Mandai
Range

Equatorial
Africa

East Lodge

Nature
Reserve

Upper
Seletar
Reservoir

Upper Seletar
Reservoir

CONTINUED ON MAP 23

WOODLANDS DR 19

WOODLANDS AVE 12

SLE

9

SELETAR

9

9km

A

Sembawang
Golf Course

**Mandai
Agro Park**

LORONG
LADA
HITAM

Orchidville
10

RD

8A

B12

B11

8B

SEMBAWANG
Flyover

MANDAI

AVE

B

MANDAI
B14
B13

Eugenia

Daffodil

Begonia
Freesia
Gardenia

Camellia

Hibiscus

**Nature
Reserve**

MANDAI
LAKE
Flyover

B09

Office

Sri Sai Sri
Crematorium
Service Halls

Entrance to
service halls

From
Car Park

Ivy

Jasmine

Kalma

B10

Pond

Departure
Pick-up point

Ash
Collection
Centre

**NEA
Mandai
Crematorium &
Columbarium**

MANDAI

C

EXPRESSWAY

NEE
SOON
Flyover

24 Hrs

B07

B08

RD

BATH RD

Nee Soon
Monopole
Base

**Children's
World Animal
Land
Pets
Corner**

**Upper
Seletar
Reservoir**

Jetty

**The
Viewing
Tower**

PCS of Upper Seletar Reservoir

**Executive
Golf Course**

UPPER
SELETAR
Flyover

B06

B02

SLE

D

**Singapore
Zoo**

Fragile
Forest

Children's
World Playland

SPH
Conservation
Centre

TRACK

CP B

**Upper Seletar
Reservoir
Park**

CP A

TRACK

7

7

Golf
Driving
Range

**Nature
Reserve**

CONTINUED ON MAP 26

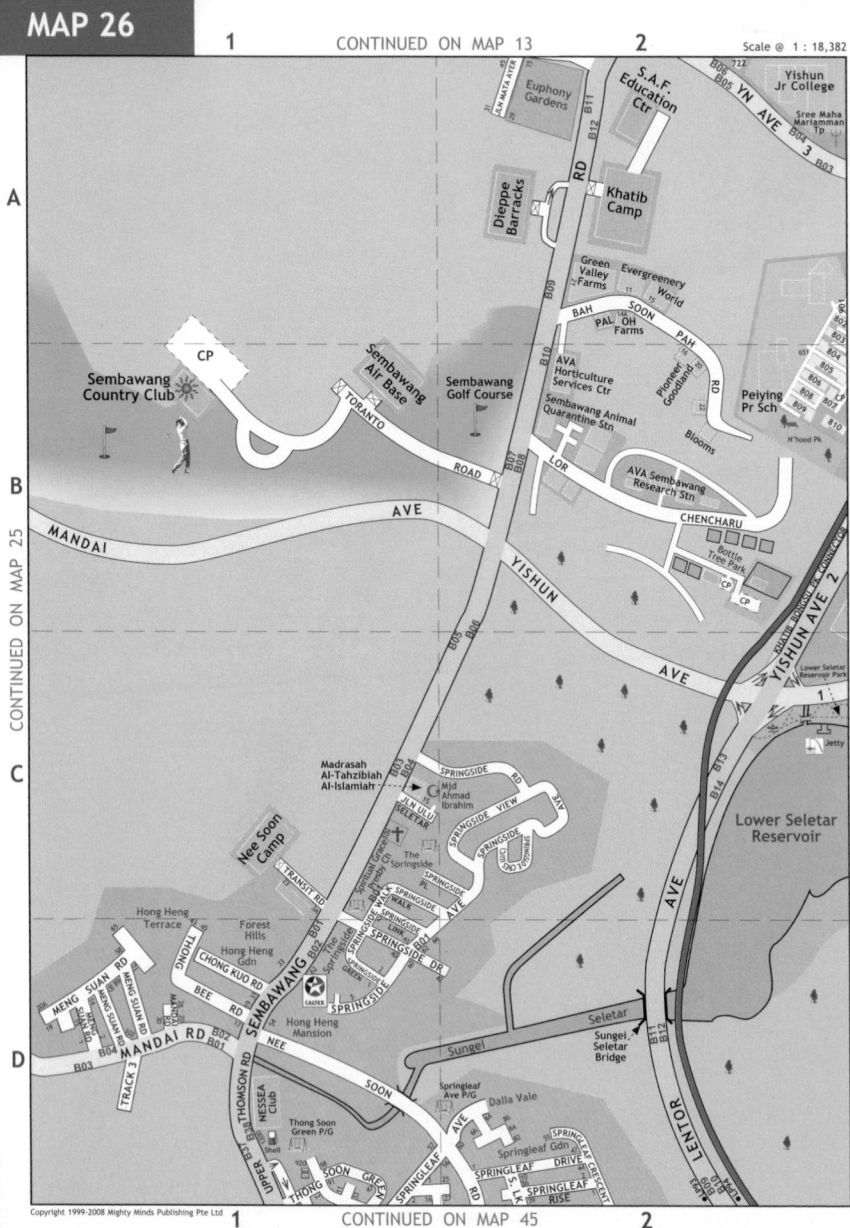

CONTINUED ON MAP 25

MAP 27

Scale @ 1 : 18,382

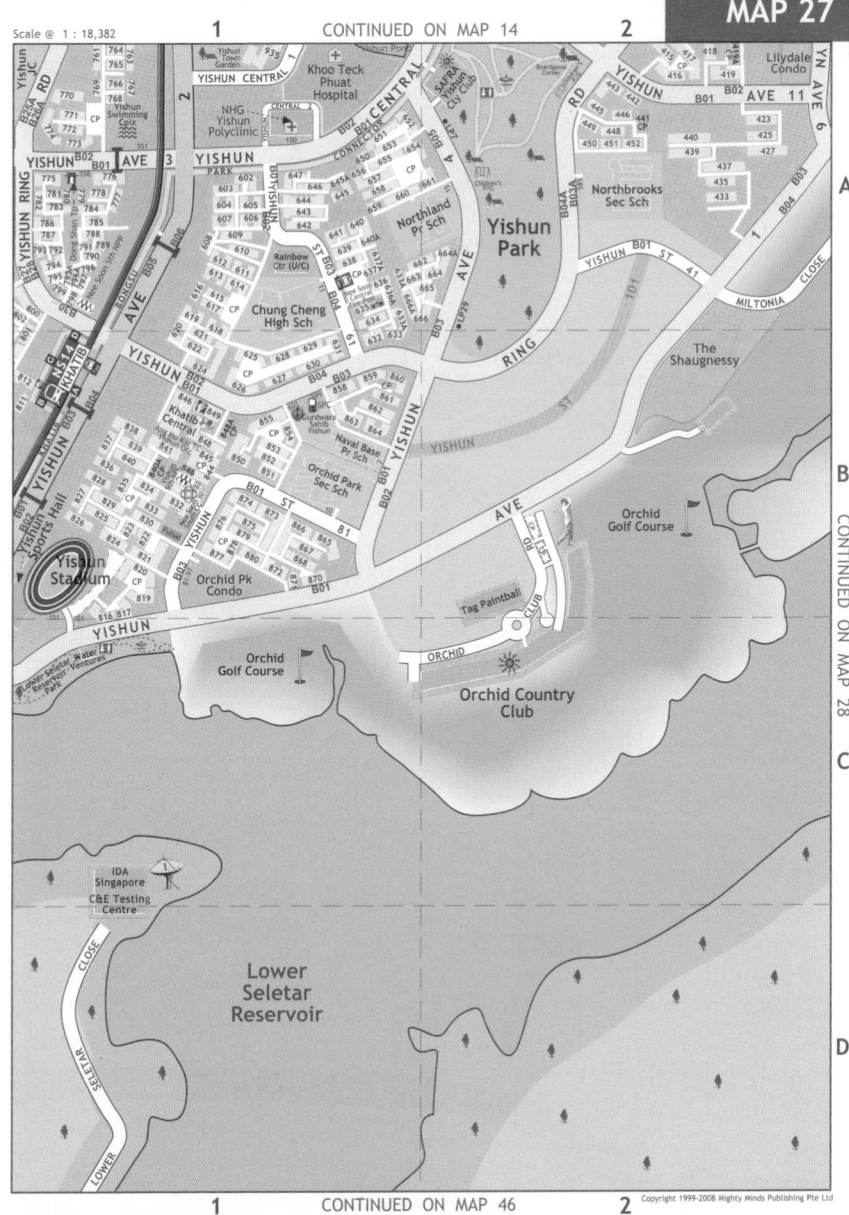

Copyright 1999-2008 Mighty Minds Publishing Pte Ltd

MAP 28

1   CONTINUED ON MAP 15   2

Scale @ 1 : 18,382

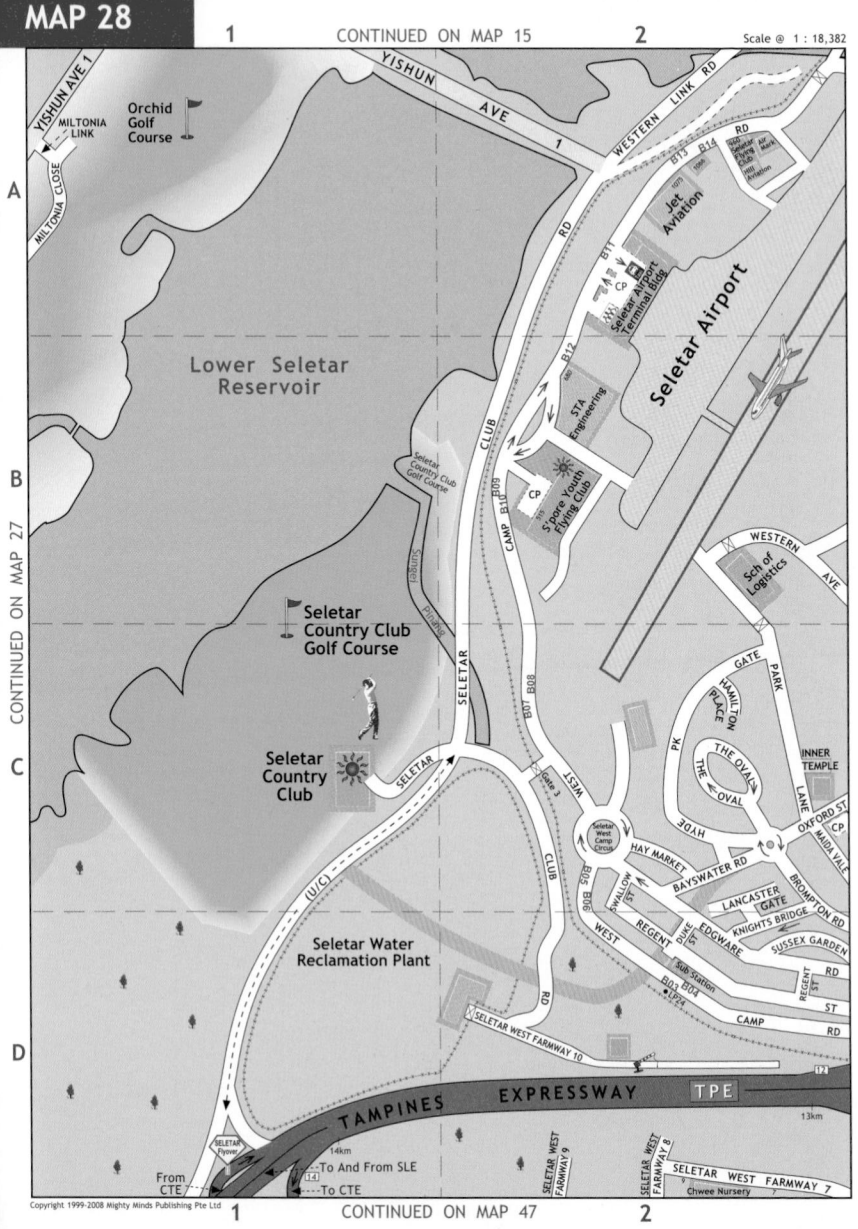

Copyright 1999-2008 Mighty Minds Publishing Pte Ltd

MAP 29

Scale @ 1 : 18,382   1   CONTINUED ON MAP 16   2

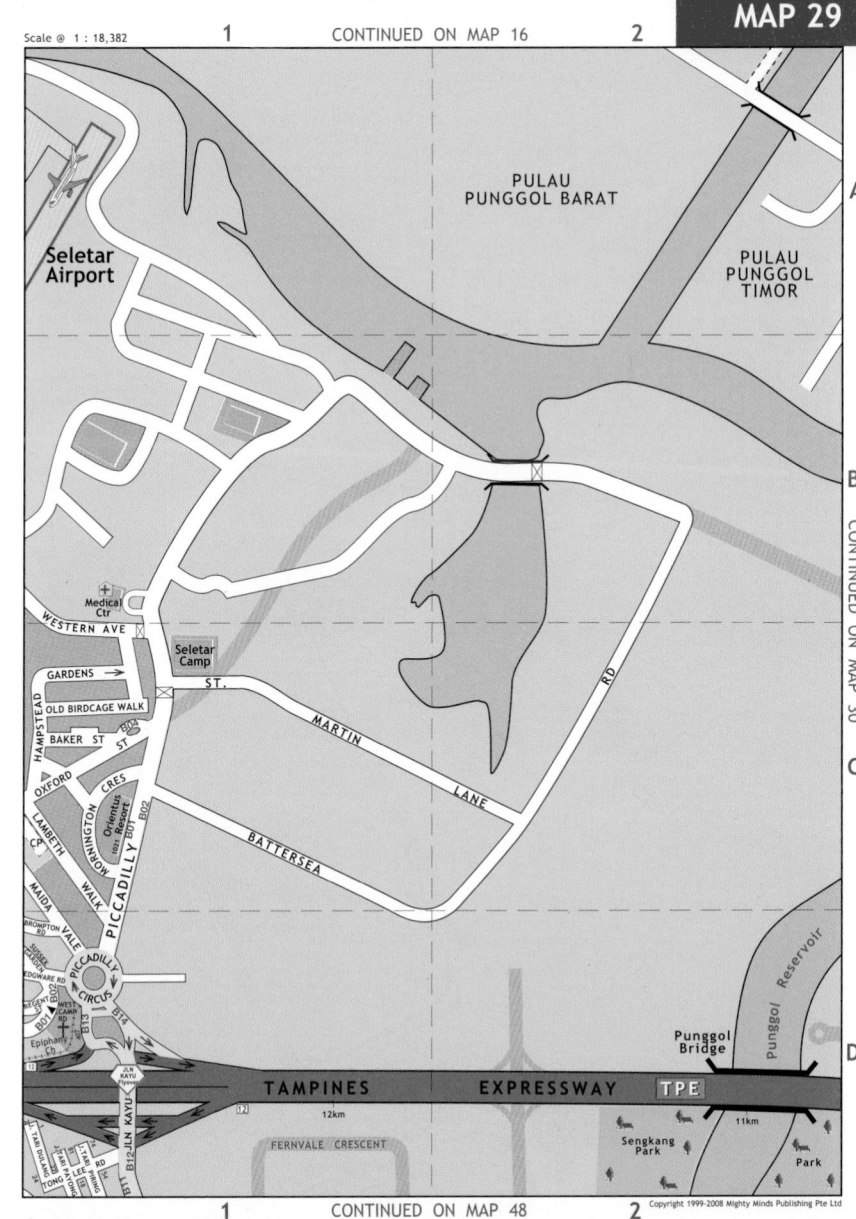

MAP 30

Scale @ 1 : 18,382

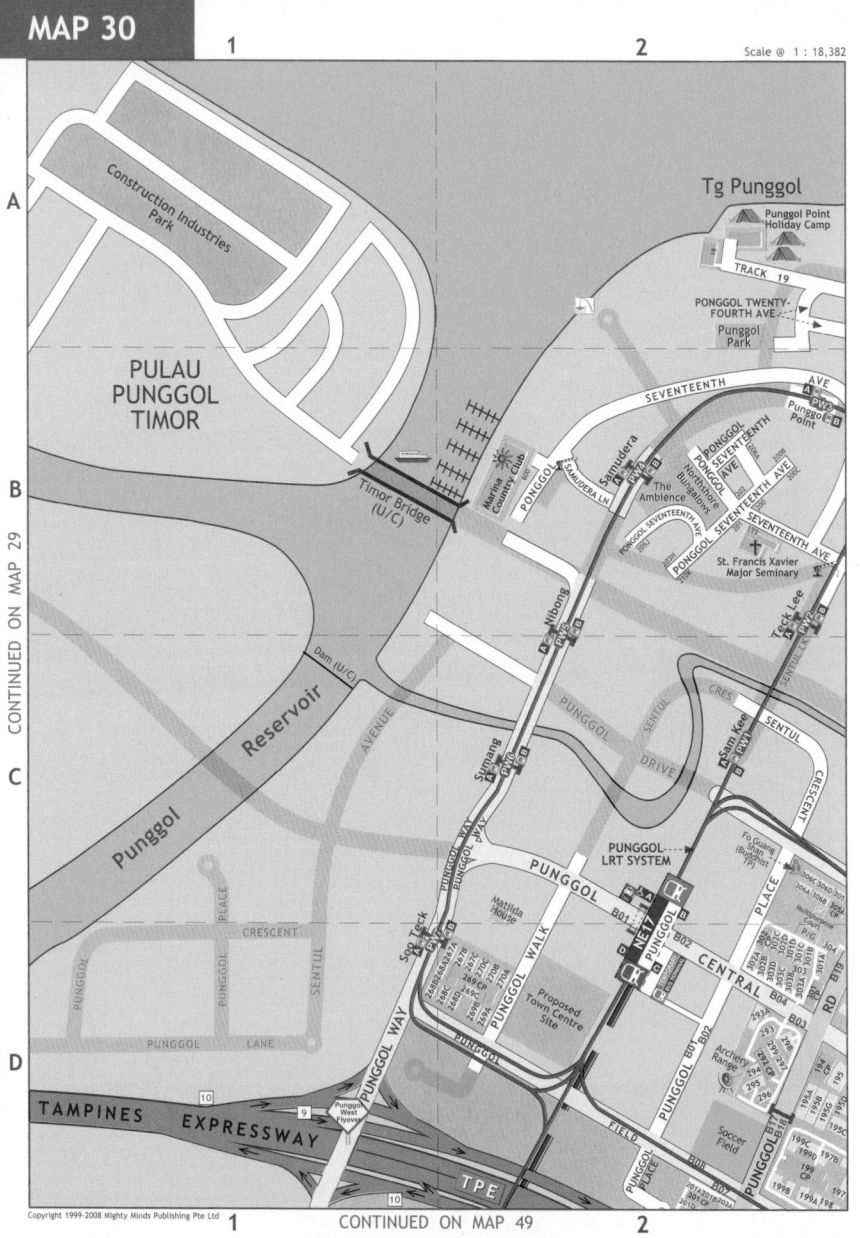

Construction Industries Park

Tg Punggol

Punggol Point Holiday Camp

TRACK 19

PONGGOL TWENTY-FOURTH AVE

Punggol Park

SEVENTEENTH AVE

Punggol Point

PULAU PUNGGOL TIMOR

Marina Country Club

PONGGOL

SAMUDERA LN

Samudera

The Ambience

PONGGOL SEVENTEENTH AVE

Northshore Bungalows

PONGGOL SEVENTEENTH AVE

SEVENTEENTH AVE

Timor Bridge (U/C)

Nibong

PONGGOL SEVENTEENTH AVE

St. Francis Xavier Major Seminary

Teck Lee

Dam (U/C)

PUNGGOL

CRES

SENTUL

Reservoir

AVENUE

PUNGGOL DRIVE

Sam Kee

SENTUL

Punggol

Sumang

PUNGGOL WAY

PUNGGOL

PUNGGOL

LRT SYSTEM

Fo Guang (Buddhist Tp)

SENTUL CRESCENT

PLACE

B01

NEL

PLACE

B02 B03

CENTRAL RD

PUNGGOL

Soo Teck

PUNGGOL WAY

PUNGGOL WALK

Matilda House

CRESCENT

PUNGGOL

PUNGGOL

SENTUL

Proposed Town Centre Site

B03 B04

Archery Range

B04

PUNGGOL LANE

PUNGGOL PLACE

Soccer Field

TAMPINES EXPRESSWAY

PUNGGOL WAY

Punggol West Flyover

PUNGGOL

TPE

MAP 31

Scale @ 1 : 18,382

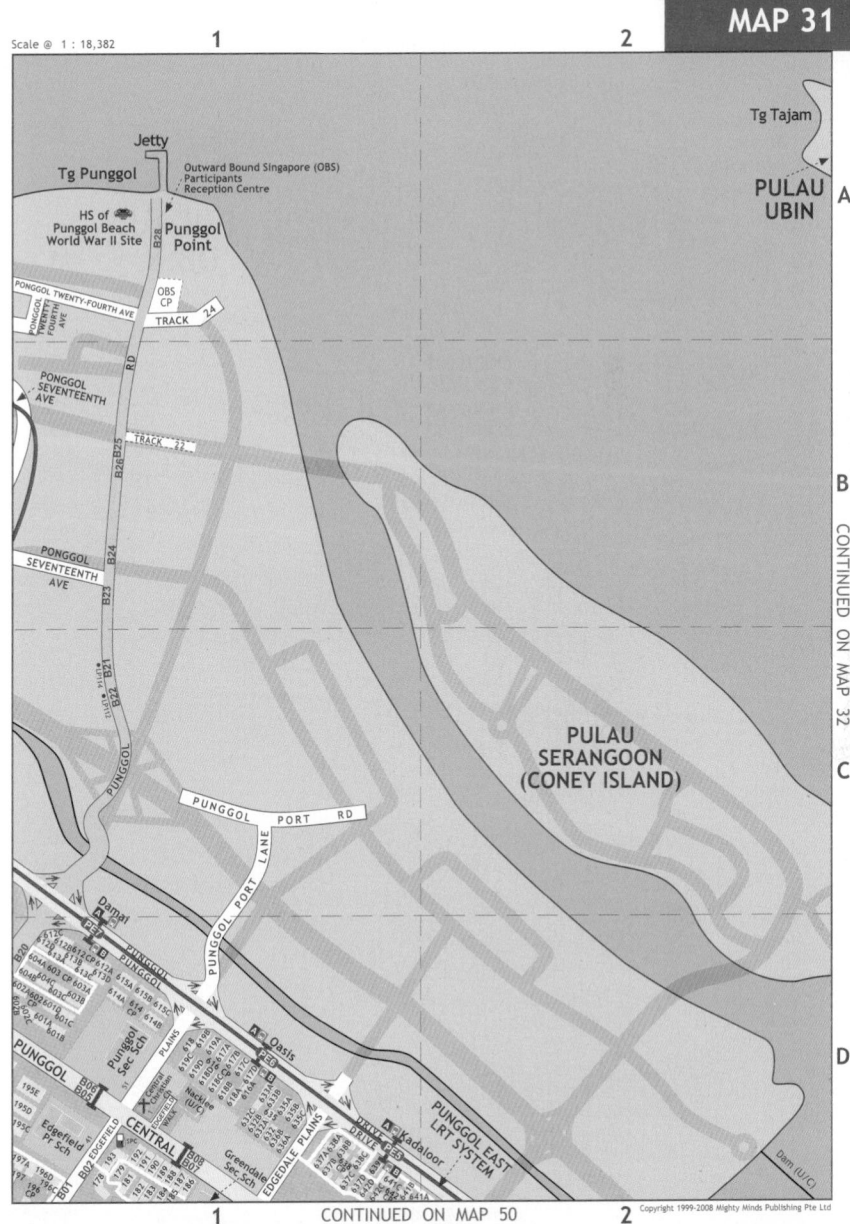

Tg Tajam

PULAU UBIN

Jetty

Tg Punggol

Outward Bound Singapore (OBS)
Participants
Reception Centre

HS of Punggol Beach World War II Site

Punggol Point

PONGGOL TWENTY-FOURTH AVE

OBS CP

TRACK 24

PONGGOL SEVENTEENTH AVE

B28

TRACK 22

B26 B25

PONGGOL SEVENTEENTH AVE

B24

B23

B22 B21

PUNGGOL RD

PUNGGOL PORT RD

PULAU SERANGOON (CONEY ISLAND)

PUNGGOL PORT LANE

Damai

PUNGGOL

Oasis

PUNGGOL EAST LRT SYSTEM

Kadaloor

Dam (U/C)

PUNGGOL

Punggol Sec Sch

Nacise (U/C)

DRIVE

EDGEDALE PLAINS

CENTRAL

Greendale Sec Sch

Edgefield Pl Sch

EDGEFIELD

CONTINUED ON MAP 32

CONTINUED ON MAP 50

MAP 32

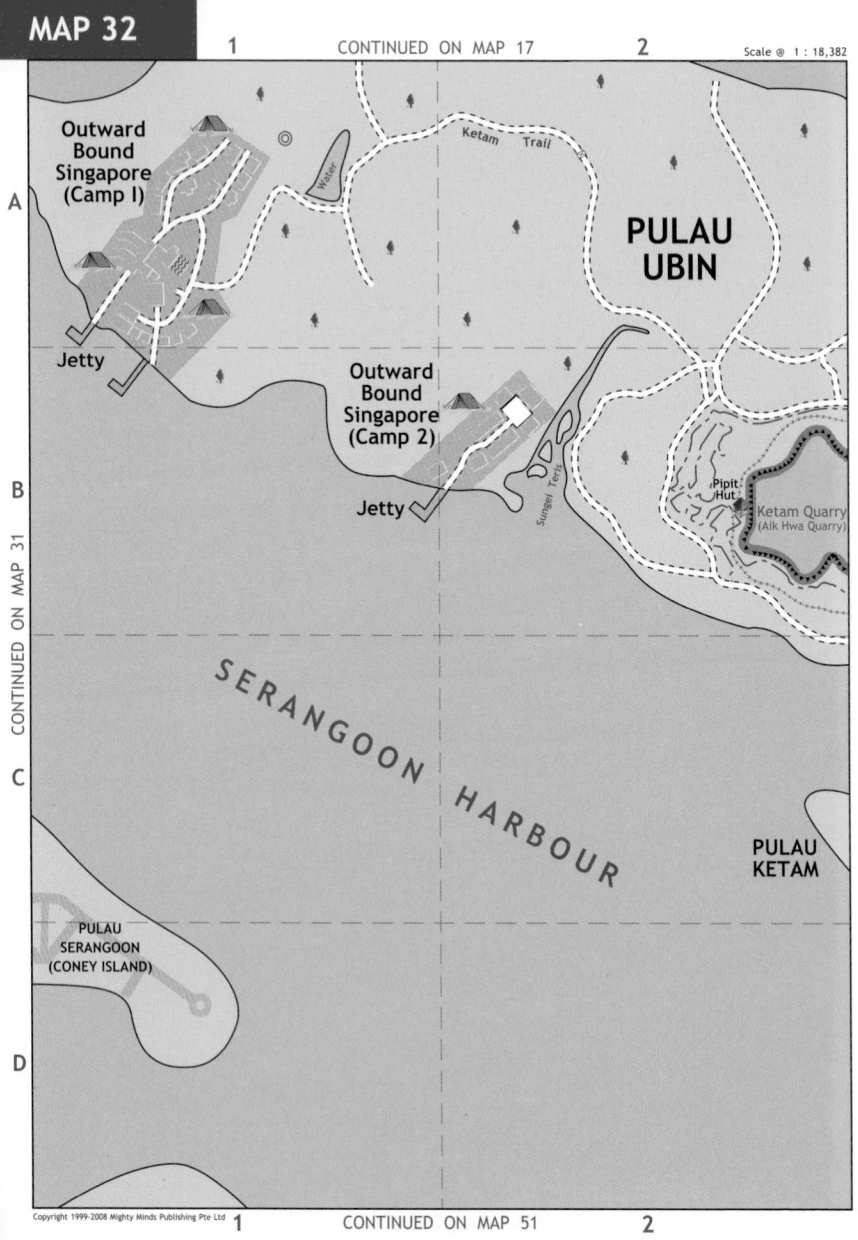

Outward
Bound
Singapore
(Camp 1)

A

Jetty

Outward
Bound
Singapore
(Camp 2)

Ketam Trail

**PULAU
UBIN**

Water

B

Jetty

Sungei Teris

Pipit
Hut

Ketam Quarry
(Aik Hwa Quarry)

S E R A N G O O N   H A R B O U R

C

**PULAU
KETAM**

PULAU
SERANGOON
(CONEY ISLAND)

D

MAP 33

Scale @ 1 : 18,382

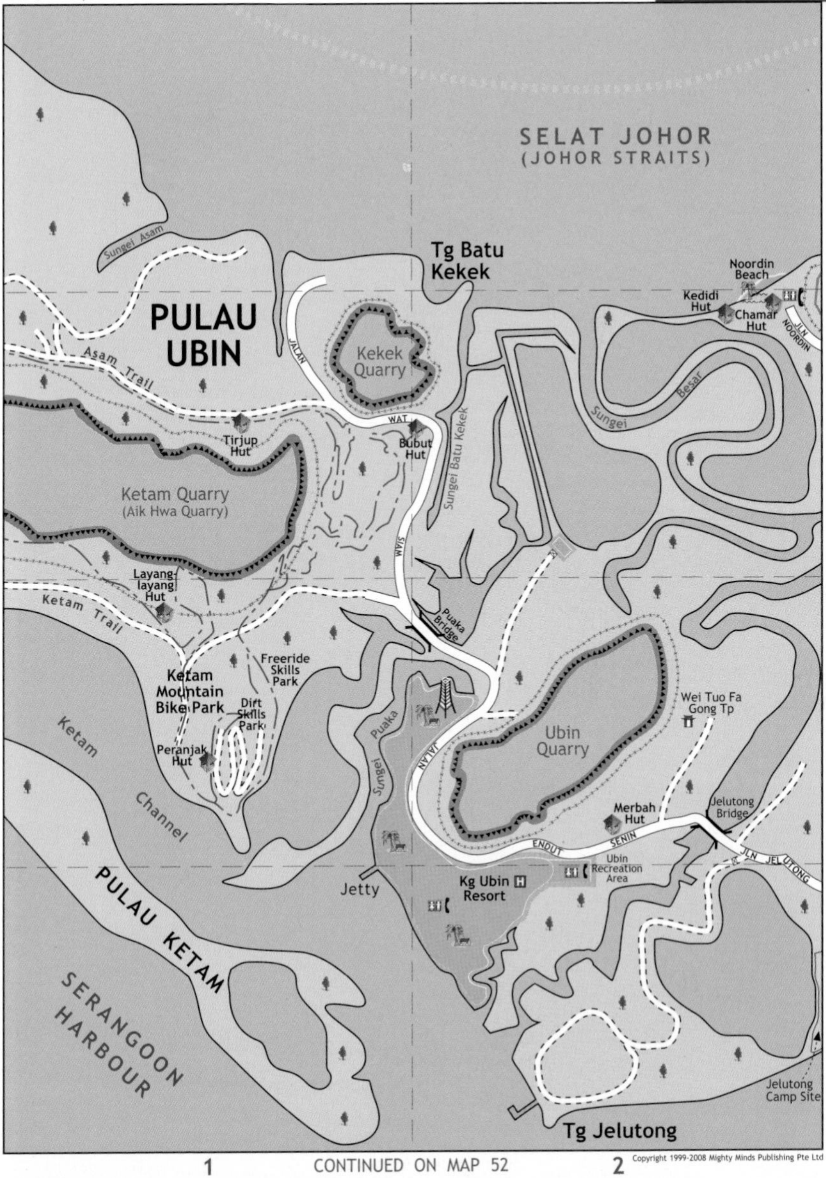

1   **2**

SELAT JOHOR
(JOHOR STRAITS)

A

Tg Batu Kekek

Noordin Beach

Kedidi Hut

Chamar Hut

Sungei Asam

Asam Trail

PULAU UBIN

Kekek Quarry

JALAN

Tirjup Hut

Bubut Hut

WAT

Sungei Batu Kekek

Sungei Besar

B

Ketam Quarry
(Aik Hwa Quarry)

Layang-layang Hut

Ketam Trail

JALAN

Puaka Bridge

Ketam Channel

Freeride Skills Park

Ketam Mountain Bike Park

Dirt Skills Park

Peranjak Hut

Sungei Puaka

JALAN

Wei Tuo Fa Gong Tp

Ubin Quarry

Merbah Hut

Jelutong Bridge

JLN JELUTONG

C

ENDUT   SENIN

Jetty

Kg Ubin Resort

Ubin Recreation Area

PULAU KETAM

SERANGOON HARBOUR

D

Jelutong Camp Site

Tg Jelutong

CONTINUED ON MAP 34

CONTINUED ON MAP 52

MAP 34

Scale @ 1 : 18,382

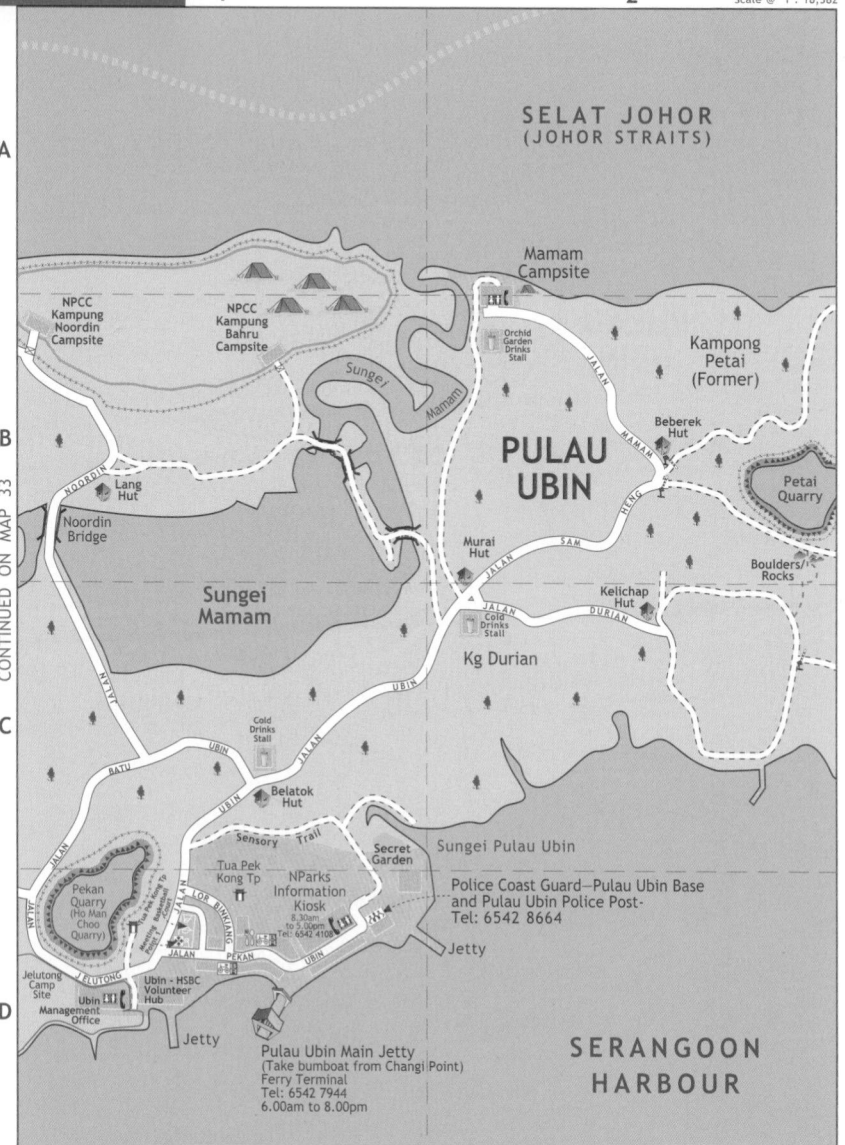

**SELAT JOHOR
(JOHOR STRAITS)**

Mamam
Campsite

Orchid
Garden
Drinks
Stall

Kampong
Petai
(Former)

NPCC
Kampung
Noordin
Campsite

NPCC
Kampung
Bahru
Campsite

Sungei
Mamam

**PULAU
UBIN**

Beberek
Hut

Petai
Quarry

Lang
Hut

Noordin
Bridge

Murai
Hut

Boulders/
Rocks

**Sungei
Mamam**

Cold
Drinks
Stall

Kelichap
Hut

Kg Durian

JALAN DURIAN

JALAN UBIN

Cold
Drinks
Stall

JALAN BATU

JALAN UBIN

Belatok
Hut

Sensory Trail

Secret
Garden

Sungei Pulau Ubin

Tua Pek
Kong Tp

NParks
Information
Kiosk
8.30am
to 5.00pm
Tel: 6542 4108

Police Coast Guard–Pulau Ubin Base
and Pulau Ubin Police Post–
Tel: 6542 8664

Pekan
Quarry
(Ho Man
Choo
Quarry)

JALAN PEKAN

LOR SINKANG

Jetty

Jelutong
Camp Site

JALAN TELUTONG

Ubin
Management
Office

Ubin – HSBC
Volunteer
Hub

Jetty

Pulau Ubin Main Jetty
(Take bumboat from Changi Point)
Ferry Terminal
Tel: 6542 7944
6.00am to 8.00pm

**SERANGOON
HARBOUR**

CONTINUED ON MAP 33

CONTINUED ON MAP 53

MAP 35

Scale @ 1 : 18,382

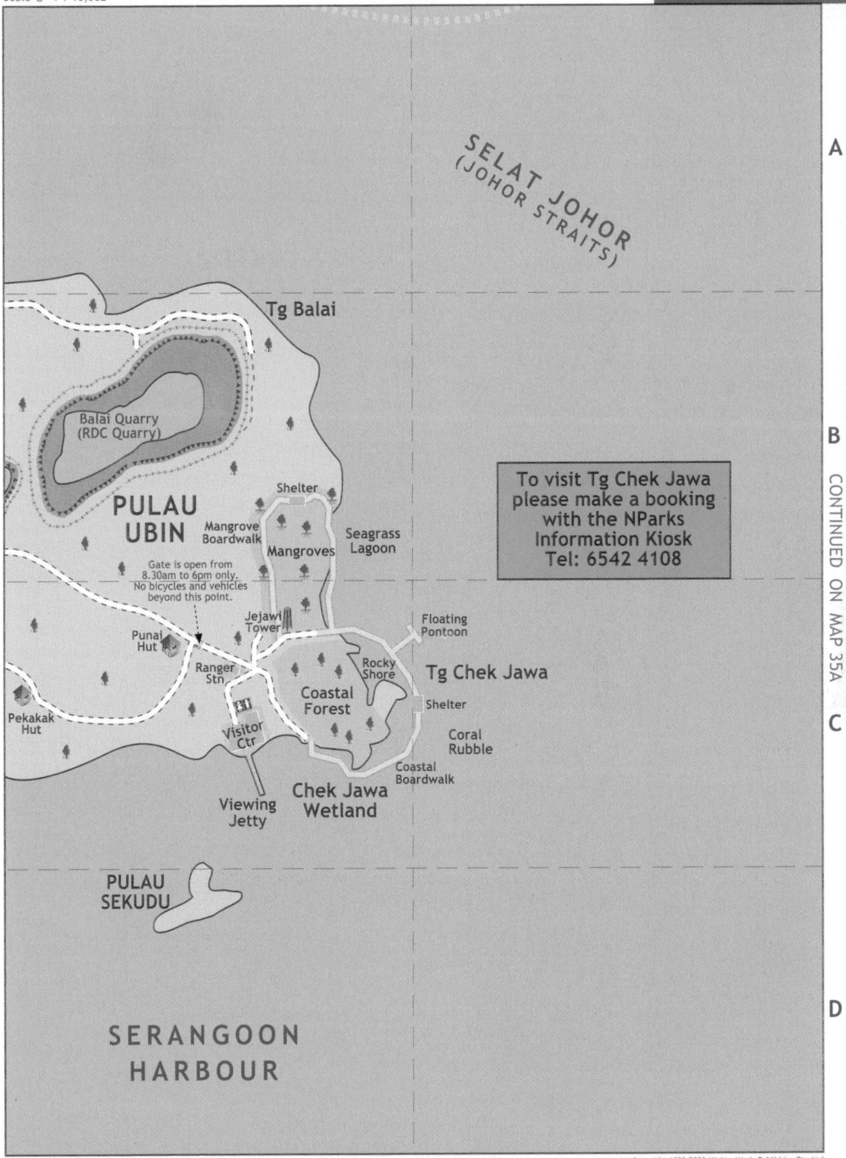

1

2

A

SELAT JOHOR
(JOHOR STRAITS)

Tg Balai

Balai Quarry
(RDC Quarry)

**PULAU
UBIN**

Mangrove
Boardwalk

Shelter

Mangroves

Seagrass
Lagoon

Gate is open from
8.30am to 6pm only.
No bicycles and vehicles
beyond this point.

Jejawi
Tower

Punai
Hut

Ranger
Stn.

Floating
Pontoon

Rocky
Shore

Tg Chek Jawa

Coastal
Forest

Shelter

Pekakak
Hut

Visitor
Ctr

Coral
Rubble

Viewing
Jetty

**Chek Jawa
Wetland**

Coastal
Boardwalk

To visit Tg Chek Jawa
please make a booking
with the NParks
Information Kiosk
Tel: 6542 4108

B

C

CONTINUED ON MAP 35A

**PULAU
SEKUDU**

D

**SERANGOON
HARBOUR**

1

CONTINUED ON MAP 54

2

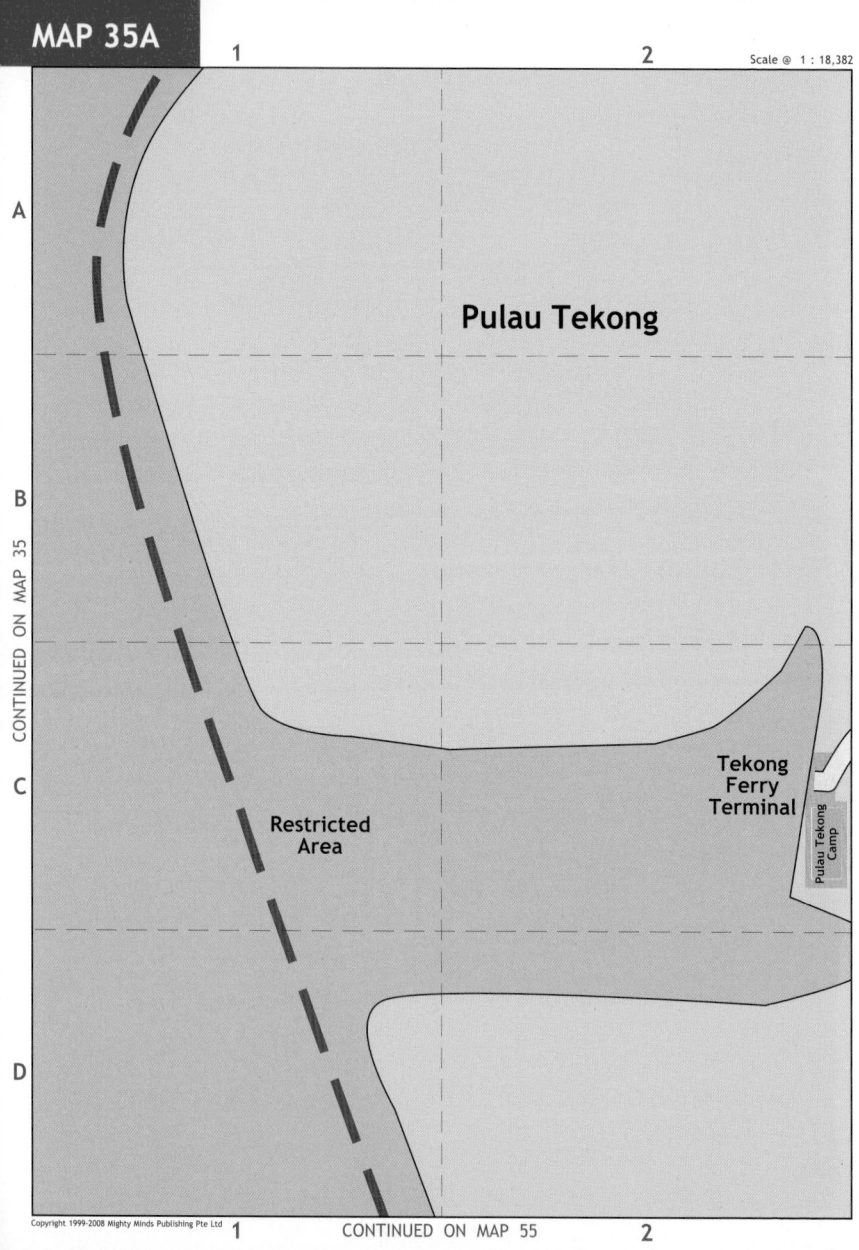

Scale @ 1 : 18,382

Pulau Tekong

CONTINUED ON MAP 35

Tekong
Ferry
Terminal

Restricted
Area

Pulau Tekong Camp

CONTINUED ON MAP 55

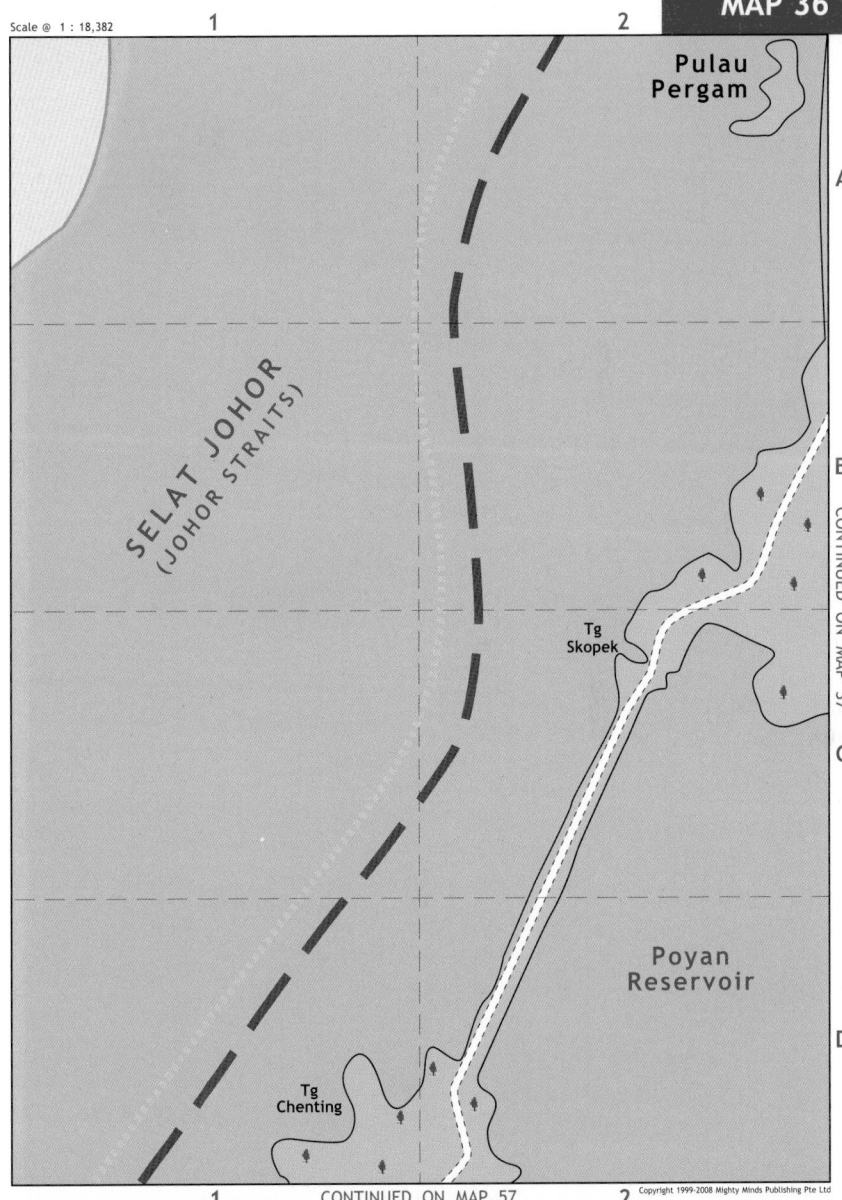

MAP 36

Scale @ 1 : 18,382

1

2

Pulau
Pergam

A

SELAT JOHOR
(JOHOR STRAITS)

B

CONTINUED ON MAP 37

Tg
Skopek

C

Poyan
Reservoir

D

Tg
Chenting

1

CONTINUED ON MAP 57

2

MAP 37

1 CONTINUED ON MAP 18 2

Scale @ 1 : 18,382

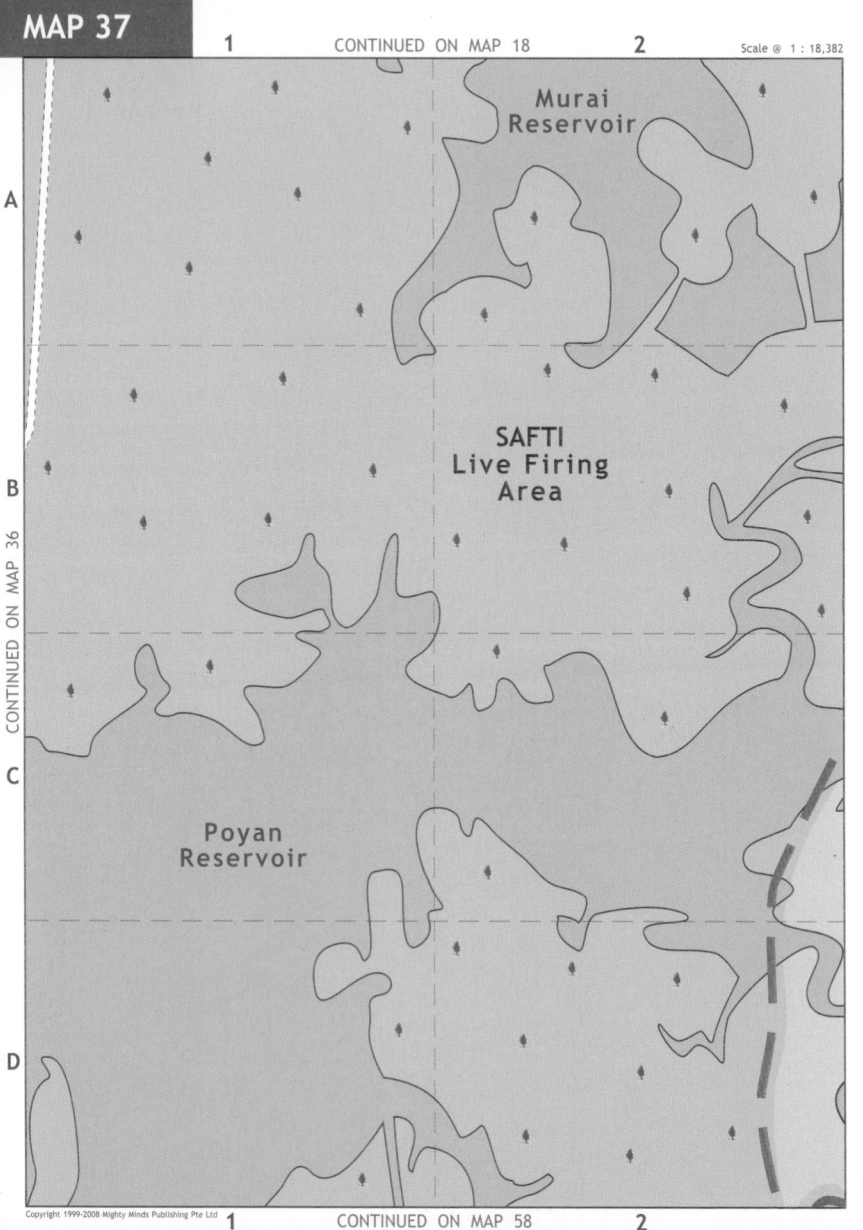

Murai
Reservoir

A

SAFTI
Live Firing
Area

B

CONTINUED ON MAP 36

C

Poyan
Reservoir

D

1 CONTINUED ON MAP 58 2

MAP 38

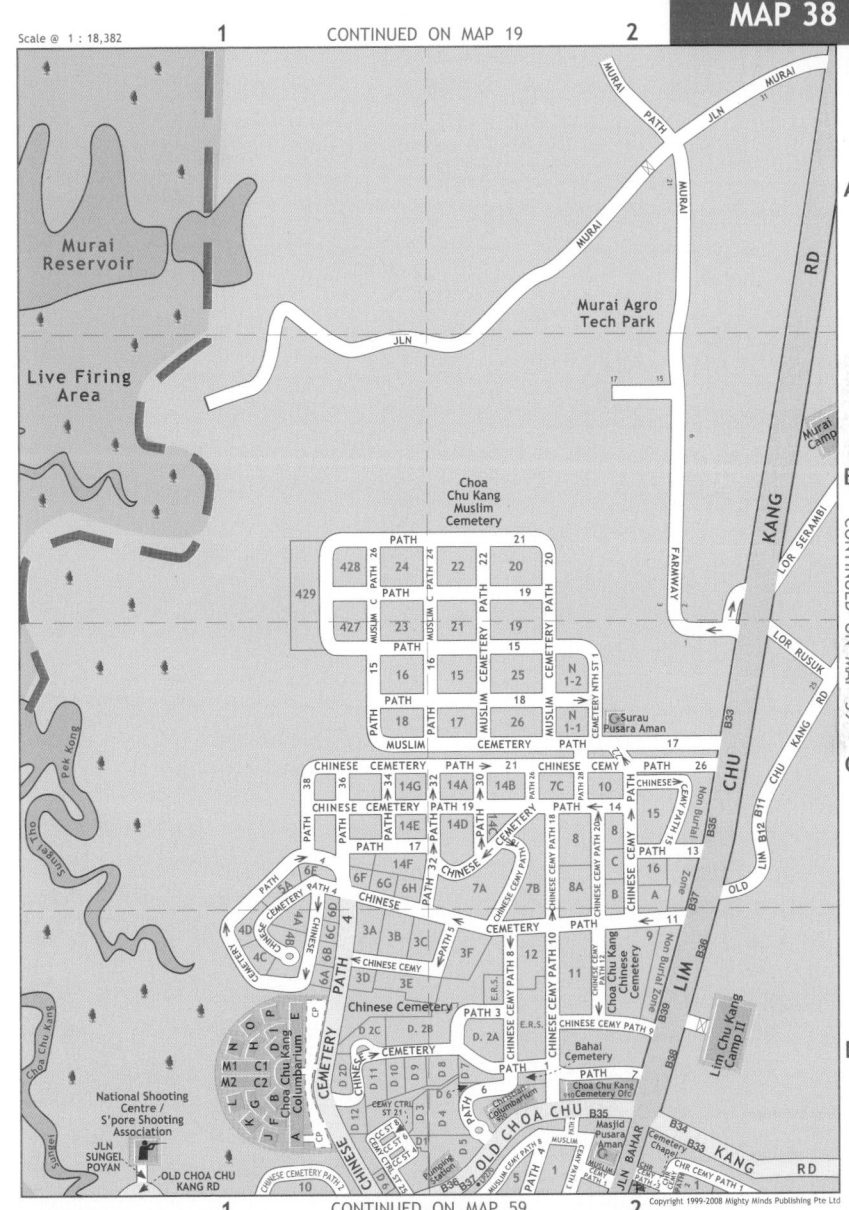

Murai
Reservoir

Live Firing
Area

Murai Agro
Tech Park

Choa
Chu Kang
Muslim
Cemetery

Surau
Pusara Aman

Choa Chu Kang
Chinese
Cemetery

Bahai
Cemetery

Choa Chu Kang
Cemetery Ofc

Chinese Cemetery

Choa Chu Kang
Columbarium

National Shooting
Centre /
S'pore Shooting
Association

Masjid
Pusara
Aman

Lim Chu Kang
Camp II

Murai
Camp

CONTINUED ON MAP 19
CONTINUED ON MAP 39
CONTINUED ON MAP 59

MAP 39

1 CONTINUED ON MAP 20 2

Scale @ 1 : 18,382

MAP 40

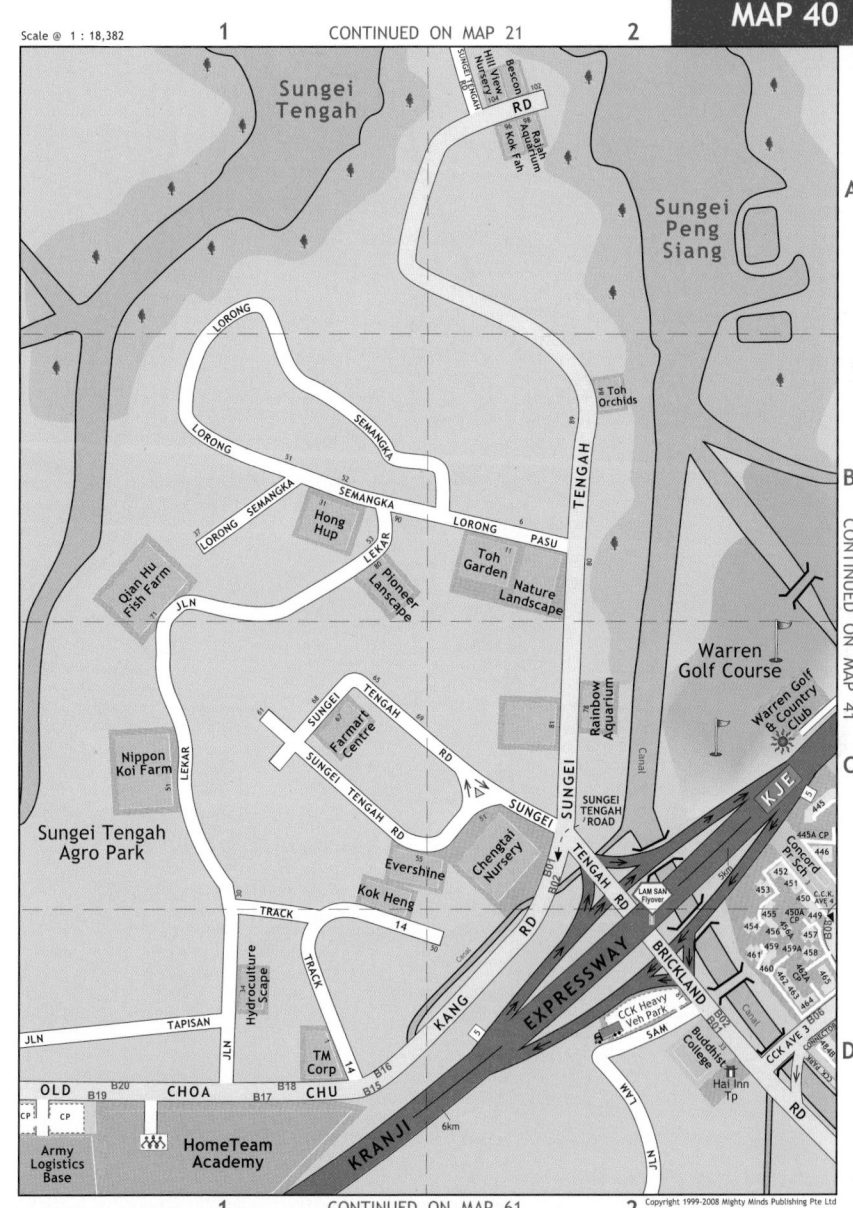

Sungei Tengah

Sungei Peng Siang

SUNGEI TENGAH RD

Hill View Nursery
Bescon
100
102
104
Rajah Aquarium
Kok Fah

LORONG

SEMANGKA

LORONG

SEMANGKA

LORONG SEMANGKA

Hong Hup

LEKAR

Pioneer Landscpe

JLN

Qian Hu Fish Farm

Nippon Koi Farm

LEKAR

Sungei Tengah Agro Park

LORONG PASU

Toh Orchids

Toh Garden

Nature Landscape

TENGAH

Rainbow Aquarium

Canal

Warren Golf Course

Warren Golf & Country Club

SUNGEI TENGAH

Farmart Centre

SUNGEI TENGAH RD

Chengtai Nursery

SUNGEI TENGAH RD

SUNGEI TENGAH ROAD

Evershine

Kok Heng

TRACK   14

Canal

TRACK

Hydroculture Scape

JLN

TAPISAN

TM Corp

JLN

KANG RD

EXPRESSWAY

BRICKLAND

KJE

Concord Pr Stch

445A CP
452
451
453
450
454
456
459
461
460
462
446
448
450A CP
C.C.K. AVE 4
457
458
459A
464
463

LAM SAN Flyover

5km

CCK Heavy Veh Park

Buddhist College

SAM

Hai Inn Tp

CCK AVE 3

RD

LAM

JLN

OLD   CHOA   CHU

B20
B19
B17
B18
B16
B15

CP   CP

HomeTeam Academy

Army Logistics Base

KRANJI   6km

MAP 41

Scale @ 1 : 18,382

Key labelled features include:

- Mowbray Camp
- Police Dog K9 Unit
- Kranji Camp
- Yew Tee Park
- Yew Tee Shopping Centre / Yew Tee Residences
- CHOA CHU KANG WAY
- CHOA CHU KANG DR
- De La Salle Sch
- Limbang Shopping Ctr
- Choa Chu Kang to Kang NPP
- Hebron Bible Presby Ch.
- Kranji Pr Sch
- Stagmont Park
- Yew Mei Green
- Windermere
- Yew Mei Pr Sch
- Regent Sec Sch
- Villa Verde
- Kranji Sec Sch
- Limbang Park
- Choa Chu Kang Swimming Complex
- Choa Chu Kang Sports Hall & Tennis Ctr
- CCK Stadium
- VERDE GROVE / VILLA VERDE / VERDE AVENUE / VERDE PLACE
- Warren Golf Course
- KRANJI EXPRESSWAY KJE
- Yew Tee Flyover
- Choa Chu Kang Park
- North Vale
- The Warren
- Choa Chu Kang Central P.O.
- Choa Chu Kang Community Library
- HDB Branch Office
- Hong Kah Town Council (Head Ofc)
- Lot 1 Shoppers' Mall
- RafflesMedical
- Bukit Panjang Govt High Sch (U/C)
- CHOA CHU KANG AVE
- SouthView Pr Sch
- South View
- Chua Chu Kang Sec Sch
- Stagmont Camp
- Pioneer Junior College
- Teck Whye Pr Sch
- Teck Whye Sec Sch
- Bukit Panjang High Sch (Temporary)
- TECK WHYE CRESCENT / TECK WHYE LANE / TECK WHYE AVE
- Teck Whye Shopping Centre
- The Church of the Incarnation
- Tembusu Park
- Choa Chu Kang Crest
- CHOA CHU KANG TER
- Chua Chu Kang Park
- Keat Hong Shopping Centre
- Comfort Gdn
- Palm Gdns
- Uttamayanmunia Buddhist Temple
- KEAT HONG
- SAN WALK
- BUKIT PANJANG LRT SYSTEM
- ITE College West (U/C)
- BUKIT BATOK RD
- HQ 4th CD DIV & Bt Batok Fire Station
- PAVILION CIRCLE
- Pavilion Pk
- BRICKLAND RD
- CHOA CHU KANG PARK CONNECTOR
- WOODLANDS RD
- Malayan Railway Track (KTM)
- CALTEX
- National Parks Board
- JLN GALI BATU
- Heavy Vehicle Park
- STAGMONT RING

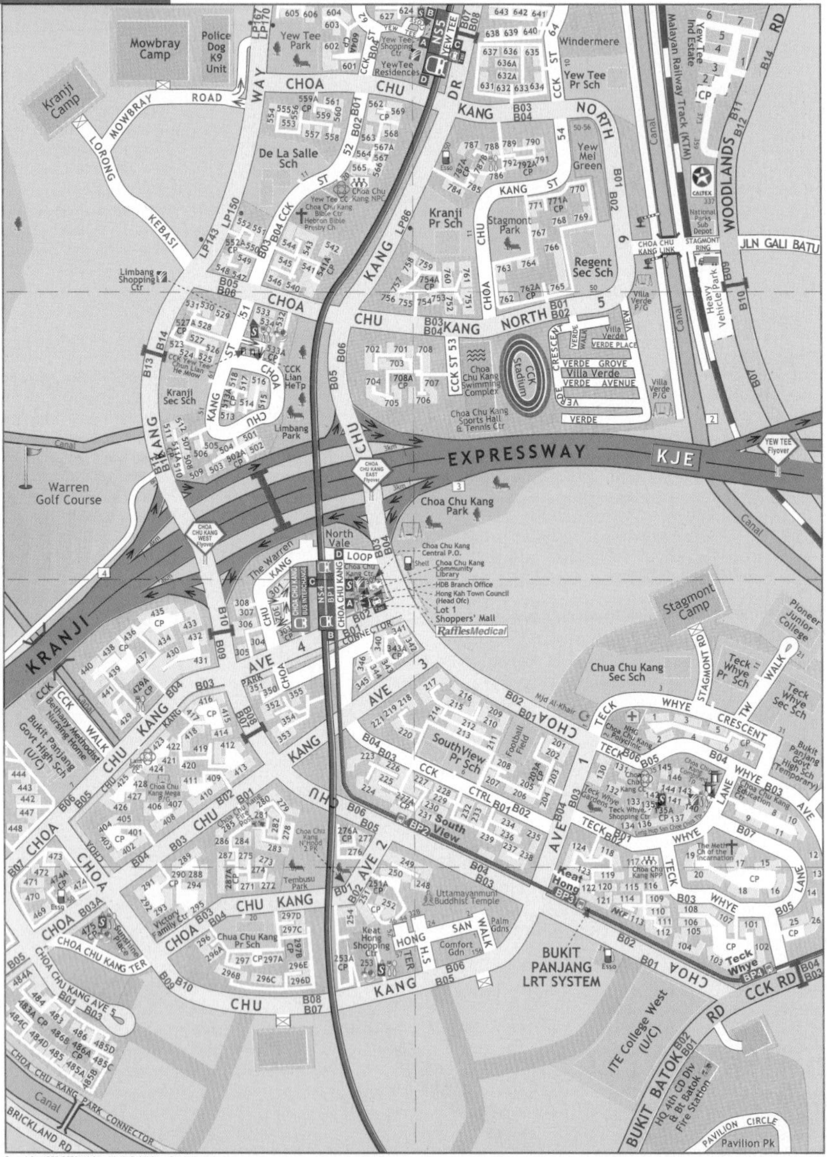

MAP 42

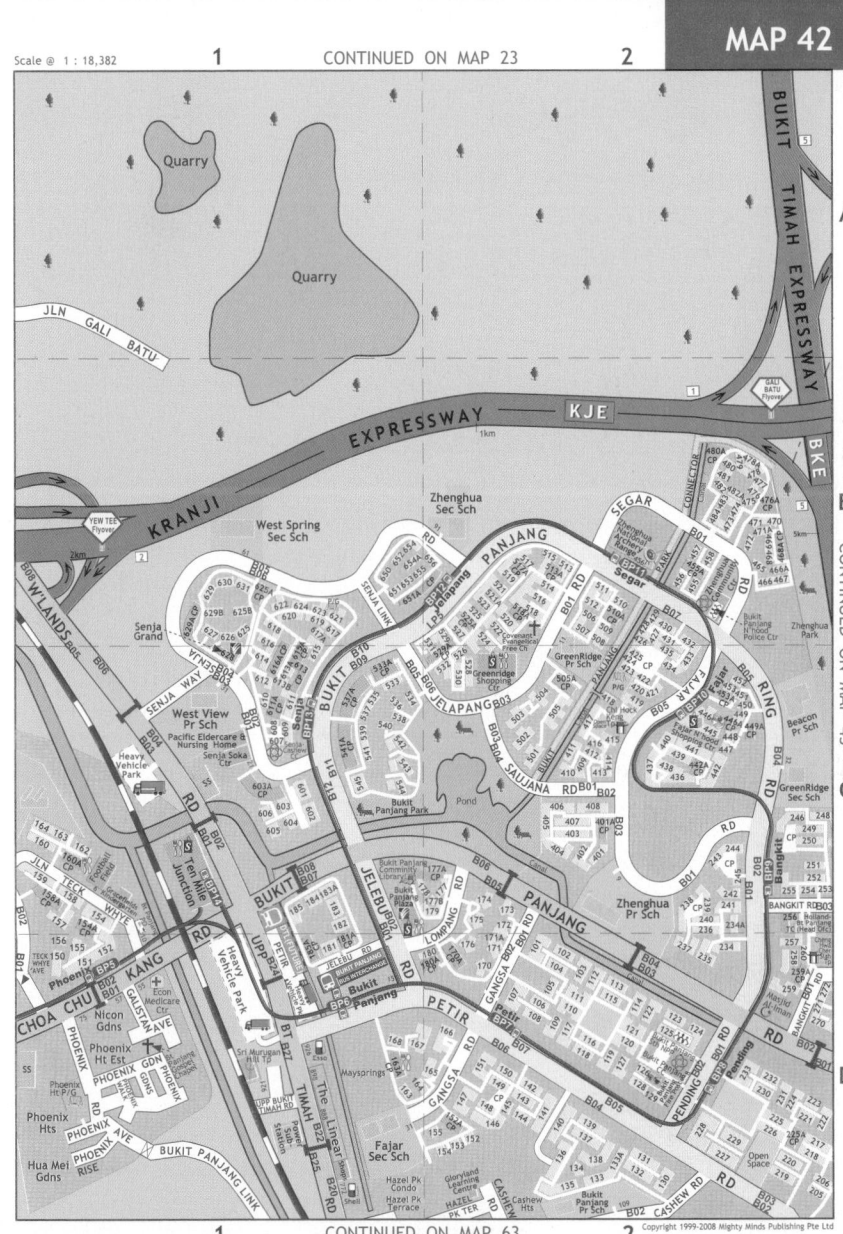

MAP 43

CONTINUED ON MAP 24

Scale @ 1 : 18,382

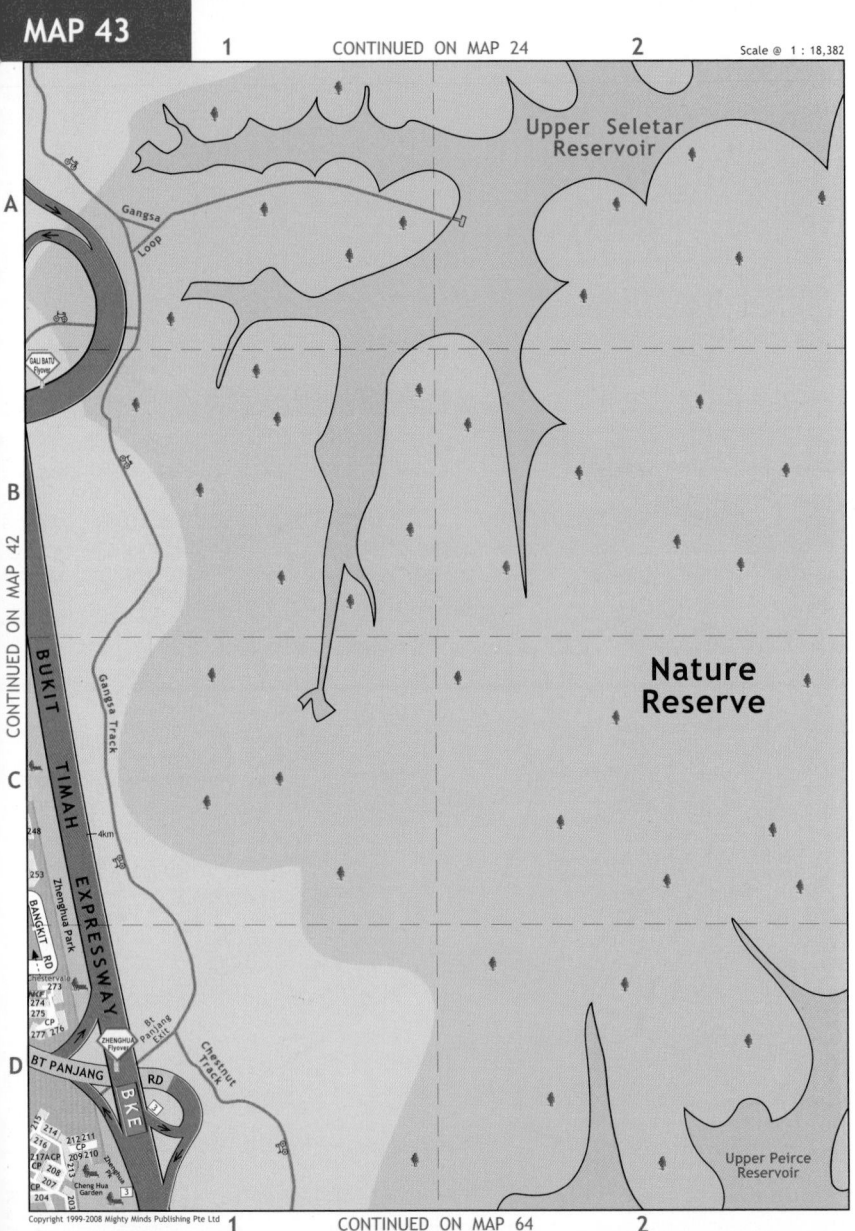

Upper Seletar
Reservoir

Gangsa Loop

DAIRY FARM
DALI BATU

BUKIT TIMAH EXPRESSWAY

Gangsa Track

Nature
Reserve

4km

Zhenghua Park

248
253

BANGKIT RD

273
274
275
CP
277 276

BT PANJANG

BKE

RD

ZHENGHUA
Flyover

Bt Panjang Exit

Chestnut Track

Cheng Hua
Garden

216 214
212 211
217 CP 209 210
CP 208 207 213
206
201 203

Upper Peirce
Reservoir

MAP 44

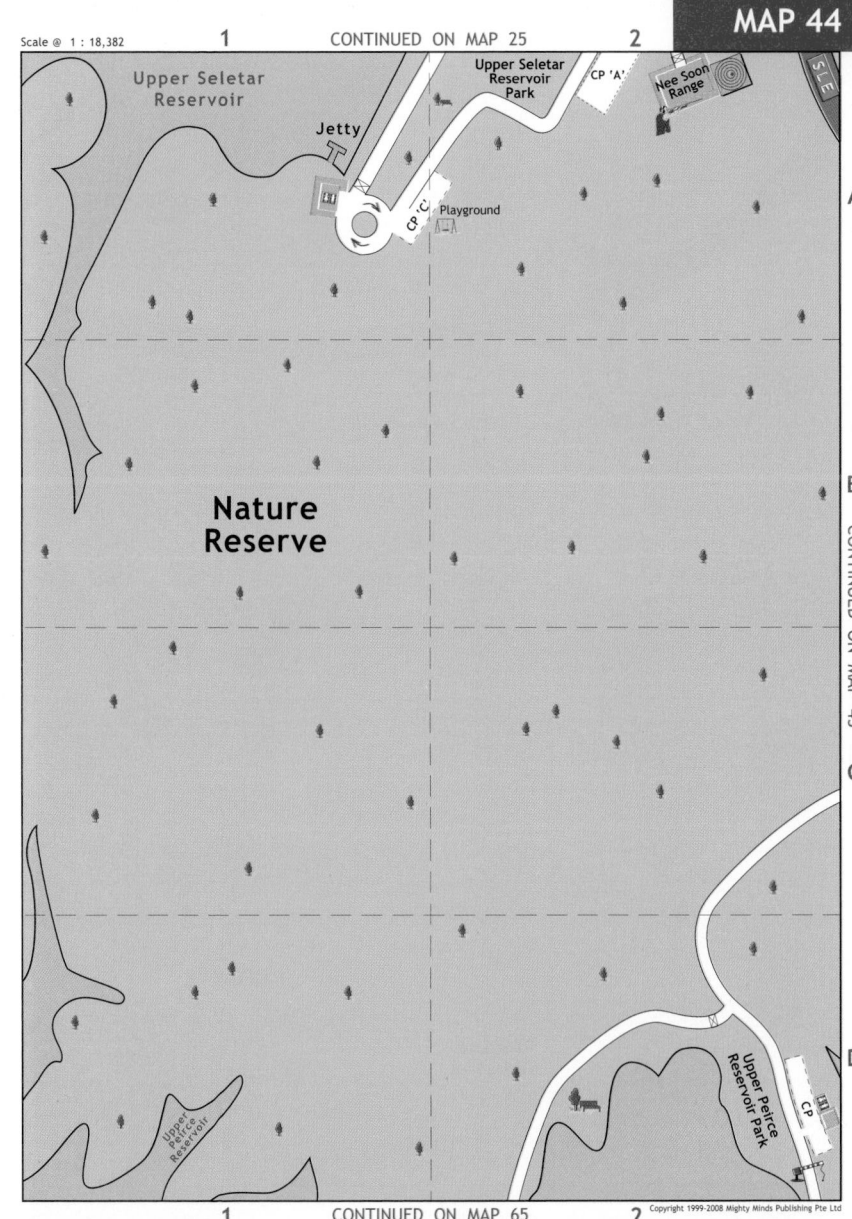

CONTINUED ON MAP 25

Upper Seletar
Reservoir

Upper Seletar
Reservoir
Park

CP 'A'

Nee Soon
Range

SLE

Jetty

CP 'C'

Playground

Nature
Reserve

CONTINUED ON MAP 45

Upper Peirce
Reservoir

Upper Peirce
Reservoir Park

CP

MAP 45

CONTINUED ON MAP 26

Scale @ 1 : 18,382

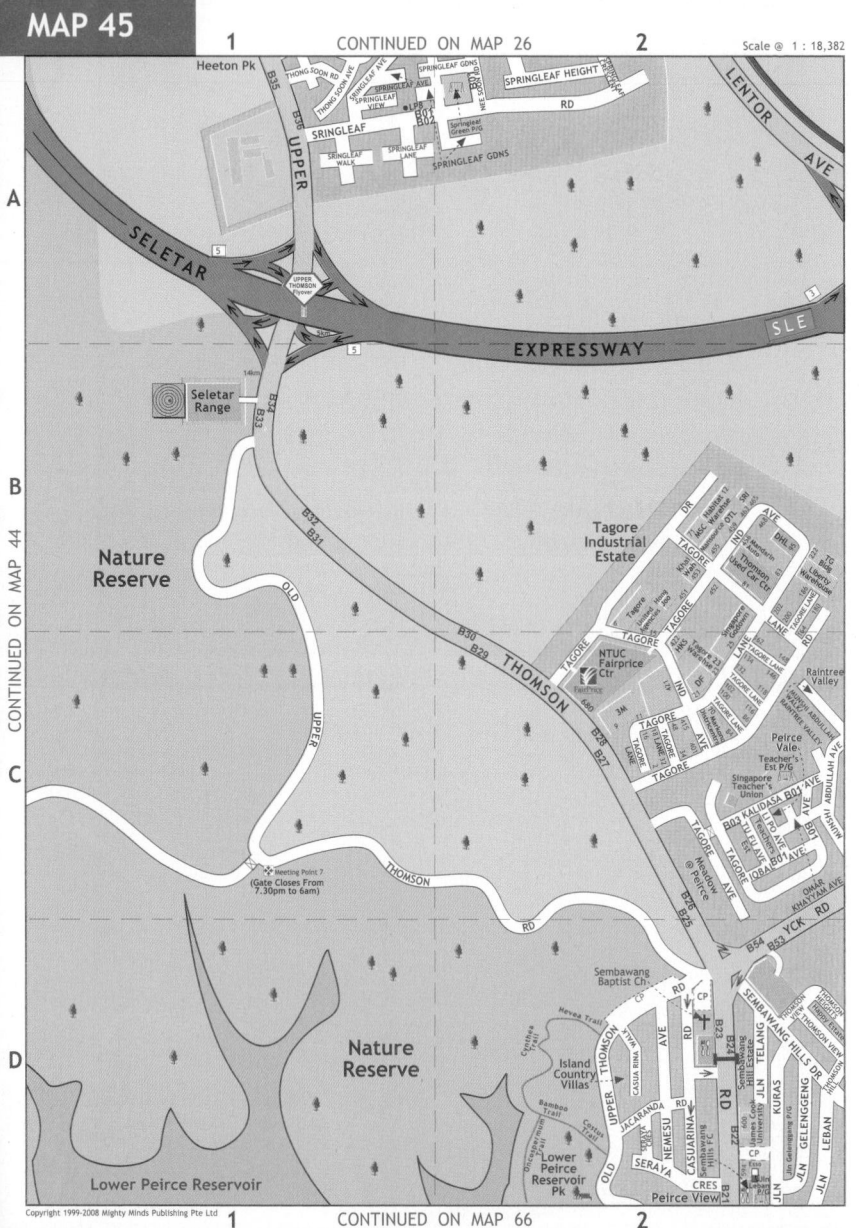

MAP 46

Scale @ 1 : 18,382

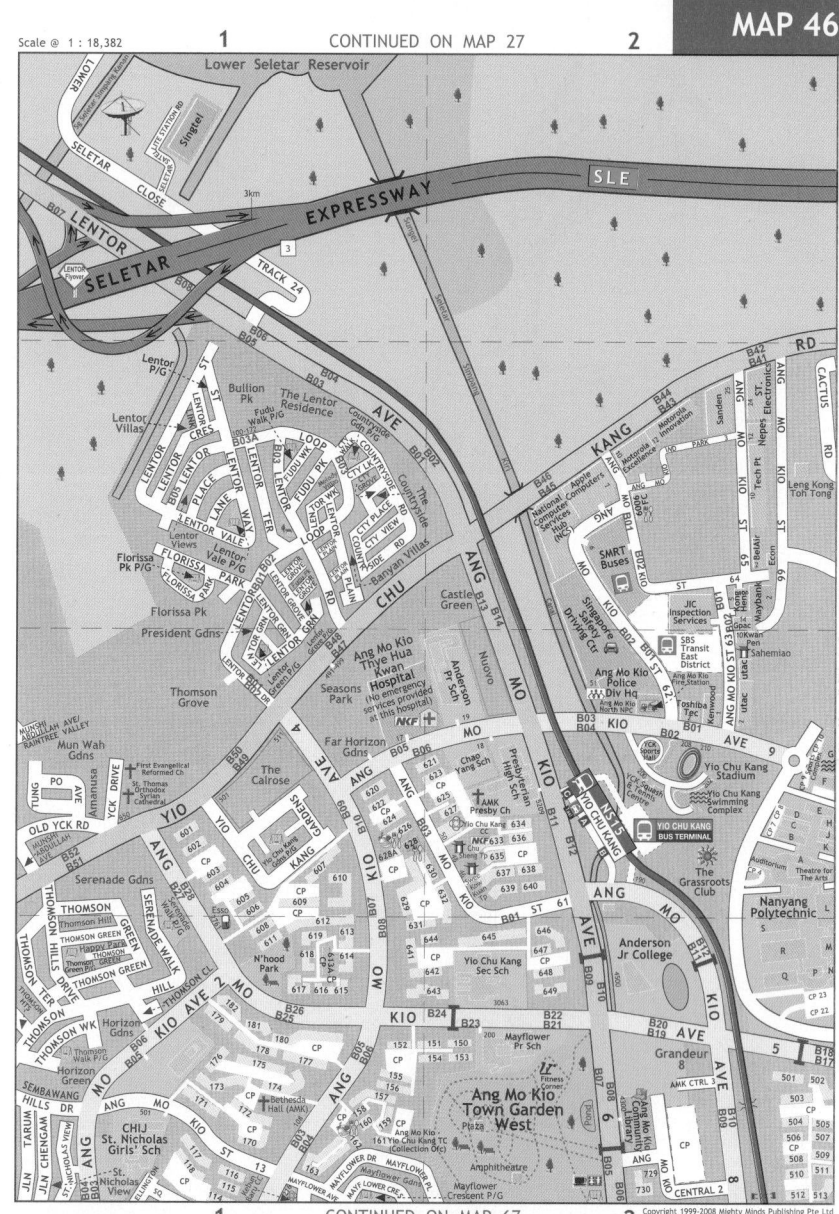

Copyright 1999-2008 Mighty Minds Publishing Pte Ltd

MAP 47

Scale @ 1 : 18,382

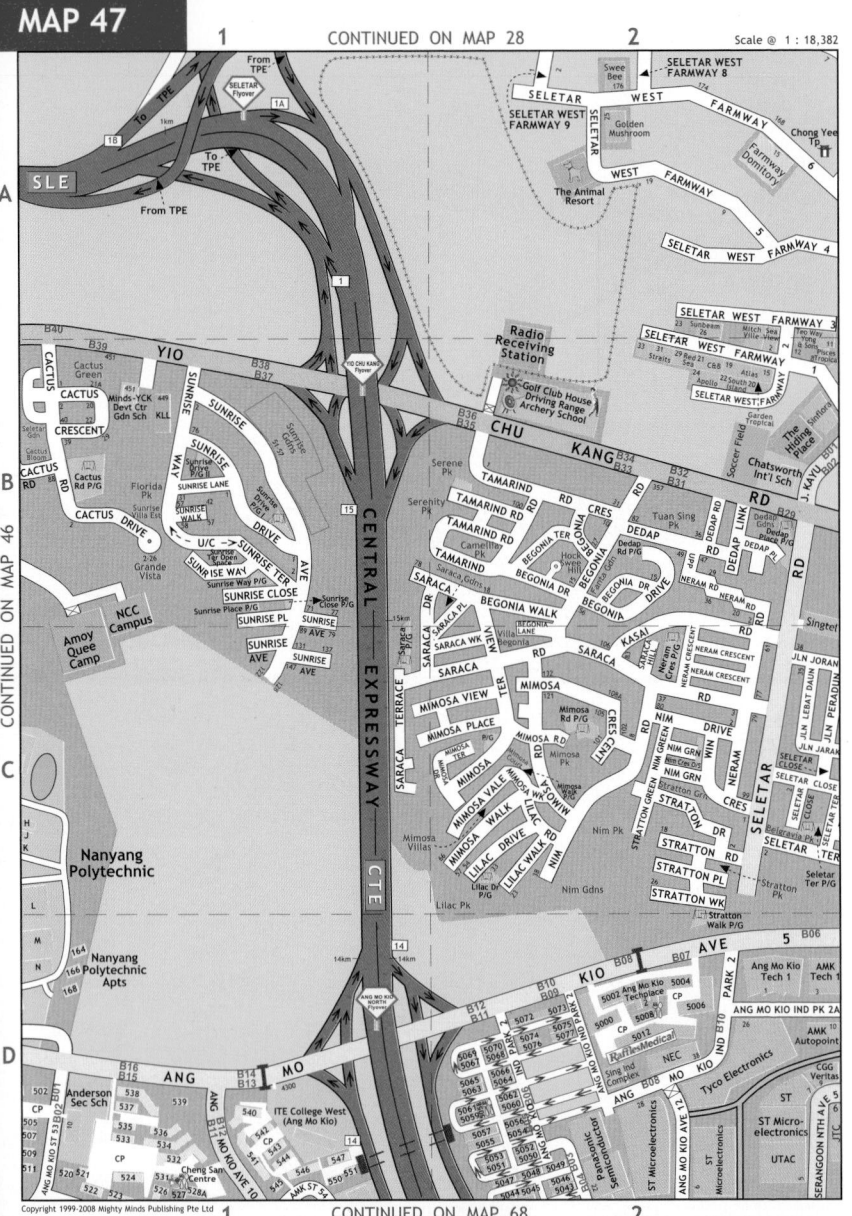

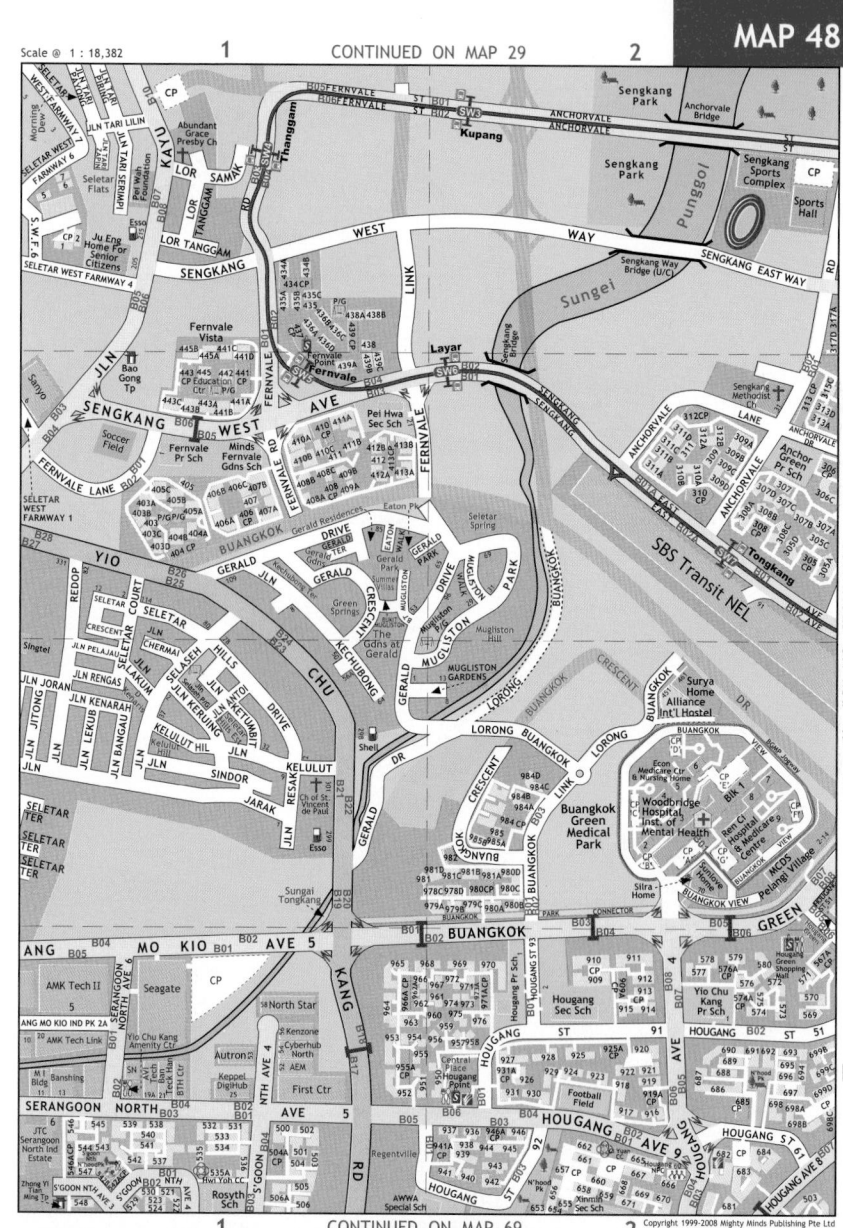

MAP 49

CONTINUED ON MAP 30

Scale @ 1 : 18,382

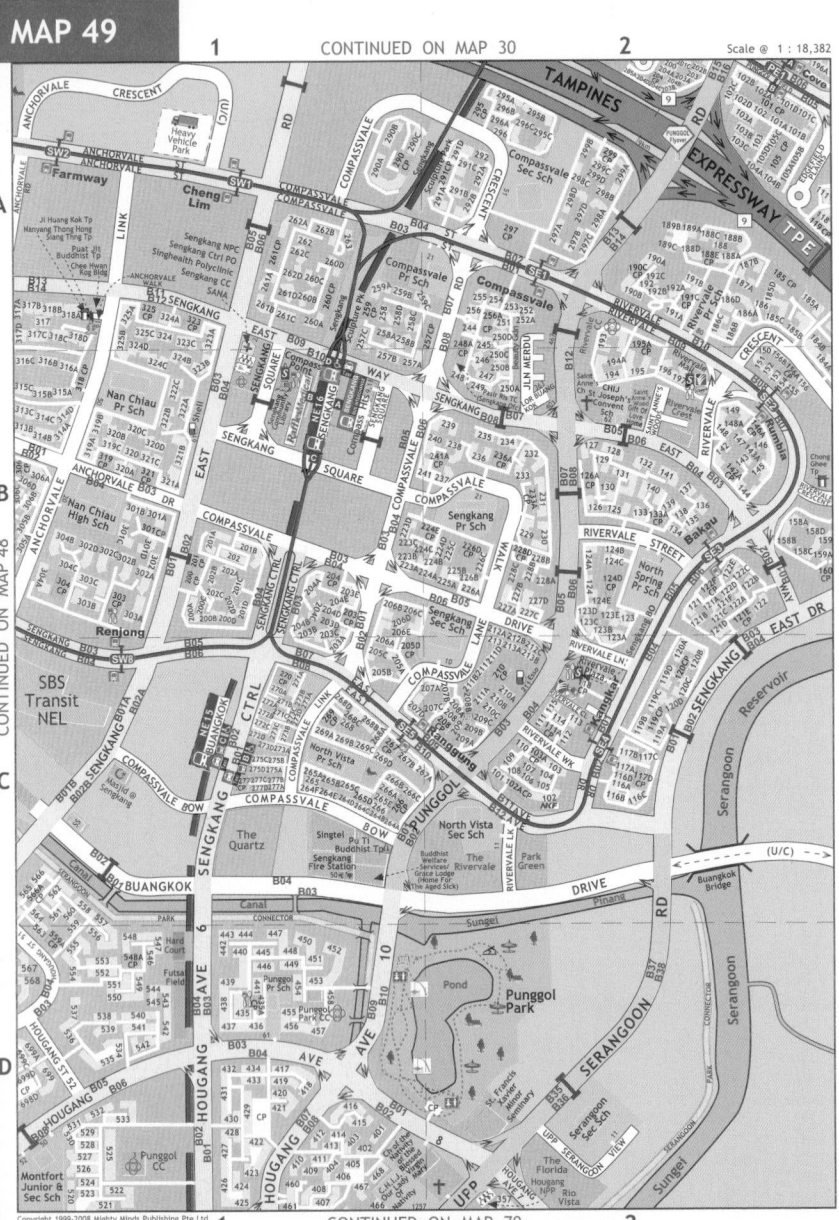

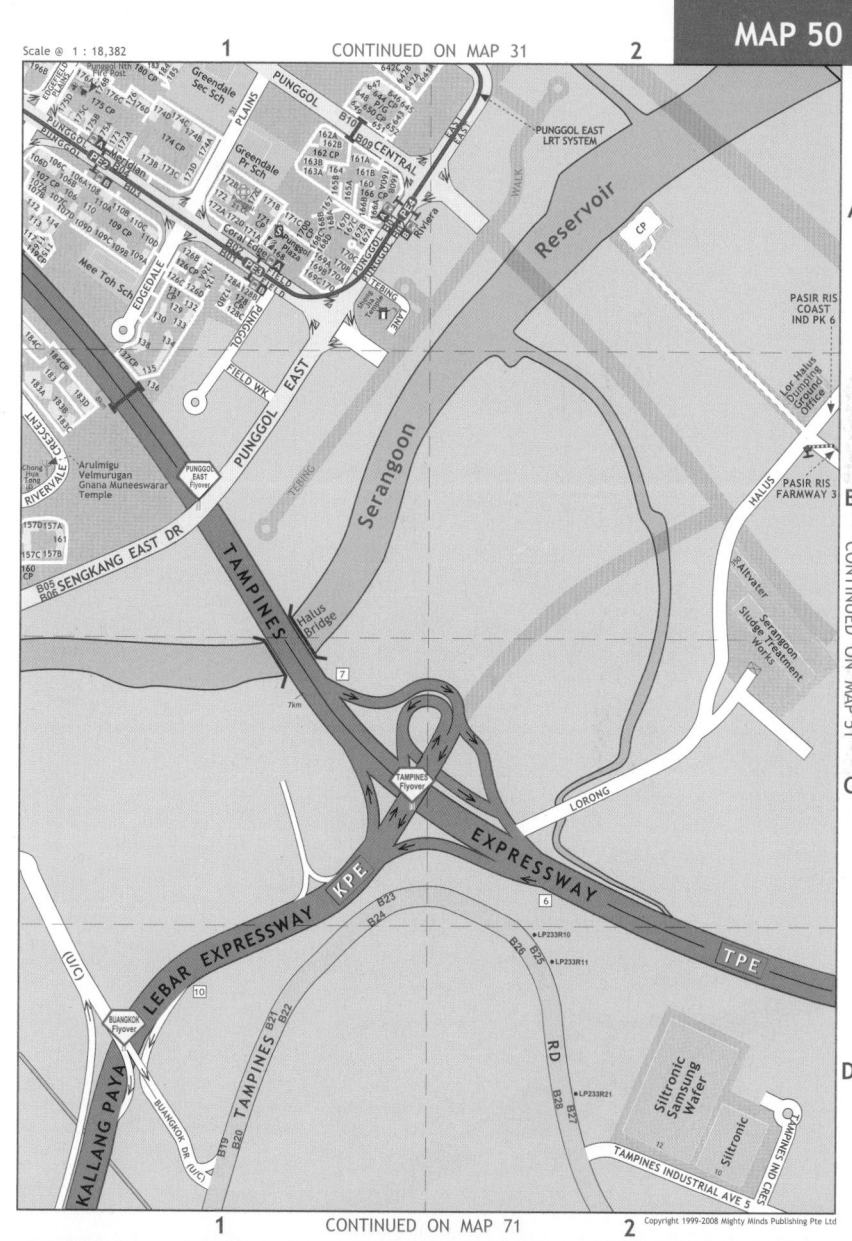

CONTINUED ON MAP 51

MAP 51

1   CONTINUED ON MAP 32   2

Scale @ 1 : 18,382

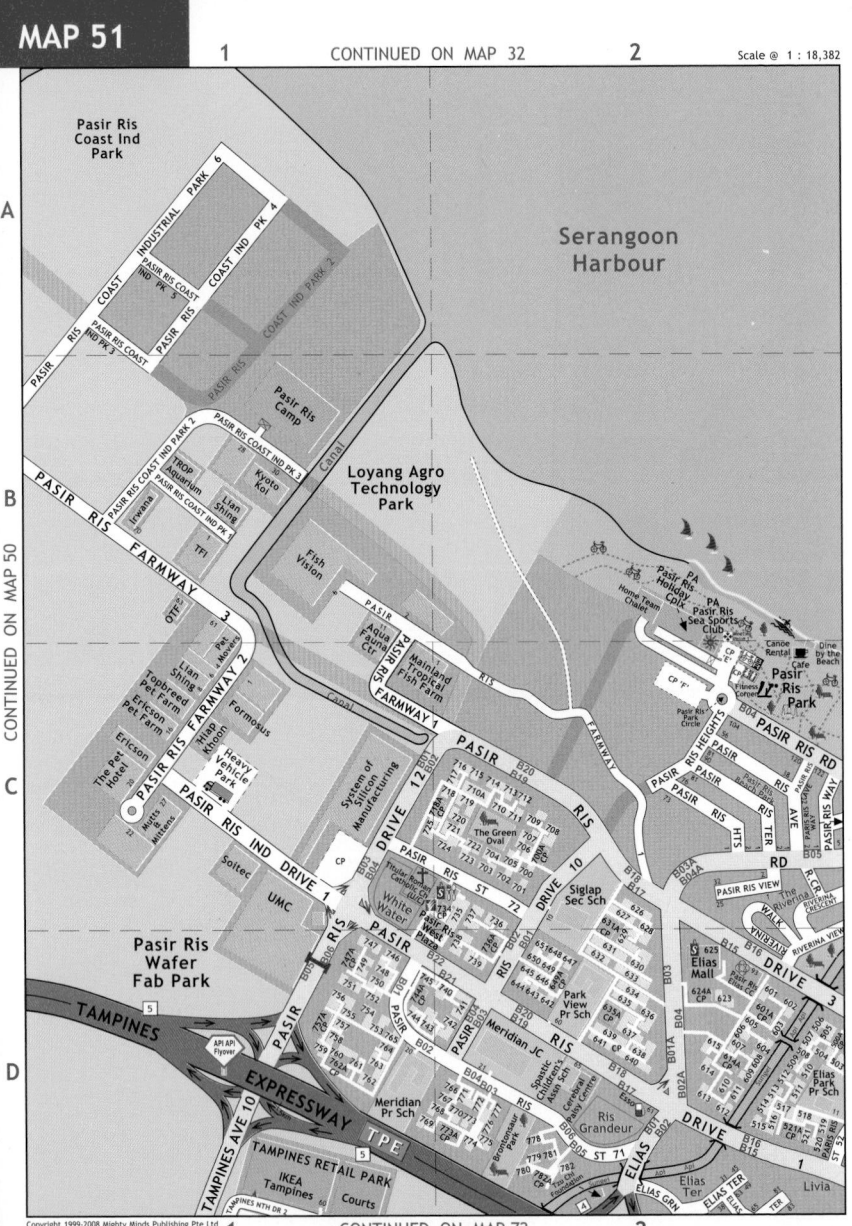

CONTINUED ON MAP 50

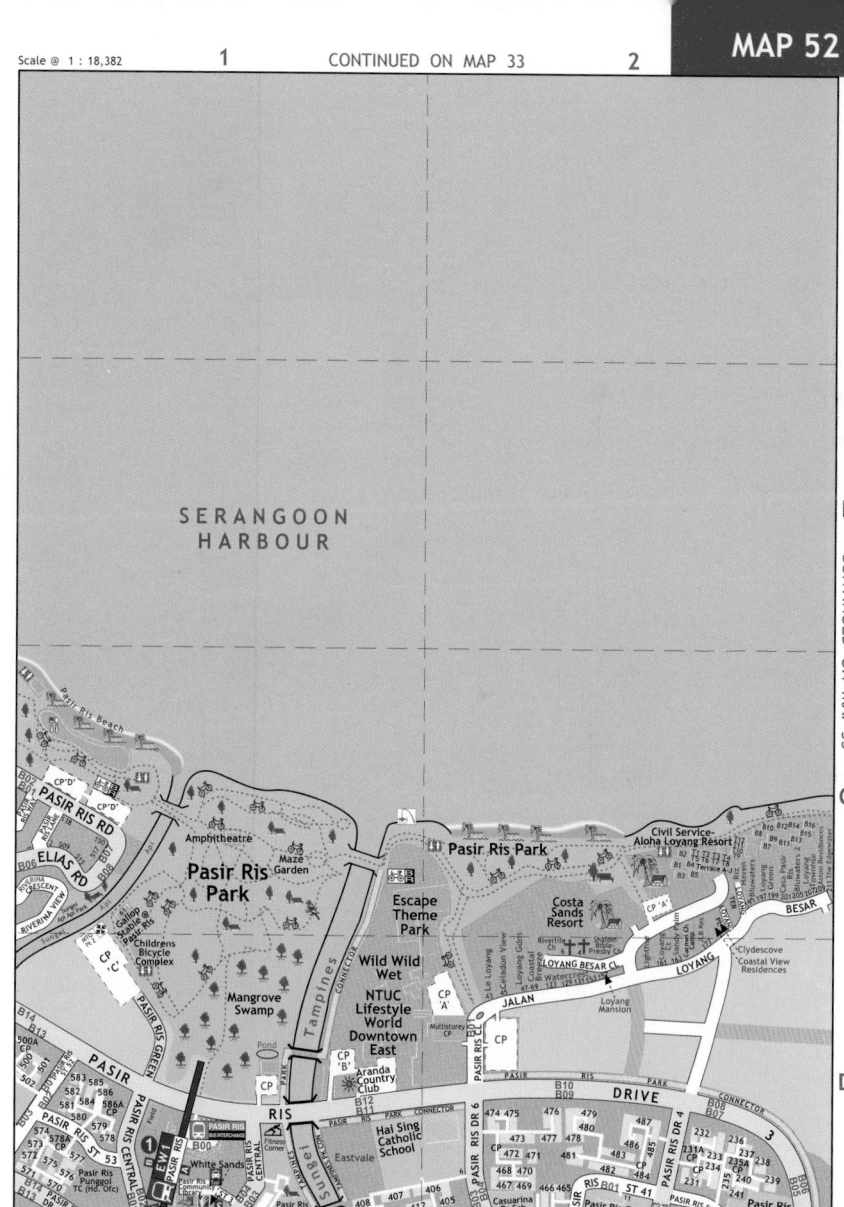

SERANGOON HARBOUR

Pasir Ris Beach

CP 'D'

PASIR RIS RD

ELIAS RD

RIVERINA VIEW

Amphitheatre

Maze Garden

Pasir Ris Park

Gallop Stable Pasir Ris

Childrens Bicycle Complex

CP 'C'

Mangrove Swamp

PASIR RIS GREEN

Pond

CP

Pasir Ris Park

Escape Theme Park

Wild Wild Wet

NTUC Lifestyle World Downtown East

CP 'A'

CP 'B'

Aranda Country Club

Multistorey CP

JALAN

Le Loyang

Celadon View

Loyang Gdn

Coastal

Waterfront

LOYANG BESAR CL

Costa Sands Resort

CP 'A'

Jade Terrace

LOYANG

Civil Service-Aloha Loyang Resort

Loyang BESAR

Loyang Mansion

Clydescove

Coastal View Residences

PASIR RIS

PASIR RIS CENTRAL

PASIR RIS ST 53

Pasir Ris Punggol

PASIR RIS DR 1

White Sands

PASIR RIS Community

PASIR RIS Town Park

Fitness Corner

PASIR RIS CENTRAL

Eastvale

Hai Sing Catholic School

Casuarina Pr Sch

RIS

DRIVE

PASIR RIS DR 6

PASIR RIS ST 41

Pasir Ris Crest Sec Sch

PASIR RIS DR 4

Pasir Ris Pr Sch

PARK CONNECTOR

CONNECTOR

MAP 53

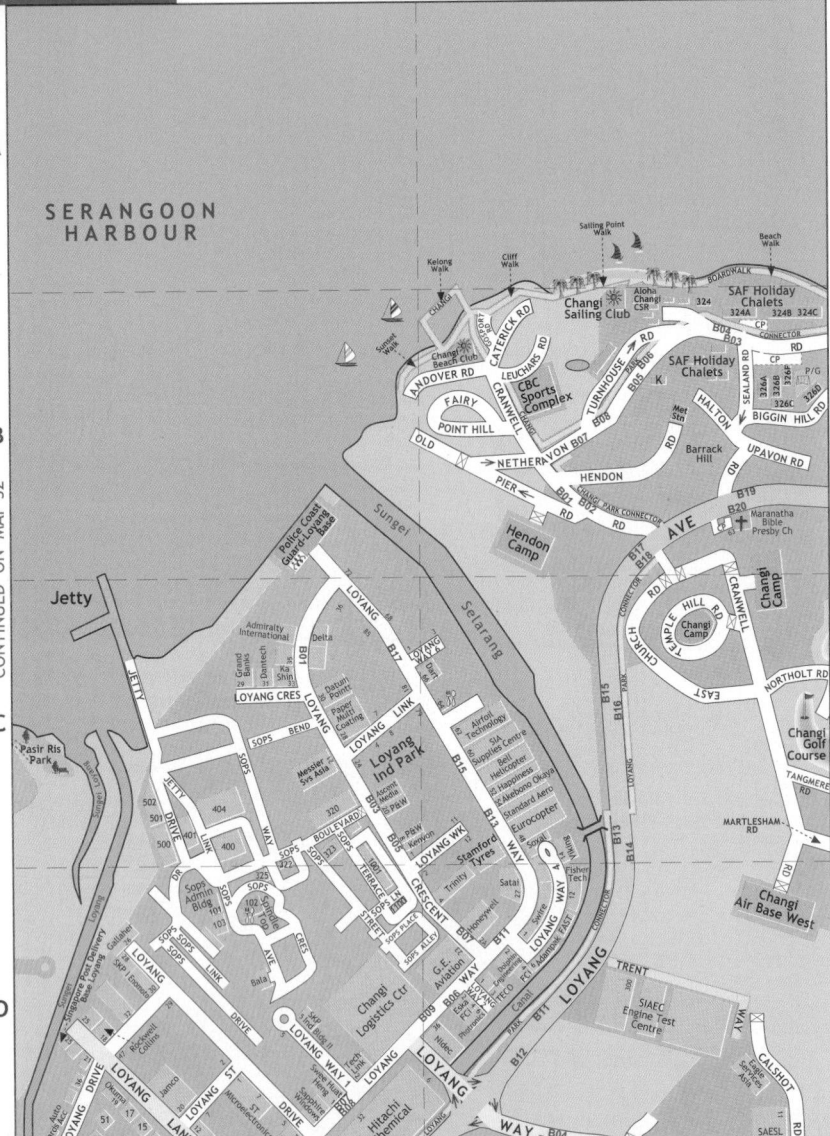

A

SERANGOON HARBOUR

Sailing Point Walk

Beach Walk

BOARDWALK

Kelong Walk

Cliff Walk

SAF Holiday Chalets

324   324A   324B 324C

Changi Sailing Club

Aloha Changi CSR

CP CONNECTOR

CATERICK RD

LEUCHARS RD

ANDOVER RD

Changi Beach Club

Sunset Walk

TURNHOUSE RD

B04

B03

SAF Holiday Chalets

SEALAND RD

P/G

CP

CBC Sports Complex

CRANWELL

B05 B06

B08

324A

326A

326B 326F

K

326C

FAIRY POINT HILL

HALTON

BIGGIN HILL RD

B

OLD

NETHERAVON B07

Met Stn

UPAVON RD

HENDON

Barrack Hill

B19

PIER

B01 B02

RD

CHANGI PARK CONNECTOR

B20

Maranatha Bible Presby Ch

Hendon Camp

AVE

B18

CRANWELL

Changi Camp

Jetty

Police Coast Guard Loyang Base

Sungei Selarang

LOYANG

B01

B17

Admiralty International

Grand Banks Damen

Delta

Datum Points

TEMPLE HILL RD

CHURCH CONNECTOR

Changi Camp

NORTHOLT RD

C

Pasir Ris Park

JETTY DRIVE

LOYANG CRES

SOPS BEND

Messier Srs Asia

LOYANG WAY

Airfoil Technology

LOYANG LINK

Loyang Ind Park

Ascent Media

SIA Supplies Centre

Bell Helicopter

Happiness

Akebono Okaya

Standard Aero

Eurocopter

EAST

Changi Golf Course

TANGMERE RD

MARTLESHAM RD

B13

B14

502

501

500

404

401

400

SOPS WAY

320

BOULEVARD

PBW

PBW Kenyon

LOYANG WK

Stamford Tyres

CRESCENT

Satai

Fishtec

LOYANG WAY

B15

Changi Air Base West

D

Sops Admin Bldg

SOPS LINK

105

102 SOPS 103

101

Bala

LOYANG CRES

TERRACE

CREST

SOPS ALLEY

G.E. Aviation

Trinity

Trent LOYANG WAY

PCS

B06 WAY

PICO

B11

TRENT

SIAEC Engine Test Centre

CALSHOT RD

LOYANG DRIVE

LOYANG LANE

LOYANG ST

DRIVE

Microelectronics

SITA

Changi Logistics Ctr

Rockwell Collins

Jamco

Hitachi Chemical

LOYANG WAY

B12

WAY B04

B03

SAESL

51

53

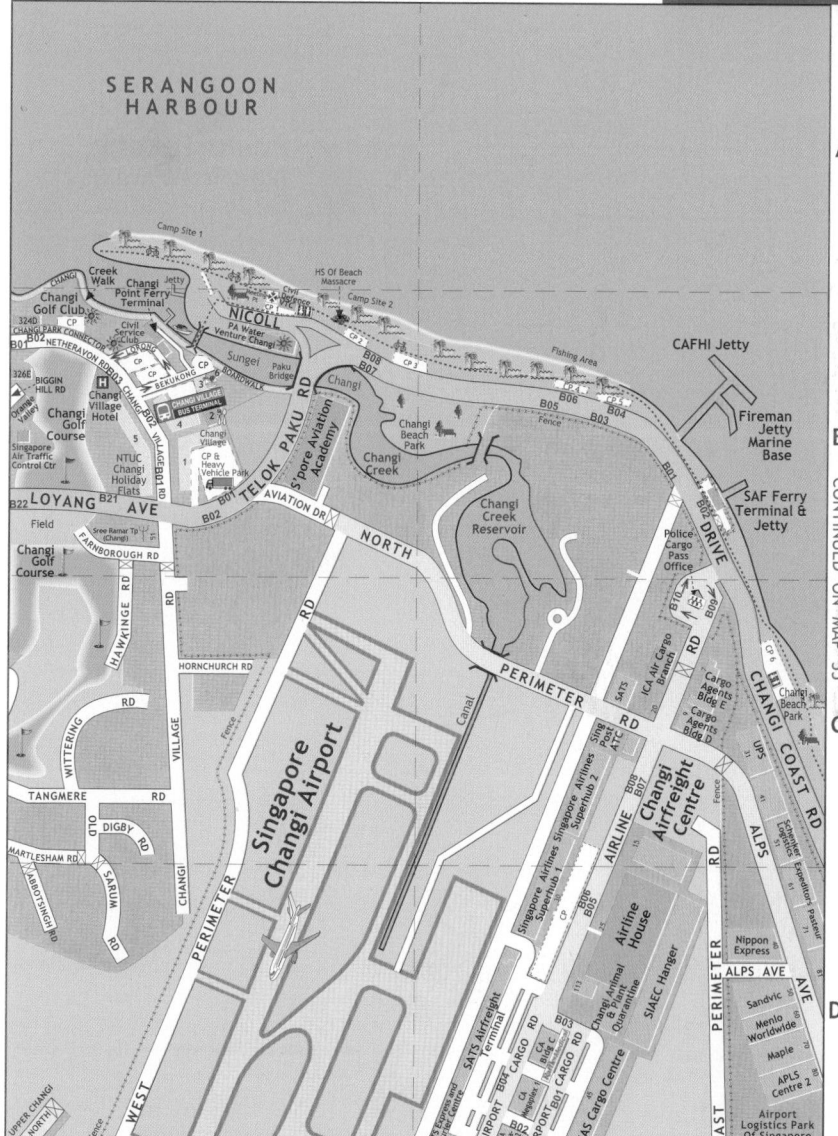

MAP 54

SERANGOON HARBOUR

A

Camp Site 1

Creek Walk

Changi Golf Club

Changi Point Ferry Terminal

Jetty

HS Of Beach Massacre

Camp Site 2

CAFHI Jetty

Civil Service Club

NICOLL

PA Water Venture Changi

CHANGI PARK CONNECTOR

NETHERAVON RD

BIGGIN HILL RD

Changi Golf Hotel

BEKUKONG

Sungei Paku

Paku Bridge

Fishing Area

Fireman Jetty Marine Base

Changi Golf Course

CHANGI VILLAGE BUS TERMINAL

S'pore Aviation Academy

Changi Beach Park

B

Singapore Air Traffic Control Ctr

NTUC Changi Holiday Flats

Changi Village

CP & Heavy Vehicle Park

Changi Creek

Fence

SAF Ferry Terminal & Jetty

LOYANG AVE

TELOK PAKU RD

AVIATION DR

Changi Creek Reservoir

DRIVE

CONTINUED ON MAP 55

Sree Ramar Tp (Changi)

Field

FARNBOROUGH RD

AVIATION DR NORTH

Police Cargo Pass Office

Changi Golf Course

HAWKINGE RD

HORNCHURCH RD

PERIMETER RD

ICA Air Cargo Branch

Cargo Agents Bldg E

CHANGI BEACH PARK

C

WITTERING RD

VILLAGE RD

CANAL

Sing Post ATC

SATS

Singapore Airlines Superhub 2

Cargo Agents Bldg D

UPS

CHANGI COAST RD

TANGMERE RD

Singapore Changi Airport

Airline House

Changi Airfreight Centre

ALPS

Schenker Logistics

OLD DIGBY RD

MARTLESHAM RD

SARUM RD

AIRBOTSINGH RD

PERIMETER RD

Singapore Airlines Superhub 1

AIRLINE RD

SIAEC Hanger

Changi Animal & Plant Quarantine

ALPS AVE

Nippon Express

Sandvic

Menlo Worldwide

D

UPPER CHANGI RD NORTH

WEST RD

Fence

SATS Airfreight Terminal

AIRPORT BLVD

AIRPORT CARGO RD

CIAS Cargo Centre

EAST PERIMETER RD

Maple

APLS Centre 2

Airport Logistics Park Of Singapore

MAP 55

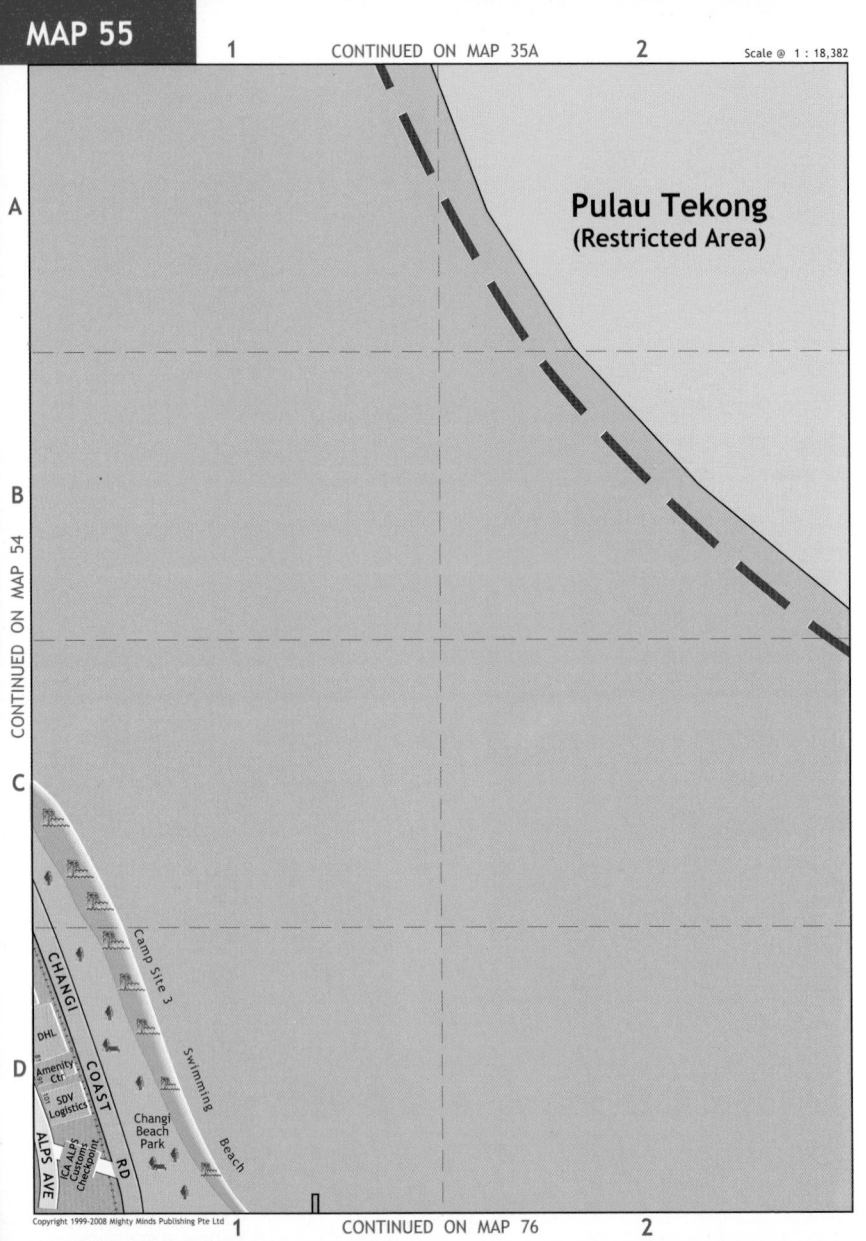

Pulau Tekong
(Restricted Area)

CHANGI COAST RD

Camp Site 3

Swimming Beach

DHL

Amenity Ctr

SDV Logistics

Changi Beach Park

ICA ALPS Customs Checkpoint

ALPS AVE

Wheel Alignment and Wheel Balancing

Do you know that Wheel Alignment and Wheel Balancing are two different things? Many people often get them confused.

Wheel Alignment

Wheel alignment consists of adjusting the angles of the wheel to get them perpendicular to the ground and parallel to each other or calibrated to 'point' straight ahead. Tyres can be nudged out of alignment by accidentally hitting them against objects such as potholes, curbs, parking blocks or a centre divider. Once a tyre is knocked out of alignment, its orientation on the vehicle is slightly off-centre. The degree of misalignment is not obvious to the human eye, but the effects will be noticeable.

The tell-tale signs of a vehicle with tyres that are out of alignment are:
- Rapid or uneven tyre wear.
- Pulling or drifting away from a straight course.
- Wandering on a straight level road.
- Spokes of the steering wheeling off to one side while driving on a straight course.

Wheel alignment helps a vehicle track straight when driving along a straight level road and achieves maximum tyre life.

Wheel Balancing

Wheel Balancing allows the tyres and wheels to spin without causing vibrations. This is achieved by checking for heavy spots on the wheel-tyre combination and compensating for it by attaching a measured lead weight on the opposite side of the wheel from where the heavy spot is.

A tyre that is out of balance will have the following symptoms:
- Vibrations in the steering wheel at certain expressway speeds.
- Vibrations in the seat or floorboard at certain expressway speeds.
- A wear pattern that is scalloped or cupped.

MAP 56

1   2   Scale @ 1 : 18,382

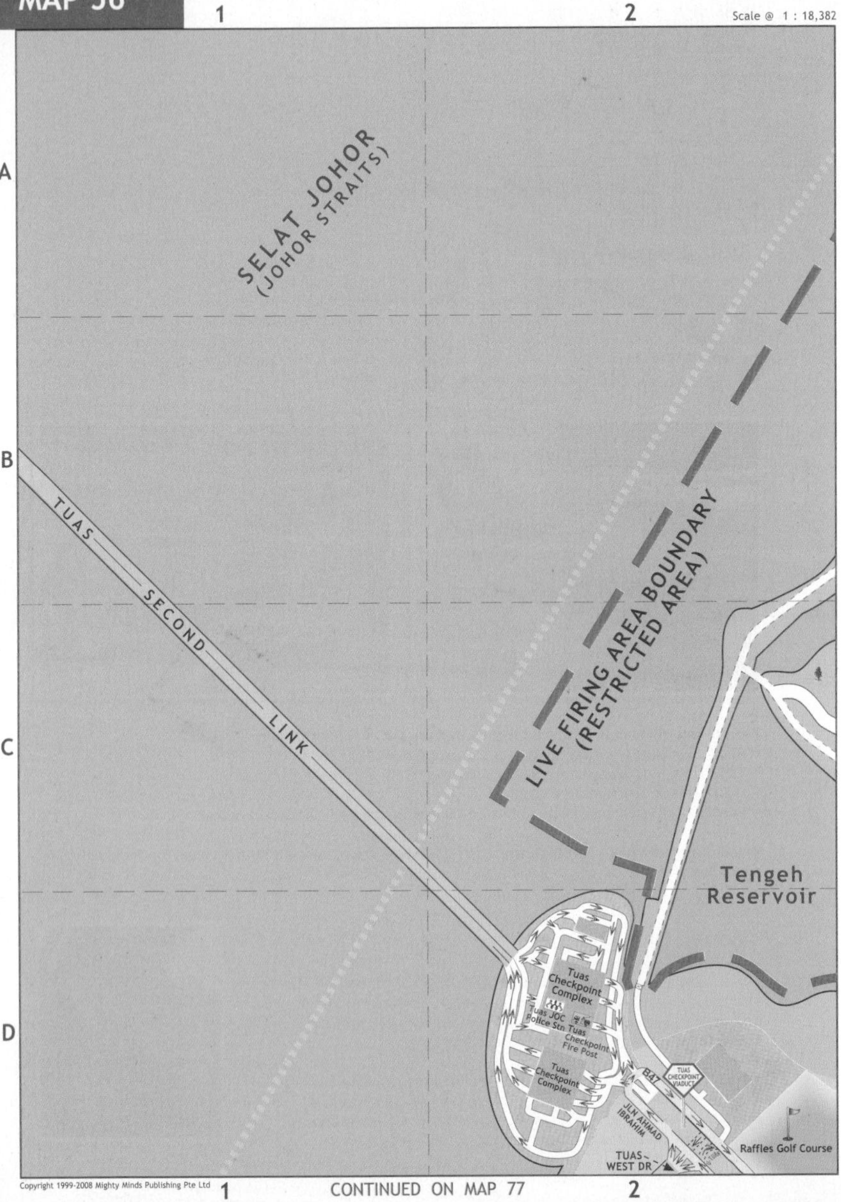

A

SELAT JOHOR
(JOHOR STRAITS)

B

TUAS SECOND LINK

LIVE FIRING AREA BOUNDARY
(RESTRICTED AREA)

C

Tengeh
Reservoir

D

Tuas
Checkpoint
Complex

Tuas JGC
Police Stn Tuas
Checkpoint
Fire Post

Tuas
Checkpoint
Complex

B47

TUAS
CHECKPOINT
INWARD

JLN AHMAD
IBRAHIM

Raffles Golf Course

TUAS
WEST DR

CONTINUED ON MAP 77

1   2

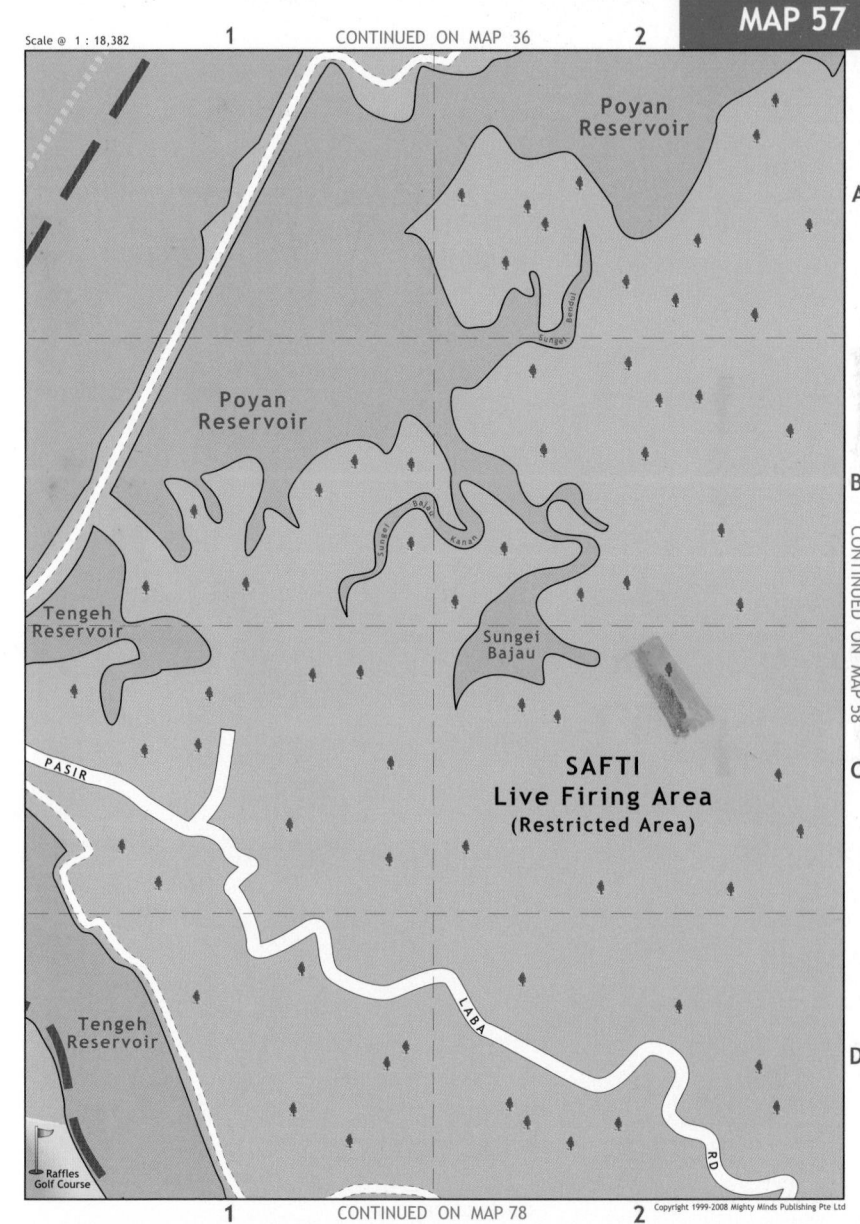

A

CONTINUED ON MAP 58

B

C

D

Poyan
Reservoir

Poyan
Reservoir

Sungei Bedok

Tengeh
Reservoir

Sungei Bajau Kanan

Sungei Bajau

PASIR

SAFTI
Live Firing Area
(Restricted Area)

LABA

Tengeh
Reservoir

RD

Raffles
Golf Course

MAP 58

1 CONTINUED ON MAP 37 2

Scale @ 1 : 18,382

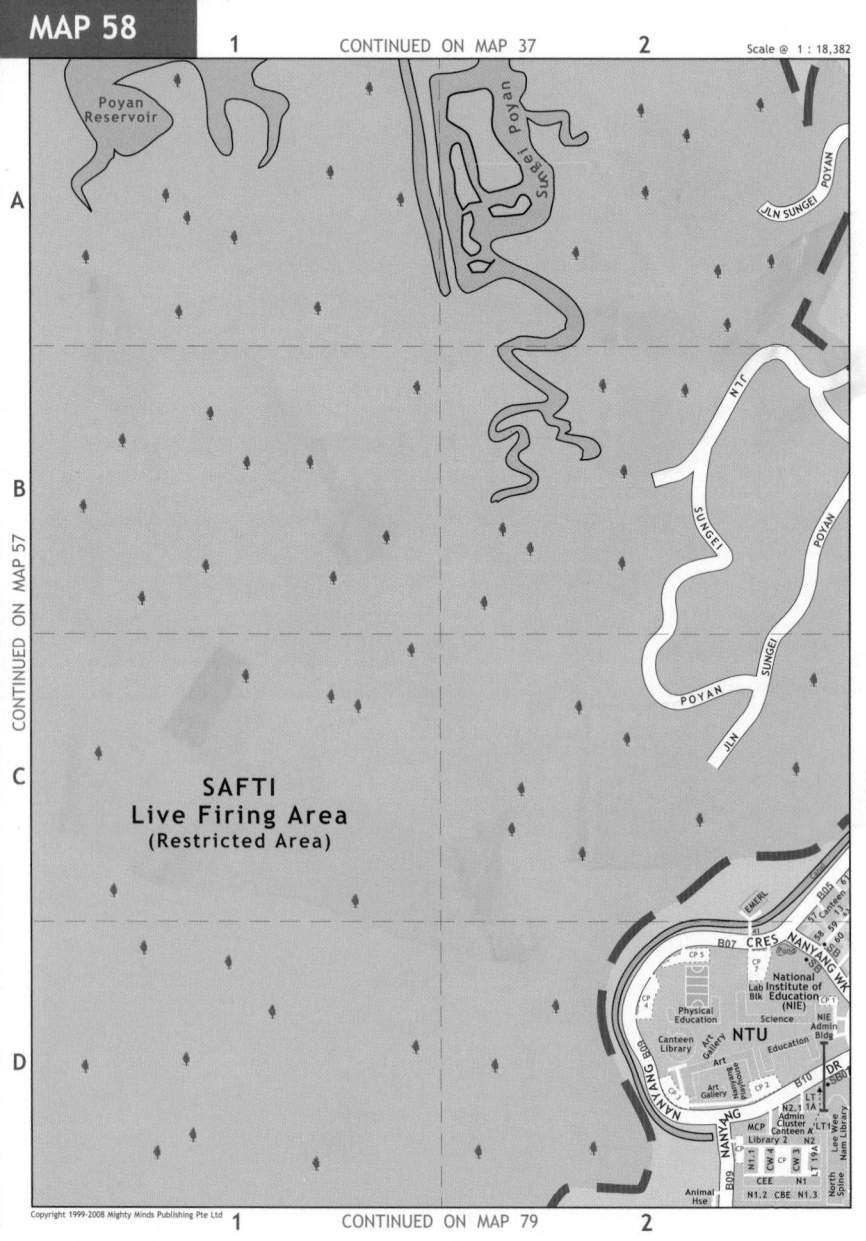

Poyan
Reservoir

Sungei Poyan

JLN SUNGEI POYAN

NTU

SUNGEI

POYAN

JLN SUNGEI POYAN

**SAFTI
Live Firing Area
(Restricted Area)**

NANYANG WK

CRES

NANYANG WK

National
Institute of
Education
(NIE)

Lab
Blk

Science

NIE
Admin
Bldg

Physical
Education

Education

Canteen
Library

NTU

Art
Gallery

Art

Nanyang
Playhouse

Art
Gallery

NANYANG DR

NANYANG DR

NANYANG

N2.1

Admin
Cluster
Canteen A

LT1

Lee Wee Nam Library

MCP

Library 2

CP

N1.1

N2

LT1

CW 4

CP 3

N1

CEE

N1

North
Spine

Animal
Hse

N1.2

CBE

N1.3

EMERL

B07

CP 5

CP
7

CP 1

CP
4

B10

B09

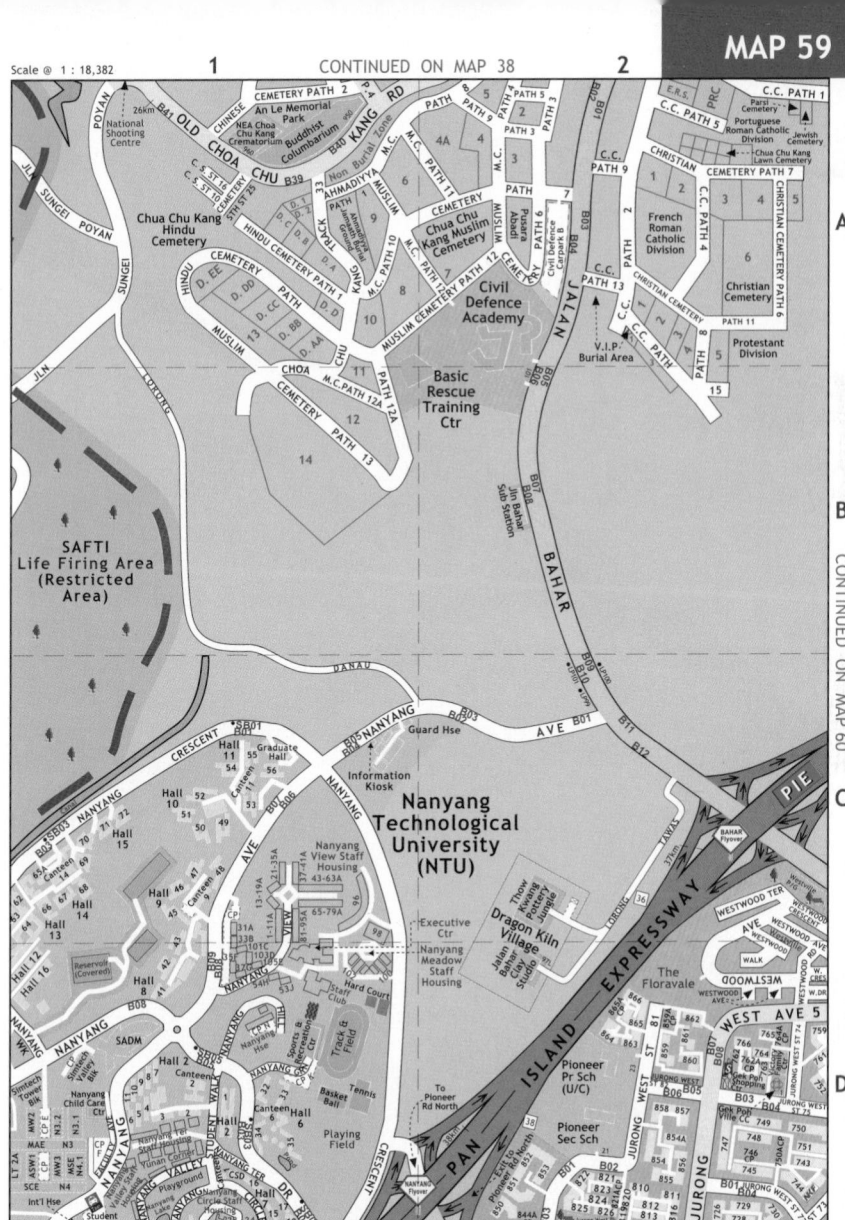

MAP 59

Scale @ 1 : 18,382

CONTINUED ON MAP 38

SAFTI
Life Firing Area
(Restricted
Area)

National Shooting
Centre

Chua Chu Kang
Hindu Cemetery

An Le Memorial
Park

REA Choa
Chu Kang
Crematorium

Buddhist
Columbarium

Chua Chu Kang
Muslim Cemetery

Civil Defence
Academy

Basic
Rescue
Training
Ctr

V.I.P.
Burial Area

French
Roman
Catholic
Division

Christian
Cemetery

Protestant
Division

Portuguese
Roman Catholic
Division

Parsi
Cemetery

Jewish
Cemetery

Chua Chu Kang
Lawn Cemetery

Jin Bahar
Sub Station

Nanyang
Technological
University
(NTU)

Guard Hse

Information
Kiosk

Graduate
Hall

Hall
11

Hall
10

Hall
15

Canteen
14

Hall
14

Hall
13

Hall
16

Hall
12

Hall
8

Reservoir
(Covered)

SADM

Hall 2

Canteen

Nanyang
Child Care
Ctr

Hall 1

Hall 6

Canteen

Playing
Field

Basket
Ball

Tennis

Track &
Field

Hard Court

Staff
Club

Sports &
Recreation
Ctr

Nanyang
Hse

Nanyang
View Staff
Housing

Nanyang
Meadow Staff
Housing

Executive
Ctr

Thow
Kwang
Pottery
Jungle

Dragon Kiln
Village

Nanyang
Bahar
Studio

To
Pioneer
Rd North

Pioneer
Pr Sch
(U/C)

Pioneer
Sec Sch

The Floravale

BAHAR
Flyover

PAN ISLAND EXPRESSWAY

PIE

WESTWOOD TER

WEST AVE 5

JURONG WEST ST 5

JURONG

Yunan Garden

Int'l Hse

Student
Svc Ctr

Simtech
Tower
Blk

NANYANG AVE

JALAN BAHAR

MAP 60

CONTINUED ON MAP 39

Scale @ 1 : 18,382

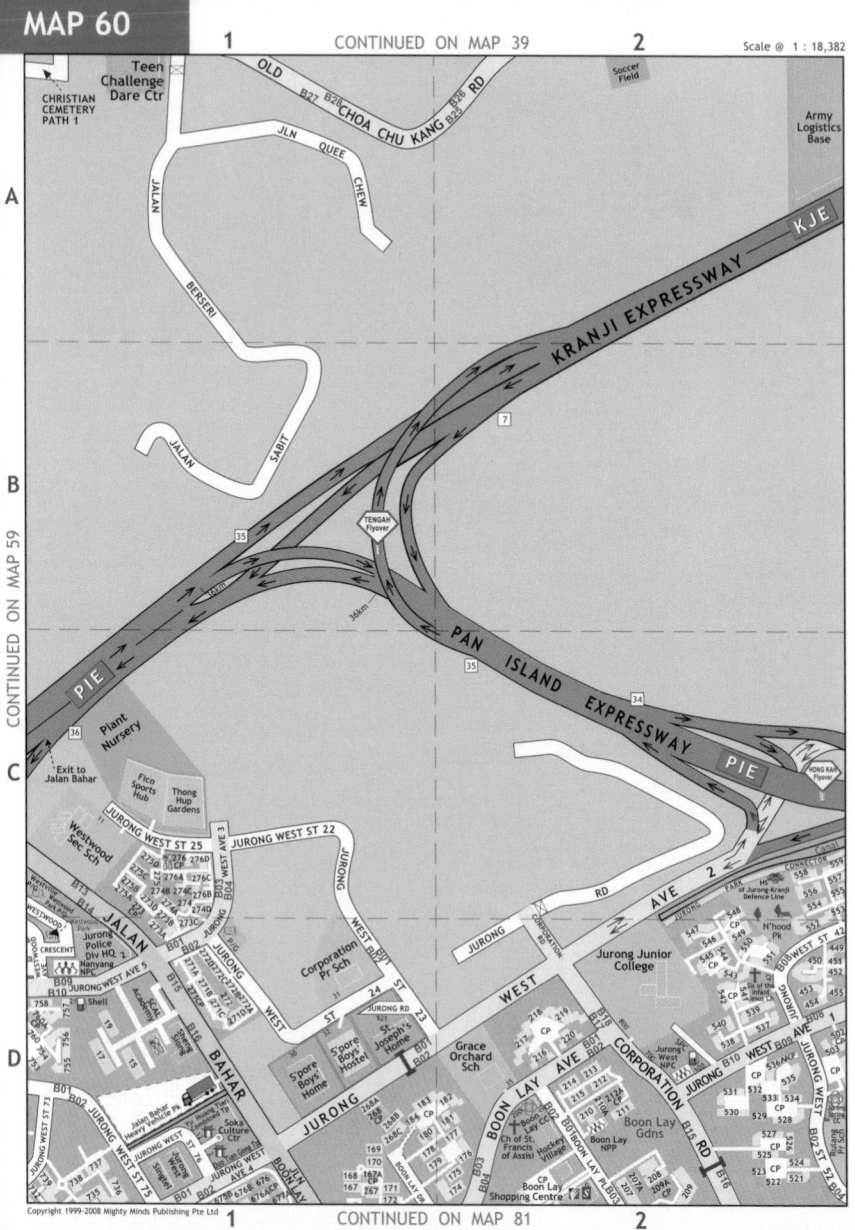

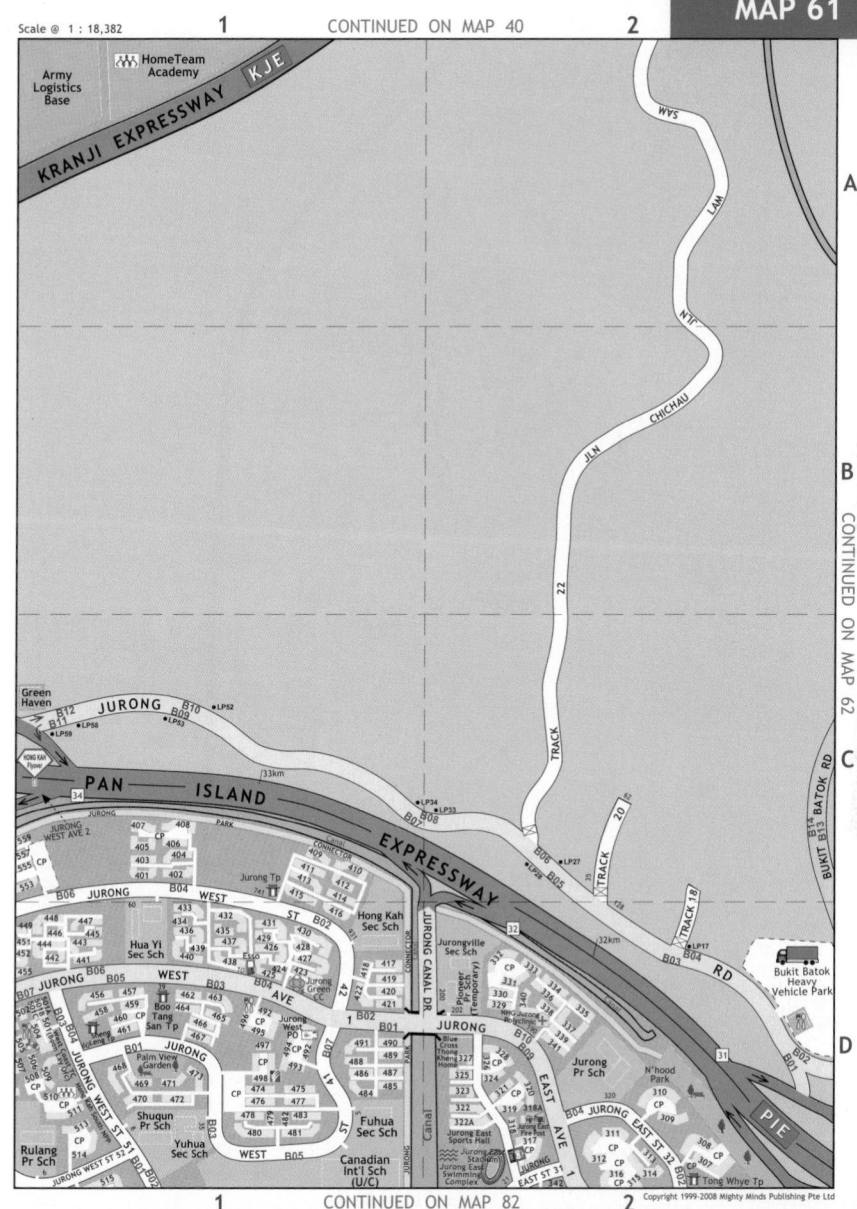

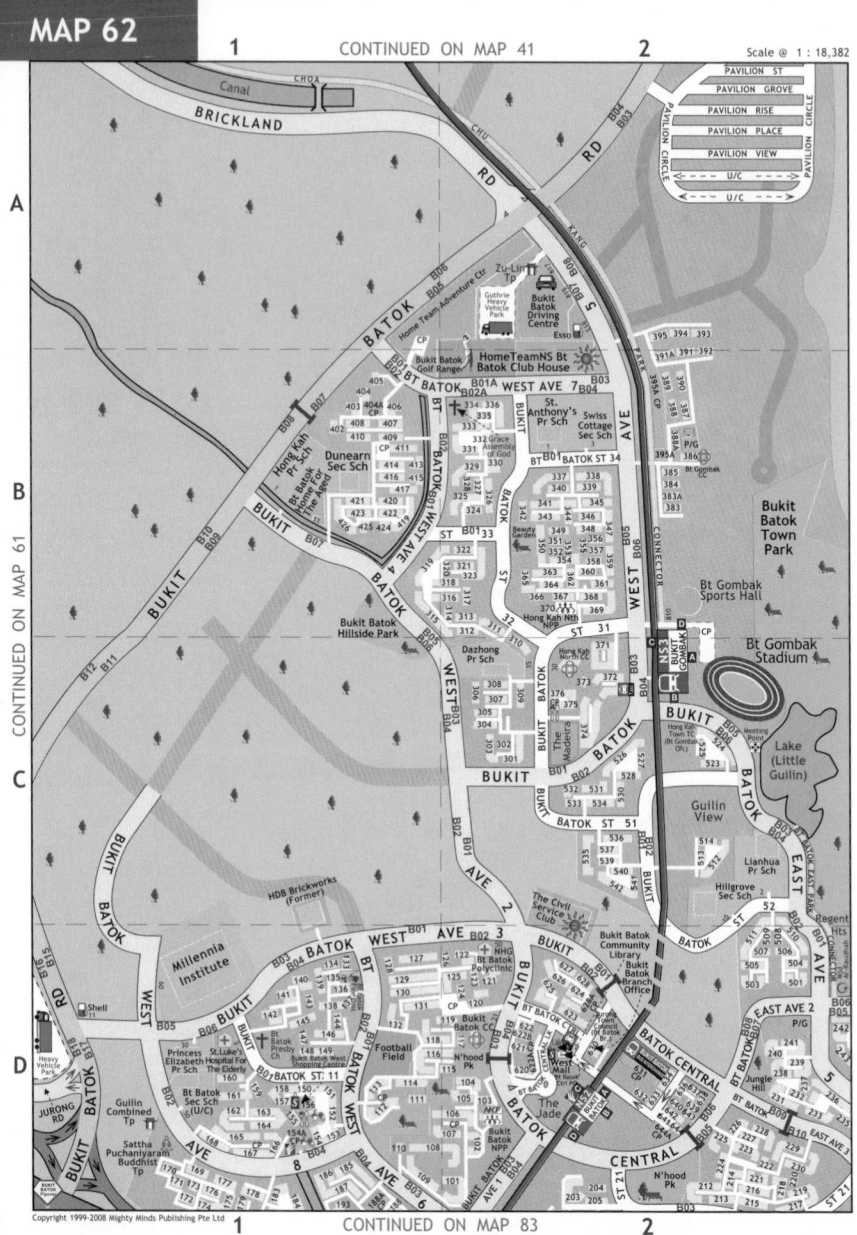

MAP 62

1   CONTINUED ON MAP 41   2

Scale @ 1 : 18,382

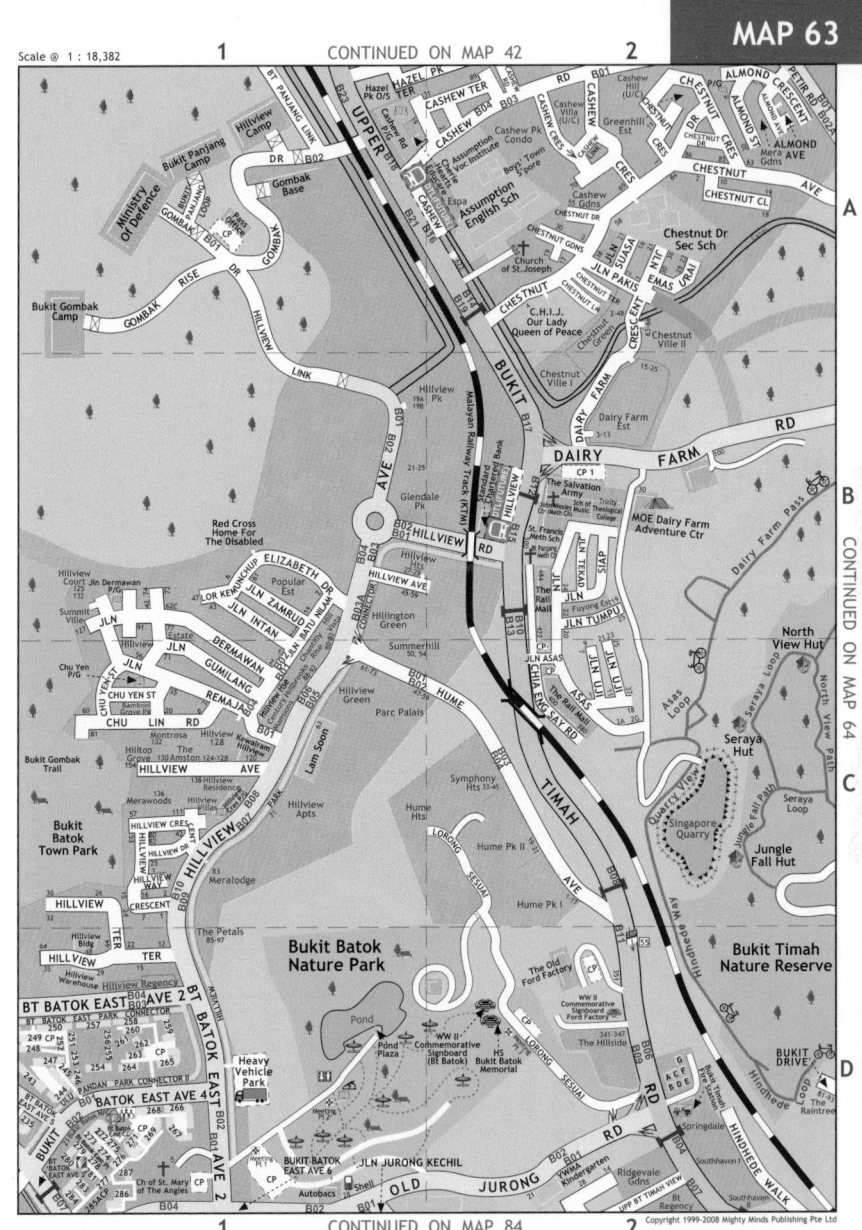

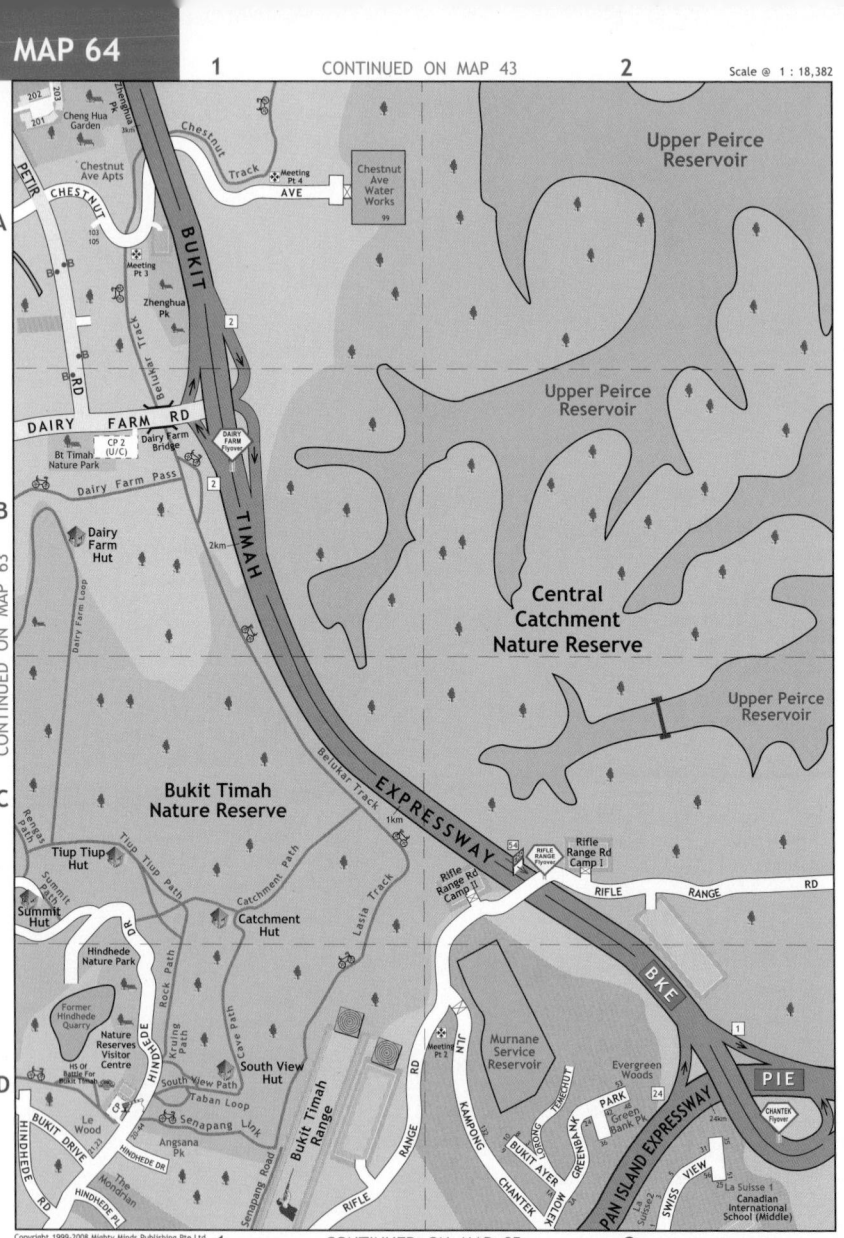

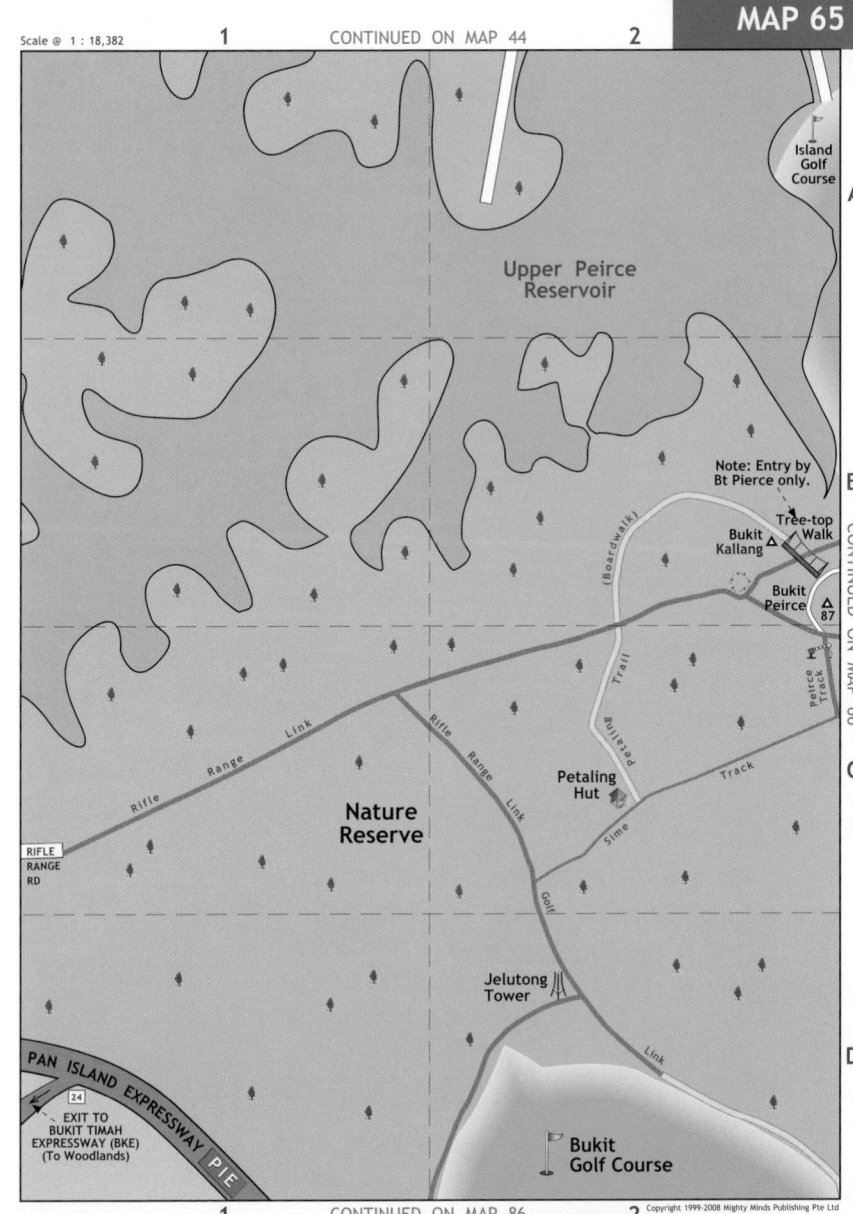

MAP 65

Scale @ 1 : 18,382   1   CONTINUED ON MAP 44   2

Island Golf Course

Upper Peirce Reservoir

Note: Entry by Bt Pierce only.

(Boardwalk)

Tree-top Walk

Bukit Kallang △

Bukit Peirce △ 87

Rifle Range Link

Rifle Range Link

Trail

Petaling Trail

Peirce Track

Petaling Hut

Sime Track

Nature Reserve

Rifle

RIFLE RANGE RD

Golf Link

Jelutong Tower

Link

Bukit Golf Course

PAN ISLAND EXPRESSWAY PIE

24

EXIT TO BUKIT TIMAH EXPRESSWAY (BKE) (To Woodlands)

MAP 66

CONTINUED ON MAP 45

Scale @ 1 : 18,382

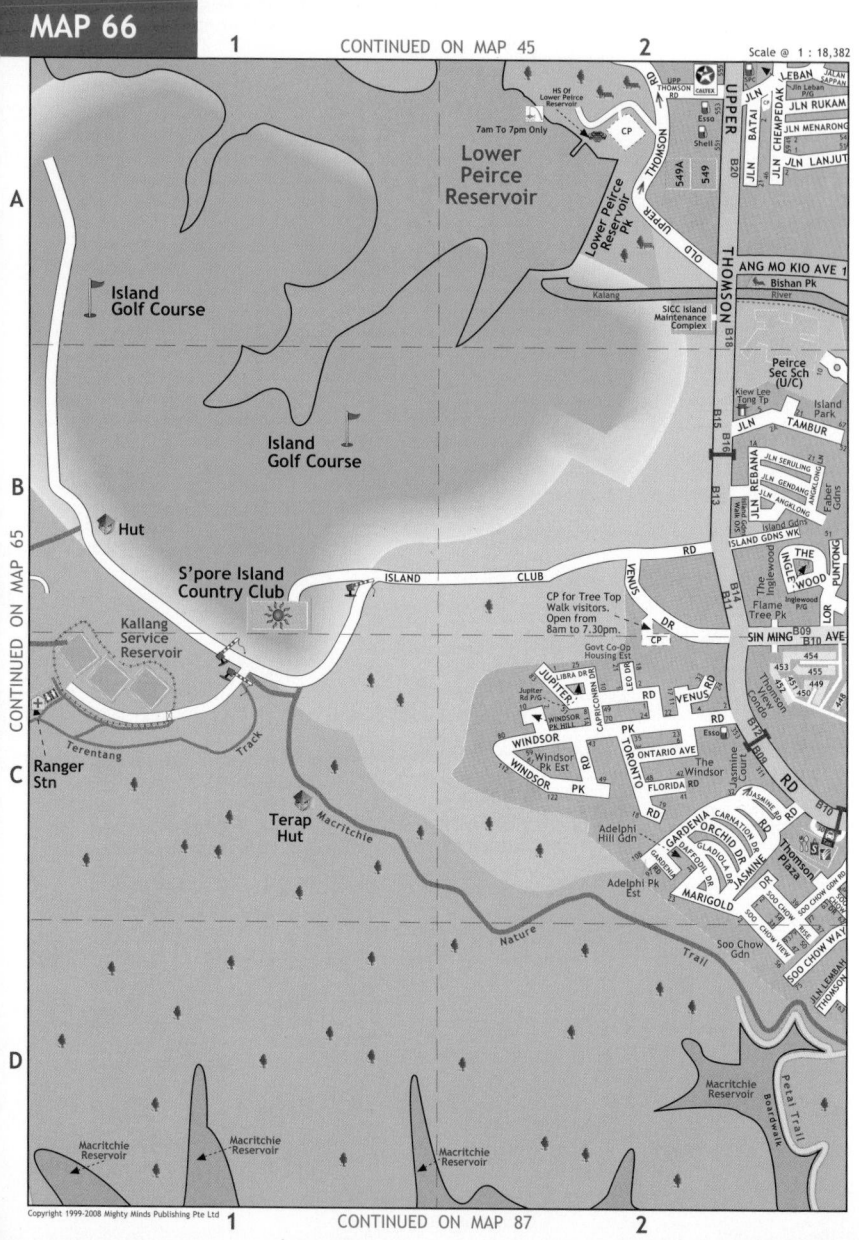

MAP 67

Scale @ 1 : 18,382

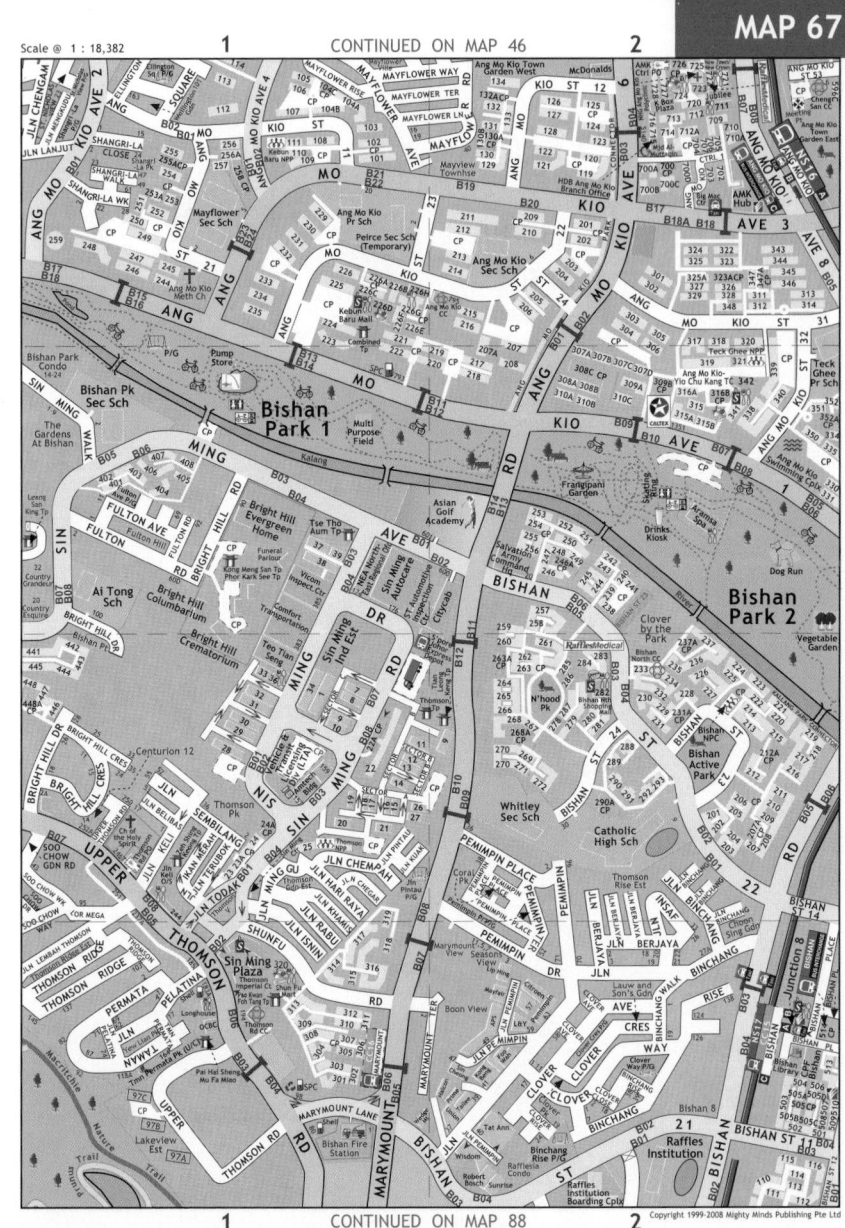

Bishan Park 1

Bishan Park 2

Copyright 1999-2008 Mighty Minds Publishing Pte Ltd

MAP 68

CONTINUED ON MAP 47

Scale @ 1 : 18,382

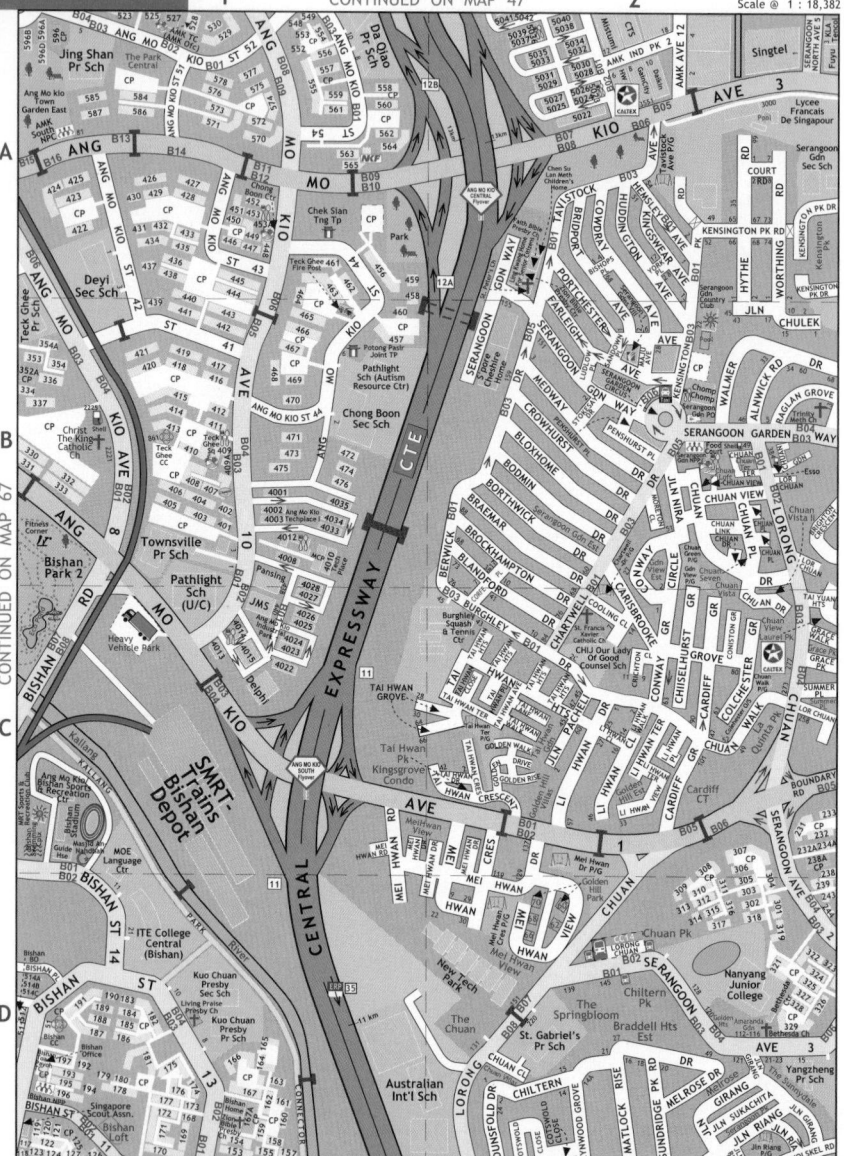

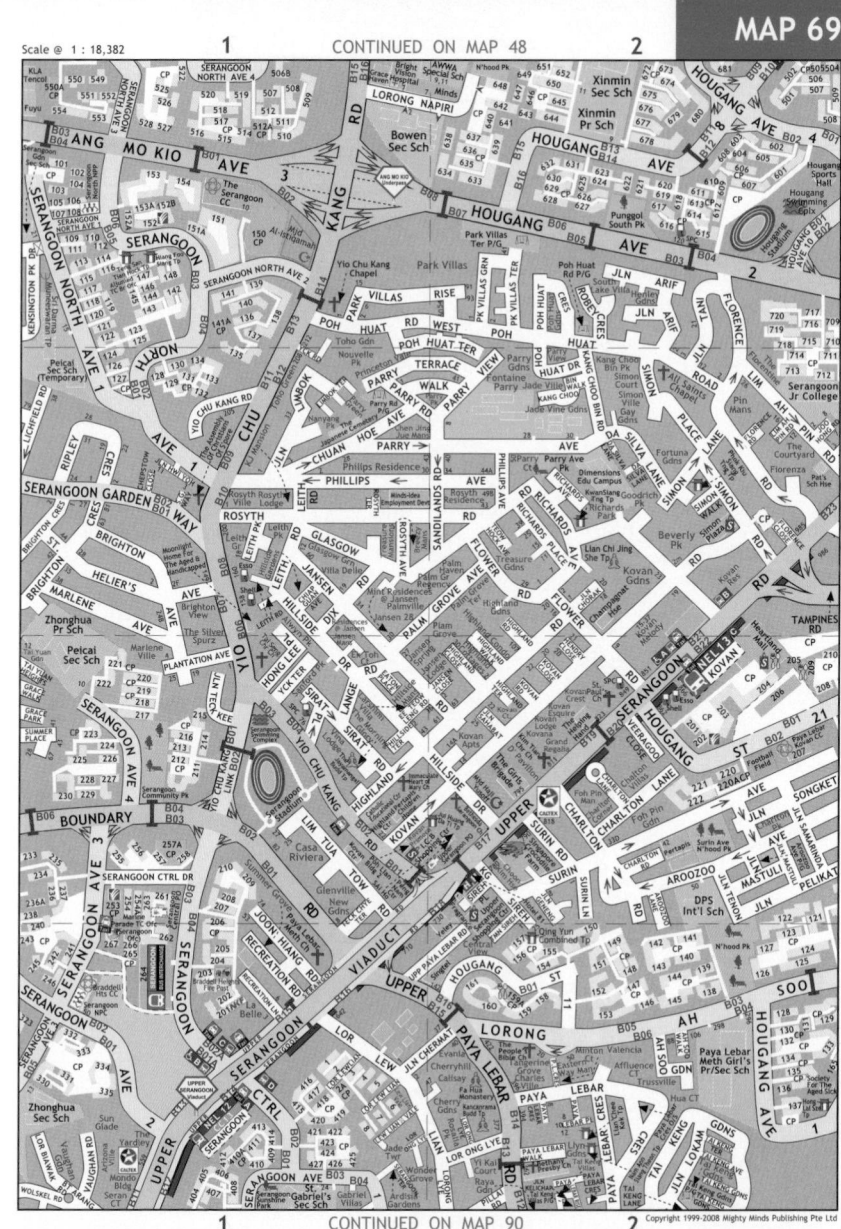

MAP 69

Scale @ 1 : 18,382

CONTINUED ON MAP 48

CONTINUED ON MAP 70

CONTINUED ON MAP 90

MAP 70

CONTINUED ON MAP 49

Scale @ 1 : 18,382

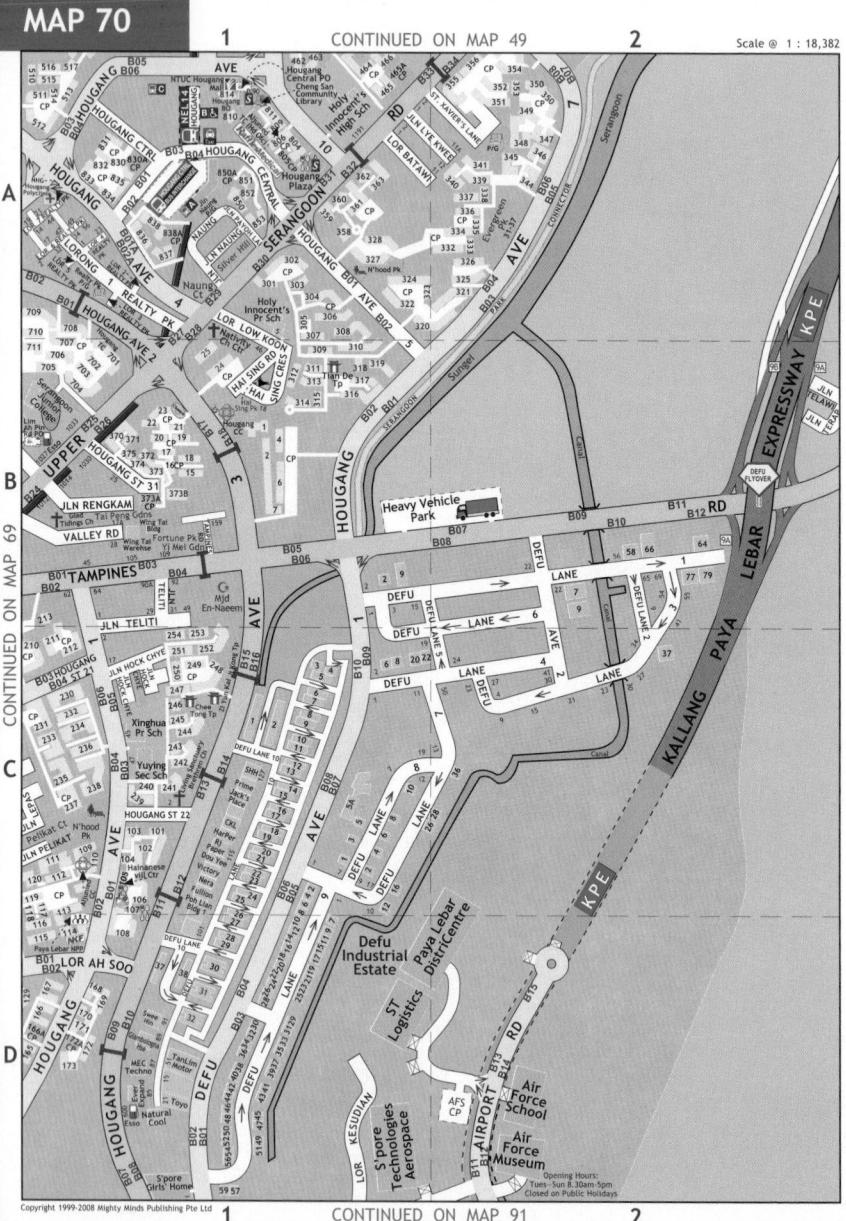

CONTINUED ON MAP 50

MAP 71

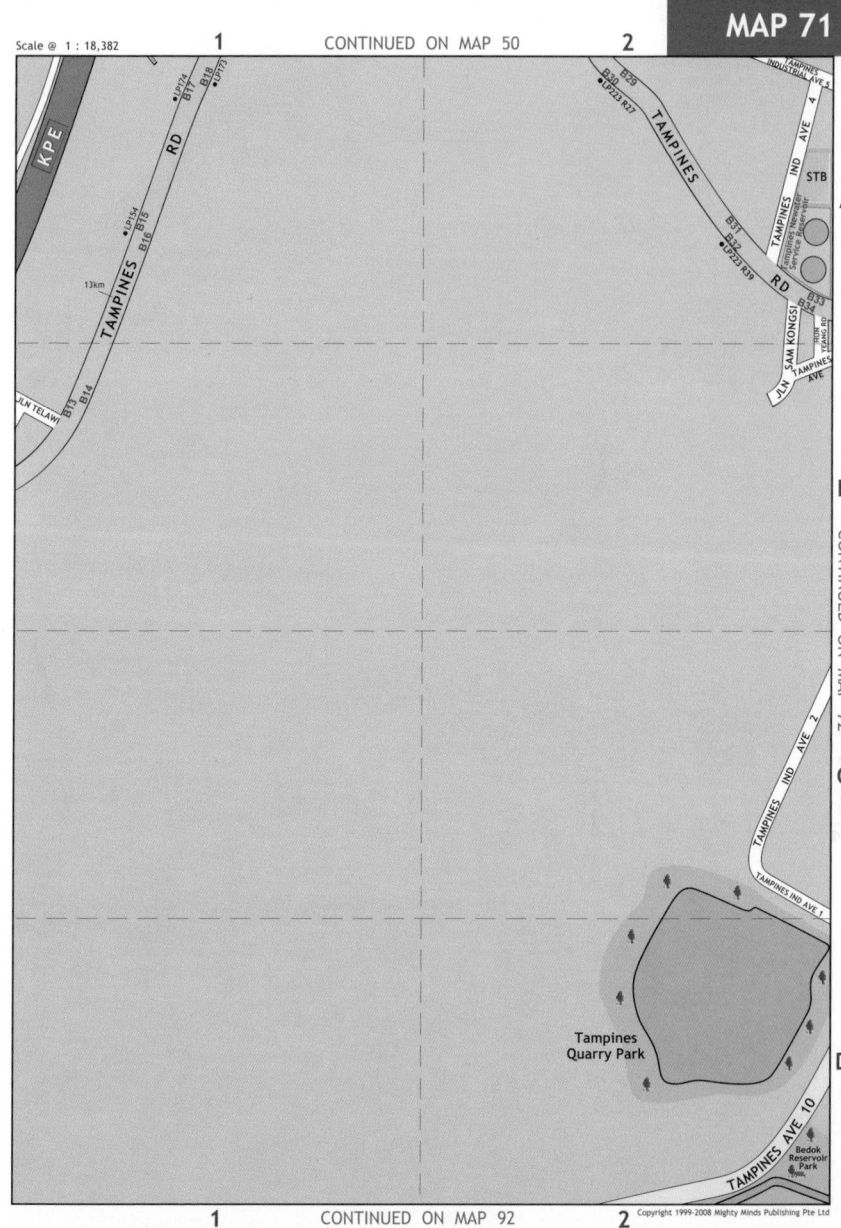

CONTINUED ON MAP 72

Tampines
Quarry Park

CONTINUED ON MAP 92

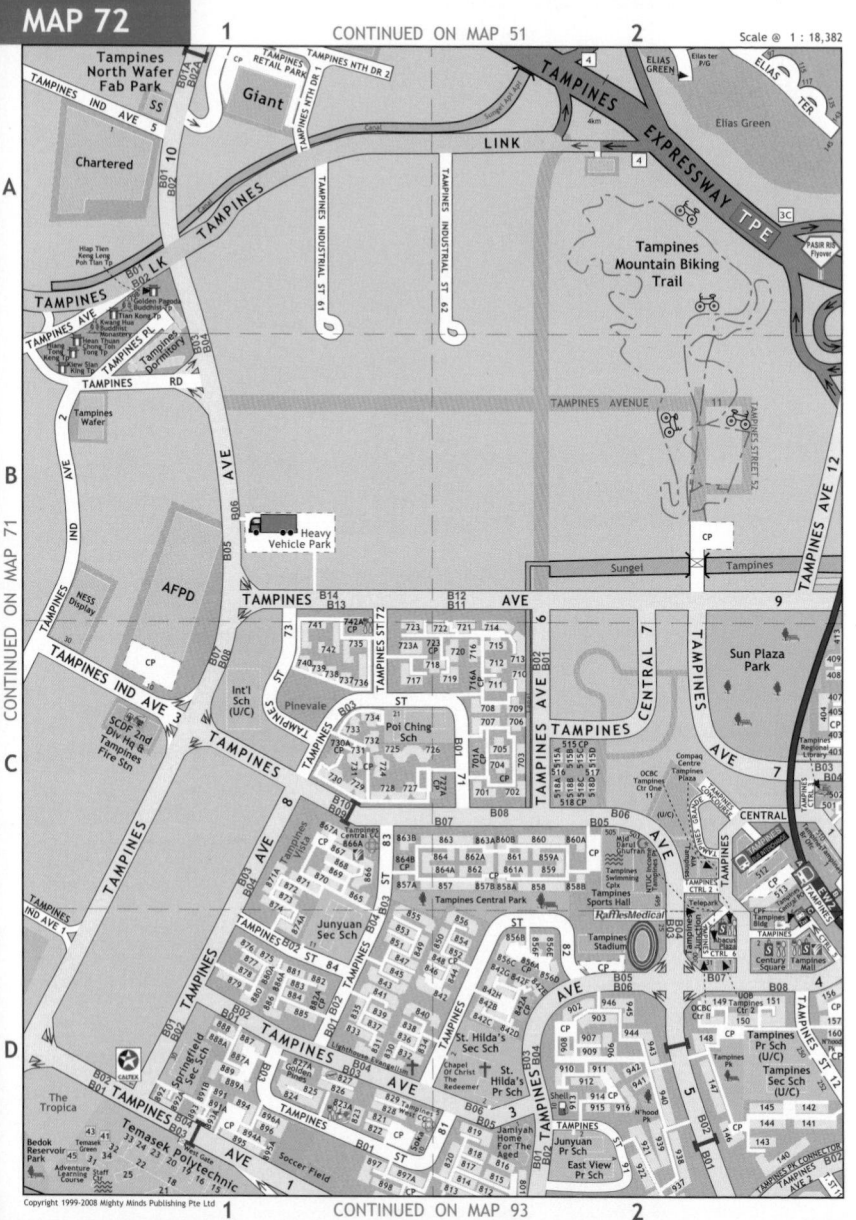

MAP 72

1
CONTINUED ON MAP 51
2

Scale @ 1 : 18,382

CONTINUED ON MAP 71

CONTINUED ON MAP 71

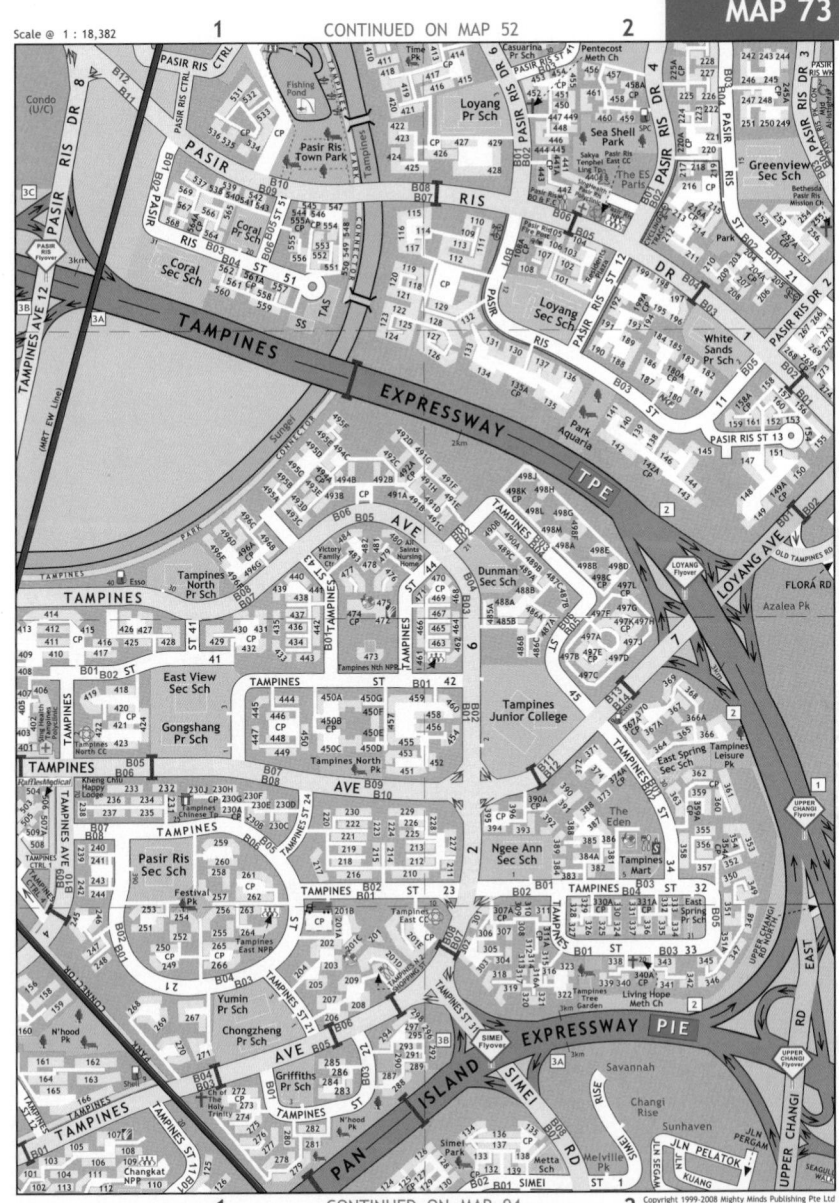

MAP 73

Scale @ 1 : 18,382

CONTINUED ON MAP 74

CONTINUED ON MAP 94

MAP 74

Scale @ 1 : 18,382

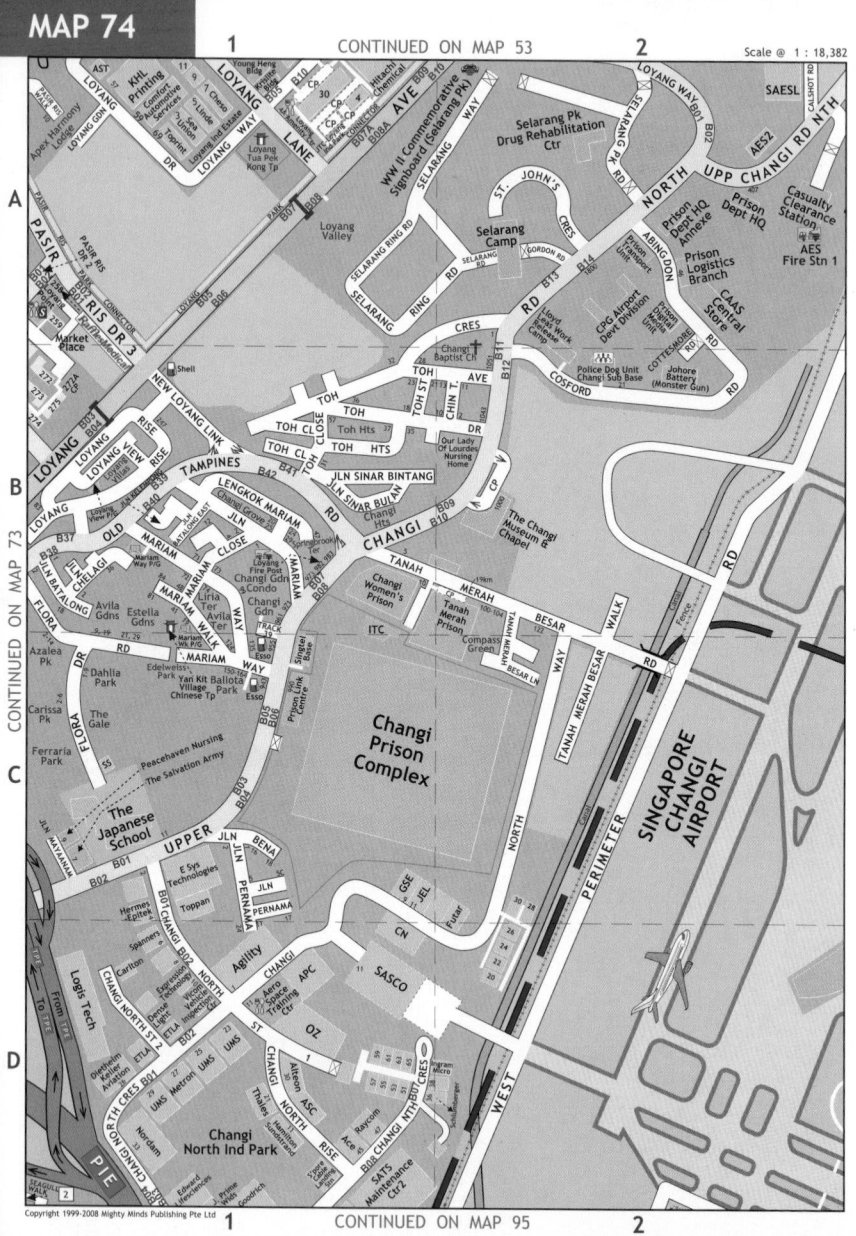

MAP 75

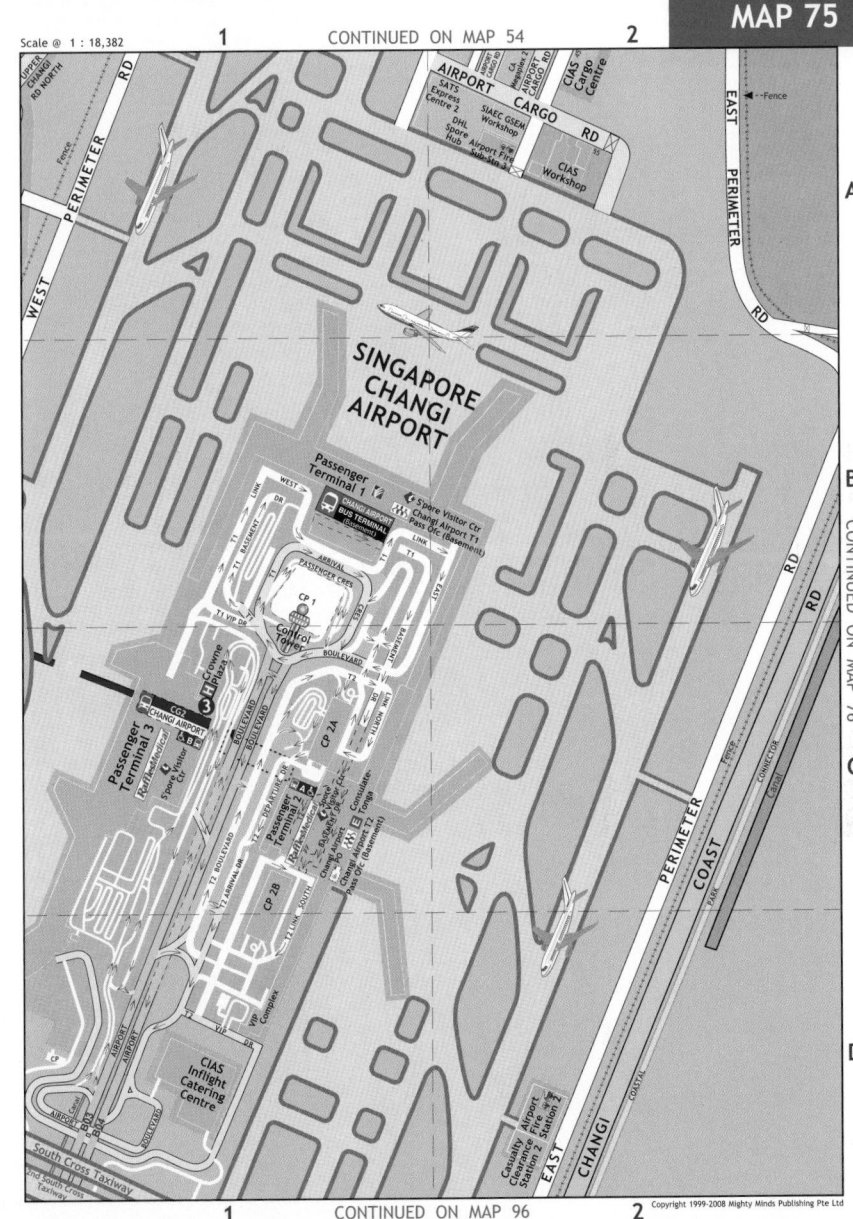

Scale @ 1 : 18,382

A

B

CONTINUED ON MAP 76

C

D

SINGAPORE
CHANGI
AIRPORT

AIRPORT CARGO

CIAS Cargo Centre

SATS Express Centre 2

SIAEC GSEM Workshop

DHL Spare Hub

Airport Fire Sub-Sta 6

CIAS Workshop

Passenger Terminal 1

Spore Visitor Ctr
Changi Airport T1
Pass Ofc (Basement)

CP 1

Control Tower

Crowne Plaza

CHANGI AIRPORT

Passenger Terminal 3

Spore Visitor Ctr

CP 2A

Passenger Terminal 2

Changi Airport T2
Pass Ofc (Basement)

CP 2B

CIAS Inflight Catering Centre

VIP Complex

Casualty Clearance Station 2

Airport Fire Station 1

EAST PERIMETER RD

WEST PERIMETER

EAST CHANGI

PERIMETER RD

COAST RD

COASTAL

MAP 76

CONTINUED ON MAP 55

Scale @ 1 : 18,382

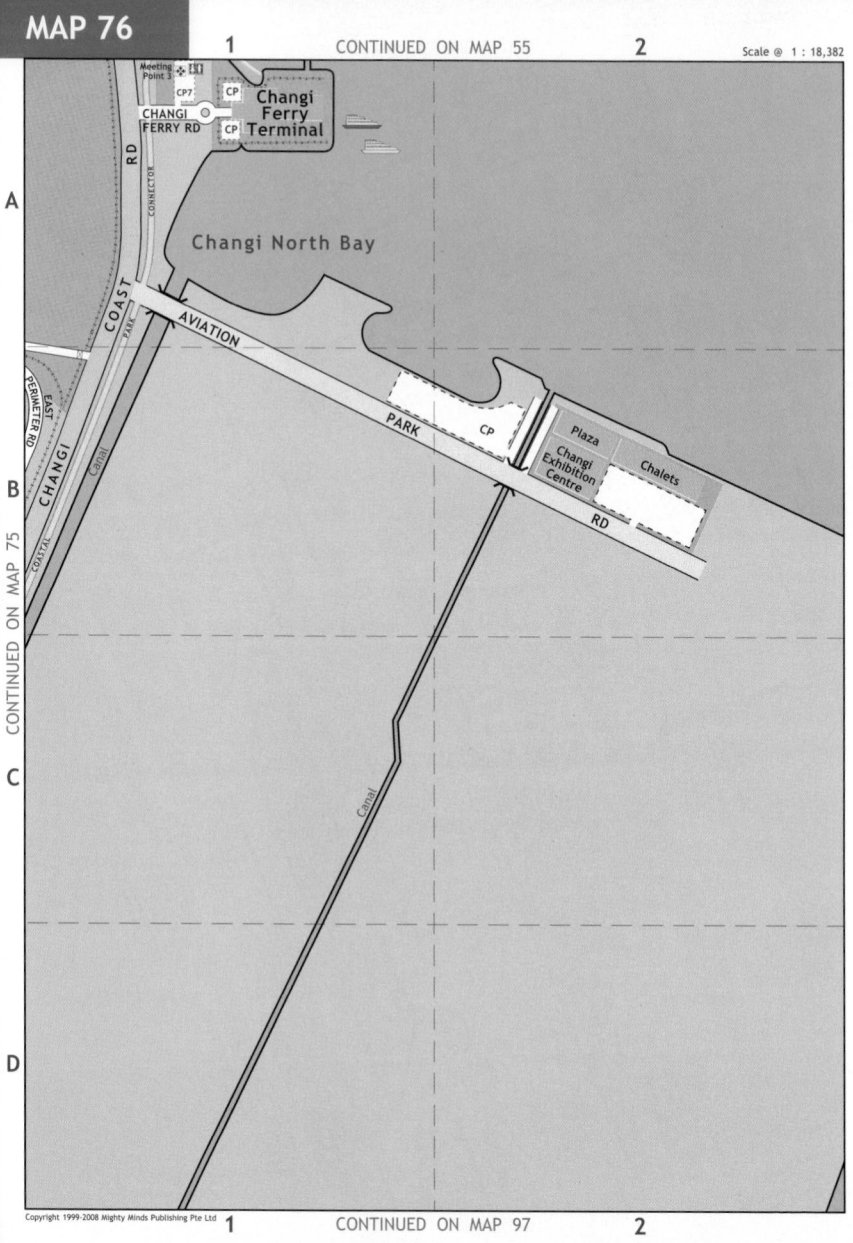

CONTINUED ON MAP 55

CONTINUED ON MAP 75

CONTINUED ON MAP 97

Look out for us

for us

Pal, 61

Taqi, 5

Alysha, 10

Audrey, 7

Shahid, 22

Lea, 23

Look out.
Stay safe.

Not all road-users have the chance to warn you of their intentions early.
Be alert and look out for them. Or, you risk losing lives.

TRAFFIC POLICE

MAP 77

1   CONTINUED ON MAP 56   2

Scale @ 1 : 18,382

Copyright 1999-2008 Mighty Minds Publishing Pte Ltd

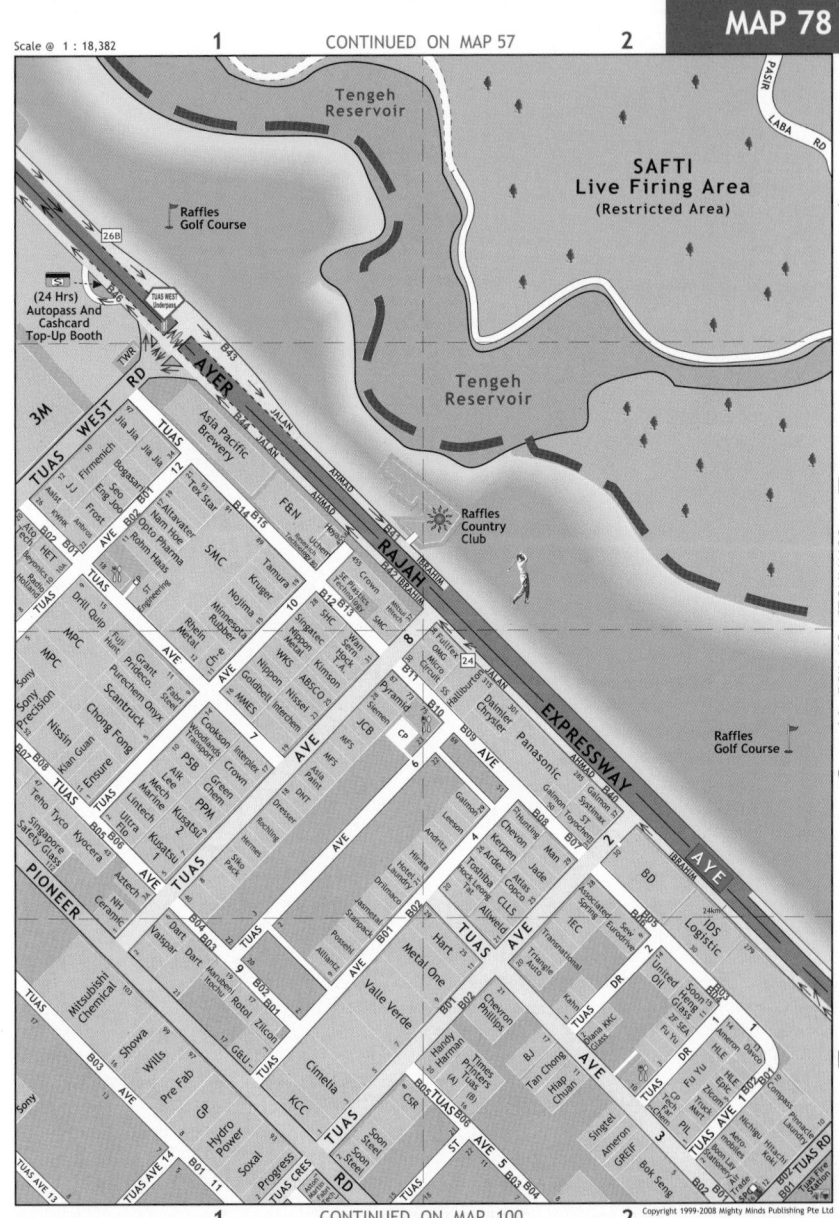

Tengeh
Reservoir

SAFTI
Live Firing Area
(Restricted Area)

Raffles
Golf Course

26B

(24 Hrs)
Autopass And
Cashcard
Top-Up Booth

TUAS WEST (Underpass)

AYER

RD

TUAS   WEST

3M

Tengeh
Reservoir

Raffles
Country
Club

Asia Pacific
Brewery

JALAN   AHMAD   IBRAHIM

RAJAH

Raffles
Golf Course

EXPRESSWAY

AYE

JALAN   IBRAHIM

PIONEER

TUAS   AVE

TUAS

KCC

TUAS   AVE   14

TUAS   AVE   13

TUAS   CRES

TUAS   RD

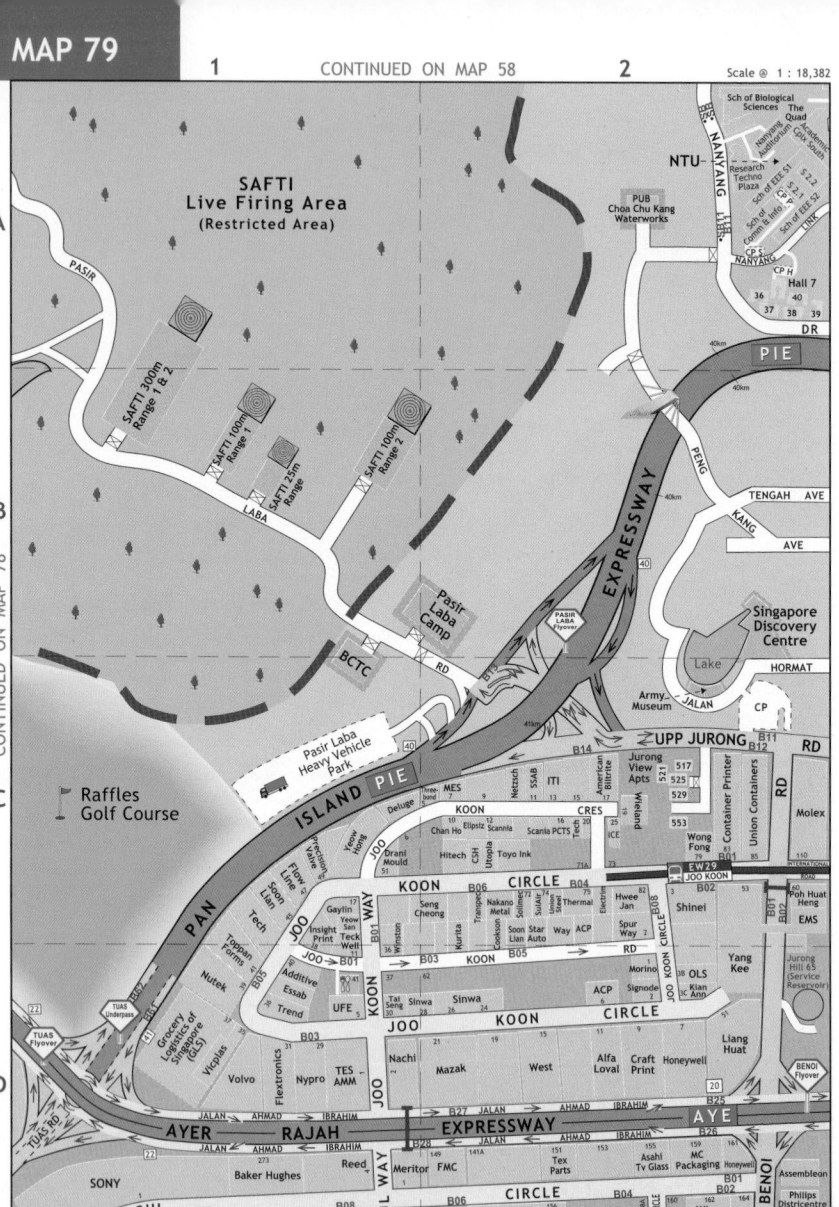

MAP 80

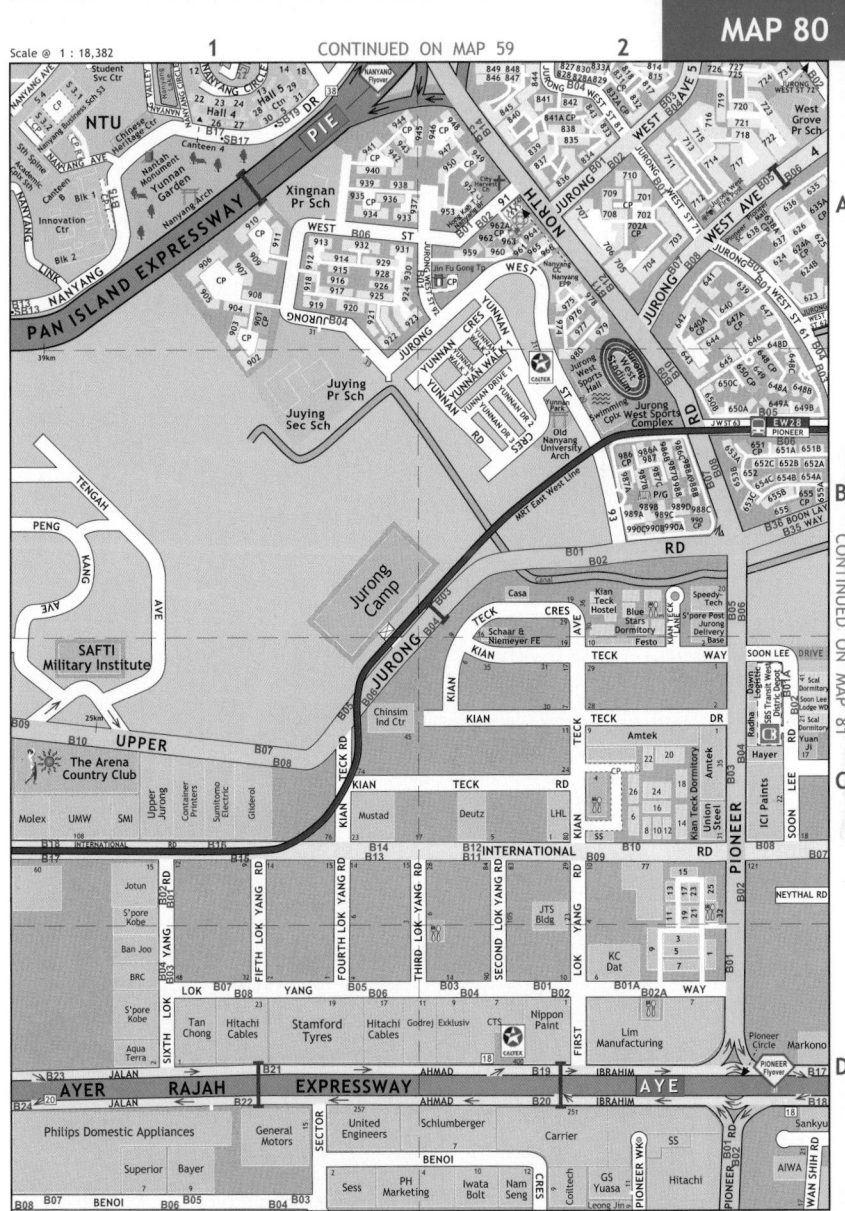

Scale @ 1 : 18,382

CONTINUED ON MAP 59

CONTINUED ON MAP 102

CONTINUED ON MAP 81

Copyright 1999-2008 Mighty Minds Publishing Pte Ltd

MAP 81

1 CONTINUED ON MAP 60 2

Scale @ 1 : 18,382

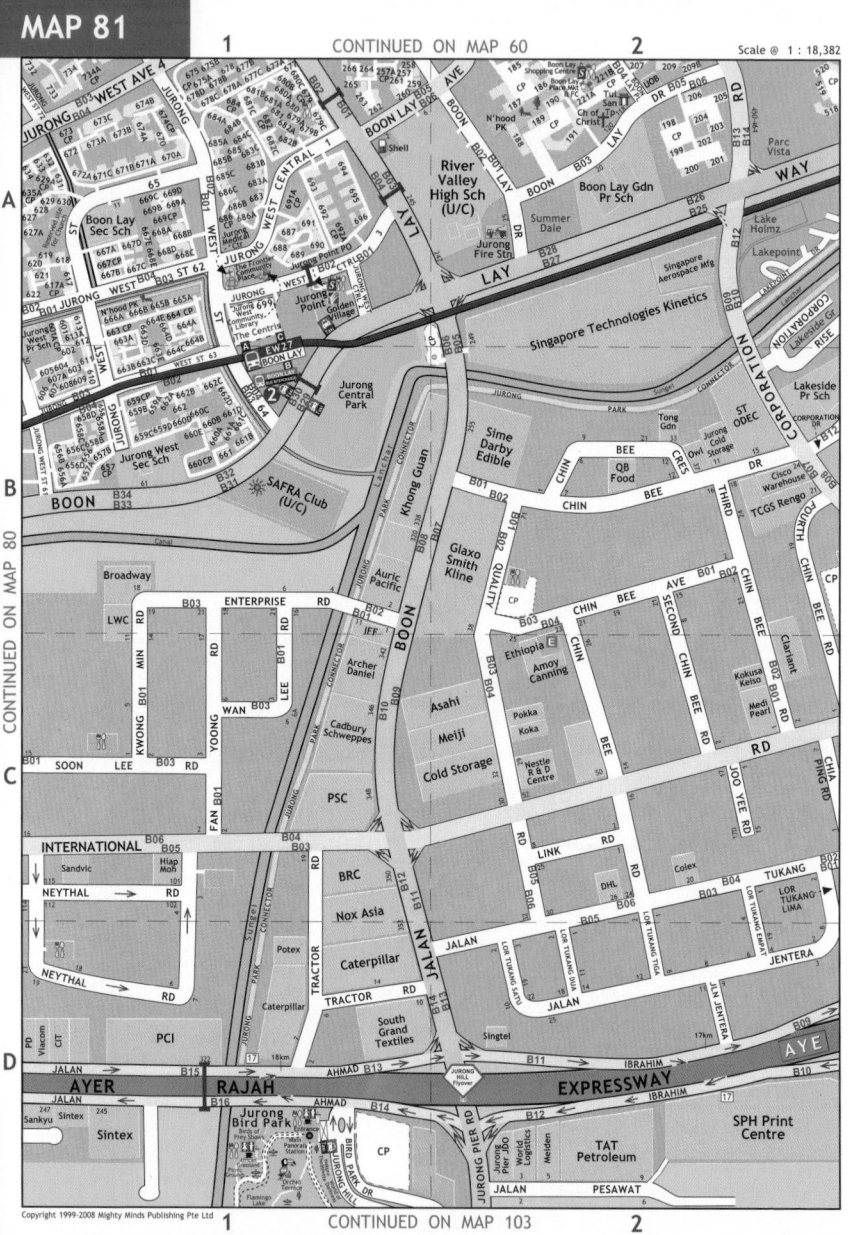

MAP 83

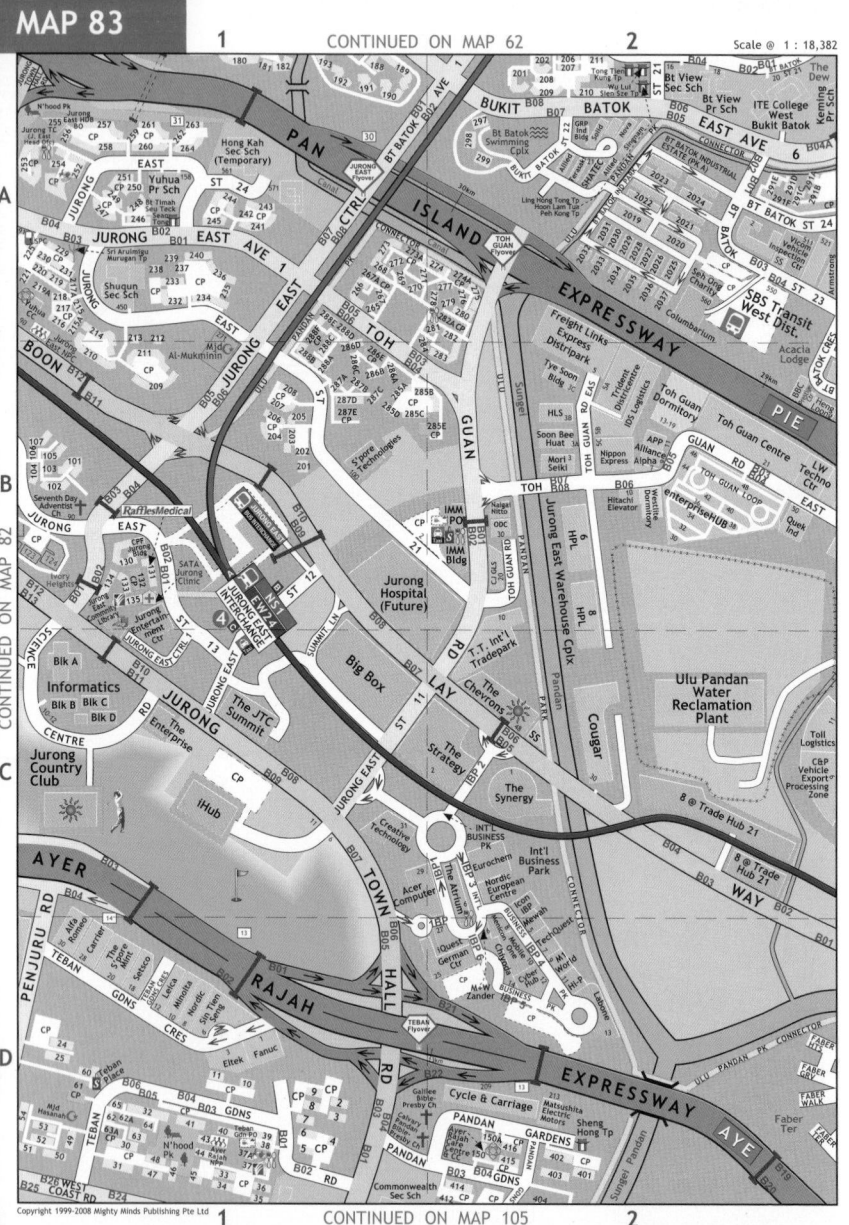

MAP 84

Scale @ 1 : 18,382

CONTINUED ON MAP 63

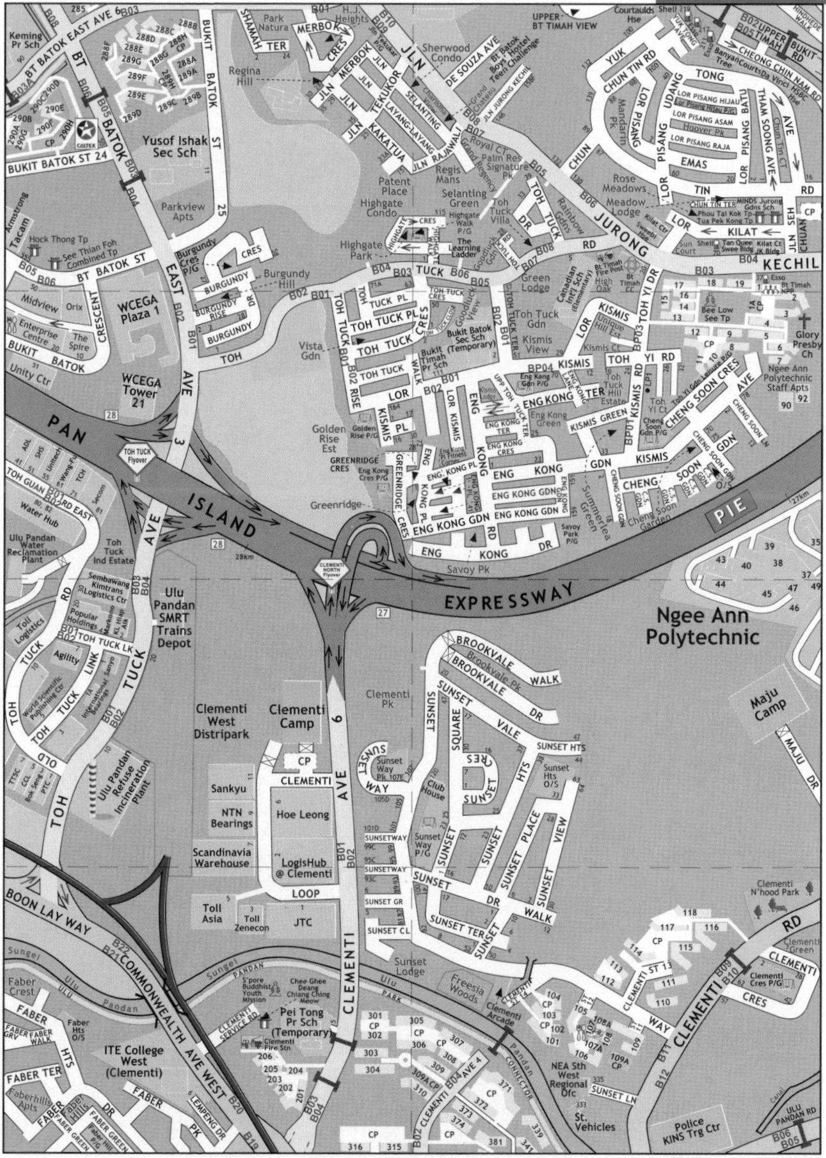

Ngee Ann Polytechnic

CONTINUED ON MAP 85

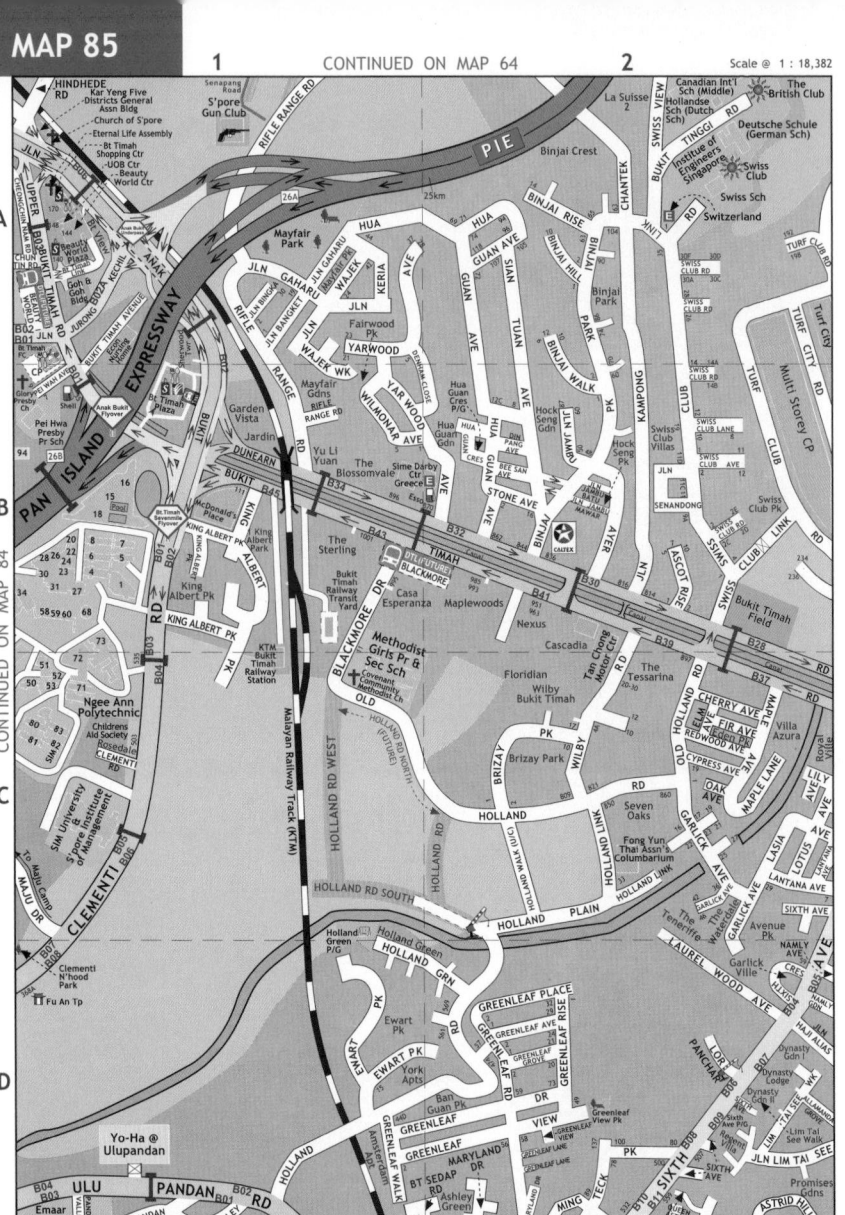

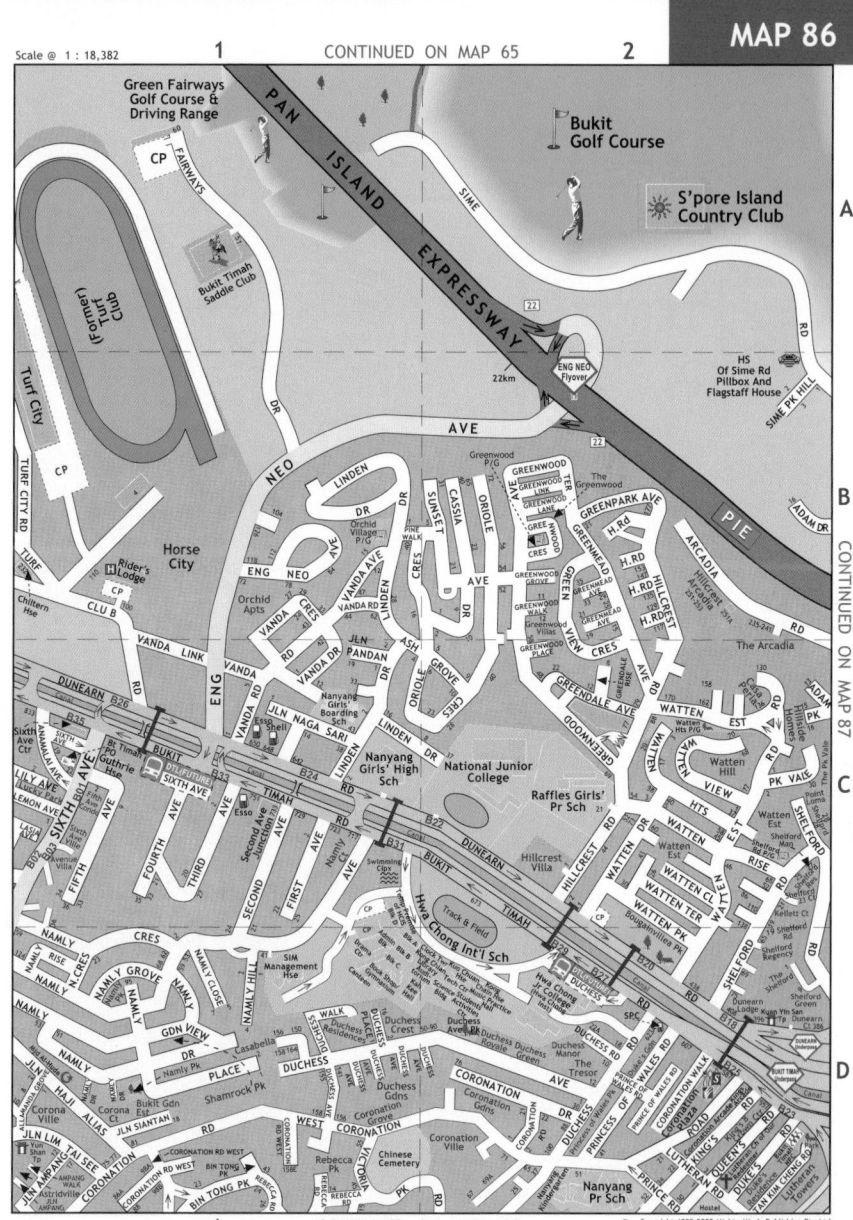

CONTINUED ON MAP 87

MAP 87

1 CONTINUED ON MAP 66 **2** Scale @ 1 : 18,382

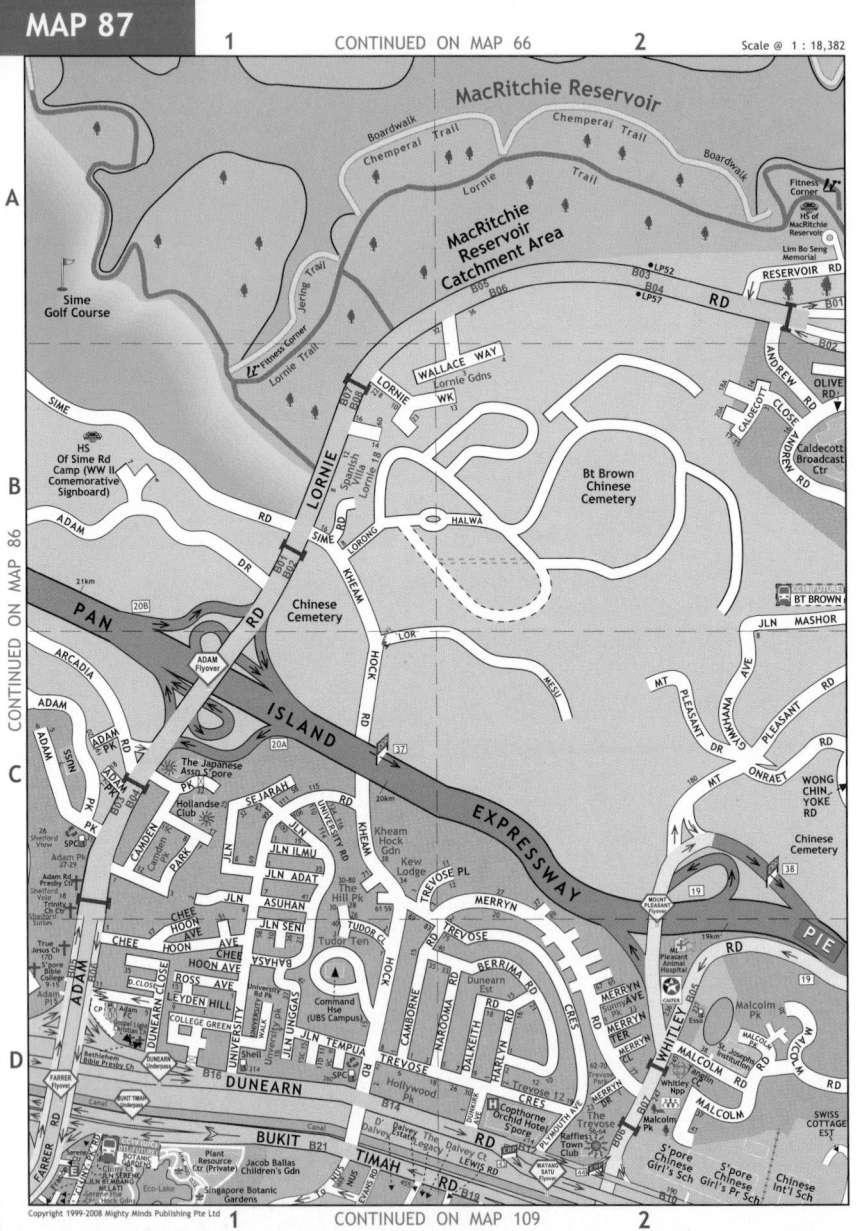

MacRitchie Reservoir

Boardwalk

Chemperai Trail

Chemperai Trail

Boardwalk

Lornie Trail

MacRitchie
Reservoir
Catchment Area

Fitness Corner

HS of
MacRitchie Reservoir

Lim Bo Seng
Memorial

Jering Trail

Fitness Corner

Lornie Trail

Sime
Golf Course

LP52

B05

B04

B06

LP57

RESERVOIR RD

B01

B02

OLIVE
RD

ANDREW

CALDECOTT

CLOSE

ANDREW

Caldecott
Broadcast
Ctr

SIME

HS
Of Sime Rd
Camp (WW II
Comemorative
Signboard)

ADAM

RD

DR

PAN

21km

20B

ARCADIA

ADAM

SSTN

ADAM

PK

ADAM

PK

ADAM

PK

LORNIE

B07

B04

WALLACE WAY

Lornie Gdns

WK

Spanish
Villa

Lornie 18

SIME

Lorong

KHEAM

Chinese
Cemetery

HALWA

Bt Brown
Chinese
Cemetery

BT BROWN

JLN MASHOR

ADAM
Flyover

ISLAND

HOCK

LOR

RD

MESU

MT

PLEASANT

JLN

CHWANA

AVE

PLEASANT

DR

MT

ONRAET

WONG
CHIN.
YOKE
RD

Chinese
Cemetery

20A

EXPRESSWAY

37

19

38

MOUNT
PLEASANT
Flyover

19

PIE

The Japanese
Assn S'pore

Hollandse
Club

SEJARAH

UNIVERSITY RD

115

KHEAM

Kheam
Hock
Gdn

Kew
Lodge

38

TREVOSE PL

MERRYN

19m

Mt
Pleasant
Animal Hospital

B05

CAMDEN

Camden
PARK

JLN ILMU

JLN ADAT

JLN ASUHAN

The
Hill Pk

TREVOSE

Tudor Ten

Tudor Pk

MERRYN

BERRIMA RD

Dunearn
Est

RD

MERRYN

AVE

MERRYN
TER

CENTER

Essa

Malcolm
Pk

St. Joseph's
Institution

MALCOLM

26
Shelford
View

SPC

CHEE
HOON AVE

JLN SENI

HOON AVE

CHEE

BAHASA

HOCK

CAMBORNE

HAROOMA

DALKEITH

HARLYN

MERRYN

WHITLEY

B07

RD

MALCOLM

Malcolm
Pk

St. Joseph's
Institution

MALCOLM

RD

Adam Pk

True
Jesus Ch
170

S'pore
Bible
College

Adam Pk

ROSS AVE

LEYDEN HILL

COLLEGE GREENWAY

JLN UNGGAS

JLN TEMPUA

University
Rd Dr

SPC

TREVOSE

Hollywood
Pk

DUNEARN CLOSE

B14

CRES

Dunearn
Est

RD

Dunearn
Est

The
Trevose

Raffles
Town
Club

MERRYN

B07

MALCOLM

MALCOLM
RD

SWISS
COTTAGE
EST

Bethlehem
Bible Presby Ch

Adam Pk

CP

Adam
Pk

FARRER
Flyover

DUNEARN

BUKIT

FARRER RD

Canal

BUKIT TIMAH

B16

B21

Canal

TIMAH

NIES

B19

RD

DALVEY

LEWIS RD

Dalvey
Estate

Dalvey
Legacy

Dalvey Ct

Copthorne
Orchid Hotel
S'pore

WATAMO
SATU

CRES

TREVOSE 12

Raffles
Town
Club

S'pore
Chinese
Girls' Sch

S'pore
Chinese
Girls' Pr Sch

Chinese
Int'l Sch

BOTANIC
GARDENS

Eco-Lake

Plant
Resource
Ctr (Private)

Jacob Ballas
Children's Gdn

Singapore Botanic
Gardens

MAP 88

Scale @ 1 : 18,382

CONTINUED ON MAP 67

CONTINUED ON MAP 89

CONTINUED ON MAP 110

MacRitchie
Reservoir

St. Theresa's Home
Raffles Junior College
RAFFLES INSTITUTION LN
Kwong Wai Siew Peck San Theng Bldg
Raffles Institution
Guangyang Pr Sch
Guangyang Sec Sch

BISHAN RD
BISHAN LANE

Westlake Gdns
HS of MacRitchie Reservoir
Pier

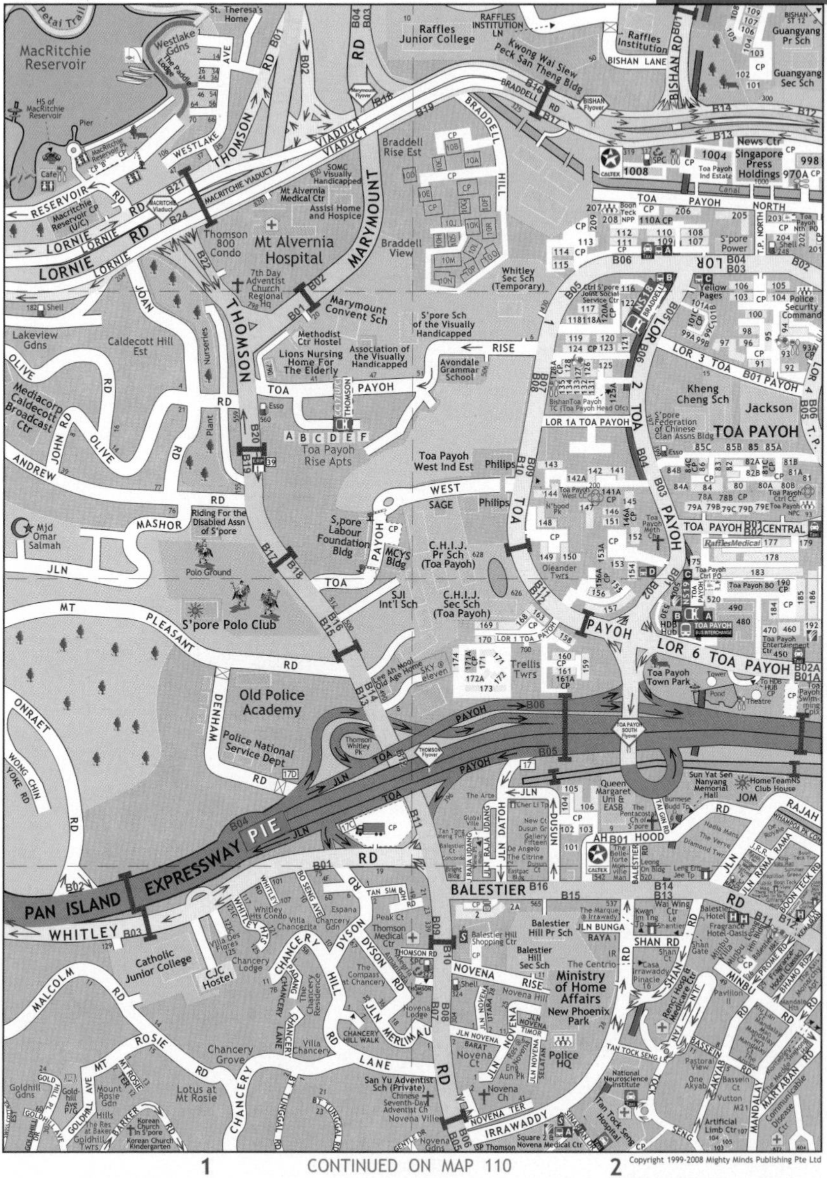

Singapore Press Holdings
News Ctr
Toa Payoh Ind Estate

THOMSON RD
WESTLAKE AVE
MACRITCHIE VIADUCT
BRADDELL RD
MARYMOUNT RD

Braddell Rise Est
SOMC Visually Handicapped
Mt Alvernia Medical Ctr
Assisi Home and Hospice

TOA PAYOH NORTH
LOR 1 TOA PAYOH

Thomson 800 Condo
Mt Alvernia Hospital
7th Day Adventist Church Regional

Braddell View
Whitley Sec Sch (Temporary)

LORNIE RD
RESERVOIR RD

Lakeview Gdns
Caldecott Hill Est
Marymount Convent Sch

S'pore Sch of the Visually Handicapped
Association of the Visually Handicapped
Avondale Grammar School

RISE

Kheng Cheng Sch
S'pore Federation of Chinese Clan Assns Bldg

TOA PAYOH

Mediacorp Caldecott Broadcast Ctr

Lions Nursing Home For The Elderly

Methodist Ctr Hostel

Toa Payoh Rise Apts
A B C D E F

TOA PAYOH
TOA PAYOH CENTRAL

OLIVE RD
JOHN RD
ANDREW RD
MASHOR RD
JLN MT

Mjd Omar Salmah

Riding For the Disabled Assn of S'pore

S'pore Labour Foundation Bldg
MCYS Bldg
C.H.I.J. Pr School (Toa Payoh)
SJI Int'l Sch
C.H.I.J. Sec Sch (Toa Payoh)

West Ind Est
WEST
SAGE
Philips
Oleander Twrs

Polo Ground
S'pore Polo Club

PLEASANT RD
MT

Old Police Academy
Police National Service Dept

Trellis Twrs
Toa Payoh Town Park

LOR 6 TOA PAYOH

ONRAET RD
WONG CHIN YOKE RD
DENHAM RD

PAN ISLAND EXPRESSWAY
PIE
TOA PAYOH

Queen Margaret
Sun Yat Sen Nanyang Memorial Hall
HomeTeamNS Club House

JLN RAJAH

WHITLEY RD
MALCOLM RD

Catholic Junior College
CJC Hostel
Chancery Lodge

Thomson Medical Ctr
Balestier Hill Shopping Ctr
Balestier Hill Pr Sch
Balestier Hill Sec Sch

BALESTIER RD
AH HOOD RD
DYSON RD
CHANCERY HILL

NOVENA RISE
Ministry of Home Affairs
New Phoenix Park

SHAN RD
JLN BUNGA RAYA

Chancery Grove
Novena Ct
Villa Chancery
CHANCERY WALK

San Yu Adventist Sch (Private)
Chinese Seventh-day Adventist Ch
Novena Villa

Police HQ
National Neuroscience Institute
Artificial Limb Ctr

ROSIE RD
GOLDHILL AVE
IRRAWADDY RD
NOVENA TER

Goldhill Gdns
Mt Rosie Gdns
Korean Church Kindergarten
Lotus at Mt Rosie

Novena Ch
Novena Medical Ctr

MANDALAY RD

MAP 89

CONTINUED ON MAP 68

Scale @ 1 : 18,382

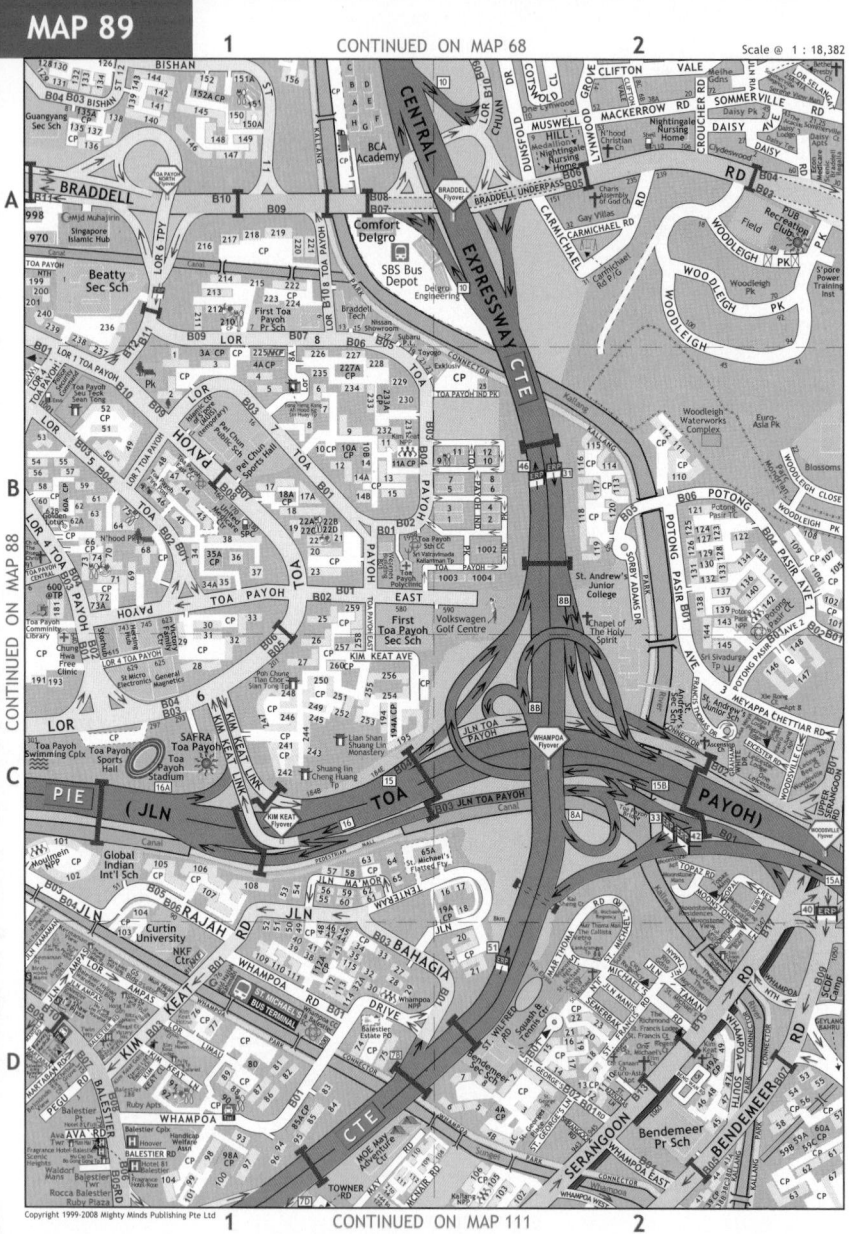

Scale @ 1 : 18,382

1 CONTINUED ON MAP 69 2

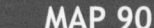

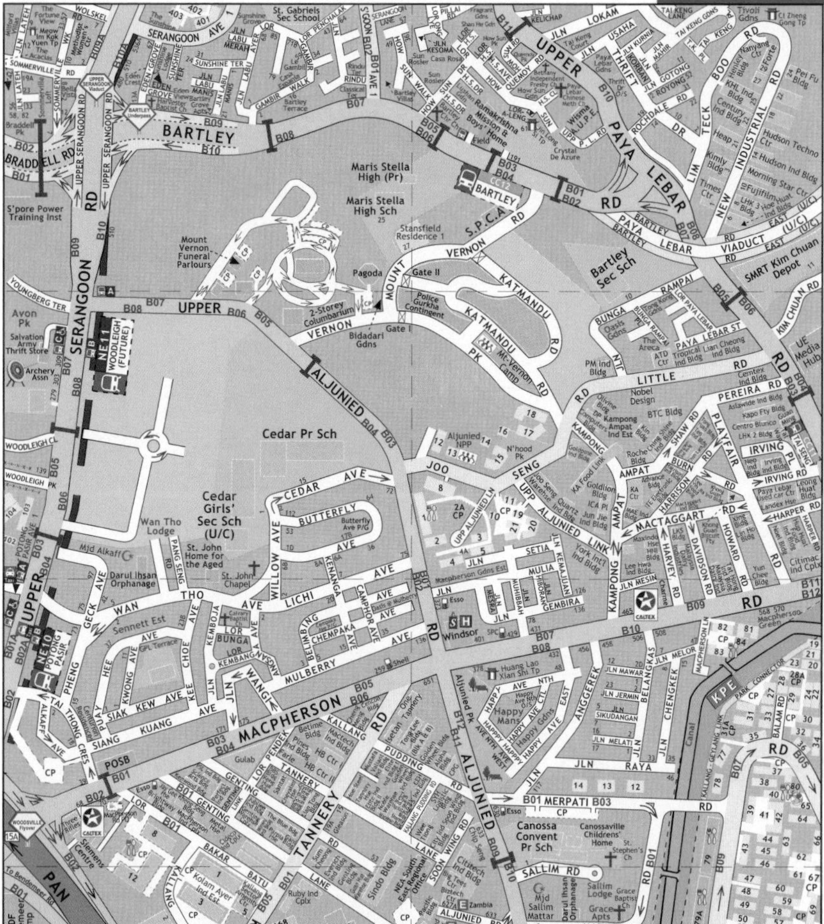

A B C D

CONTINUED ON MAP 91

1 CONTINUED ON MAP 112 2

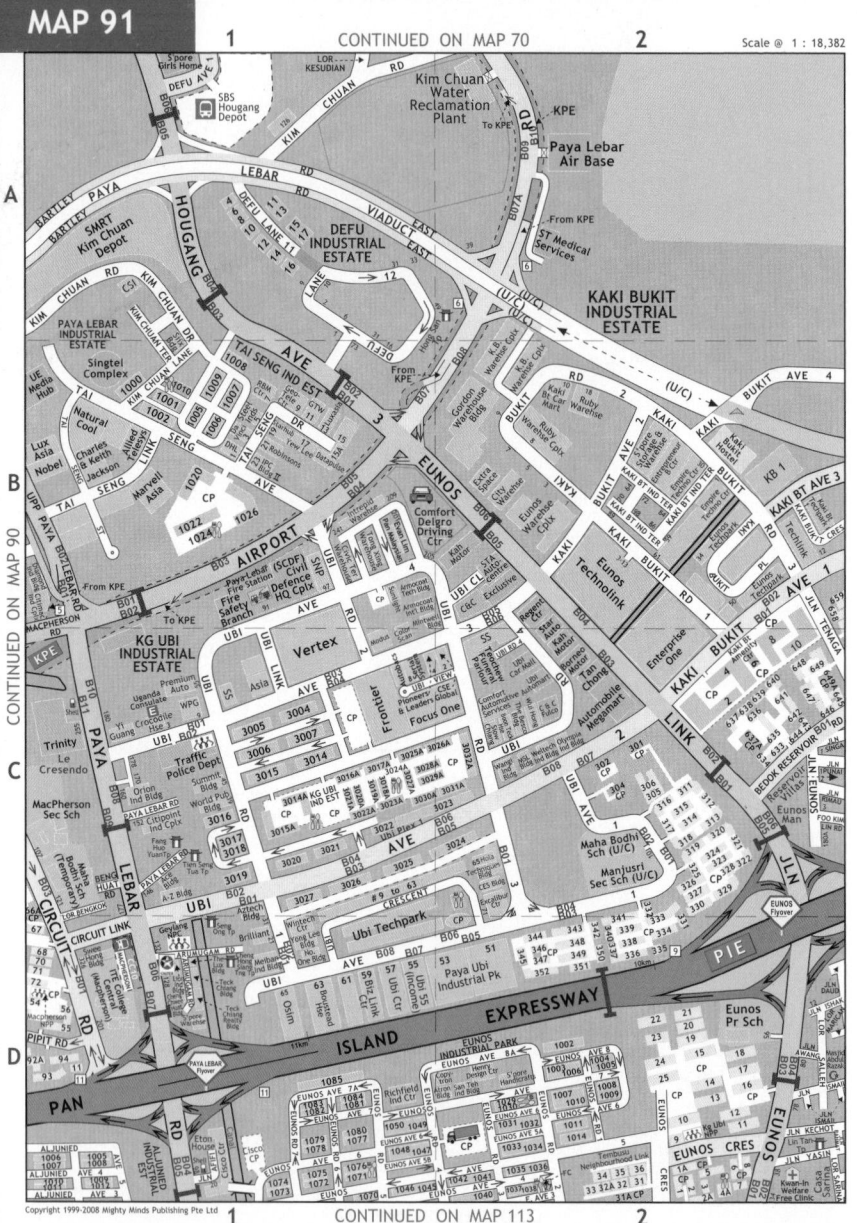

CONTINUED ON MAP 90

MAP 92

TAMPINES AVE 10

Canal

EAST

RD

Bedok
Reservoir

A

SAF Driving
Circuit

KAKI BUKIT

KAKI BUKIT Viaduct

PUB
KAKI BUKIT AVE 6

PUB Bedok
Waterworks

Kaki
Bukit
Camp

Jln Eunos Service
Reservoir

KAKI BUKIT RD

Meeting
Pt 2

Bedok
Reservoir
Park

RD

AVE 5

Fitness
Corner

CONNECTOR

Playground

Vicom
Insp.
Ctr

5 Star

BARTLEY

KAKI BUKIT

RD

Kaki Bukit Ctr
(Prison Sch)

B11

BEDOK

RESERVOIR

743 742A 740
742 741 739
246 745 738

CP

CP CP

737 CP

CP
740A

B17
B18

RD

Damai
Sec Sch

B

KAKI BT AVE 3

Techview

Shun Li
Ind Pk II

B12

Kato-
spring

Dou
Tree
Bldg

701

702

B14

715

716

B15 B16

714

717

718

Mid
Alkafi Kg
Melayu

702

CP

705 704

BEDOK IND PK C

706

Damai
Pr Sch

712 711 719 720

713 710

721

KAKI BUKIT AVE 1

KAKI
BUKIT
CRES

BUKIT

AVE 1

B07

B08

151

149

148

142

Bedok
North
Sec Sch

628

Eunos NPP

621

Bedok West
Pr Sch

709

BEDOK

B04
B03

KAKI BUKIT

JLN

657
656 665
654 666 667
653 668
652 669
651 670
650 671

664

663

B05

B06

147

146

145

143

141

140

136

626

627

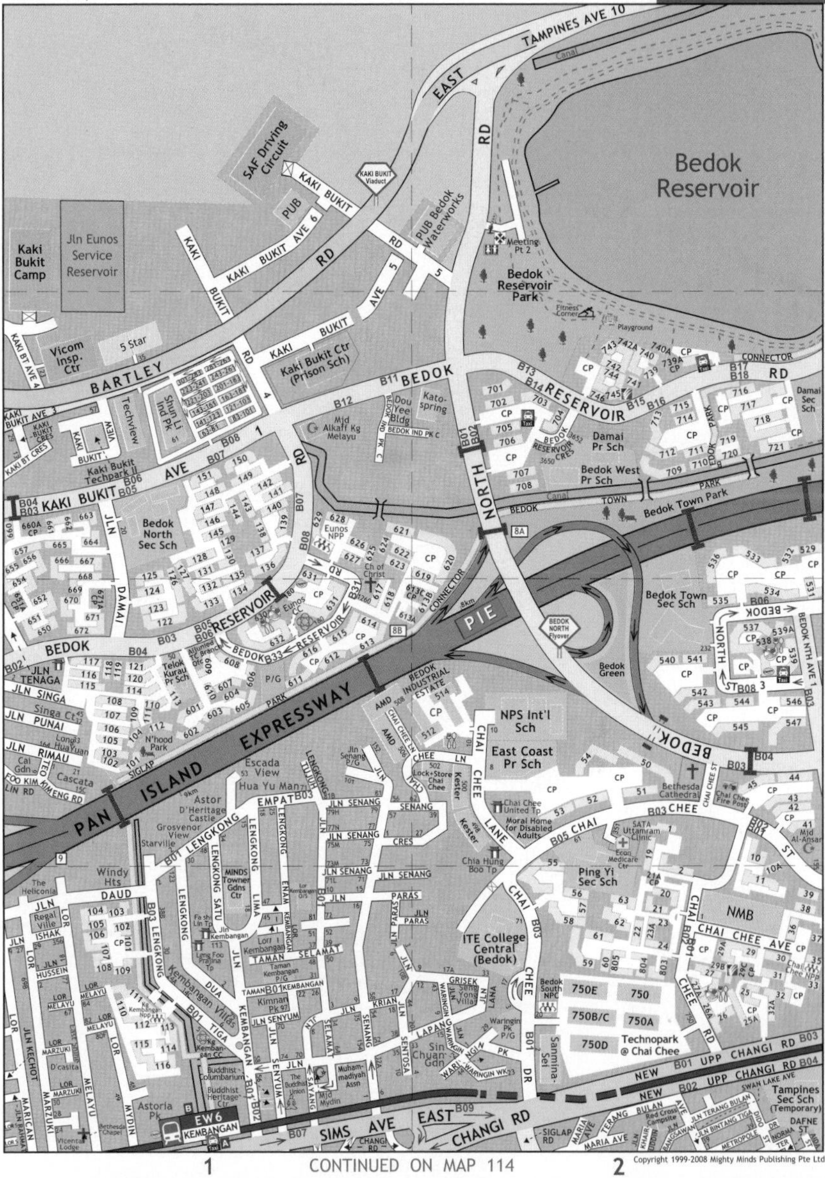

620

Ch of
Christ

623
619

CP

618

Bedok Town Park

BEDOK

NORTH

8A

533

532

531

529

Bedok Town
Sec Sch

536

CONTINUED ON MAP 93

DAMAI

BEDOK

131

130

138

137

629
625 624

B08

622

617

CP

P/G

616

670

135

134

133

132

124

123

122

633

614A

614

BEDOK

C

B02

JLN
TENAGA

116
115

611
610
609

Telok
Kurau
Pr Sch

608

CONNECTOR

613

615

612

Bedok
Green

535

534

531A

534

537
538

538A

539A

539

BEDOK NTH AVE 3

B08 3

Singa Cres

114

607

606

605

604

603

P/G

540 541

542

543

544

546

547

545

JLN PUNAI

110
107 106
104

108 109

113

112

BEDOK

RESERVOIR

AMD

602

601

BEDOK
INDUSTRIAL
ESTATE

AMD

512

CHAI CHEE LN

511

NPS Int'l
Sch

East Coast
Pr Sch

CP

50

51

CP

52

Bethesda
Cathedral

B04

B03

44

43

42

41

JLN
RIMAU

105

PAN

ISLAND

EXPRESSWAY

BEDOK

Mid
Al-Ahsan

Escada
View

Hua Yu Man

513

Lock+Store Chai
Chee

Chai Chee
(United) Tp
Moral Home
for Disabled
Adults

53
52

CHEE

CHAI

CHEE

CHAI

CHEE

AVE

D

Astor
D'Heritage
Castle

EMPAT

B03

JLN SENANG

514

JLN SENANG

Keller

LANE

55

51

SAT
Uttamram
Clinic

Store
Medicare

Ping Yi
Sec Sch

39

Grosvenor
View

Starville

LENGKONG

CRES

Chia Hung
Boo Tp

63

62

NMB

10A

Windy
Hts

JLN
DAUD

The
Heliconia

JLN
Regal
Ville

105

104

103

102

LENGKONG SATU

MINDS
Towner
Gdns
Ctr

JLN SENANG

JLN SENANG

JLN
PARAS

59

60
B05

58

61

22

23A

23

24

21

CHAI CHEE

CHAI CHEE AVE

CHEE

32

31

29

JLN
ISTAH

106

108

109

Jhu
Fou
Kiw

Lor 1
Kembangan

TAMAN
SELAMAT

TAMAN
KEMBANGAN

59

57

60

ITE College
Central
(Bedok)

CHEE

56

B04

26

25

31A
B01

29

38

37

750E

750

LOR
MELAYU

112

113

114
115

116

B01

LENGKONG

TIGA

LENGKONG

DUA

Asphangkam Villas

JLN SENYUM

GRISEK

Kinmao

JLN
PRIAN

Bedok
South NPC

750B/C

750A

750D

Technopark
@ Chai Chee

RD

32

CP

D

LOR
MARUKU

D'casita

JLN
KECHOT

JLN
MARUKU

KEMBANGAN

Kembangan
MRT

JLN SENYUM

Buddhist
Columbarium

Buddhist
Heritage

TAMAN
KEMBANGAN

Muham-
madiyah
Assn

SIN
CHUAN
GAN

WARING

WK23

Sammnau-
Sei

UPP CHANGI RD

UPP CHANGI RD

B03

Tampines
Sec Sch
(Temporary)

MARICAN

Astoria
Pk

EW6
KEMBANGAN

Bethesda
Chapel

Waverley
Lodge

B07

SIMS

CHANGI
RD

AVE

The
Buddha

B09

EAST

CHANGI RD

NEW

SIGLAP
RD

MARIA AVE

DAFNE

MAP 93

CONTINUED ON MAP 72

Scale @ 1 : 18,382

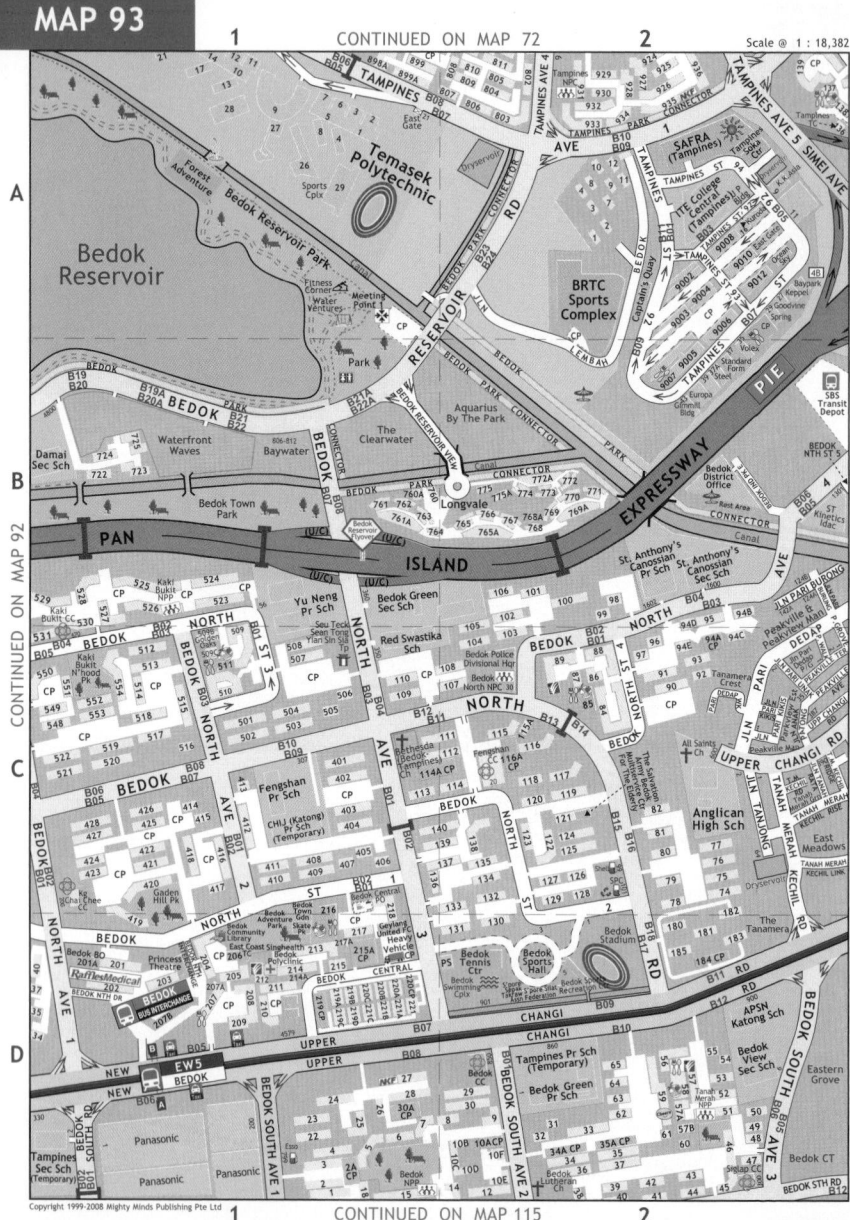

CONTINUED ON MAP 92

CONTINUED ON MAP 115

Copyright 1999-2008 Mighty Minds Publishing Pte Ltd

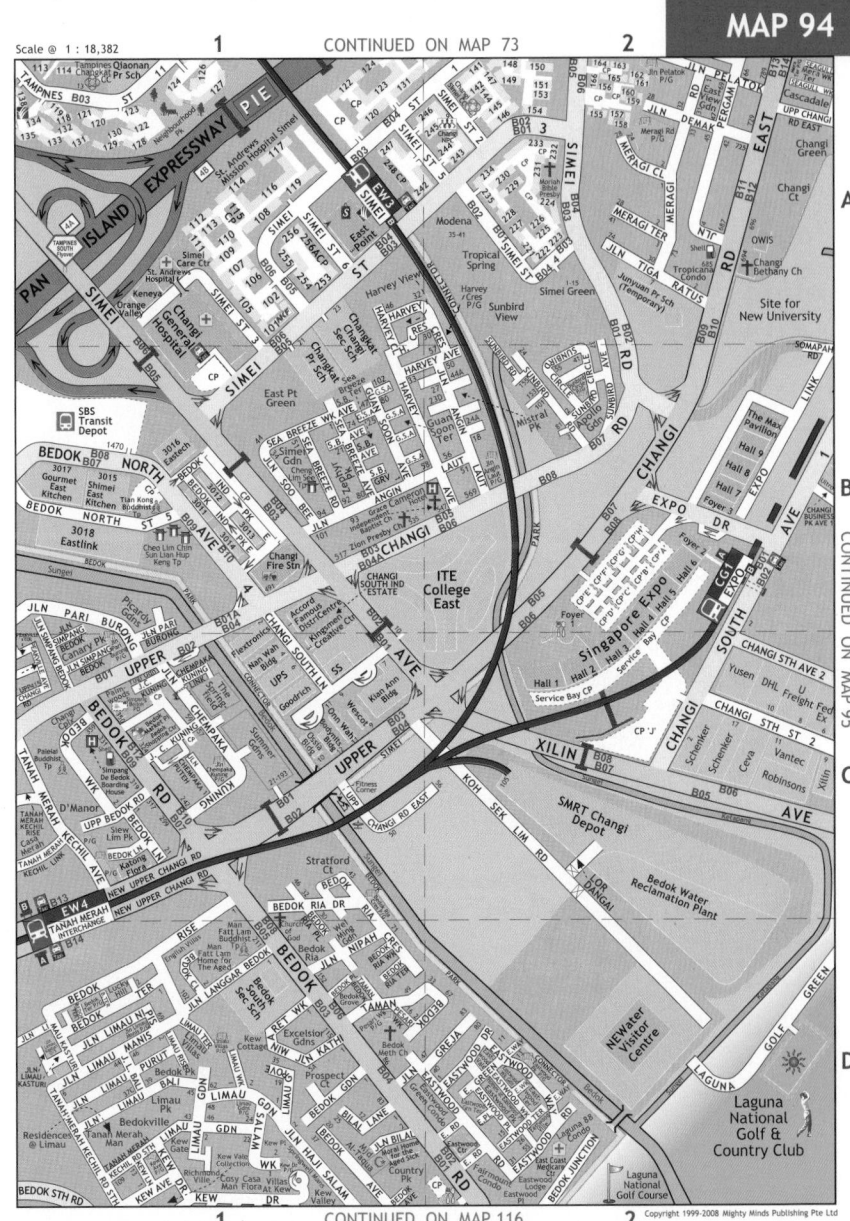

MAP 94

Scale @ 1 : 18,382

CONTINUED ON MAP 73

MAP 95

CONTINUED ON MAP 74

Scale @ 1 : 18,382

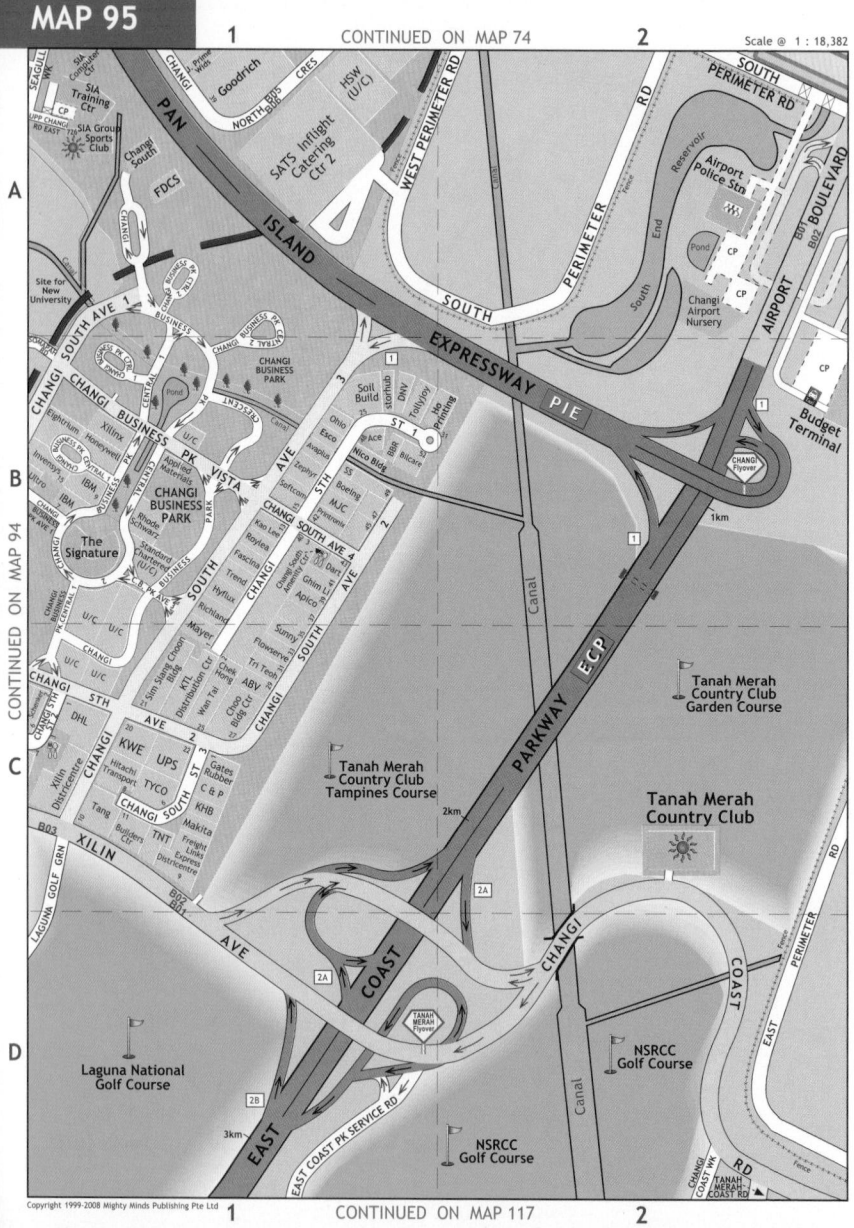

MAP 96

Scale @ 1 : 18,382

CONTINUED ON MAP 75

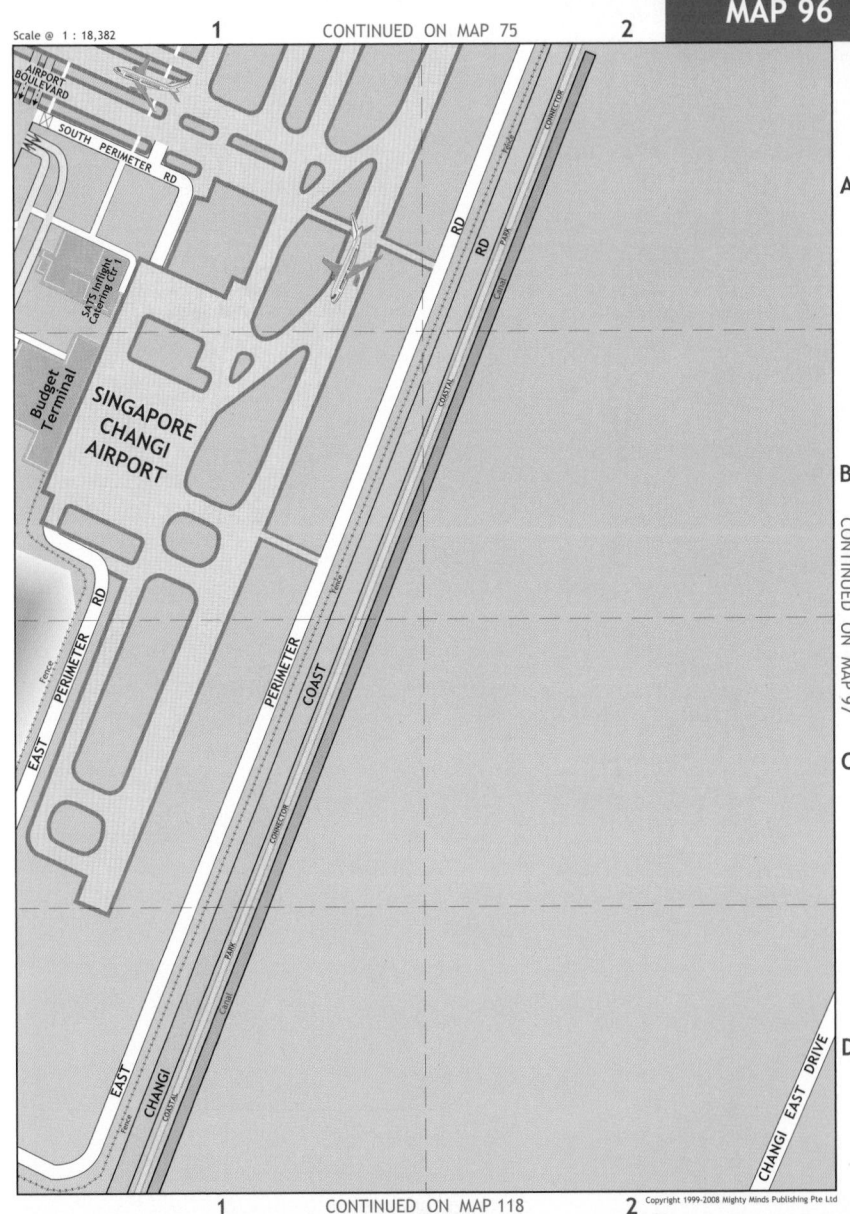

AIRPORT BOULEVARD

SOUTH PERIMETER RD

SATS Inflight Catering Ctr

Budget Terminal

SINGAPORE CHANGI AIRPORT

EAST PERIMETER RD

Force

PERIMETER

COAST

COASTAL RD

COASTAL RD

CONNECTOR

EAST CHANGI COASTAL

CONNECTOR

CHANGI EAST DRIVE

Copyright 1999-2008 Mighty Minds Publishing Pte Ltd

MAP 97

CONTINUED ON MAP 76

Scale @ 1 : 18,382

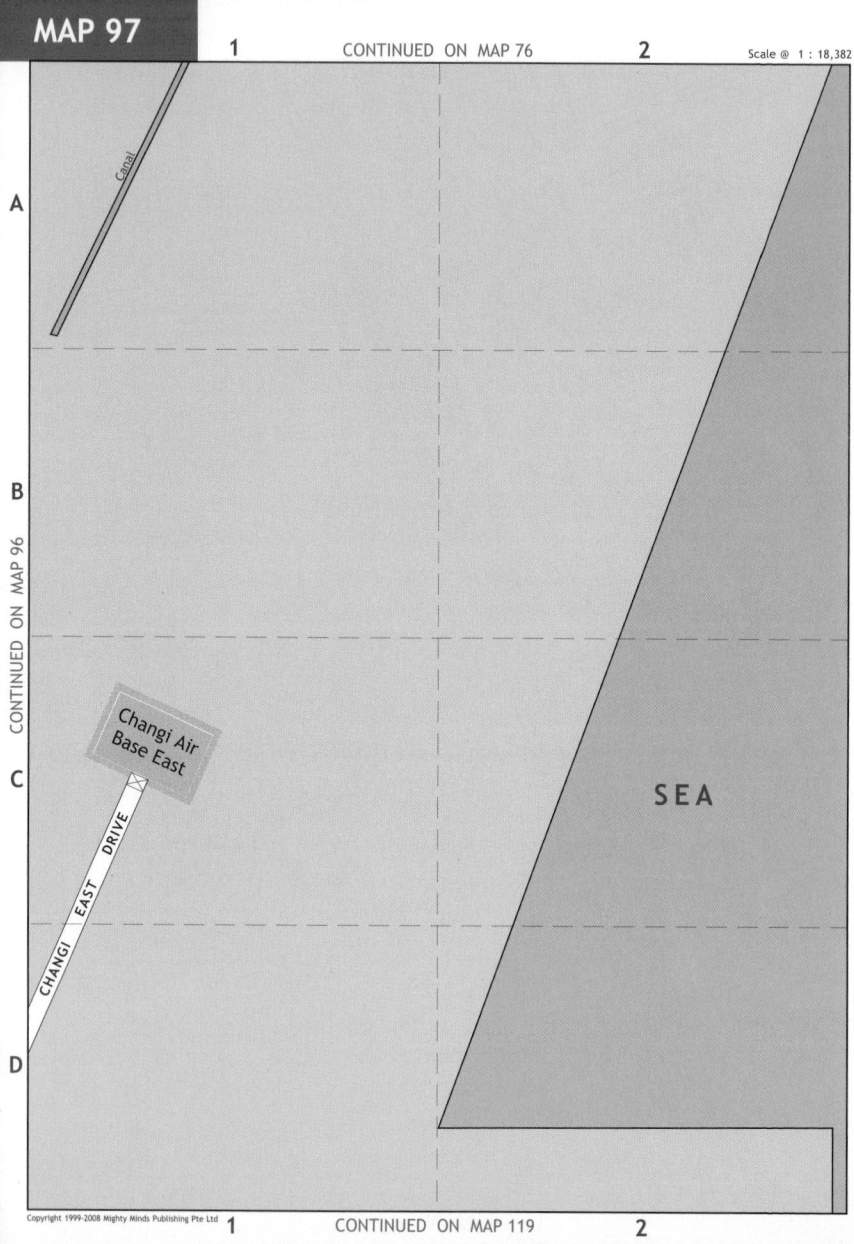

Canal

A

B

C

D

1

2

Changi Air
Base East

SEA

CHANGI   EAST   DRIVE

MAP 98

Scale @ 1 : 18,382

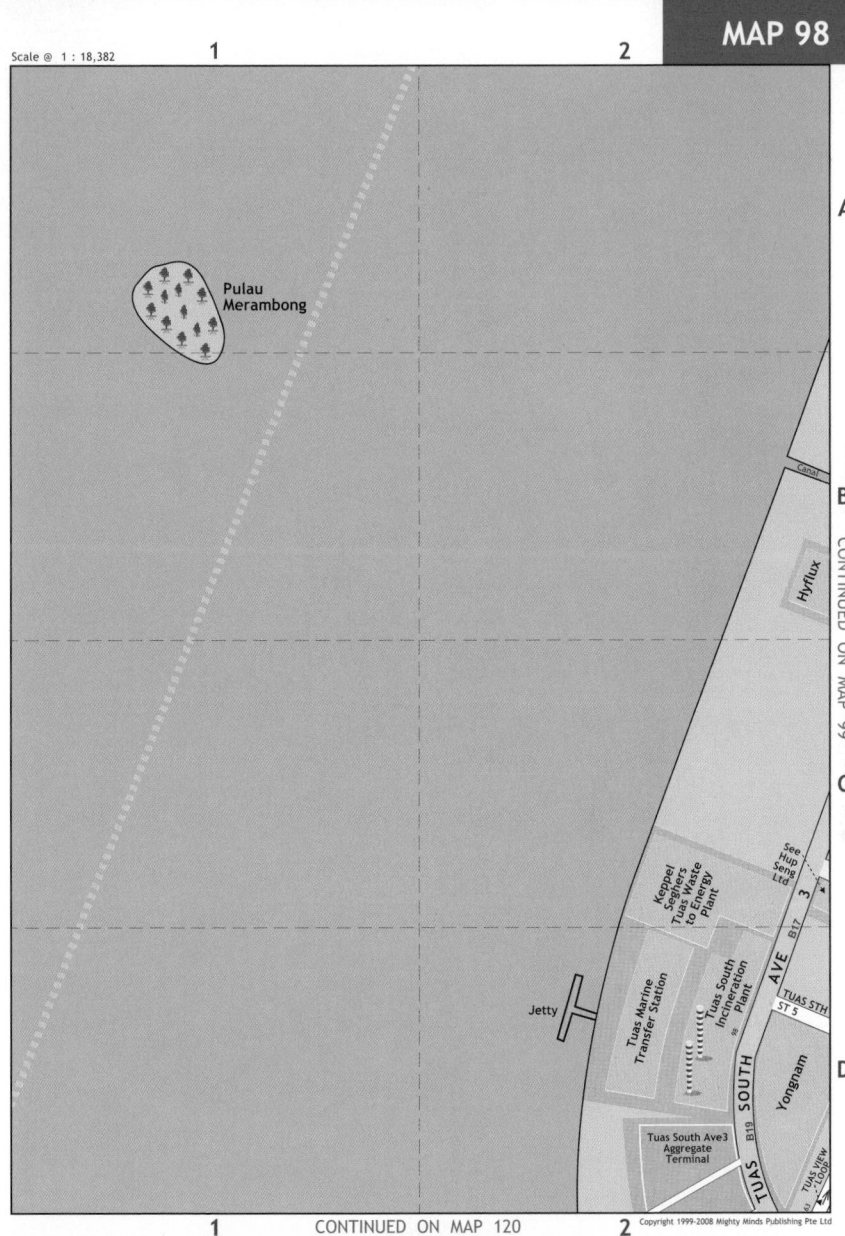

Pulau Merambong

Canal

Hyflux

CONTINUED ON MAP 99

Keppel Seghers Tuas Waste to Energy Plant

See Hup Seng Ltd

B17

AVE

TUAS 5TH

ST 5

Tuas Marine Transfer Station

Tuas South Incineration Plant

Jetty

SOUTH

Yongnam

B19

Tuas South Ave3 Aggregate Terminal

TUAS

TUAS VIEW LOOP

Copyright 1999-2008 Mighty Minds Publishing Pte Ltd

MAP 99

Scale @ 1 : 18,382

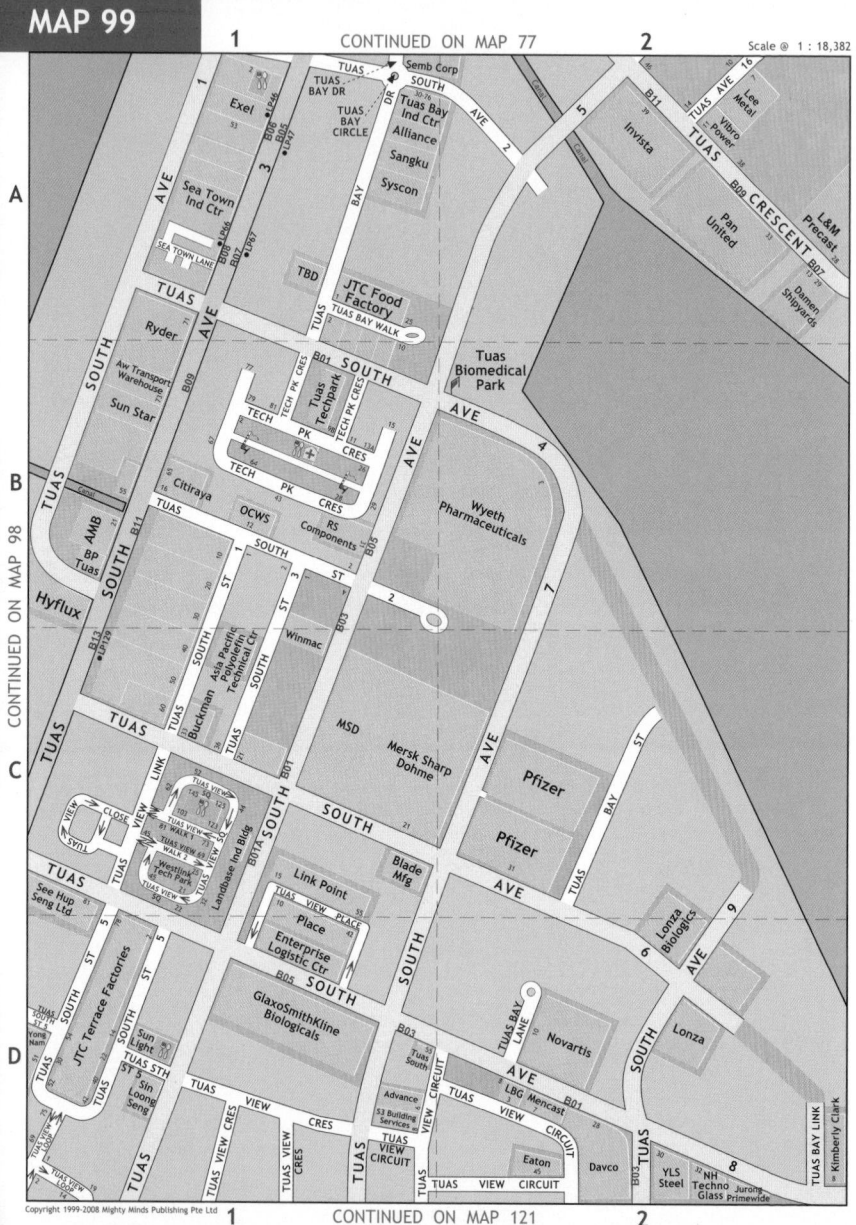

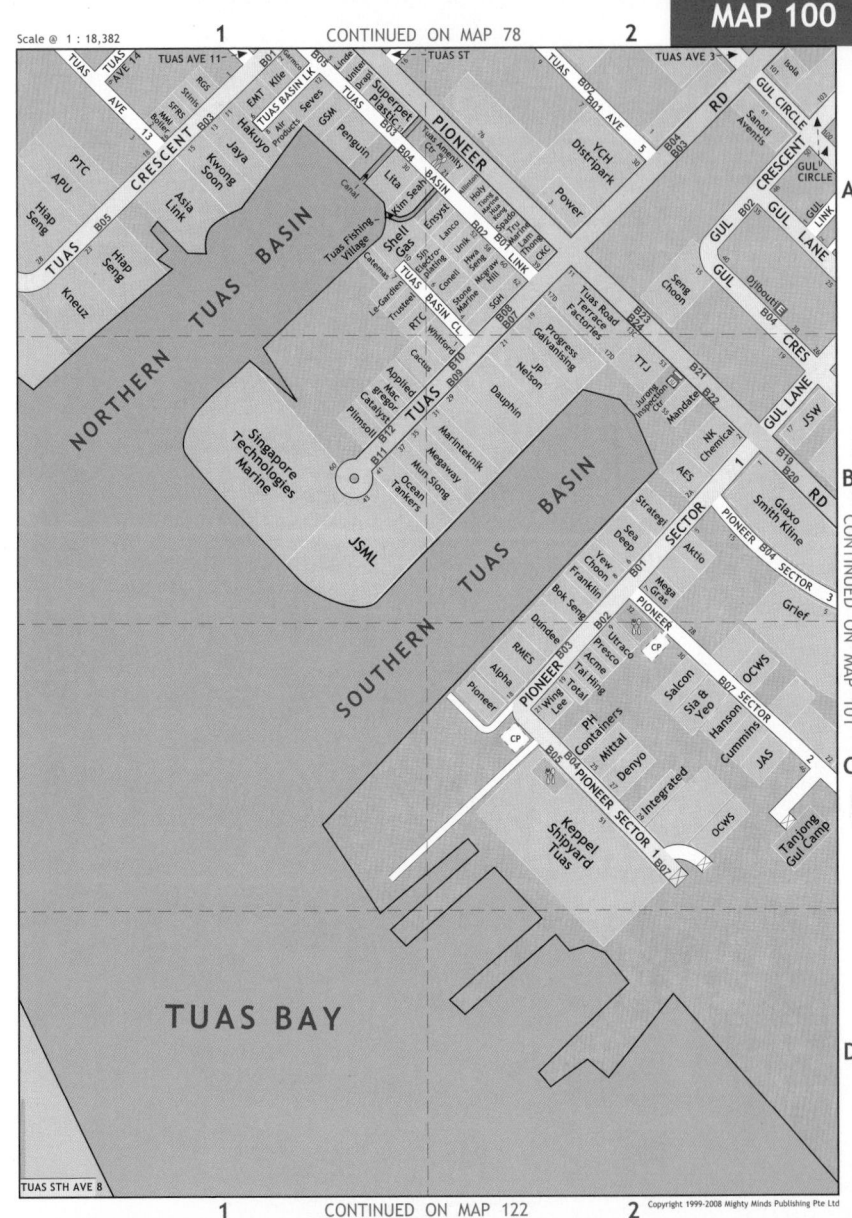

A

B

CONTINUED ON MAP 101

C

D

NORTHERN TUAS BASIN

Singapore Technologies Marine

JSML

SOUTHERN TUAS BASIN

Keppel Shipyard Tuas

TUAS BAY

Tanjong Gul Camp

MAP 101

Scale @ 1 : 18,382

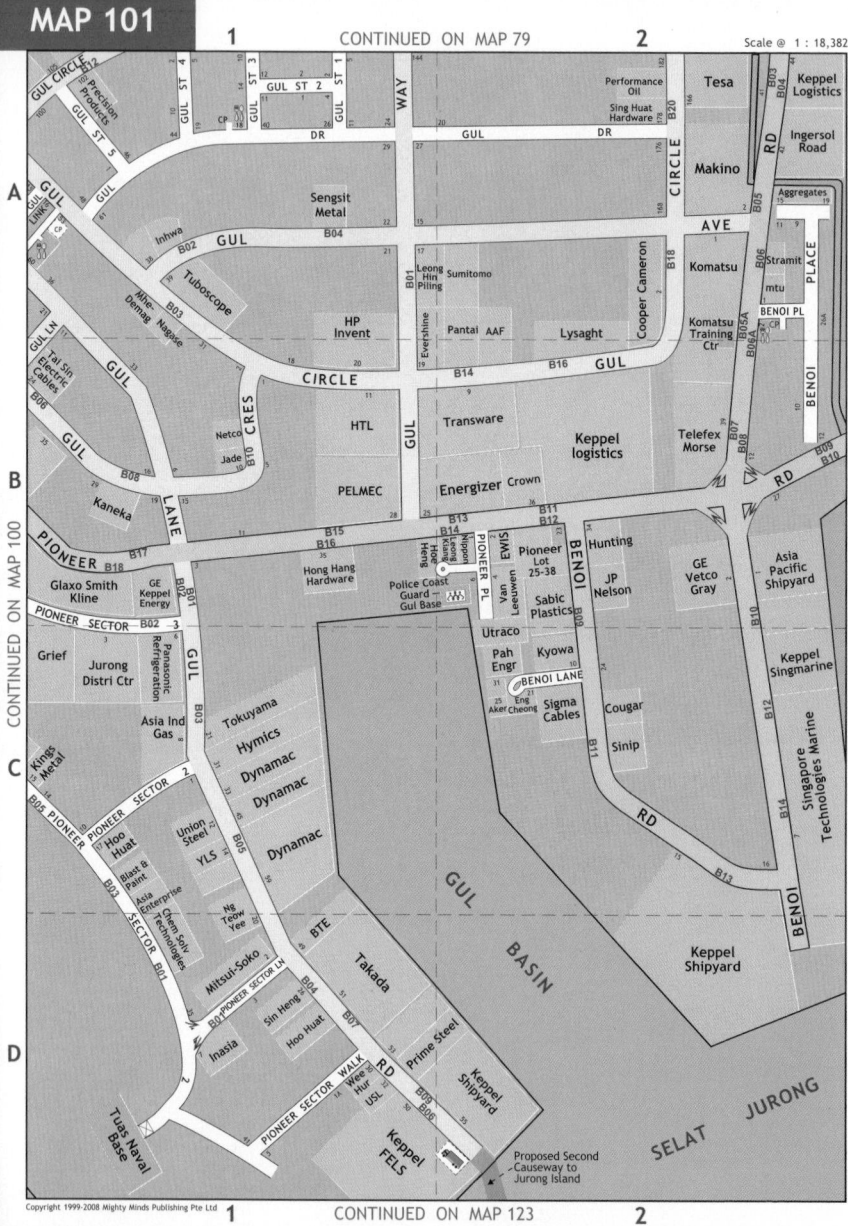

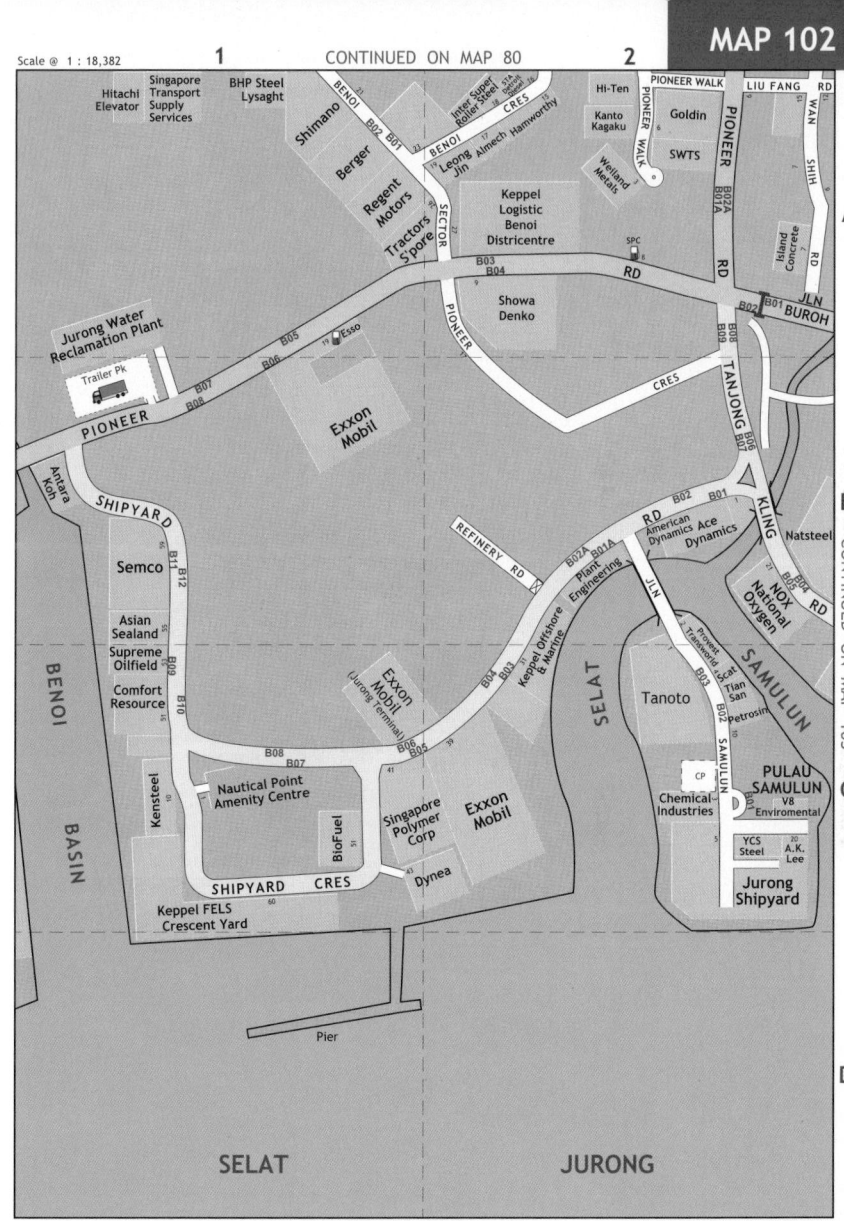

MAP 103

CONTINUED ON MAP 81

Scale @ 1 : 18,382

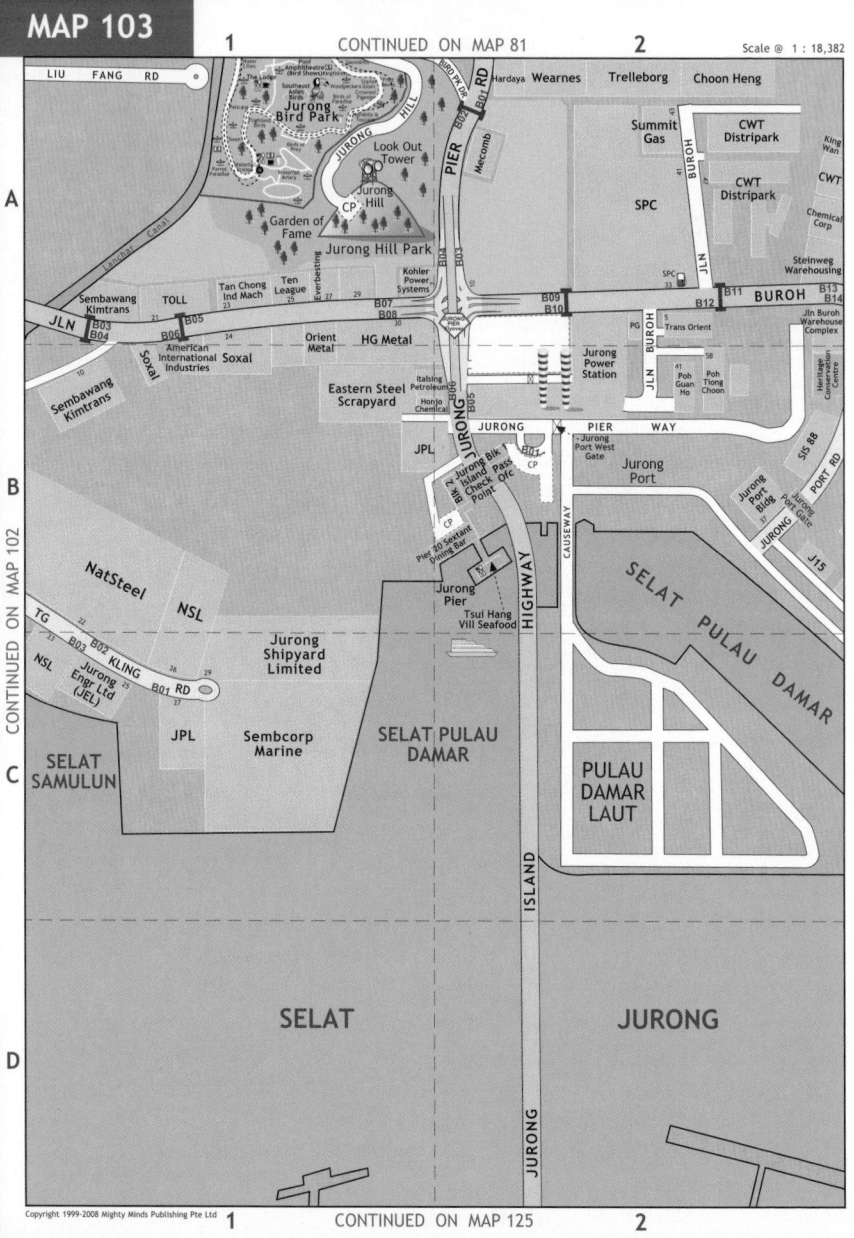

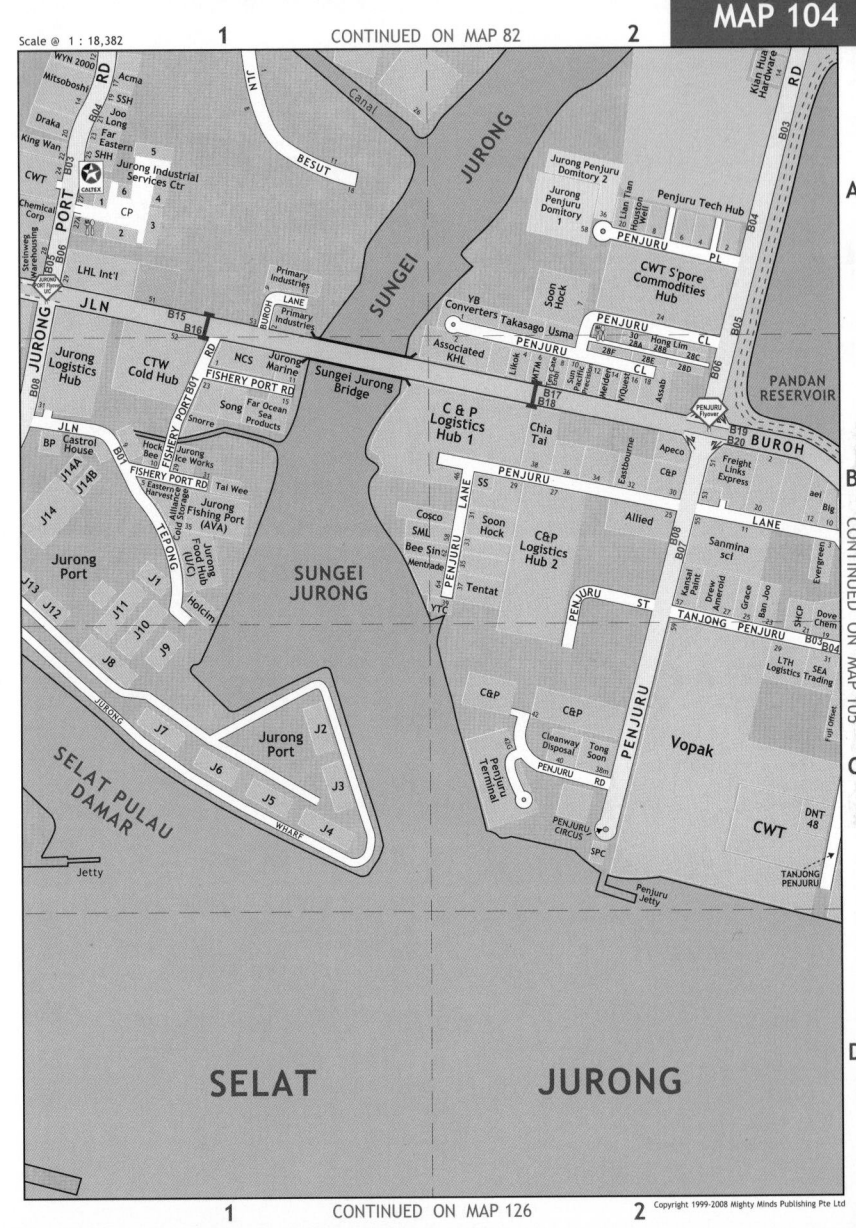

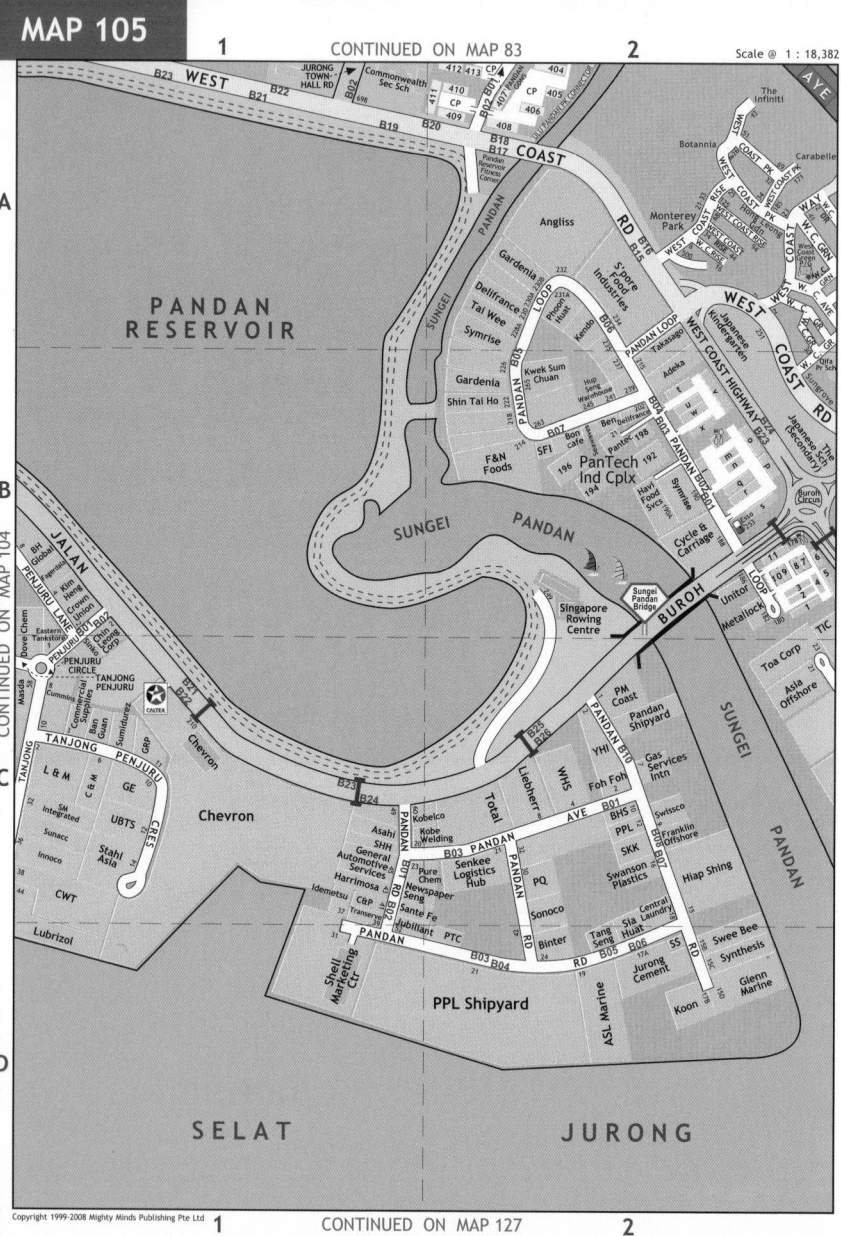

Copyright 1999-2008 Mighty Minds Publishing Pte Ltd

MAP 106

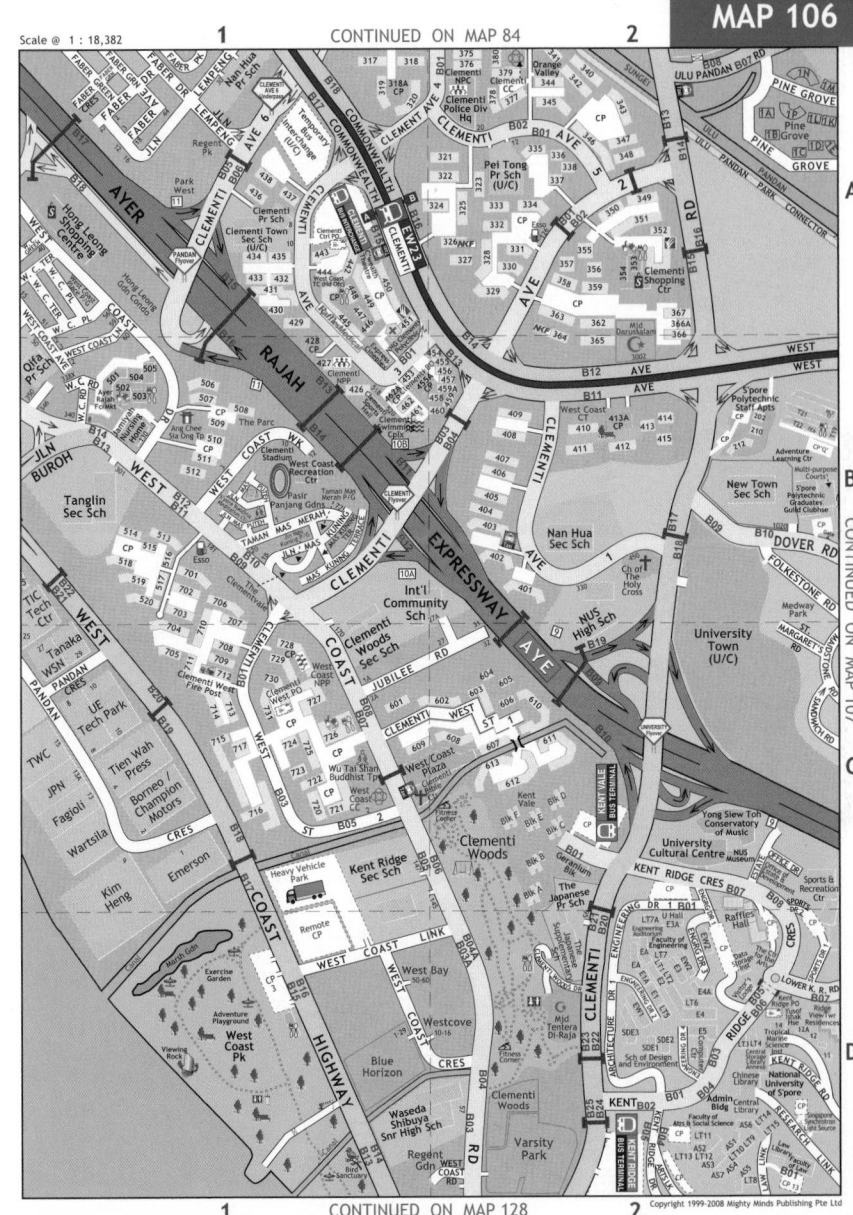

MAP 107

CONTINUED ON MAP 85

Scale @ 1 : 18,382

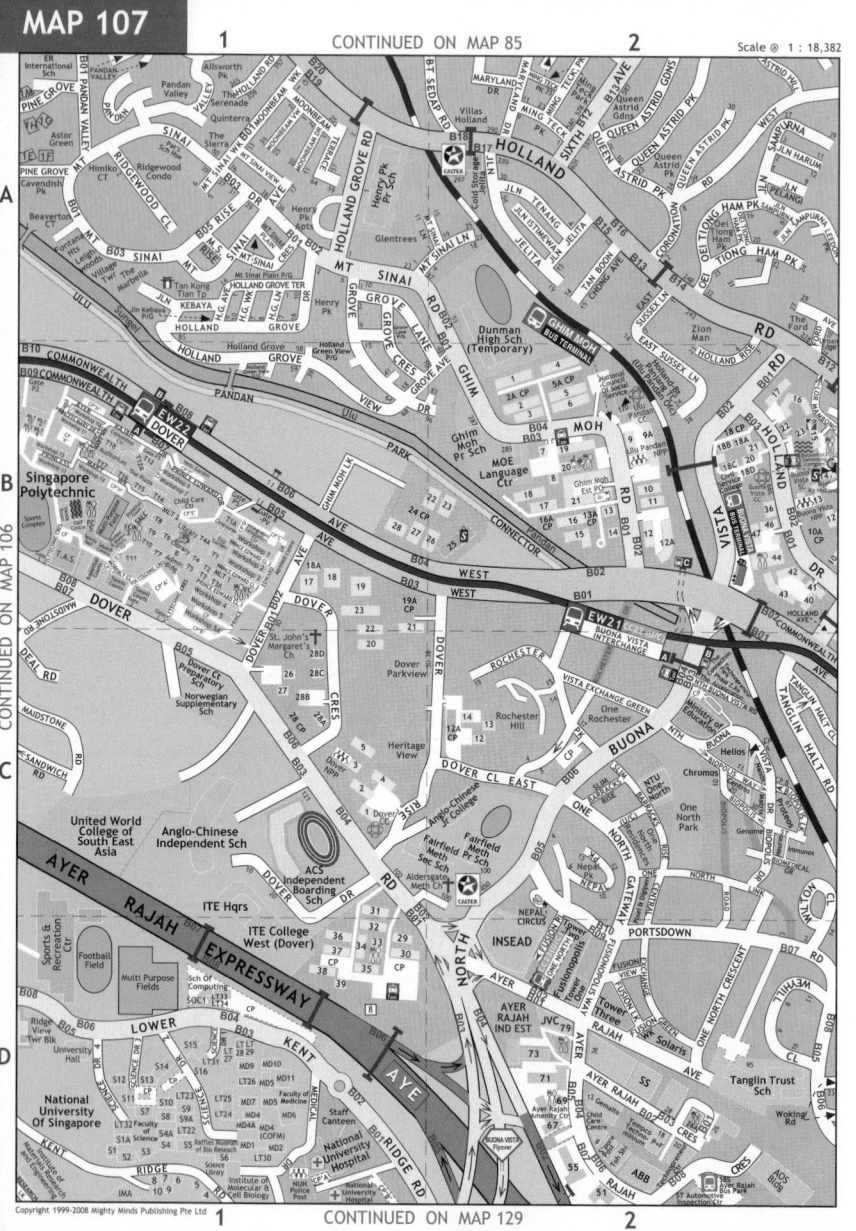

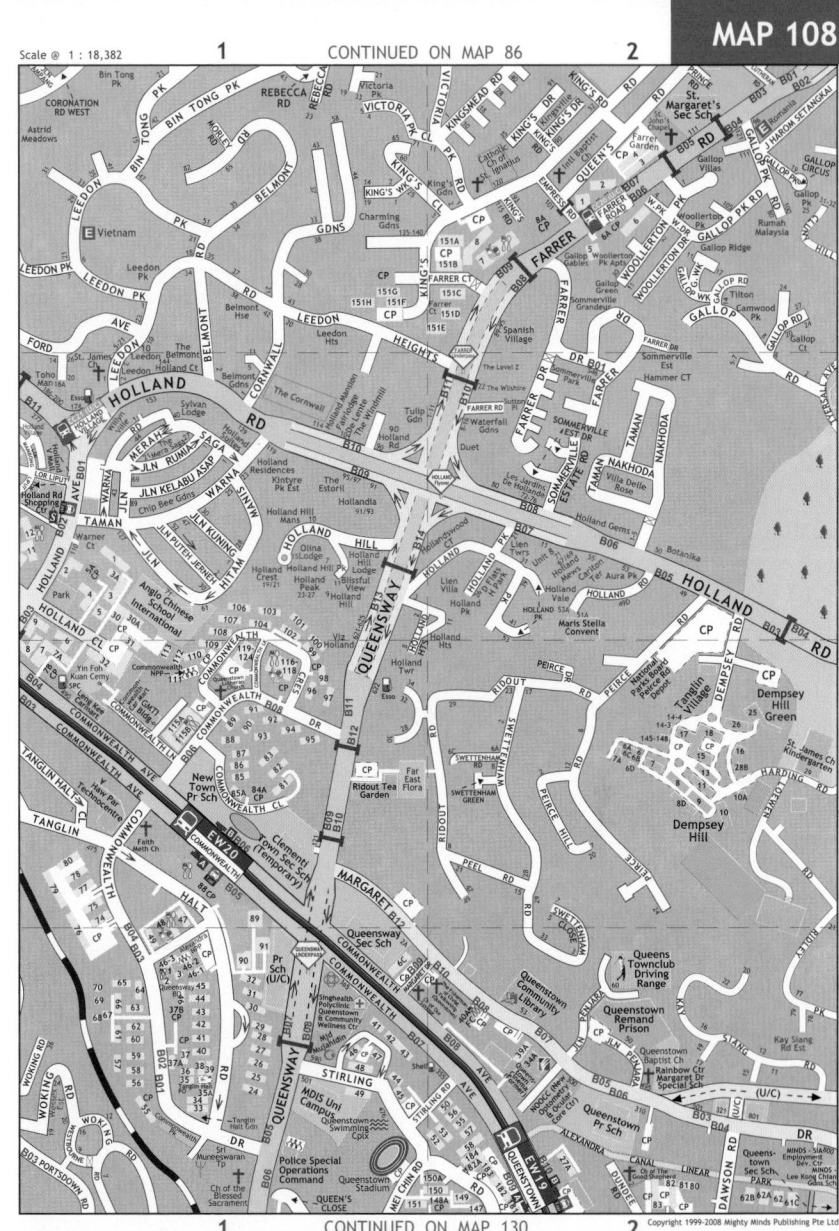

MAP 109
WITH ENLARGED SECTIONS

Scale @ 1 : 18,382

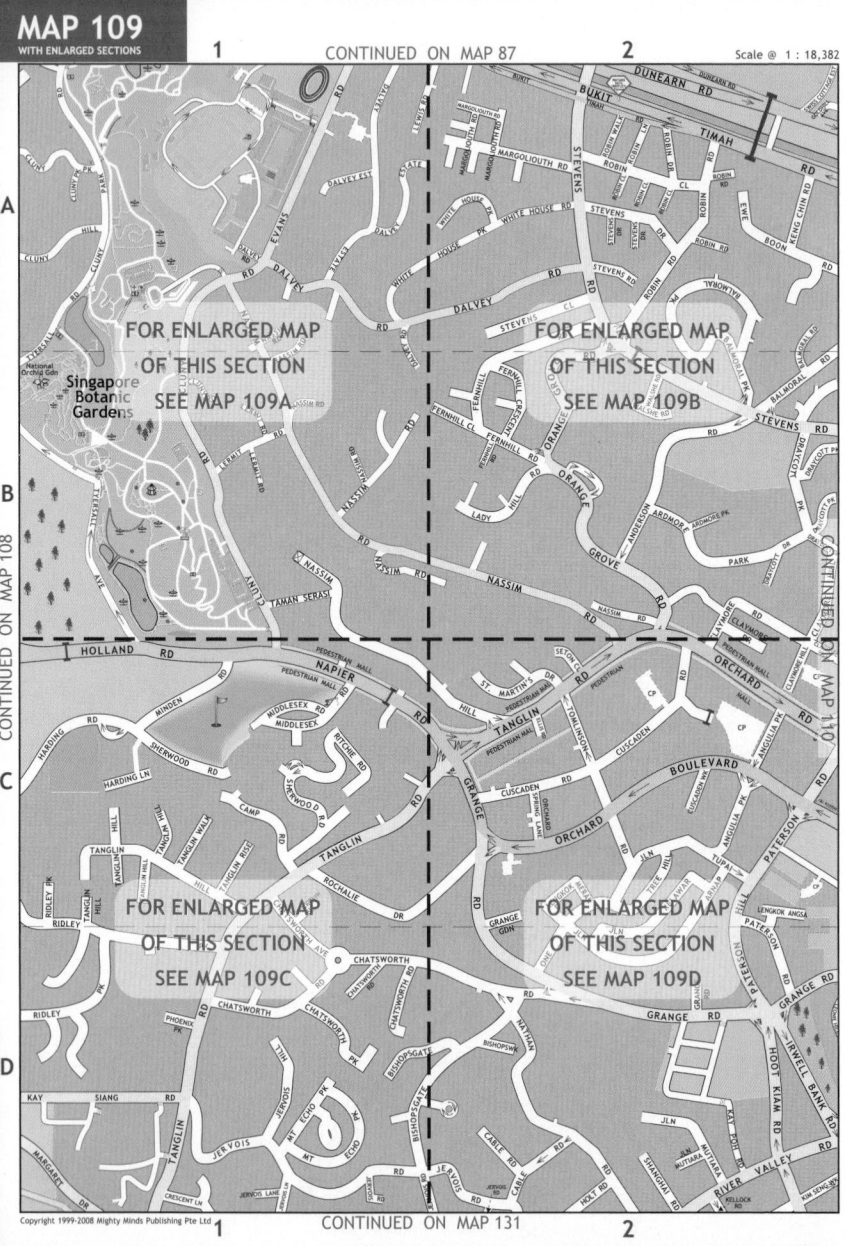

CONTINUED ON MAP 87

DUNEARN RD

FOR ENLARGED MAP
OF THIS SECTION
SEE MAP 109A

FOR ENLARGED MAP
OF THIS SECTION
SEE MAP 109B

Singapore
Botanic
Gardens
National
Orchid Gdn

FOR ENLARGED MAP
OF THIS SECTION
SEE MAP 109C

FOR ENLARGED MAP
OF THIS SECTION
SEE MAP 109D

CONTINUED ON MAP 108

CONTINUED ON MAP 110

MAP 109A
ENLARGED MAP

Scale @ 1 : 9,191

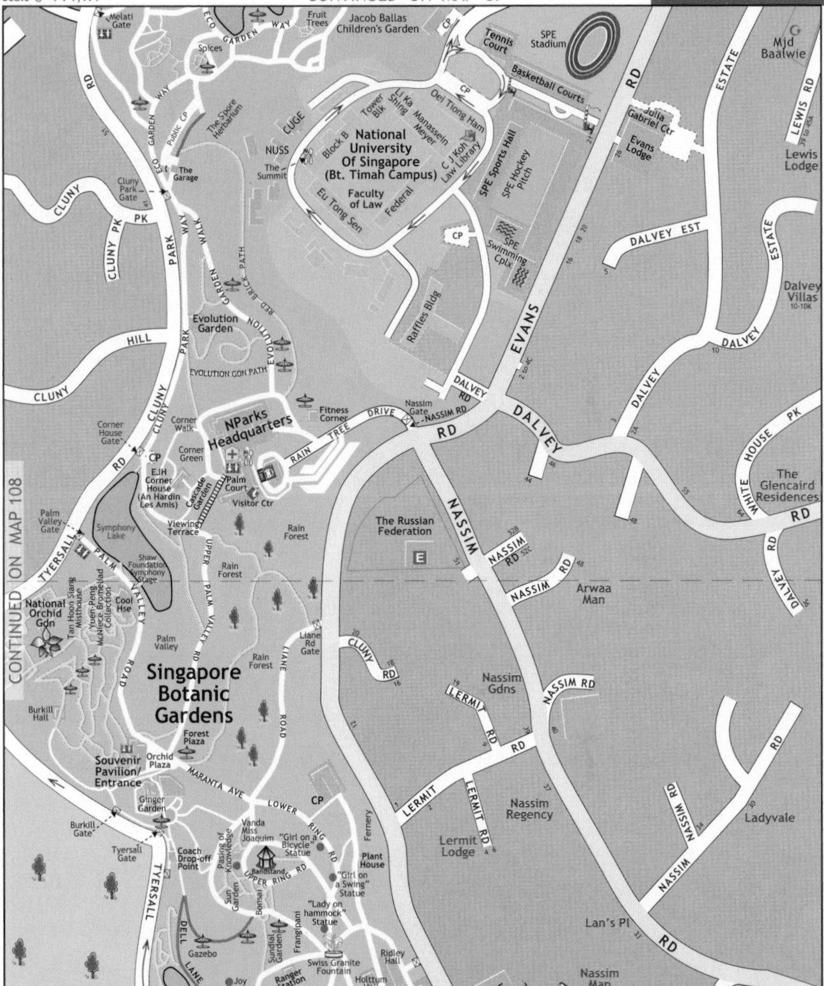

CONTINUED ON MAP 108

CONTINUED ON MAP 109B

Melati Gate

ECO GARDEN WAY

Fruit Trees

Jacob Ballas Children's Garden

Spices

The Shore Herbarium

Tennis Court

SPE Stadium

Basketball Courts

Mjd Baalwie

ESTATE

LEWIS RD

Lewis Lodge

CLUNY RD

Public CP

The Garage

NUSS

The Summit

Block B

Tower Blk

Sri Ka Shing

Manaseh Meyer

Del Tiong Ham

Julia Gabriel Ctr

Evans Lodge

CLUNY PARK GATE

Cluny Park Gate

National University Of Singapore (Bt. Timah Campus)

CLIGE

Eu Tong Sen

C J Koh Law Library

SPE Sports Hall

SPE Hockey Pitch

Evans Lodge

DALVEY EST

CLUNY PK

Faculty of Law

Federal

Raffles Bldg

CP

SPE Swimming Cpls

DALVEY VILLAS 10-10K

Dalvey Villas

HILL

Evolution Garden

EVOLUTION GDN PATH

EVANS RD

DALVEY RD

DALVEY

A

CLUNY

Corner House Gate

Corner Walk

Corner Green

NParks Headquarters

Fitness Corner

DRIVE

Nassim Gate

NASSIM RD

WHITE HOUSE PK

The Glencaird Residences

RD

RD

CP

CLUNY RD

EJH Corner House (An Hardin Les Amis)

Palm Court

Cascade Gardens

Visitor Ctr

RAIN TREE

RD

DALVEY RD

Palm Valley Gate

Symphony Lake

Viewing Terrace

Rain Forest

The Russian Federation

E

NASSIM RD

Arwaa Man

NASSIM RD

CONTINUED ON MAP 109B

TYERSALL

Shaw Foundation Symphony Stage

Rain Forest

NASSIM

National Orchid Gdn

Tan Hoon Siang Misthouse

Khoo-Teck Puat Mistouse Orchidarium

Cool Hse

RD

PALM VALLEY ROAD

LIANE ROAD

Liane Rd Gate

CLUNY RD

Nassim Gdns

LERMIT RD

Burkill Hall

Palm Valley

Rain Forest

Singapore Botanic Gardens

Forest Plaza

NASSIM RD

RD

Ladyvale

Souvenir Pavilion Entrance

Orchid Plaza

MARANTA AVE

LOWER

RING

Ginger Garden

Vanda Miss Joaquim

"Girl on a Bicycle" Statue

CP

Nassim Regency

LERMIT RD

NASSIM RD

Burkill Gate

TYERSALL

Tyersall Gate

Coach Drop-off Point

Spice Garden

Bandstand

UPPER RING RD

ROAD

Frangipani

"Girl on a Swing" Statue

Plant House

Fernery

Lermit Lodge

B

Sundial Gardens

Frangipani

"Lady on a hammock" Statue

Lan's Pl

DELL LANE

Gazebo

Joy

Ranger Station

Sundial Gardens

Swiss Granite Fountain

Holttum Hall

Ridley Hall

OMF International

NASSIM

Nassim Man

AVE

Swan Lake

Flight of Swan

Gazebo

Swing me mama Statue

TANGLIN

GATE

Marsh Garden

Green Pavilion

CLUNY RD

TAMAN SERASI

Botanic Gdns View

Botanic Gdns Man

HILL

NASSIM RD

Tanglin Gate

Gleneagles Medical Ctr

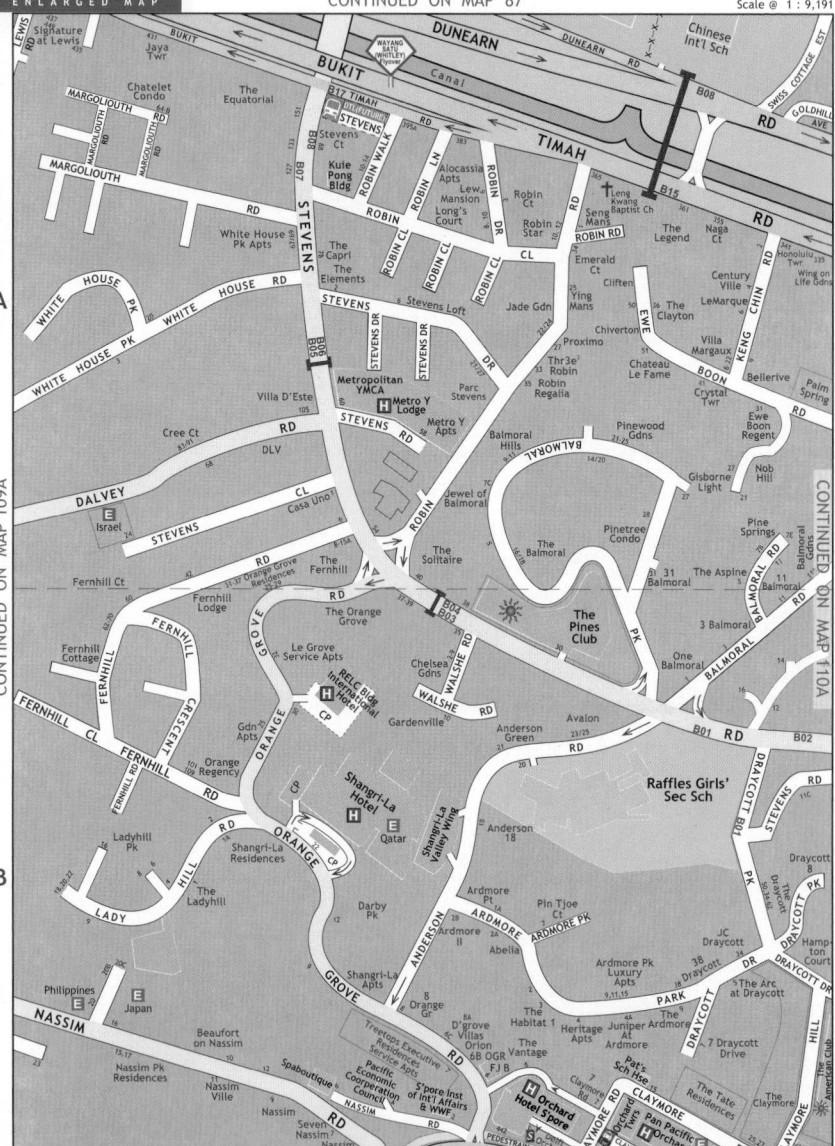

Scale @ 1 : 9,191

TYERSALL AVE
B02
B01
HOLLAND RD
Singapore Botanic Gardens
CLUNY RD
Gleneagles Hospital
8 Napier
NASSIM
Nassim Woods 19
HILL
NAPIER
PEDESTRIAN MALL
B04
B03
RD
B01 B02
30 British Council
Dempsey Hut
CP
MINDEN
RD
Tanglin Golf Course
MIDDLESEX RD
RD
27
USA
Highwood
CP
HARDING
RD
SHERWOOD
St. George's Ch (Tanglin)
Tanglin Fields
Ebenezer Chapel
CP
HARDING LANE
MIDDLESEX
25
Australia
RITCHIE RD
UK
100
B01 B02
C
RD
CP
Ministry of Foreign Affairs HQ Cplx
SHERWOOD
China
CAMP
RD
150
RD
TANGLIN HILL
TANGLIN HILL
TANGLIN HILL
TANGLIN WALK
TANGLIN RISE
Tanglin Hill Condo
ROCHALIE
DR
12
17
TANGLIN
HILL
CONTINUED ON MAP 108
RIDLEY PK
TANGLIN HILL
Tanglin Hill Meadows
CHATSWORTH AVE
CHATSWORTH AVE
CONTINUED ON MAP 109D
RIDLEY
PK
2
Tanglin Pk
B07
CHATSWORTH
RD
CHATSWORTH RD
CHATSWORTH RD
RIDLEY
PK
CHATSWORTH
RD
CHATSWORTH PK
BISHOPSGATE
PHOENIX PK
B06
CHATSWORTH
Brunei
D
HILL
JERVOIS
ECHO PK
Mt Echo Pk
BISHOPSGATE
KAY
SIANG RD
Gate B
CP
Gate C
Gate A
S'pore Youth Olympic Games Organising Committee
TANGLIN
JERVOIS
MT ECHO
MT ECHO
New York University (NYU) Tisch Sch of Arts (Asia)
CP
MARGARET DR
B01
MINDS Lee Kong Chian Gdns Sch
Esso
Grace Assembly of God Ch
Jervois Green
Casa Jervois
Jervois Grove
JERVOIS LN
RD
Dormer Pk
Jervois Regency
JERVOIS RD
ALEXANDRA CANAL LINEAR PK
B02
CRESCENT LN
Clydesview
JERVOIS LN
Crescent Girls Sch
Spore Sch For The Deaf
ICA Academy

Copyright 1999-2008 Mighty Minds Publishing Pte Ltd

CONTINUED ON MAP 109C

CONTINUED ON MAP 110C

The Loft

St. Martin's Residence

NASSIM RD
NASSIM RD

SETON CL

NASSIM MALL

ORCHARD TWRS
Palais Renaissance

B20

Claremont Plaza Apts
Claremont Apts

CLAYMORE DR

CLAYMORE HILL
Pakistan

Thailand

Int'l Bldg

Shaw Ctr

St. Martin's Lodge

Tanglin Residence

ST MARTIN'S DR

Friven & Co.
Tanglin PO

NAPIER RD

TANGLIN

HILL

Myanmar

Tudor Ct Shopping Gallery

Tanglin Mall

Traders Hotel S'pore

Regent S'pore

ELLIS RD

TOMLINSON RD

Tanglin Place

St. Regis Hotel

St. Regis Residences (U/C)

Tanglin Shopping Ctr

Multi Storey CP

Ming Arcade

Orchard Parade Hotel

Forum The Shopping Mall

CLAYMORE RD PEDESTRIAN

Hilton Hotel

Far East Shopping Ctr

ORCHARD RD

Liat Twrs

Borders

Netherlands

Wheelock Place

CP

HPL Hse

Nanyang Moral Uplifting General Society

Four Seasons Hotel

Cuscaden Residence

The Biltmore (U/C)

B03

ANGULLIA PK

BOULEVARD

The Parisian

Ion Orchard

3RD BOUNDARY

C

Grange Residences

GRANGE

CUSCADEN

S'pore Tourism Board Tourism Ct

Camden Medical Centre

ORCHARD

SPRING LANE

ALLANBROOKE RD

Pk Hse

B05

The Tomlinson

The Boulevard Residences (BLVD)

CUSCADEN WK

Cuscaden Walk

Four Seasons Pk

Boulevard Vue

Cuscaden Royale

ANGULLIA PK

Skyline Angullia

Angullia Mans

Orchard View

The Marq (on Paterson Hill)

The Paterson Edge

PATERSON RD

Paterson Lodge

ISS Int'l Sch (Elementary Sch)

Gate

CP

ROCHALIE DR

Westwood Apts

Orchard Bel Air

Beverly Mai

Kum Hing Ct

TUPAI

HILL

KELAWAR

ARNAP

ISS Int'l Sch (Middle Sch)

CP

CP

SANA

Residence 8

31 to 45

LENGKOK MERAK

TREE

JLN

One Tree Hill Gdns

Kim Lin Pk

LENGKOK ANGSA

Paterson Suites

25B Overseas Family Ctr

25C

25D

The Grange (U/C)

GRANGE GDN

Parkview Eclat

One Tree Hill Residence

JLN ONE

One Tree Hill Mans

JLN

Paterson Twr

HILL

PATERSON

PATERSON

Paterson Residence

The Paterson

Egypt

CHATSWORTH

Indonesia

Indonesia Embassy Residential Units

Grange Rd Apts

NATHAN

Rainbow Man

One Chatsworth

Cliveden at Grange

Beverly Hill

Colonnade

GRANGE RD

Manhattan Man

Grange CT

Grange 80

B04

B03

B02

Lucky Twr

Spring Grove

MOE Teachers Network

Grange 70

PATERSON RD

GRANGE RD

HOOT KIAM RD

GR

The Paterson

LEONIE HILL

D

BISHOPSGATE

BISHOPSGATE

Bishops Walk

BISHOPSWALK

Regency Pk

CABLE RD

JERVOIS

Jervois Lodge

JERVOIS RD

Jervois View

Malaysia

Nathan Pl

HCM Residential Cplx

The Horizon

Regency Lodge

CABLE RD

HOLT RD

No 1 Holt Road

Shanghai One

Studio 3

SHANGHAI

Queensberry Nathan Lodge Res

Bishops

Nathan RD

BLK 2

BLK 3

BLK 4

BLK 5

BLK 1

i-care lodge

Kay Poh Rd Baptist Ch

JLN

The Montana

Latitude

KAY POH

JLN MUTIARA

Mutiara Crest

Mutiara View

Charleston

B14A

B14

B13

Kasturina Lodge

The Aston

Kellock Lodge

RIVER

Ch of St. Bernadette

Zion Full Gospel Ch

Edward Lee Apts

IRWELL BANK RD

VALLEY RD

ZION RD

KELLOCK RD

KIM SENG WK

The Tiara

Great World Service Apt

Copyright 1999-2008 Mighty Minds Publishing Pte Ltd

CONTINUED ON MAP 131

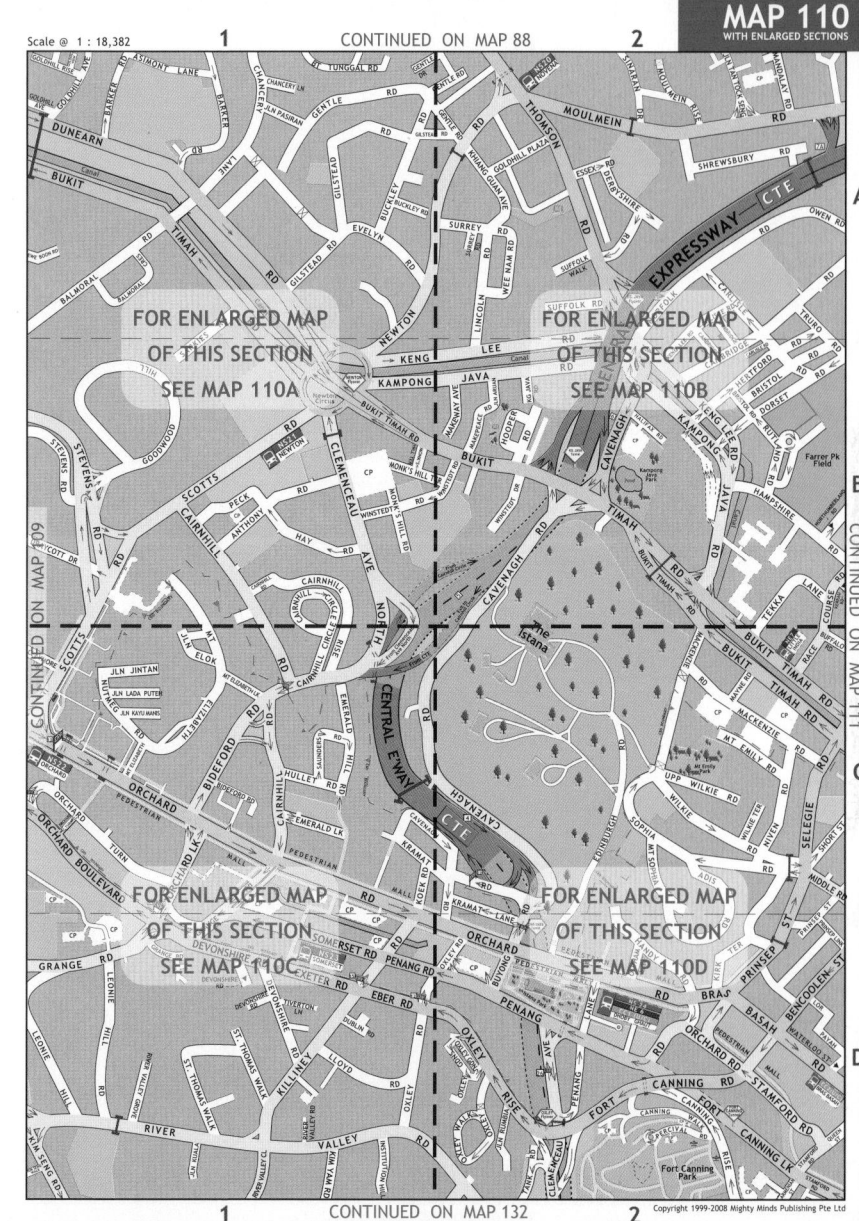

FOR ENLARGED MAP
OF THIS SECTION
SEE MAP 110A

FOR ENLARGED MAP
OF THIS SECTION
SEE MAP 110B

FOR ENLARGED MAP
OF THIS SECTION
SEE MAP 110C

FOR ENLARGED MAP
OF THIS SECTION
SEE MAP 110D

CONTINUED ON MAP 109

CONTINUED ON MAP 111

CONTINUED ON MAP 132

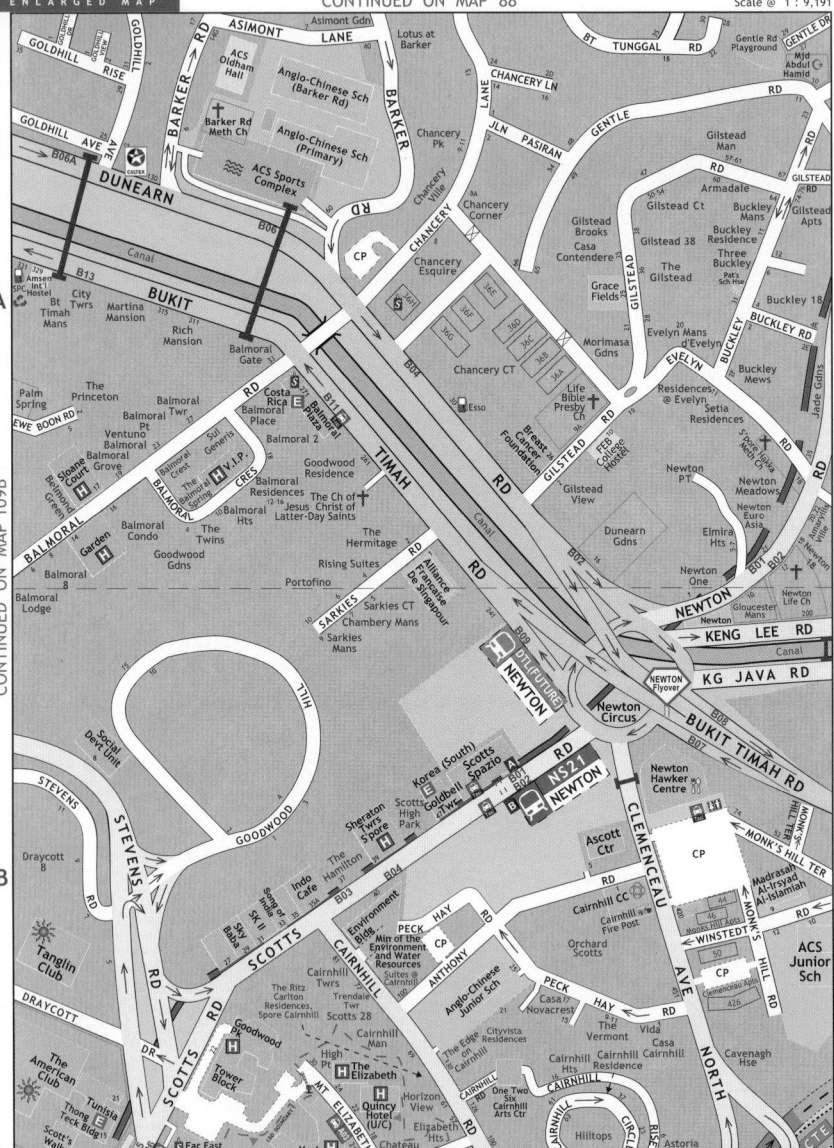

CONTINUED ON MAP 109B

CONTINUED ON MAP 110C

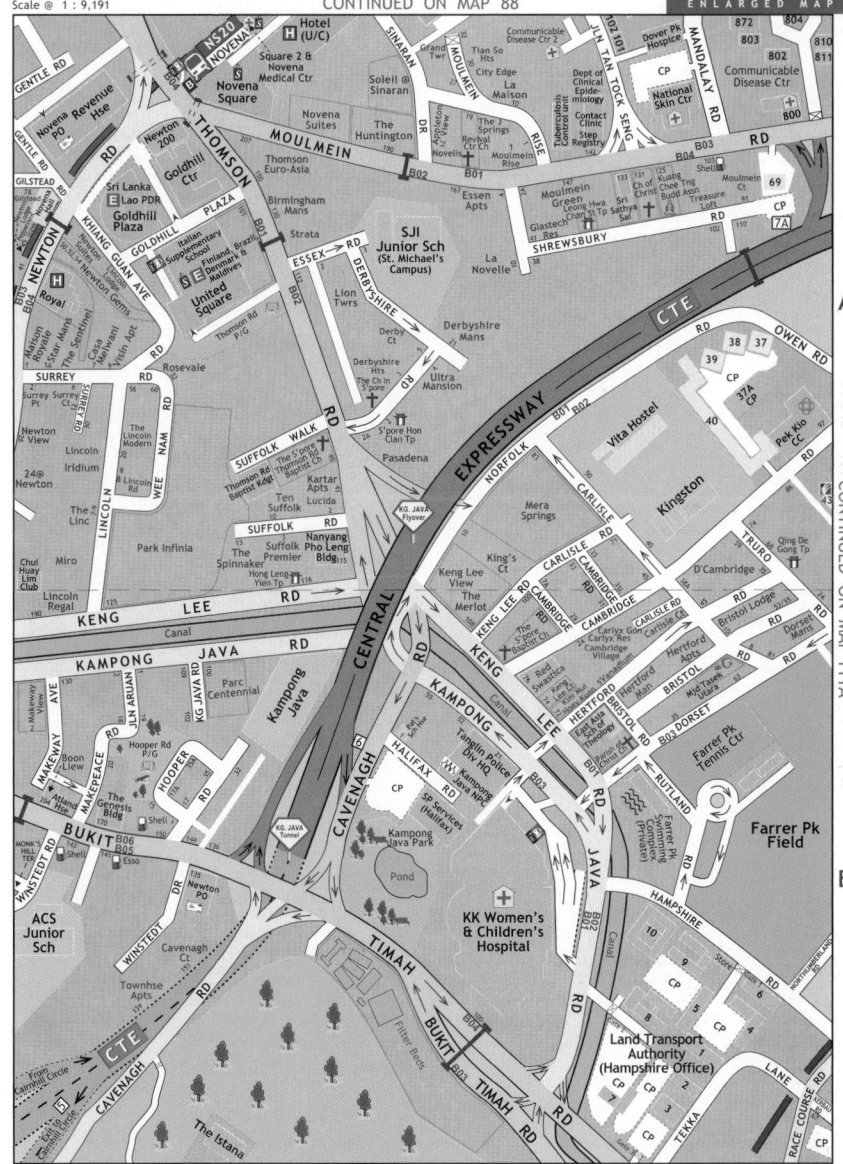

CONTINUED ON MAP 109D

CONTINUED ON MAP 132A

Copyright 1999-2008 Mighty Minds Publishing Pte Ltd

Roads and places:

SCOTTS RD · CLAYMORE HILL · JLN ELOK · MT ELIZABETH LK · CAIRNHILL RD · CAIRNHILL CIRCLE · CLEMENCEAU AVE NTH · CENTRAL EXPRESSWAY · CTE

Royal Plaza · Pacific Plaza · Far East Plaza · The Esquire · Comoros Cairnhill · Helios · The Light · The Cairnhill · Astoria Apts · Kimsia CT · JLN JINTAN · JLN LADA PUTEH · JLN KAYU MANIS · JLN NUTMEG · Grand Hyatt S'pore · Scotts square · Scotts Ctr · Shaw Hse · Elizabeth Twrs · Rhapsody on Mt Elizabeth · SomerSet Compass · Tan Chin Tuan Man · Cairnhill Crest · Emerald Lodge · Top Teh Apt · KG JAVA TUNNEL · Cavenagh Fortuna · Cavenagh Lodge · Cavenagh Gdn · Water Scape @ Cavenagh

Mt Elizabeth Hospital · Richmond Pk · Mt. Elizabeth Medical Ctr · Paragon Medical · Hill CT · Urban Resort · Emerald Man · Cavenagh Mans

S'pore Marriott · Tangs Plaza · Lucky Plaza · Lucky Plaza PO · ORCHARD RD · Ion Orchard · NS22 ORCHARD · Wisma Atria · Poland · Thong Sia Bldg · Mjd Al-Falah · Cairnhill Place (CP) · Somerset Grand Cairnhill · Char Yong Gdns · HULLET RD · Hullet Rise · 8 Hullet Rd · HulletCT · Chatsworth Int'l Sch · Sian Teck Tng Tp · Starhub Ctr · Holiday Inn Park View · SAUNDERS RD · EMERALD HILL · CBD BOUNDARY

Orchard Park Suites · Orchard Residences · ORCHARD BOULEVARD · ORCHARD TURN · Takashimaya Shopping Ctr · Ngee Ann City · Fiji · Orchard PO · New Zealand · The Paragon · BIDEFORD RD · Park Hotel Orchard S'pore · 268 · The Heeren · EMERALD LINK · Pacific Plaza · Meritus Mandarin · Mandarin Orchard · Mandarin Shopping Arcade · ORCHARD LINK · Centrepoint Apartments · Cuppage Plaza · KRAMAT · Pregnation Place · The CentrePoint · SomerSet Orchard · Orchard PO · KOEK RD

Twr A · Twr B · Chatsworth Orchard · Chelbourne Orchard · GRANGE RD · SOMERSET RD · Orchard Bldg · ORCHARD RD · Orchard Shopping Centre · Specialists Shopping Centre · Orchard Central (U/C) · Penang House · Penang Rd Oc'l · Killiney Rd PO · PENANG RD

25G · 25H · 25J · 25K · Overseas Family Sch · Overseas Family College · CP · Garden · S'pore Power Bldg · Nat'l Youth Council · S'pore Youth Pk · Somerset Central (U/C) · Sweden · Swedish Supplementary Sch · B01 RD · NS23 SOMERSET · Skate Pk · Saudi Arabia · Samoa · Winsland House II · Goethe Institut

GRANGE RD · LEONIE HILL · Grange Infinite · Grangeford Apt · India · Lumos · Leonie View · Horizon Twrs (East Twr) · Leonie Parc View · DEVONSHIRE RD · The Beaumont · The Metz · Devonshire Lodge · EXETER RD · Comcentre · Comcentre II · Singtel · Comcentre III · EBER RD · Orchard NPC · Eber Gdns · Oxley Man · Villa Madeleine

Leonie Studio · Leonie Gdn · Horizon Twrs (West Twr) · Ritz Residences · Sam Klang Man · St. Thomas Suites · Devonshire Apts · Devonshire Bldg · The Bayron · TIVERTON LN · Tong Stan Tng Tp · DUBLIN RD · Dublin Lodge · Dublin Rd Flats · The SKA Villa

LEONIE HILL · Leonie Twrs (B) · Leonie Hill Residences · Futura · Grange Hts · Riveria Gardens · St. Thomas Lodge · St. Thomas CT · St. Thomas Ville · St. Thomas View · The Abode at Devonshire · One Devonshire · CGH Bldg · Brentwood · LLOYD RD · Lloyd CT · Lloyds Inn · Lloyd Man

Leonie Twrs (A) · Riva Lodge · Leonie Condotel · Luma · RIVER VALLEY GROVE · ST. THOMAS WALK · SkyPark · Phoenix CT · KILLINEY RD · Killiney Apt · Meng Gdn Apts · The Botanic On Lloyd · OXLEY RISE

River-shire · Riverdale Residence · Wilmer Hse · Airview Twrs · La Crystal · Claremont · Residences at 338A · AA Ctr · Valley Hse · Stardus Clubhouse · Valley Man · VALLEY RD

KIM SENG RD · The Cosmopolitan · ERC Institute · RIVER VALLEY RD · JLN KUALA · RIVER VALLEY CL · The Morningside · The Regalia · Urbana · Riveria Pt · Langston Ville · KIM YAM RD · Aspen Hts · Valley Lodge

The Trillium · Great World Service Apt · Yong An Pk · River Valley Pr Sch · Pacific Man · Euro-Asia CT · Martin Place · The S'pore Buddhist Lodge · INSTITUTION HILL

Scale @ 1 : 9,191

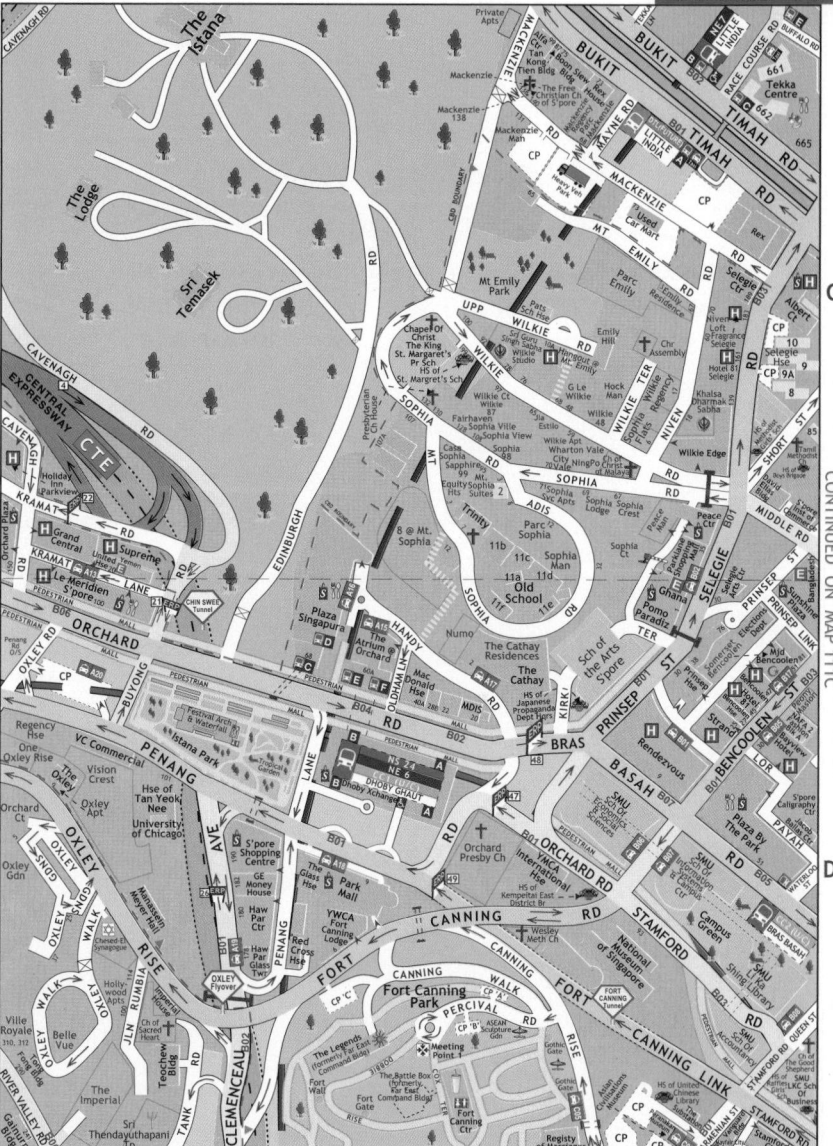

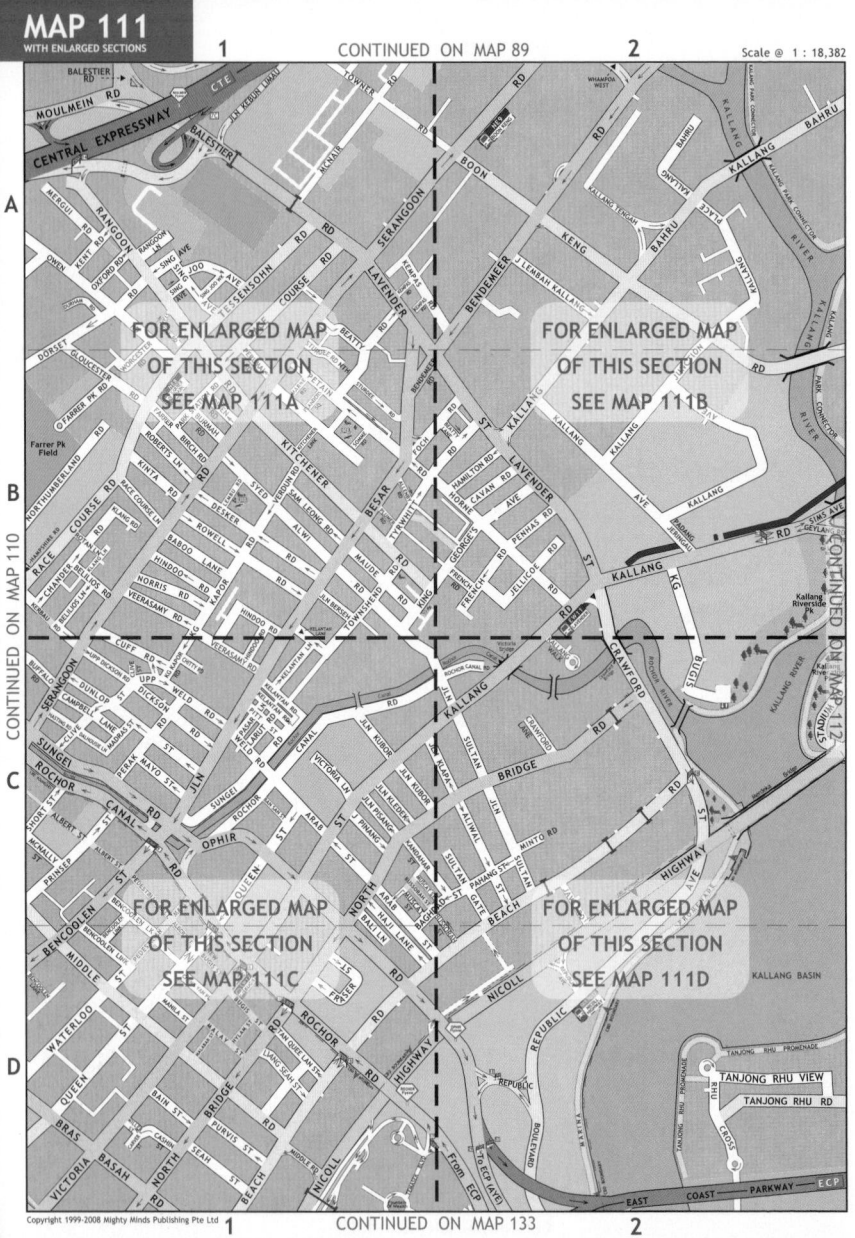

FOR ENLARGED MAP
OF THIS SECTION
SEE MAP 111A

FOR ENLARGED MAP
OF THIS SECTION
SEE MAP 111B

FOR ENLARGED MAP
OF THIS SECTION
SEE MAP 111C

FOR ENLARGED MAP
OF THIS SECTION
SEE MAP 111D

CONTINUED ON MAP 110

CONTINUED ON MAP 112

Scale @ 1 : 9,191

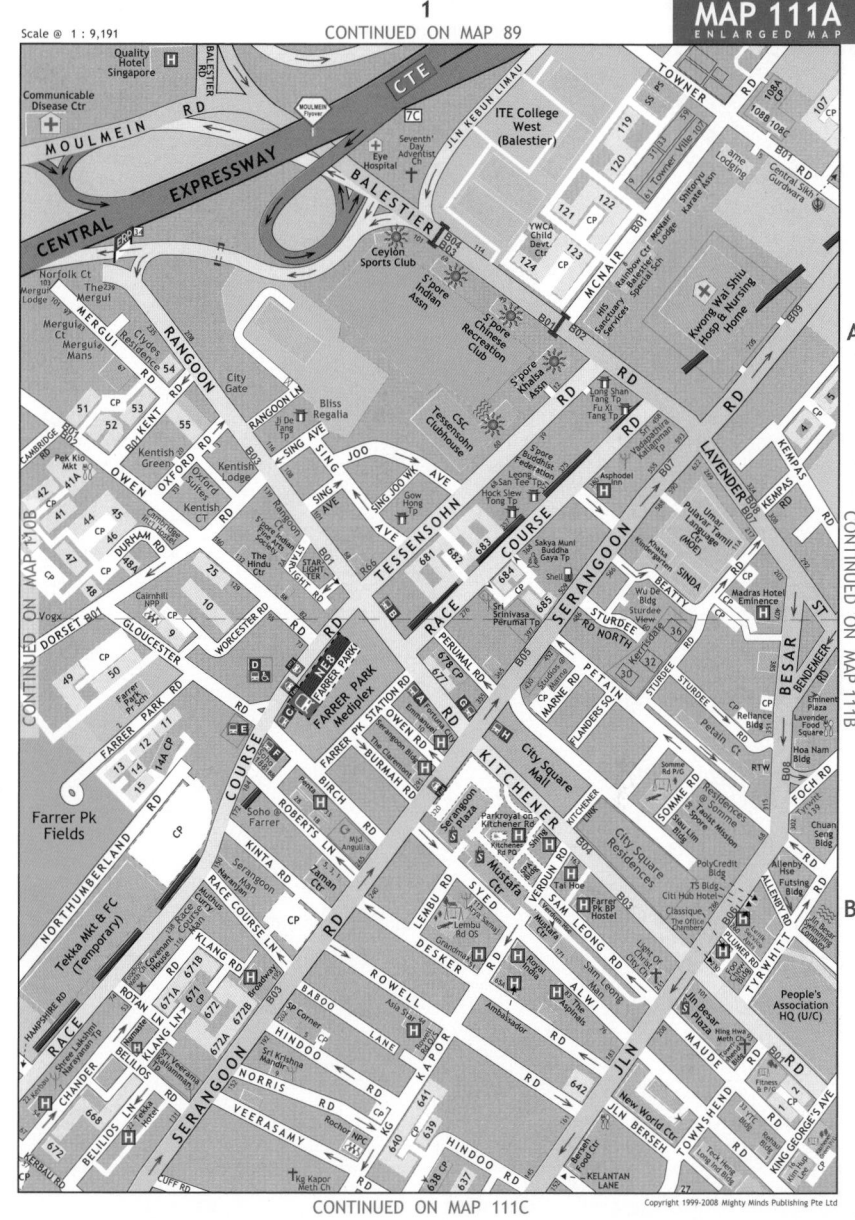

CONTINUED ON MAP 130B

CONTINUED ON MAP 111B

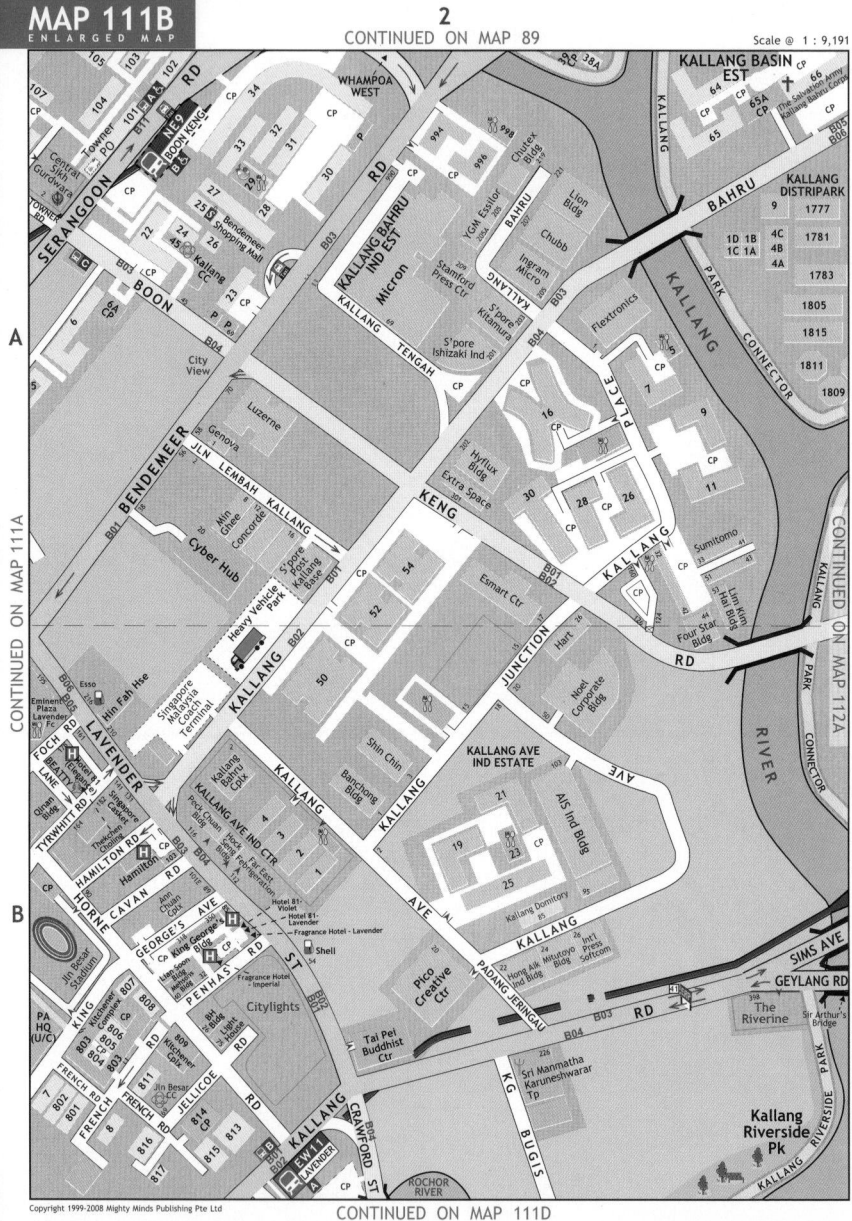

CONTINUED ON MAP 111A

CONTINUED ON MAP 111D

CONTINUED ON MAP 112A

Scale @ 1 : 9,191

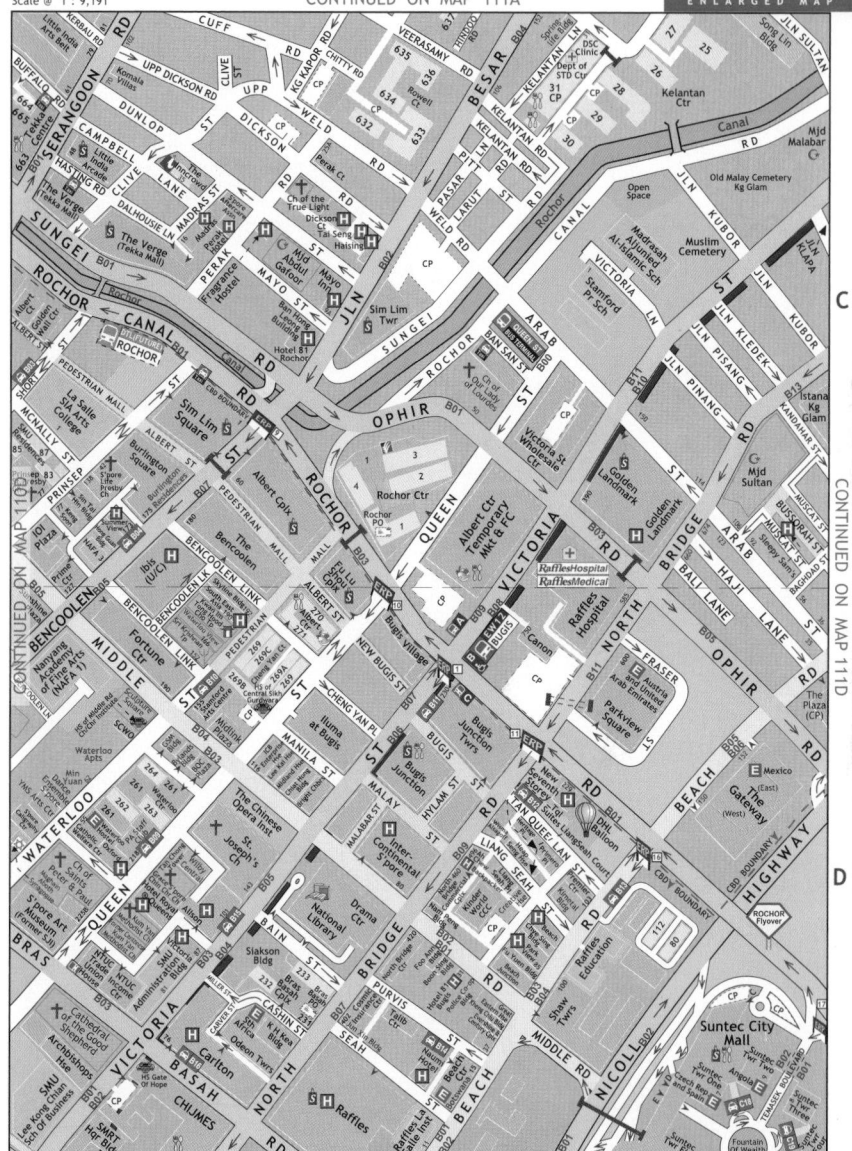

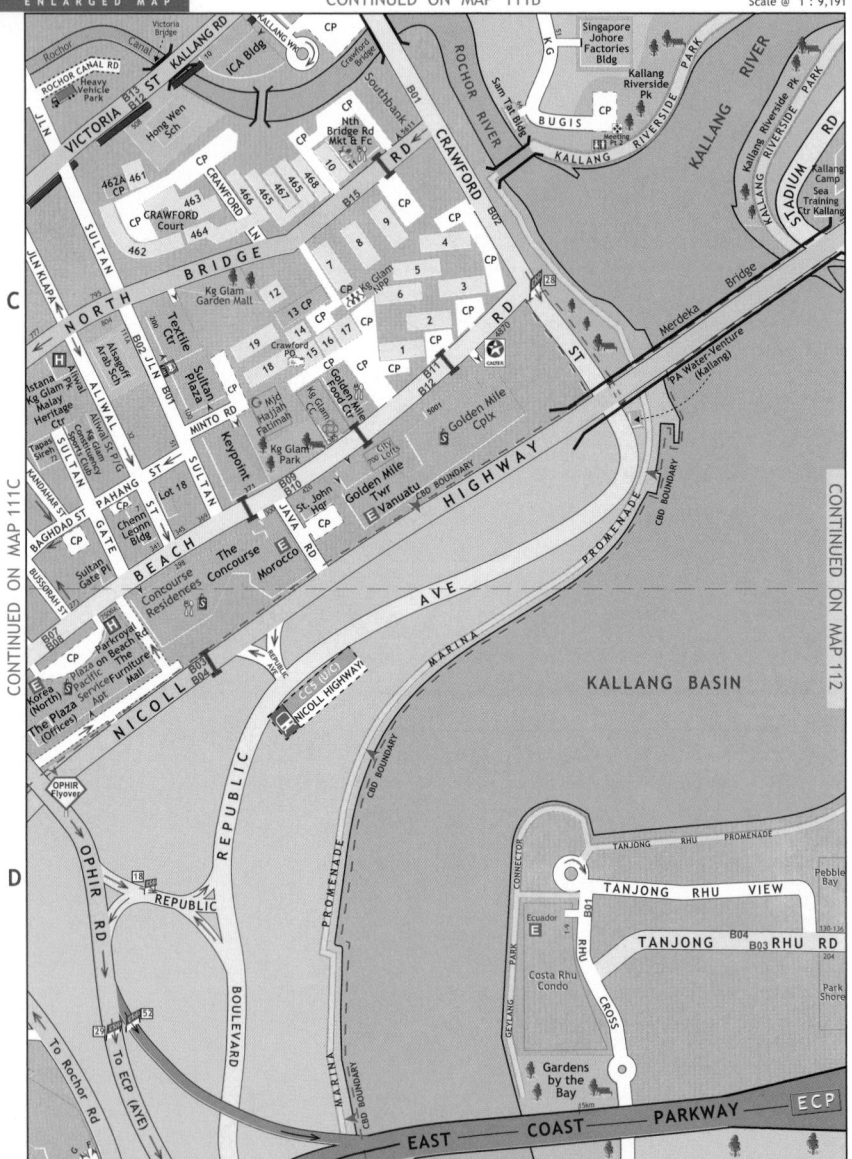

CONTINUED ON MAP 111C
CONTINUED ON MAP 111B
CONTINUED ON MAP 112
CONTINUED ON MAP 133

KALLANG BASIN

KALLANG RIVER

CONTINUED ON MAP 90

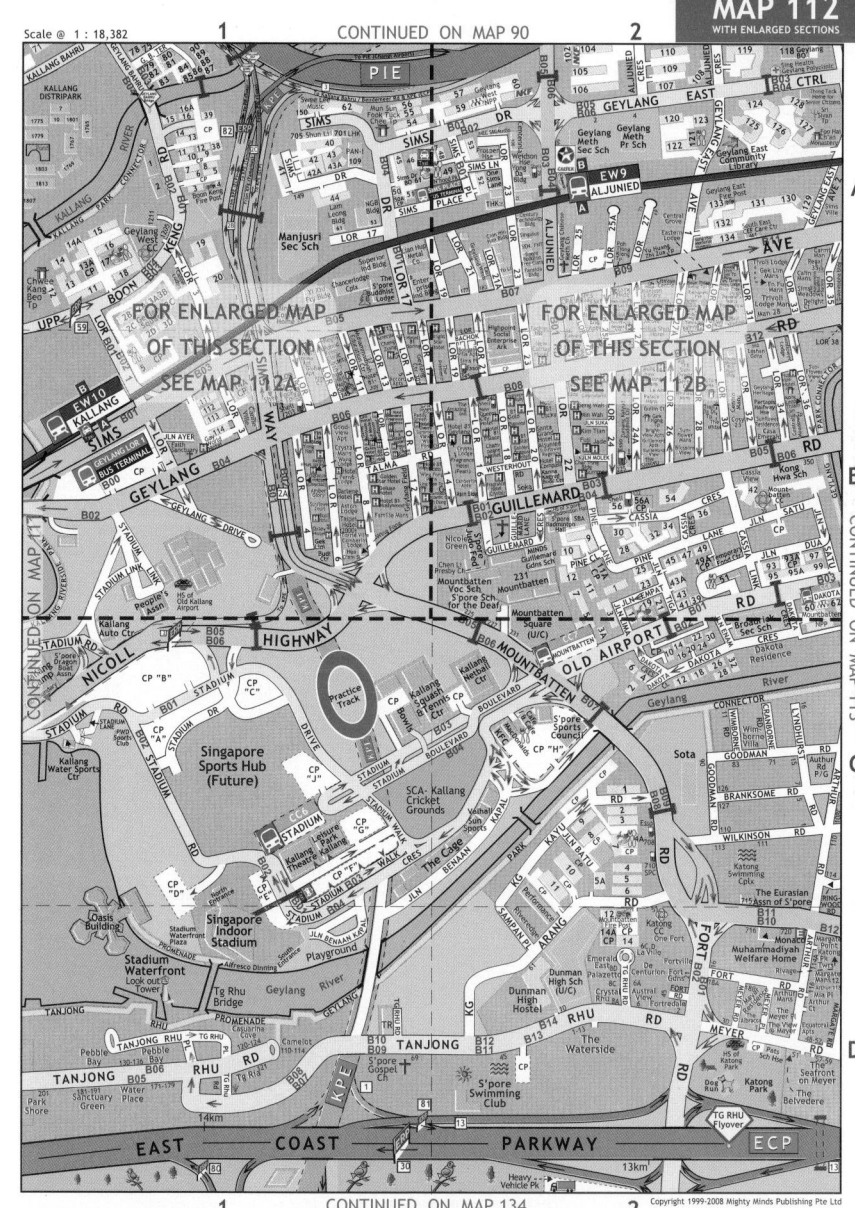

FOR ENLARGED MAP OF THIS SECTION SEE MAP 112A

FOR ENLARGED MAP OF THIS SECTION SEE MAP 112B

Singapore Sports Hub (Future)

Singapore Indoor Stadium

CONTINUED ON MAP 134

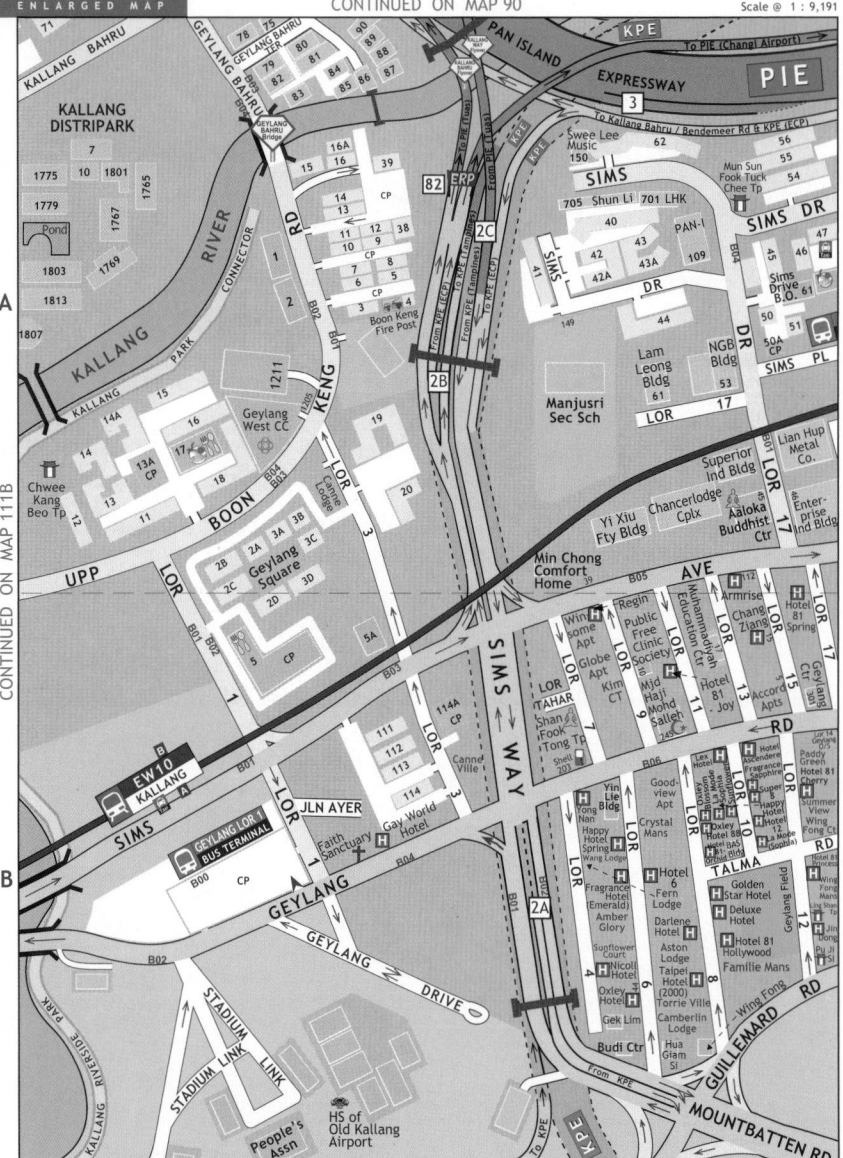

CONTINUED ON MAP 111B

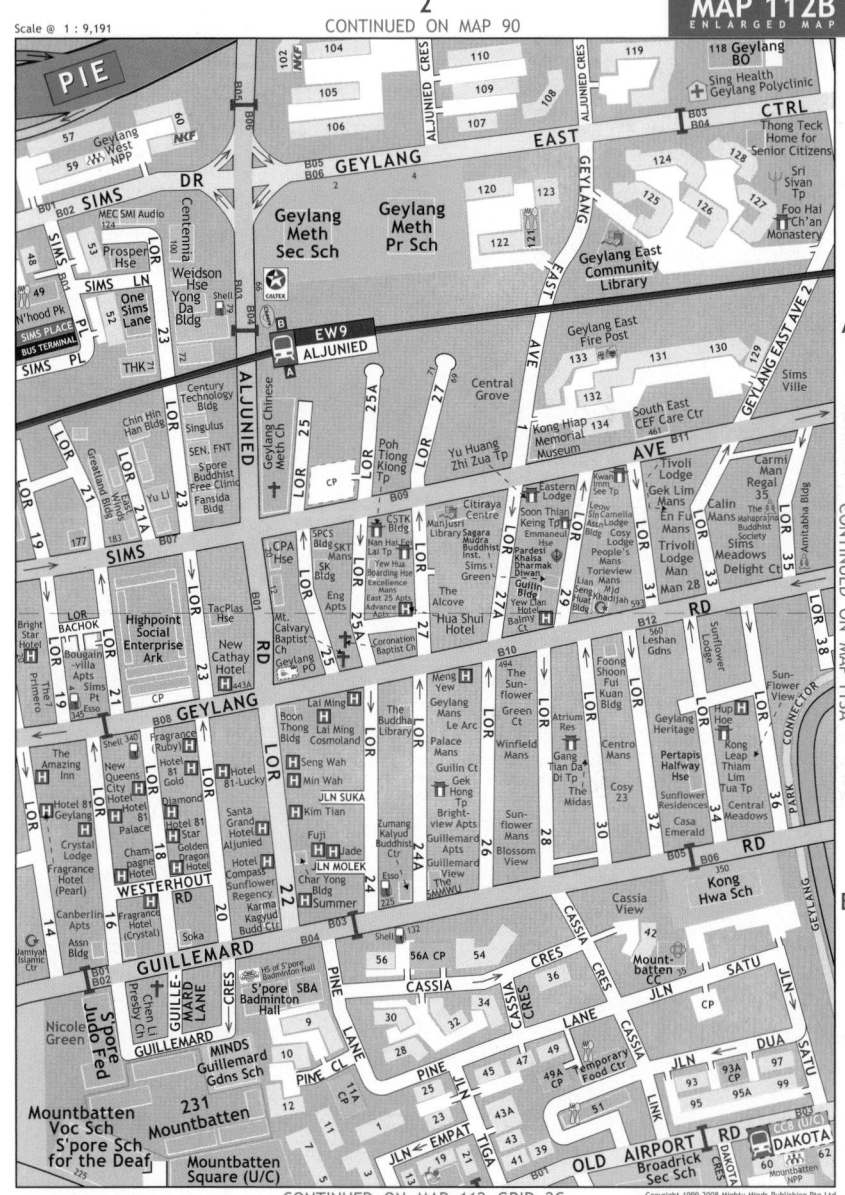

Scale @ 1 : 9,191

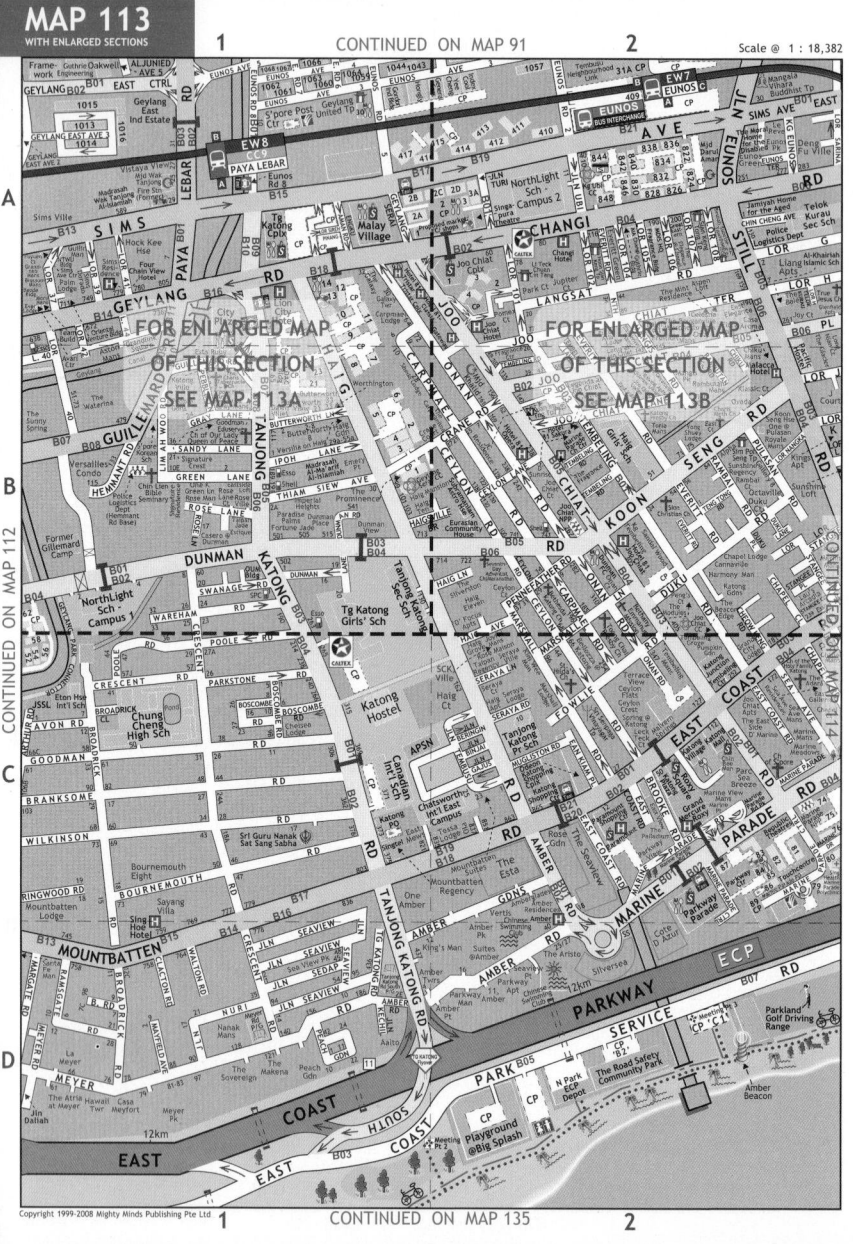

CONTINUED ON MAP 112

CONTINUED ON MAP 114

FOR ENLARGED MAP
OF THIS SECTION
SEE MAP 113A

FOR ENLARGED MAP
OF THIS SECTION
SEE MAP 113B

Scale @ 1 : 9,191

Framework
Oakwell
Guthrie
Engineering
ALJUNIED AVE 5
B01 EAST CTRL
GEYLANG EAST B02
EUNOS AVE
1068 1067
1066
4
EUNOS AVE 6
1044 1043
1062 1061
1063 1060
1064 1059
EUNOS
3
Gordon Ind Bldg
Hongly
1015
Geylang East Ind. Estate
S'pore Post Ctr
Geylang United Tp
30
CP
1013
1016
GEYLANG EAST AVE 3
1014
EW8 CC9
PAYA LEBAR
415
417 416
B17
GEYLANG EAST AVE 2
Vistaya View
B15
AVE
GEYLANG SERAI
2B 2C
2A
A
Mjd Wak Tanjong
Madrasah Wak Tanjong Al-Islamiah
Fire Stn (Former)
29
Proposed market/ FC/ shops
Sims Ville
589
SIMS
B13
Tanjong Katong Cplx
CP
L. SIREH
AMAN RD
ENGKU
Malay Village
Guilin Man
Hock Kee Hse
PINANG
B18
ONAN RD
970
The Galaxy
Fuyuen Ct
HTWU Bldg
Sims Ave Ctr
Sims Residence
LOR 41
PAYA
845
Galaxy Twr
Grandneo Mans
Blossom Mans
Palm Lodge
LOR 39
Four Chain View Hotel
Lion City Hotel
14
13
12
CP
Carpmael Lodge
CP de Dilg Mons
Oriental Venture Bldg
779
780
805
HAIG
10
11
CP
GEYLANG
736
610
16
15
8
9
CARPMAEL RD
CONTINUED ON MAP 113B
B14
LEBAR
City Plaza
CP
654 470 471
Team Build
LOR 42
Grandlink Square
511
Esta Ruby
GUILLEMARD RD B11
B
Avari Ctr
E550
Aston Mans
Canal
Geylang
601
The Charis Tabernacle Ch
Katong Ville
S'pore Nat'l Wushu Federation
Gray Mans
PEBBLE LN
CDAC Bldg
22 23
21
CP
Sheda Lodge
LOR 40
The Waterina
GUILLEMARD
LIM AH WOO RD
Pebble Gdns
GRAY LANE
Signature Crest
Goodman Eduserve
Dawn Ville
Butterworth View
3
Worthington
6
The Sunny Spring
40
B07 B08
Ch of Our Lady Queen of Peace
BUTTERWORTH LANE
Versilia on Haig
Butterworth 8
Haig Gdn
5
Versailles Condo
HEMMANT
S'pore Korean Sch
SANDY LANE
2
TANJONG
LANE
296-354
4
Police Logistics Dept (Hemmant Rd Base)
Chin Lien Bible Seminary
GREEN LANE
One K Green Ln
Eastside Loft
IPOH LANE
Esso
Madrasah Al-Ma'arif Al-Islamiah
Emery Pt
46
Geylang Serai CC
3
Signature Residence
Rose Man
Rose Lane Ct
Rose Ville
Shell
SIEW AVE
THIAM
The Prominence
Haig Mansion
Haig Ten
HAIGOVILLE DR
KATONG
ROSE LANE
19
13A
ROSE LN
5A
Taipan Jade Estique
Casero @ Dunman
489
Imperial Heights
Paradise Palms
Fortune Jade
Dunman Place
DUNMAN RD
541
543
Dunman View
B03 B04
RD
501
505
515
713
714
Former Guillemard Camp
B01 B02
DUNMAN
CRESCENT RD
SWANAGE RD
OUM Bldg
DUNMAN RD
516
19
20
B03 B04
RD
Tanjong Katong Sec Sch
B04
62
CP
GEYLANG PARK CONNECTOR
NorthLight Sch - Campus 1
WAREHAM RD
WAREHAM RD
33
SPC
Esso
Tg Katong Girls' Sch

Copyright 1999-2008 Mighty Minds Publishing Pte Ltd

EUNOS AVE 3

Index Cool
General Cars
Yee Cheong Cars
CP

EUNOS RD 2

1057

Tembusu Neighbourhood Link
31A
CP
CP

EW7 EUNOS
A
B
C
CP
409

JLN

Mangala Vihara Buddhist Tp

EUNOS BUS INTERCHANGE

SIMS AVE EAST

B01

LOR SARINA

SIMS AVE
B21

413 411
414 412 410
B19

JLN EUNOS 2

The Moral Home for the Disabled
Eunos Green
KG
Le Reve
Eunos Pk
Deng Fu Ville
EUNOS TER
283
251 277

838 836
844 842 840 834 822
846 830 832 824
848 828 826
Eunos Fire Post
Mjd Darul Aman

NorthLight Sch-Campus 2

Singapura Theatre

SIMS

JLN UBI

Kg Ubi CC

EUNOS RD
B06

A

2D
3A
TURI
2 3
CP
Proposed market/ FC/ shops
1

Jamiyah Home for the Aged

CHIN CHENG AVE

Police Logistics Dept

Telok Kurau Sec Sch

CHANGI RD
60
B04 CHANGI
MDIS HQ
Great Eastern @ Changi
Sian Keng Yong Tp
Beulah
Sunrise

STILL RD

G

Joo Chiat Cplx
1 2 3 4
CP

Changi Hotel
CALTEX

Hoon Sian Keng Tp
Everitt Green
LIA Changi
Guthrie Bldg
Fragrance Bldg

LOR 105 CHANGI
LOR 106 CHANGI
LOR 107 CHANGI
LOR 108 CHANGI

The Elegance @ Changi

Poh Hian Cho Tp

Liang Apts

True Jesus Church
Al-Khafiah Islamic Sch

LOR 101
LOR 102 CHANGI
EVERITT RD
LOR 104 CHANGI

Li Teck Chuan Cin Tang
Park Jupiter Ct

The Mint Residence

TER

The Bale
The Joy Ct
The Glacier

PL

Nilam Ct

CONTINUED ON MAP 113A

Pomex Ct
Joo Chiat Hotel

LANGSAT

NTH

CHIAT

Celestia
The Bougainville Maisonette Apts
Palm Loft
Joo Chiat Mans
Flora East

Aspen Loft
East Elegance

B05

Pacific Hostel

JOO

Gateway Hotel

Fragrance Ctr

JOO

TEMBELING LANE
EVERITT

MANGIS

Euro-Asia Lodge
Lotus at Joo Chiat
Fruition

CHIAT

Chiku Mans
Casa Aroma

LOR J

TEMBELING RD
B03

The Geranium

RAMBUTAN
CHIKU RD

Malacca Hotel

Mrd Khalid

JOO

JC Residence
Hotel 81 Sakura

Legenda at Joo Chiat
Vitra Legenda

Gideon's Flock
Joo Chiat Lodge
East Ville
Kuan Jim Ting Tp

Mangis Pk
Rambutan Mans

Klassic Ct
Ovada

Koon Seng Hse

LOR K

Kings Apt

ONAN RD

CARPMAEL RD

CRANE RD

CEYLON

Crane Flats

Hotel 81 Opera

LANE
CHIAT
JOO

The Fragrance
D' Sunrise

Katong Presby Ch
Torie Mans

Charis Meth Ch

Tian Ct

Yong Shuey Lodge

D'Fresco
East Ct

One @ Pulasan
Royale Mans

LOR L

Sunshine Loft

B

Suramadana Astro Hse

Hotel 81 Opera

TEMBELING RD

Haig Girls' Sch

S'pore Gujarati Sch

SENG

RAMBAI

PULASAN

Alpha
Sim Poh Seng Tp
Gallery

Sunshine Regency

Octaville
Cantiz
Duku Ct

CEYLON RD

Joo Chiat Ct

KOON

Sandal Wood

EVERITT RD

TENG TONG RD

Rambai Ct

DUKU LANE

LOR STANGEE

HAIGSVILLE DR

Eurasian Community Housing

Joo Chiat NPP

Sion Christian Ch

Kg Tembeling Hoo Jia Tp

Chapel Lodge
Cannaville

Maya Merlin Man

DUNMAN RD
B06 B05

Shell

D'Sunrise
FC

CP

Harmony Man

Katong Gdns

Lau's Arcadia

722 723 741 743

Seventh-Day Adventist Ch (Maranatha)

Onan Ct

DUKU RD

Peng's Ct
The Modules

Tembeling Mans

STANGEE PL

HAIG LN

The Silverston
Haig Eleven
'D' Focus Apts

HAIG AVE

PENNEFATHER RD

CARPMAEL RD

Ceylon Ct

Bethesda Katong Ch

MARSHALL RD

Bethany Mission

Toong Chai Presby Ch

Joo Chiat CC

CHEOW KENG RD

EAST COAST RD

MAP 114

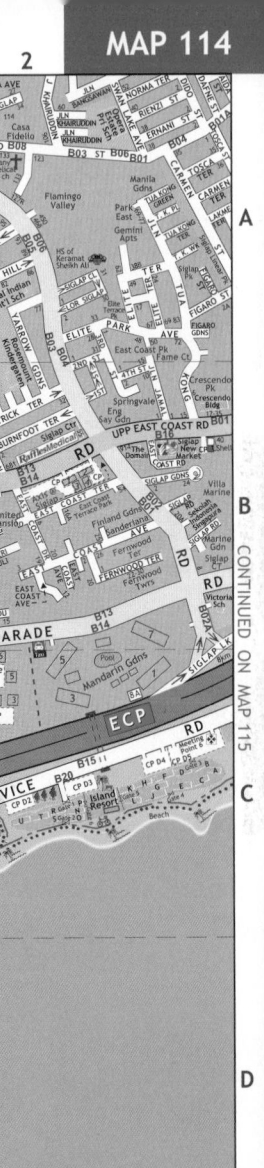

CONTINUED ON MAP 113

CONTINUED ON MAP 115

SIMS AVE EAST

CHANGI

ROAD

FRANKEL

TELOK KURAU

JOO CHIAT PLACE

JOO CHIAT

TELOK KURAU

SIGLAP

FRANKEL AVE

DUNBAR

ROSEBURN

COLDSTREAM

EAST COAST

KATONG

PATTERSON

MARINE

PARADE

MARINE

SOUTH

EAST

COAST

PARKWAY

SERVICE

ECP

St. Patrick's Sec Sch

CHIJ Katong Convent

Ngee Ann Pr Sch

Victoria Junior College

Tao Nan Sch

EAST COAST PARK

Marine Cove

ECP Police Post & Life Guard

Park Land Golf Driving Range

Mandarin Gdns

Neptune Ct

MAP 115

CONTINUED ON MAP 93

Scale @ 1 : 18,382

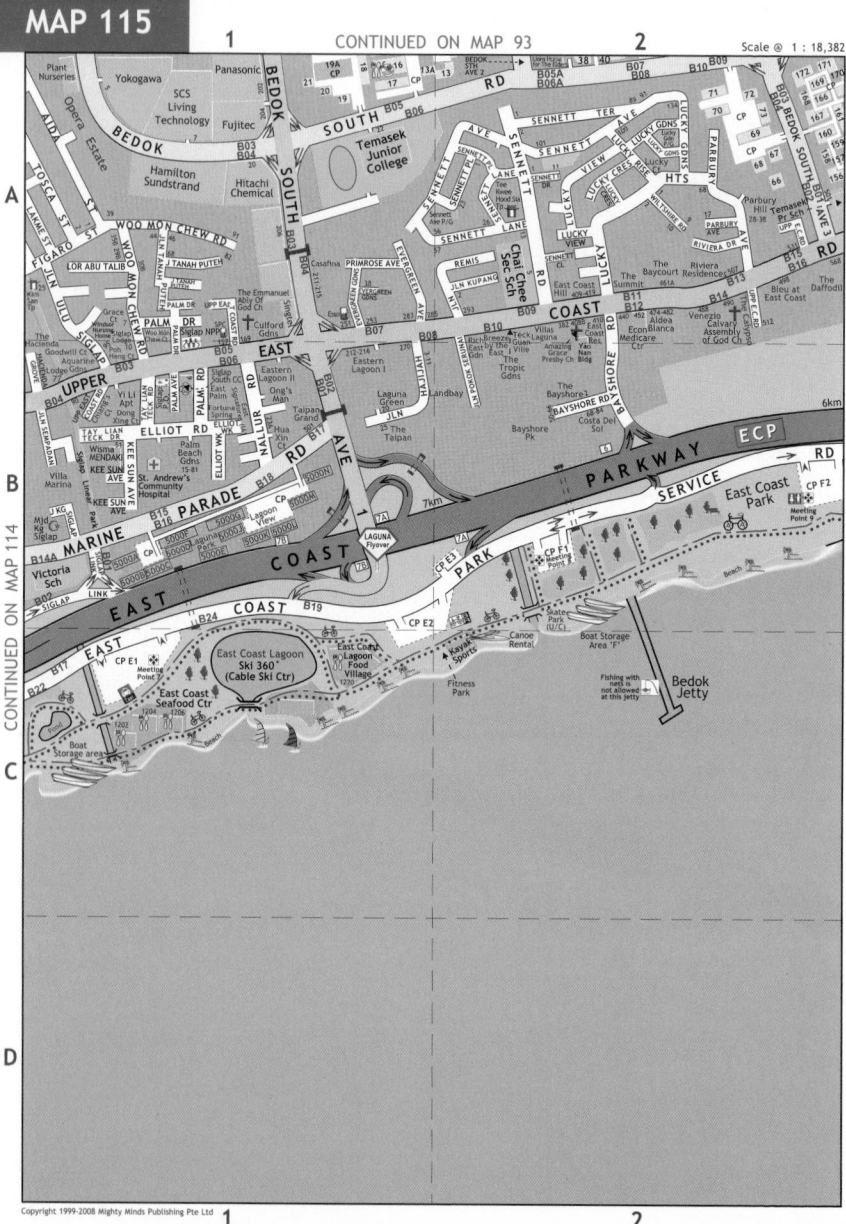

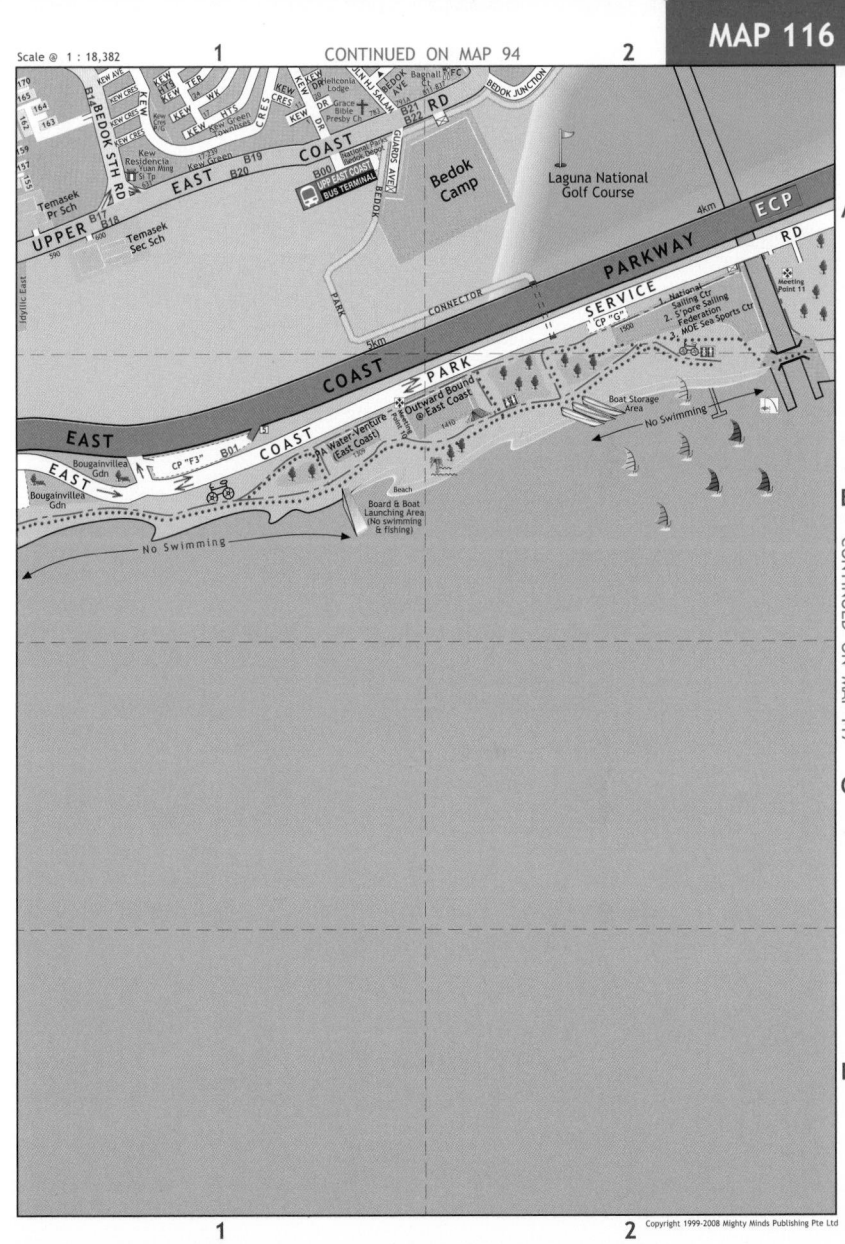

CONTINUED ON MAP 117

MAP 117

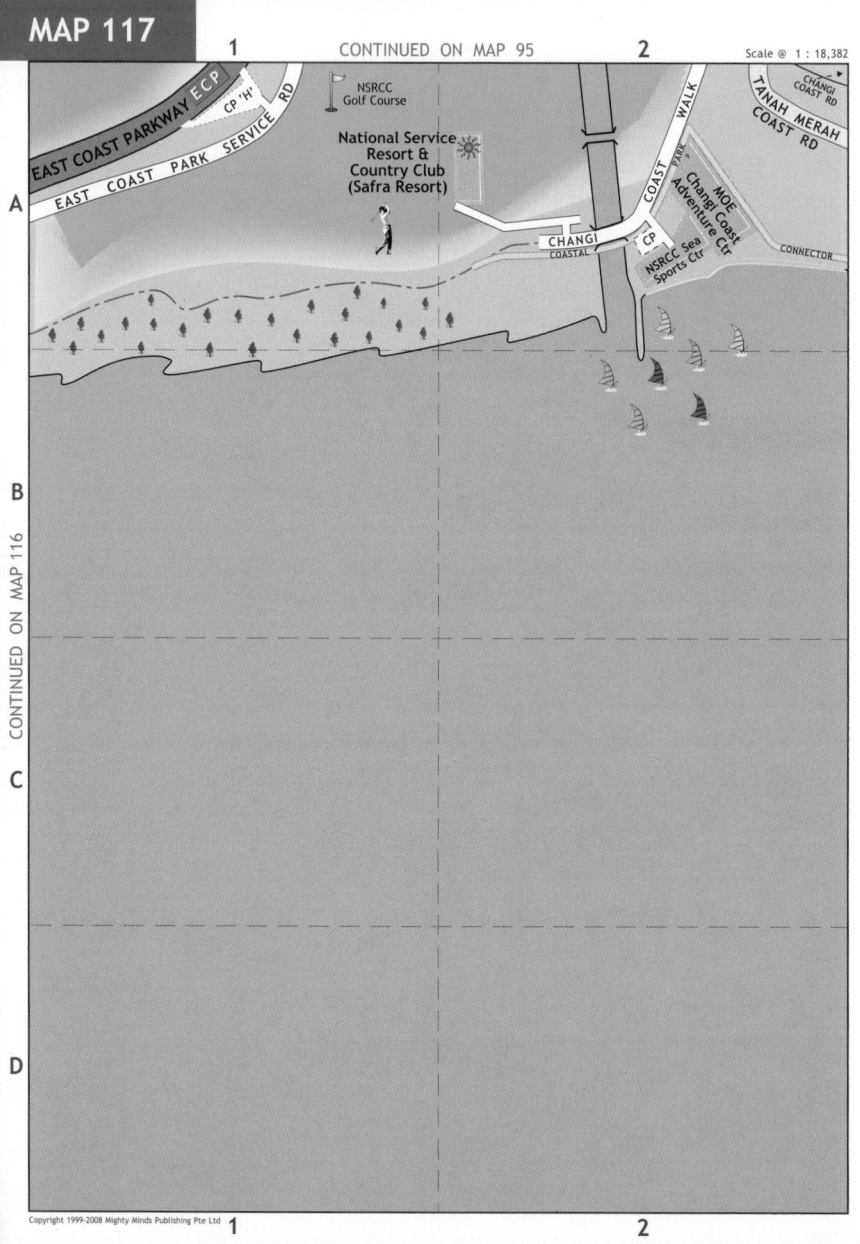

EAST COAST PARKWAY ECP

CP 'H'

NSRCC Golf Course

National Service Resort & Country Club (Safra Resort)

EAST COAST PARK SERVICE RD

CHANGI COASTAL

COAST PARK WALK

CP

NSRCC Sea Sports Ctr

MOE Changi Coast Adventure Ctr

TANAH MERAH COAST RD

CHANGI COAST RD

CONNECTOR

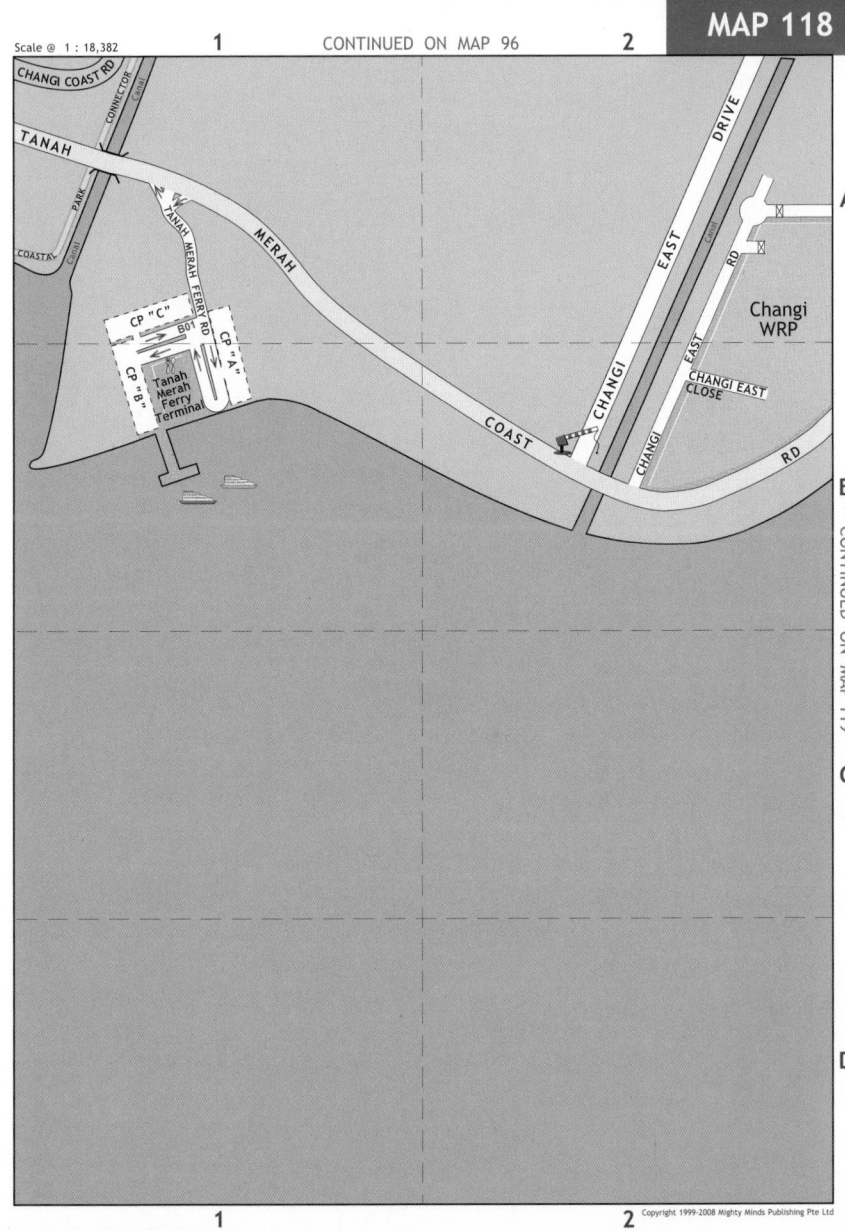

CHANGI COAST RD

TANAH

PARK

COAST RD

TANAH MERAH FERRY RD

MERAH

CP "C"

B01

CP "A"

CP "B"

Tanah
Merah
Ferry
Terminal

COAST

CHANGI

EAST

DRIVE

RD

Changi
WRP

CHANGI EAST
CLOSE

EAST

CHANGI

RD

A

B

C

D

CONTINUED ON MAP 119

MAP 119

CONTINUED ON MAP 97

Scale @ 1 : 18,382

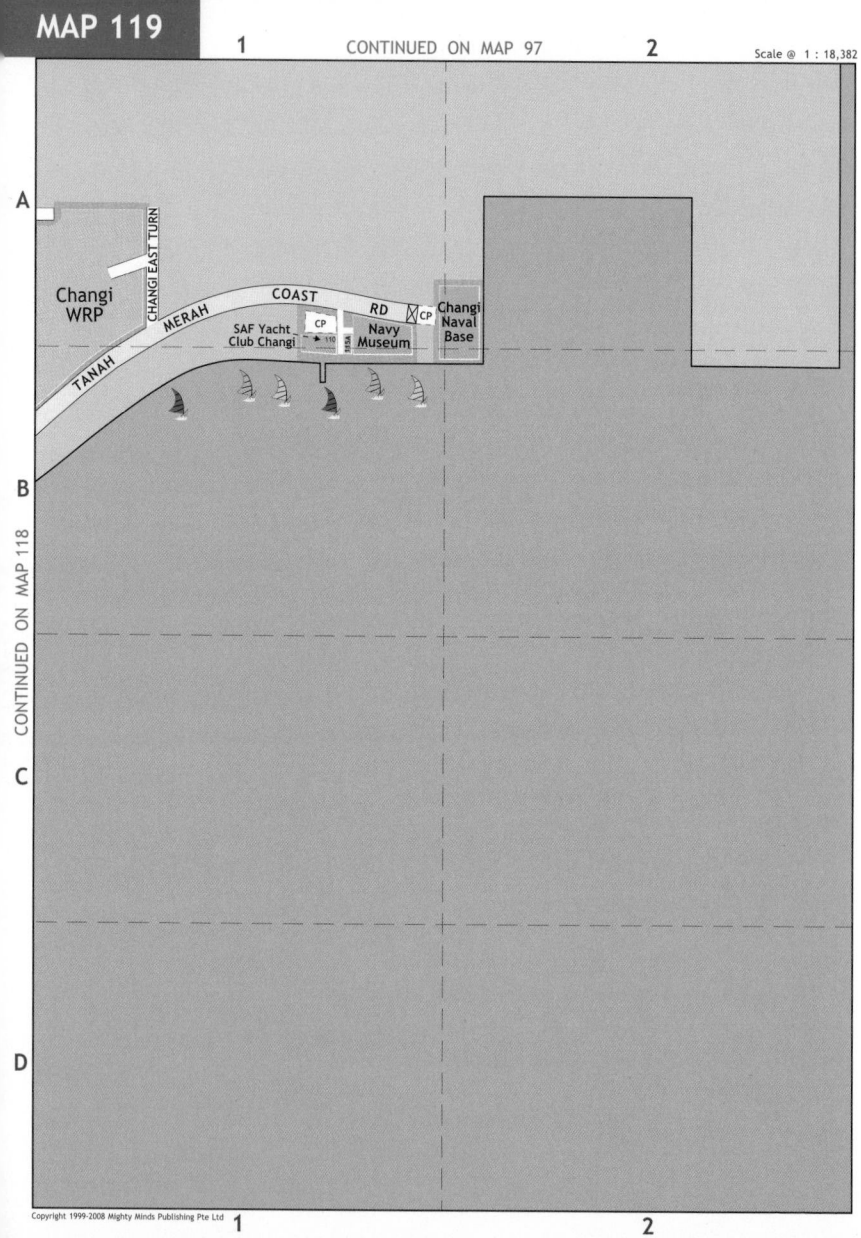

CONTINUED ON MAP 118

Changi WRP

CHANGI EAST TURN

COAST

TANAH MERAH

RD

SAF Yacht Club Changi

CP

Navy Museum

CP

Changi Naval Base

Scale @ 1 : 18,382

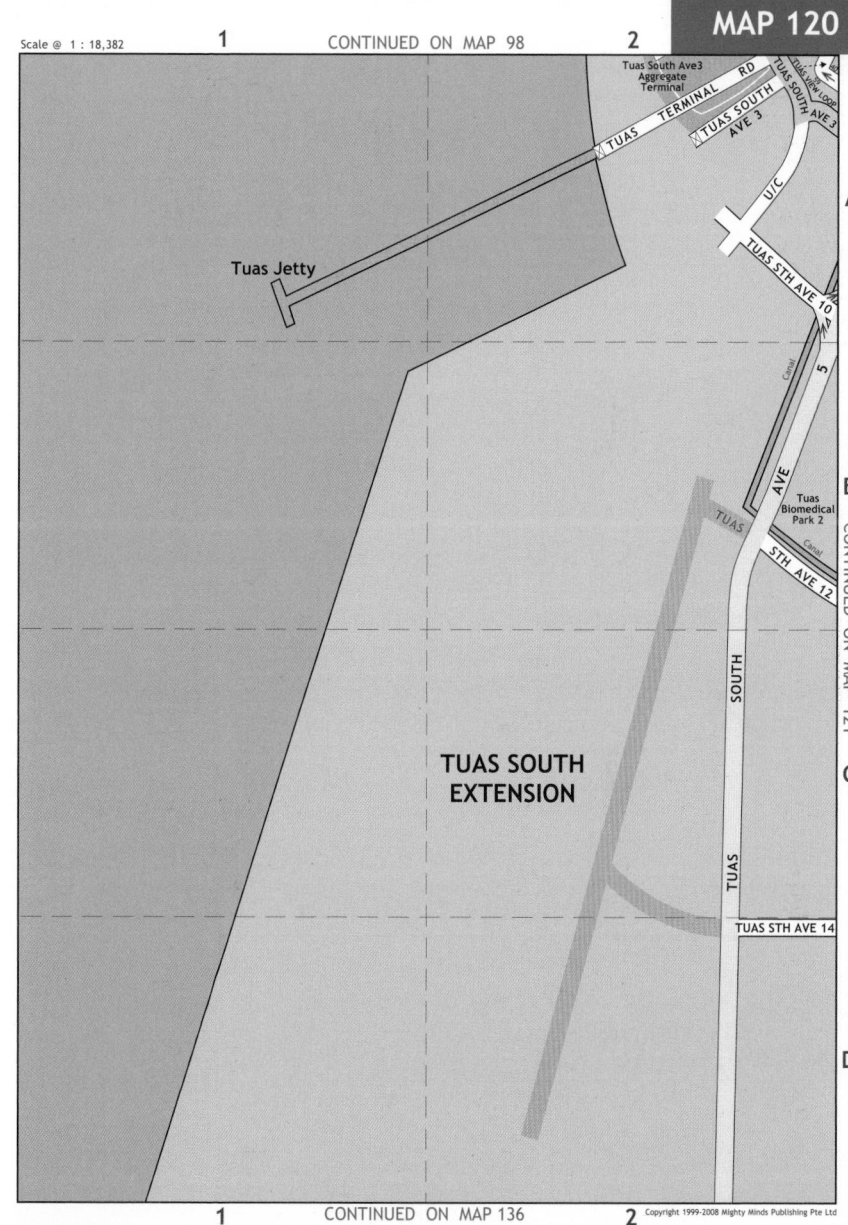

Tuas South Ave3
Aggregate
Terminal

TUAS TERMINAL RD

TUAS SOUTH AVE 3

TUAS SOUTH AVE 3

U/C

TUAS STH AVE 10

Tuas Jetty

Canal

5

TUAS AVE

Tuas
Biomedical
Park 2

Canal

STH AVE 12

SOUTH

TUAS

TUAS STH AVE 14

**TUAS SOUTH
EXTENSION**

A

B

C

D

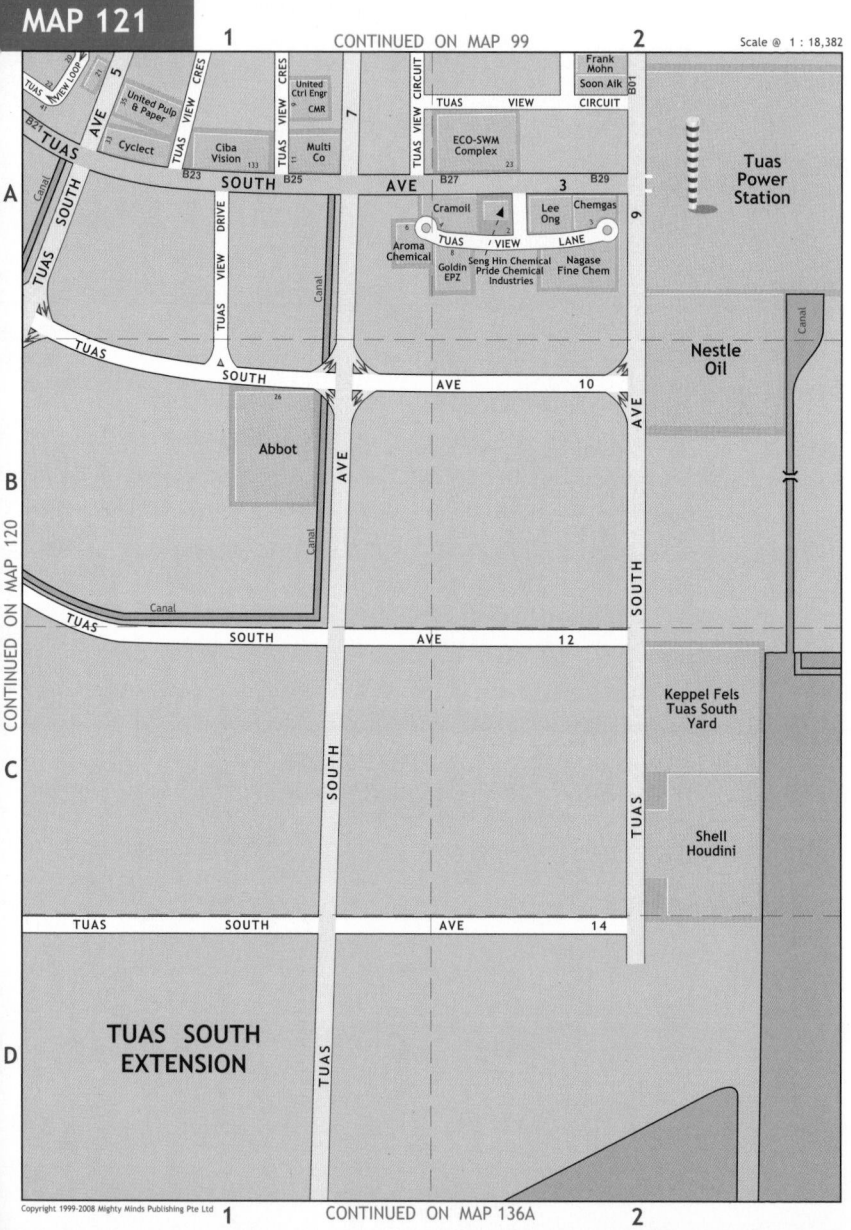

MAP 121

CONTINUED ON MAP 99

Scale @ 1 : 18,382

Frank Mohn
Soon Alk

United Pulp & Paper
Cyclect
United Ctrl Engr
CMR
Ciba Vision
133
Multi Co

ECO-SWM Complex
23

Tuas Power Station

B21 TUAS SOUTH
TUAS SOUTH

B23 SOUTH B25 AVE B27

TUAS VIEW CRES
VIEW LOOP
5
AVE
TUAS VIEW CRES
7
TUAS VIEW CIRCUIT
TUAS VIEW CIRCUIT
B01
3
B29
9

A

TUAS VIEW DRIVE
Canal

Cramoil
Lee Ong
Chemgas
6
TUAS / VIEW LANE
2
1
5

Aroma Chemical
Goldin EPZ
Seng Hin Chemical
Pride Chemical Industries
Nagase Fine Chem

TUAS SOUTH
AVE
10

Nestle Oil

Canal

Abbot
26

AVE

SOUTH

B

CONTINUED ON MAP 120

Canal

TUAS SOUTH
AVE
12

SOUTH

Keppel Fels Tuas South Yard

C

TUAS

Shell Houdini

TUAS SOUTH
AVE
14

TUAS SOUTH EXTENSION

SOUTH

TUAS

D

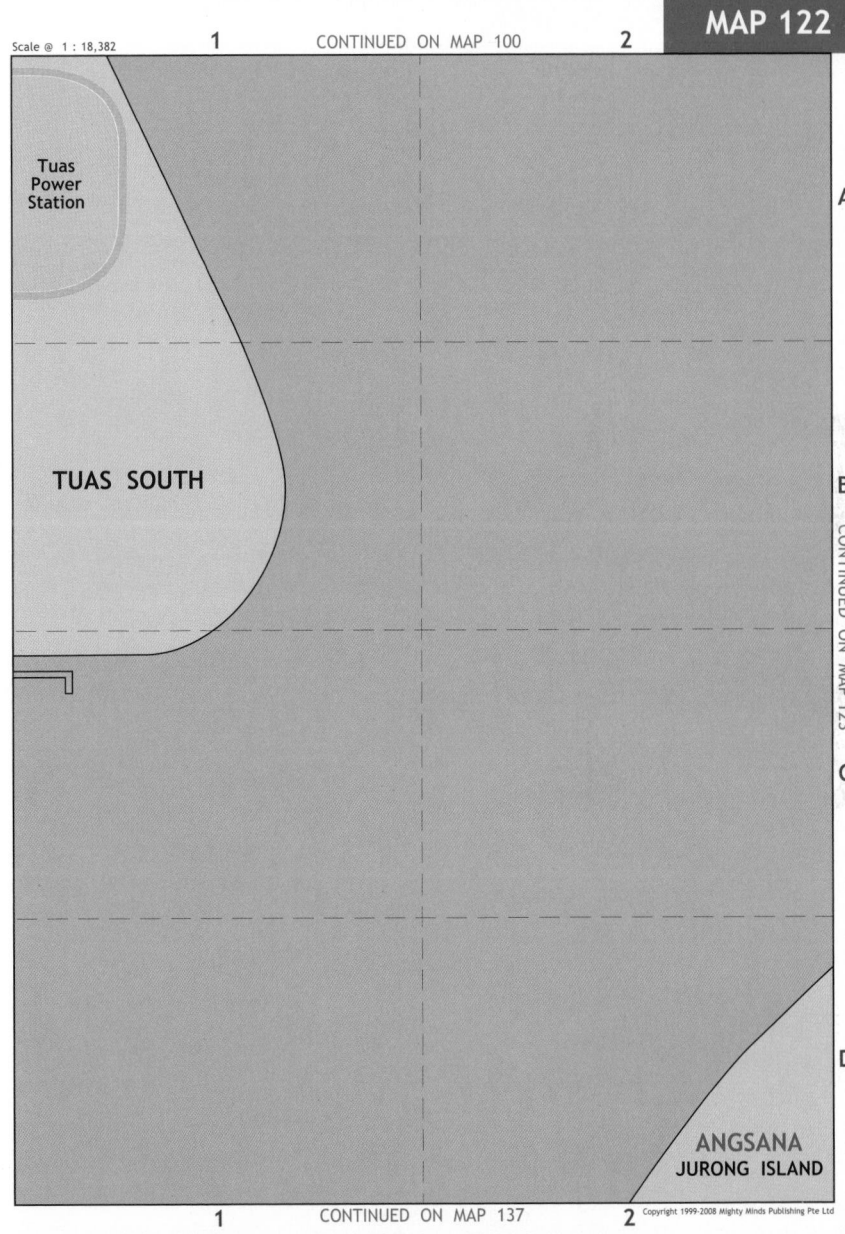

MAP 122

Scale @ 1 : 18,382

1   CONTINUED ON MAP 100   2

A

Tuas
Power
Station

TUAS SOUTH

B

C

D

ANGSANA
JURONG ISLAND

MAP 123

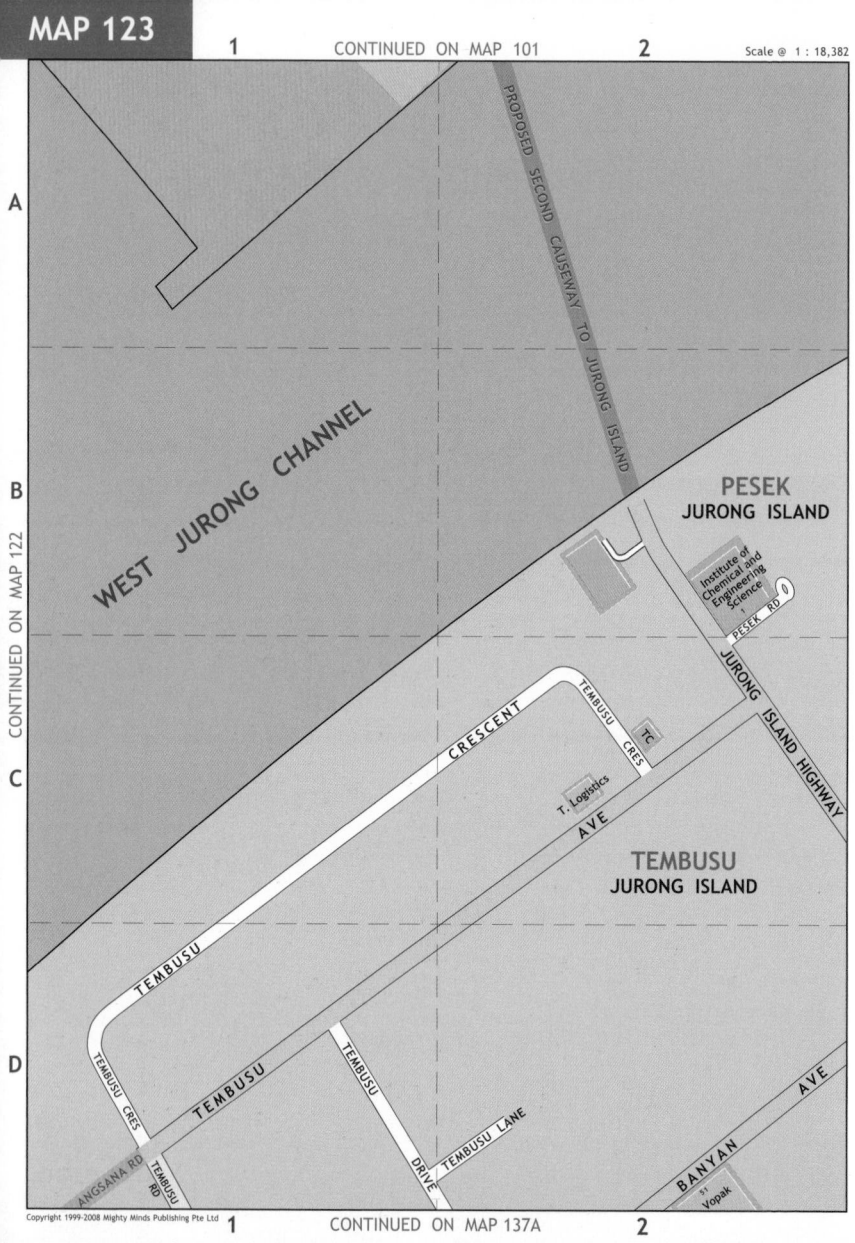

A

B

PROPOSED SECOND CAUSEWAY TO JURONG ISLAND

WEST JURONG CHANNEL

PESEK
JURONG ISLAND

Institute of Chemical and Engineering Science

PESEK RD

C

CRESCENT

TEMBUSU CRES

TC

T. Logistics

AVE.

JURONG ISLAND HIGHWAY

TEMBUSU
JURONG ISLAND

D

TEMBUSU

TEMBUSU CRES

TEMBUSU RD

TEMBUSU

TEMBUSU DRIVE

TEMBUSU LANE

BANYAN AVE.

ANGSANA RD

Vopak

MAP 124

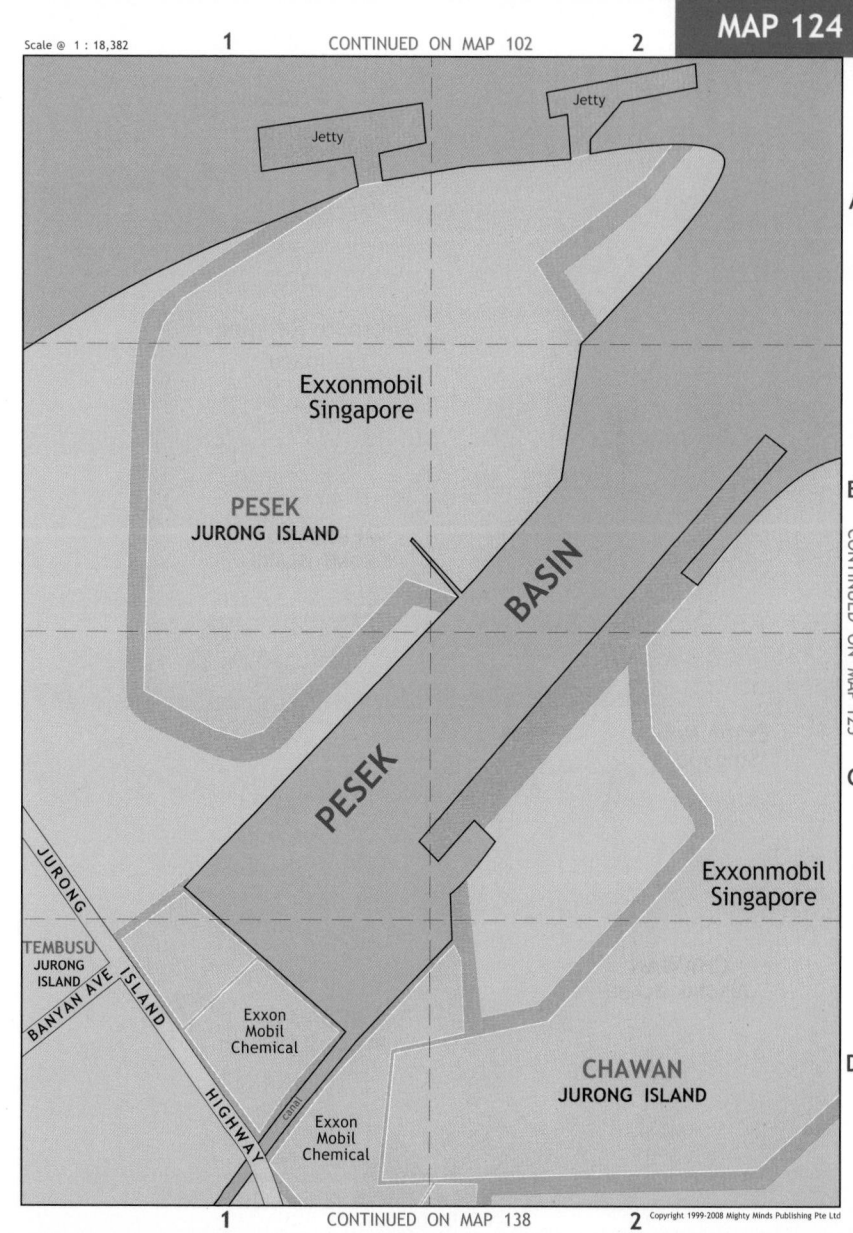

Jetty

Jetty

A

Exxonmobil
Singapore

PESEK
JURONG ISLAND

B

CONTINUED ON MAP 125

BASIN

PESEK

C

Exxonmobil
Singapore

JURONG ISLAND

TEMBUSU
JURONG
ISLAND

BANYAN AVE

Exxon
Mobil
Chemical

CHAWAN
JURONG ISLAND

D

HIGHWAY

Canal

Exxon
Mobil
Chemical

MAP 125

CONTINUED ON MAP 103

Scale @ 1 : 18,382

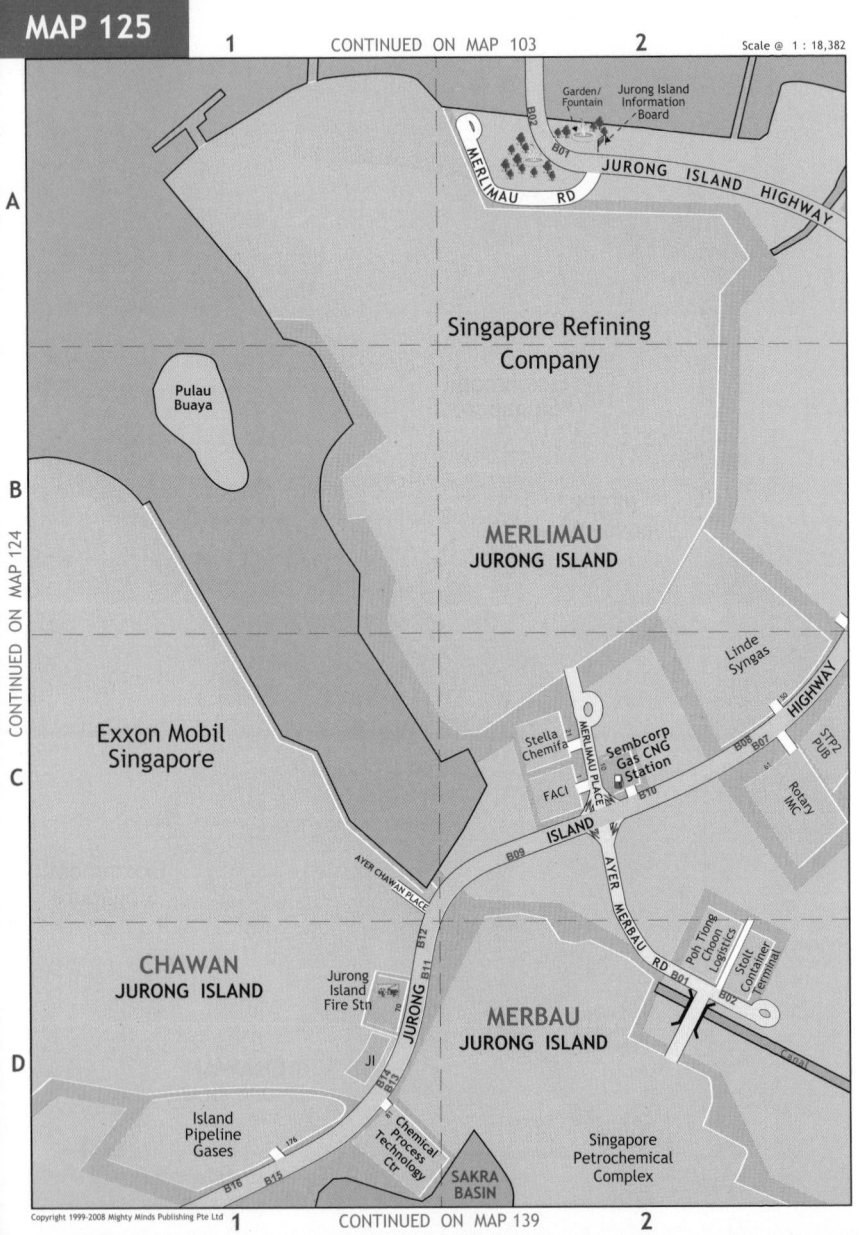

Garden/
Fountain

Jurong Island
Information
Board

B02

B01

MERLIMAU RD

JURONG ISLAND HIGHWAY

**Singapore Refining
Company**

Pulau
Buaya

**MERLIMAU
JURONG ISLAND**

Linde
Syngas

HIGHWAY

**Exxon Mobil
Singapore**

Stella
Chemifa

MERLIMAU PLACE

Sembcorp
Gas CNG
Station

B06 B07

STP2
PUB

FACI

B10

Rotary
IMC

ISLAND

B09

AYER MERBAU RD

AYER CHAWAN PLACE

B12

Poh Tiong
Choon
Logistics

Stolt
Container
Terminal

**CHAWAN
JURONG ISLAND**

Jurong
Island
Fire Stn

B11

B01

B02

**MERBAU
JURONG ISLAND**

JI

Canal

Island
Pipeline
Gases

176

B16 B15

Chemical
Process
Technology
Ctr

**SAKRA
BASIN**

**Singapore
Petrochemical
Complex**

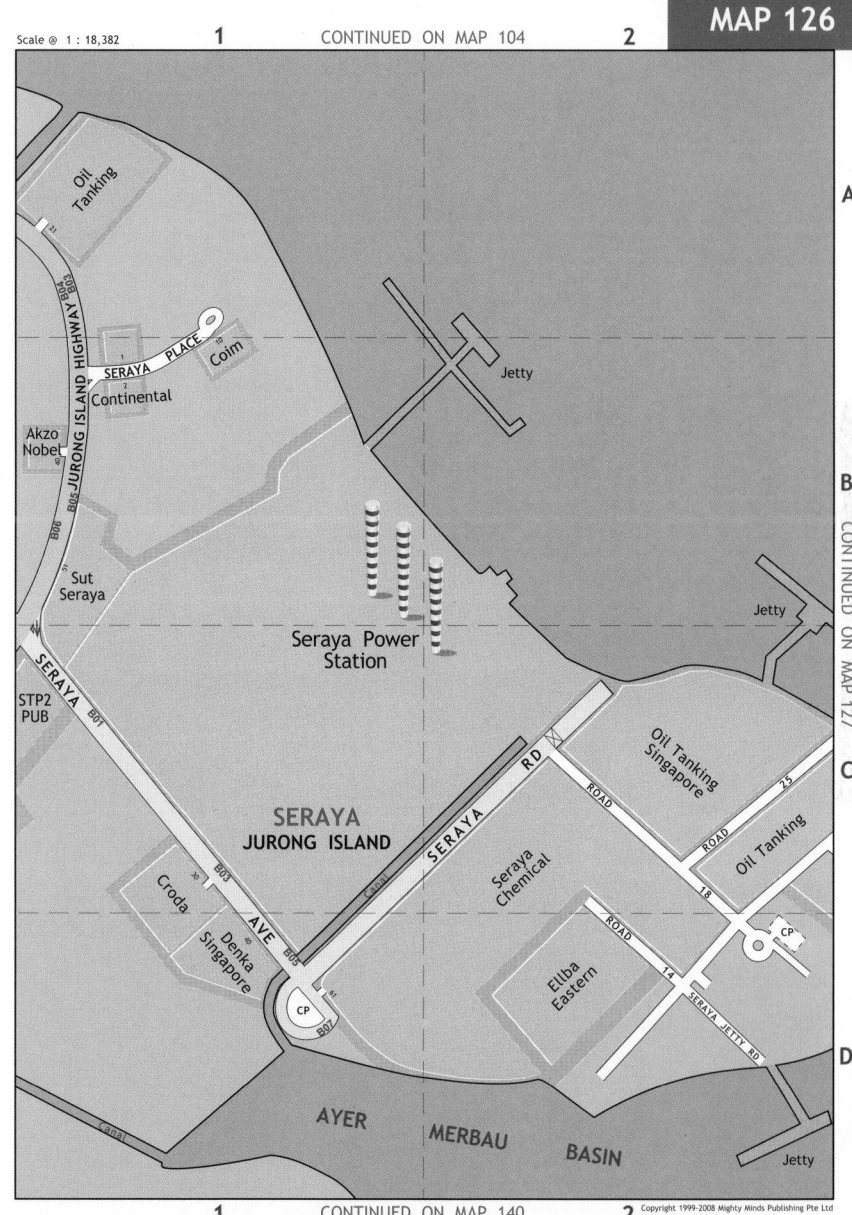

MAP 127

1   CONTINUED ON MAP 105   2

Scale @ 1 : 18,382

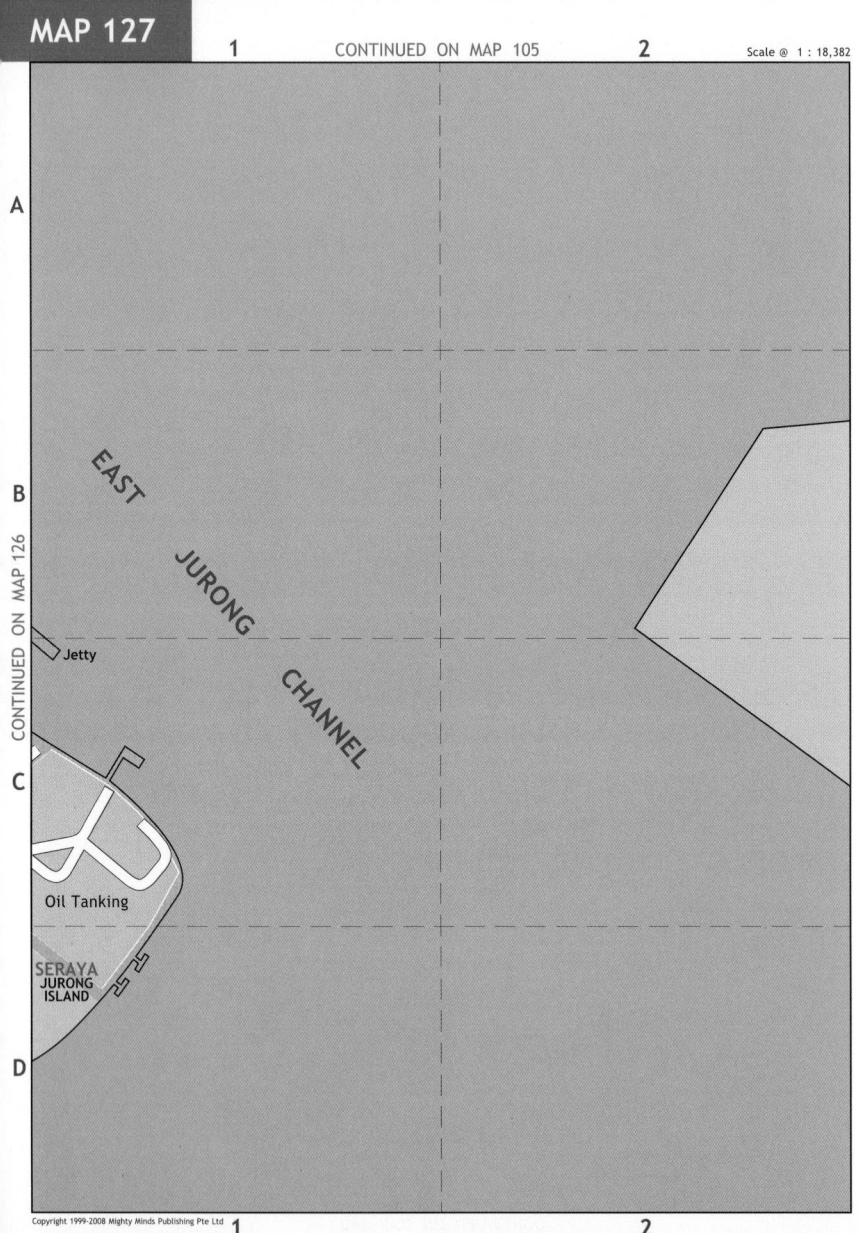

A

CONTINUED ON MAP 126

B

EAST

JURONG

Jetty

CHANNEL

C

Oil Tanking

SERAYA
JURONG
ISLAND

D

MAP 128

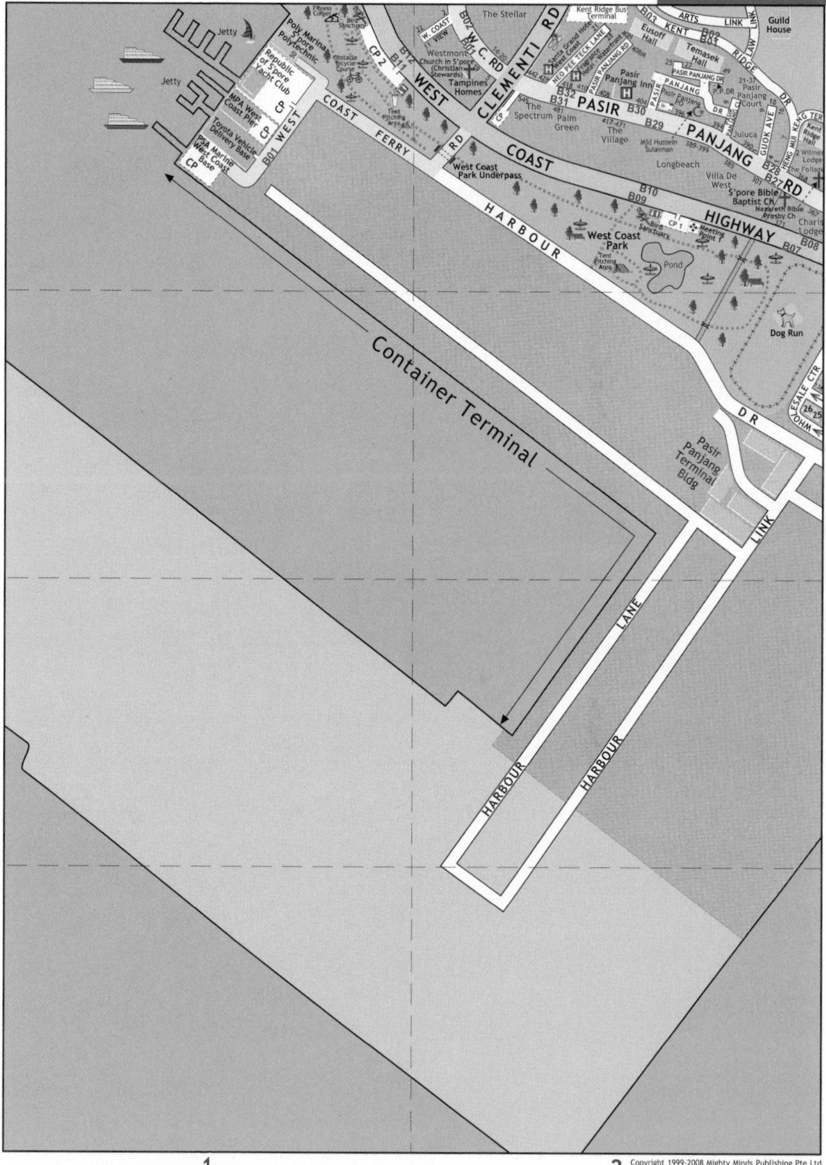

Jetty

Jetty

Phon Collegiate

Poly Marina

Republic Of S'pore Yacht Club

MPA West Coast Pier

Toyota Vehicle Delivery Regional

S'pore Marine West Coast Base

Cp

Cp 2

Republic Poly-technic

Westmont Church In S'pore (Christian Stewards) Tampines Homes

Cp2

W. COAST

W.COAST RD

The Stellar

Kent Ridge Bus Terminal

Guoff Hall

Temasek Hall

ARTS LINK

Guild House

KENT RIDGE DR

PASIR PANJANG RD

Pasir Panjang Inn

B31

B30

21-23 Pasir Panjang Court

B29

The Spectrum Palm Green

The Village

PASIR PANJANG RD

Juluca

B32

Villa De West

Longbeach

Mid Hussin Sulaiman

B27

Charis Lodges

HIGHWAY

B10

B09

S'pore Bible Baptist Ch.

Napkent Bible Presby Ch

B08

B07

Charis Lodges

COAST FERRY RD

BLK WEST

BLK WEST

West Coast Park Underpass

HARBOUR

COAST

West Coast Park

Tent pitching area

Sanctuary

Cp1

Resting area

Pond

Dog Run

Container Terminal

D R

SCALE TER

KHM

18-25

Pasir Panjang Terminal Bldg

LINK

LANE

HARBOUR

HARBOUR

A

B

C

D

MAP 129

CONTINUED ON MAP 107

Scale @ 1 : 18,382

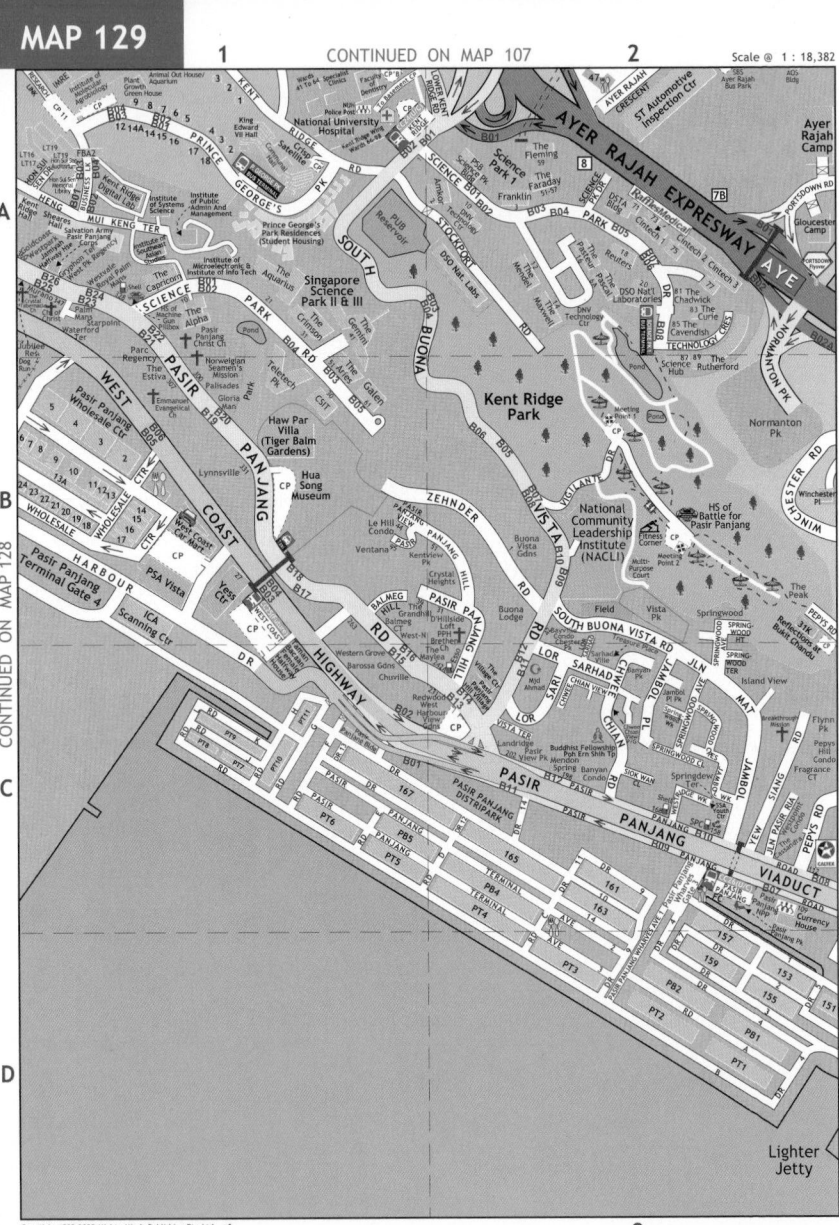

Scale @ 1 : 18,382

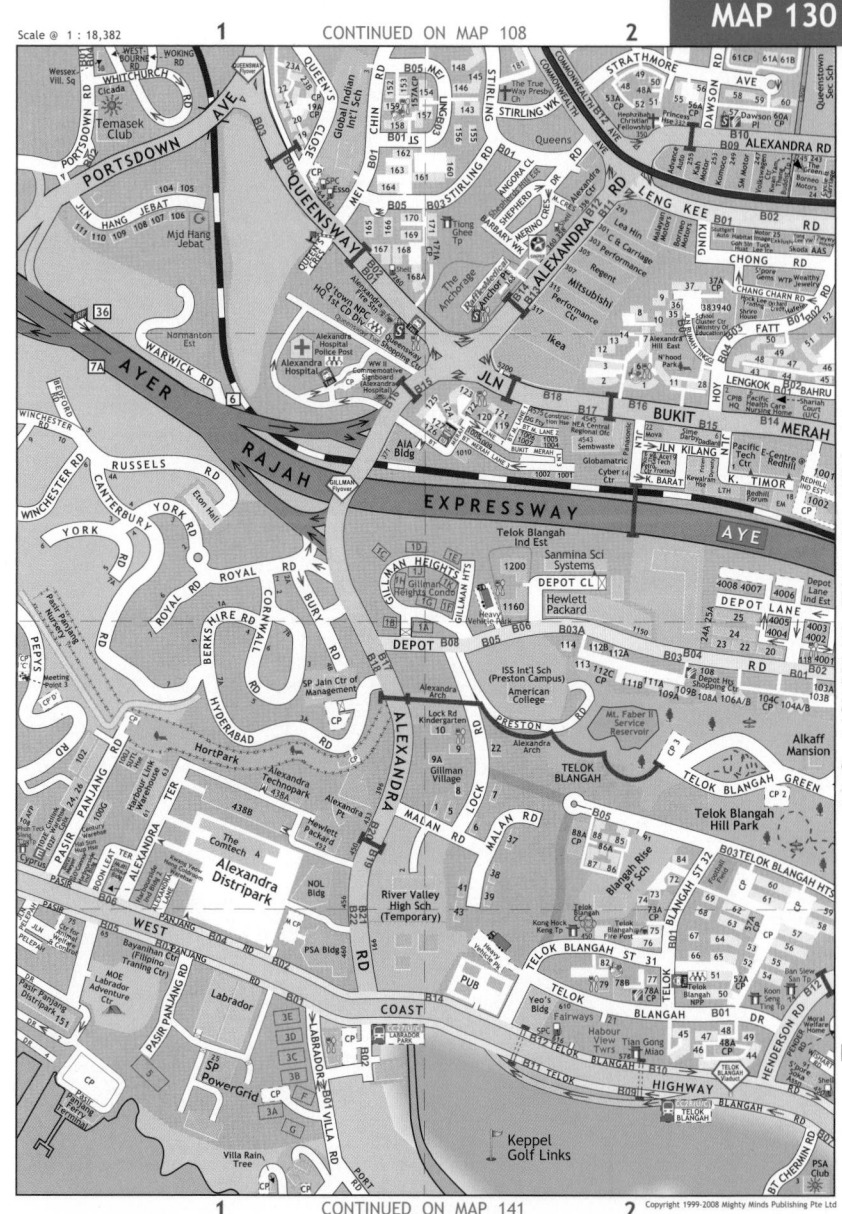

MAP 131

CONTINUED ON MAP 109

Scale @ 1 : 18,382

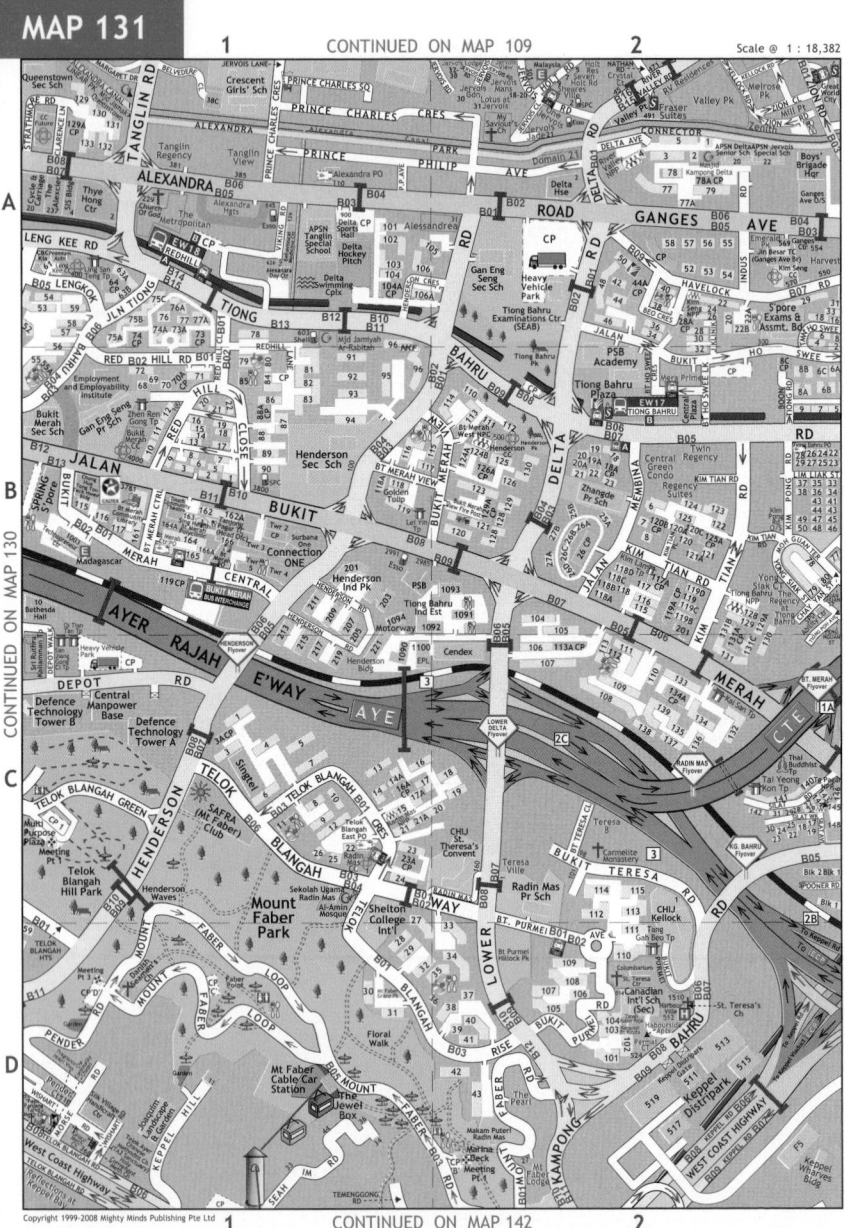

CONTINUED ON MAP 110

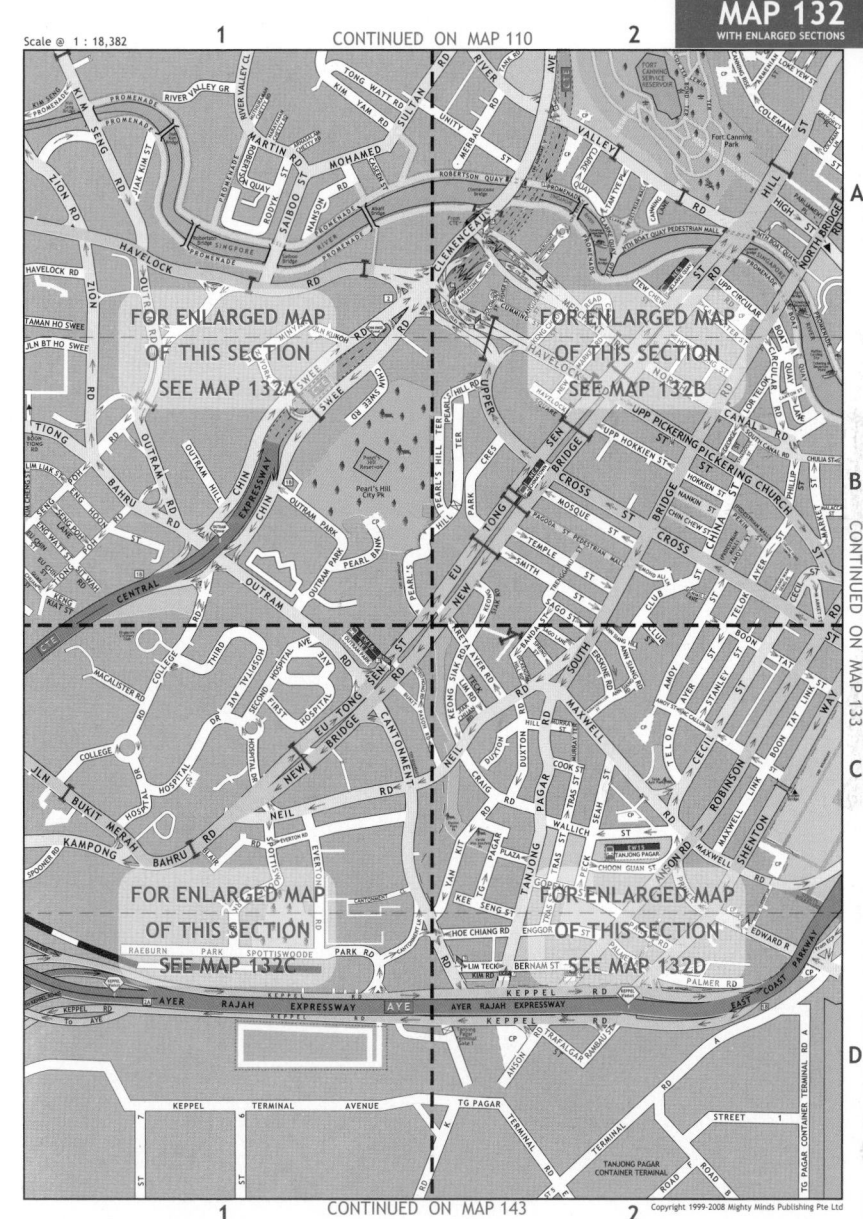

FOR ENLARGED MAP
OF THIS SECTION
SEE MAP 132A

FOR ENLARGED MAP
OF THIS SECTION
SEE MAP 132B

FOR ENLARGED MAP
OF THIS SECTION
SEE MAP 132C

FOR ENLARGED MAP
OF THIS SECTION
SEE MAP 132D

CONTINUED ON MAP 133

CONTINUED ON MAP 143

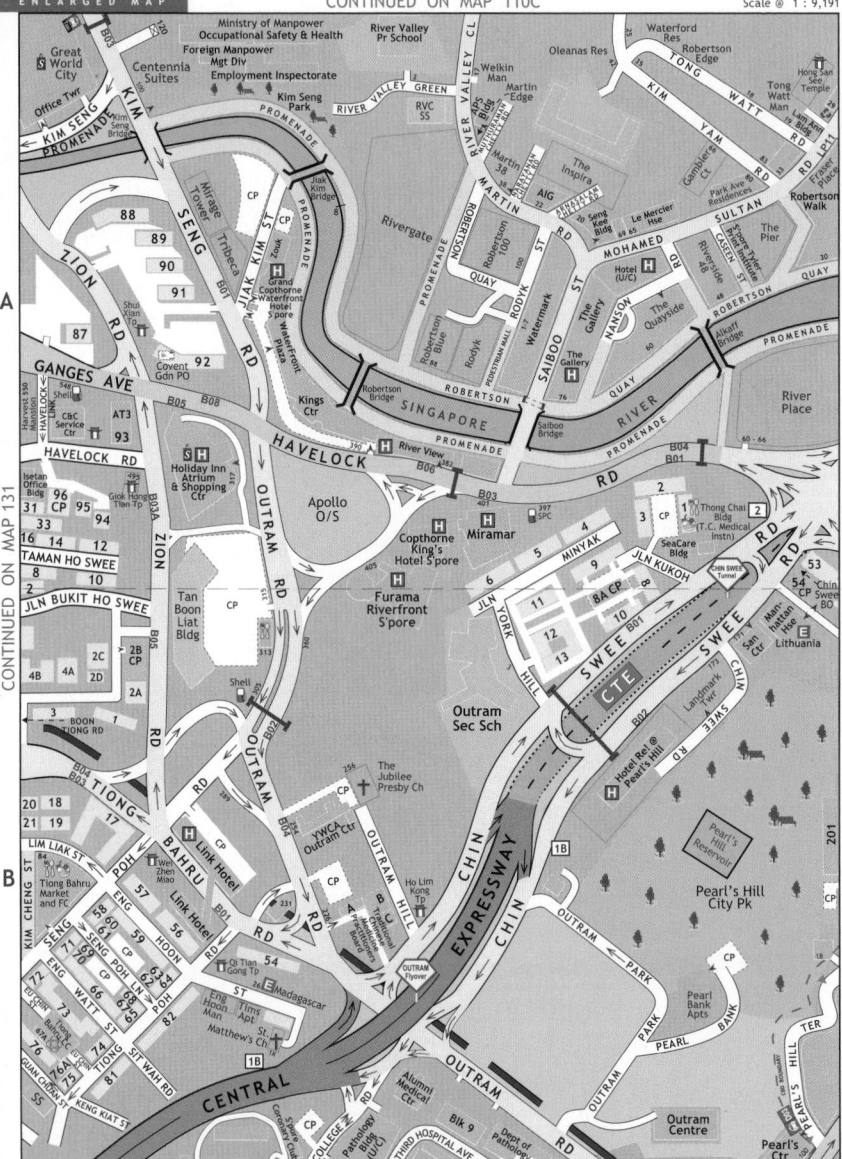

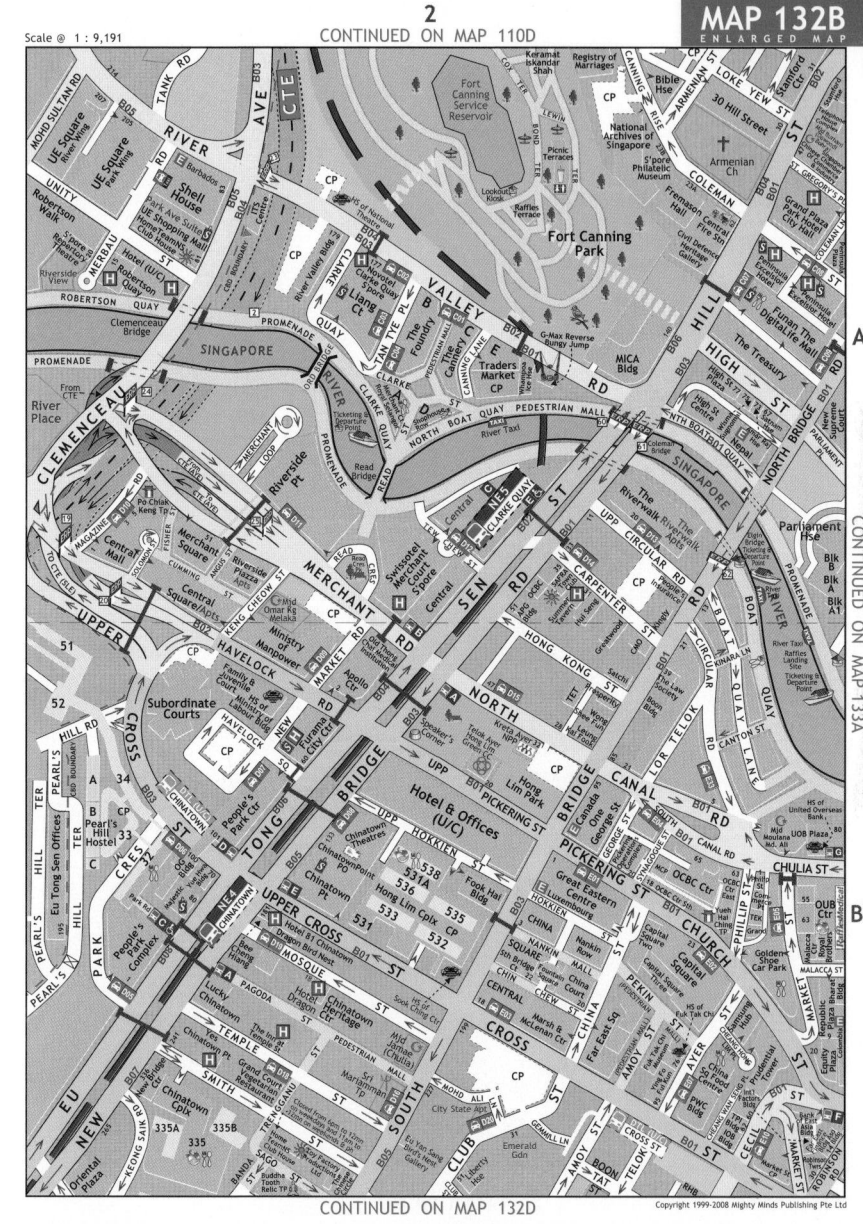

CONTINUED ON MAP 133A

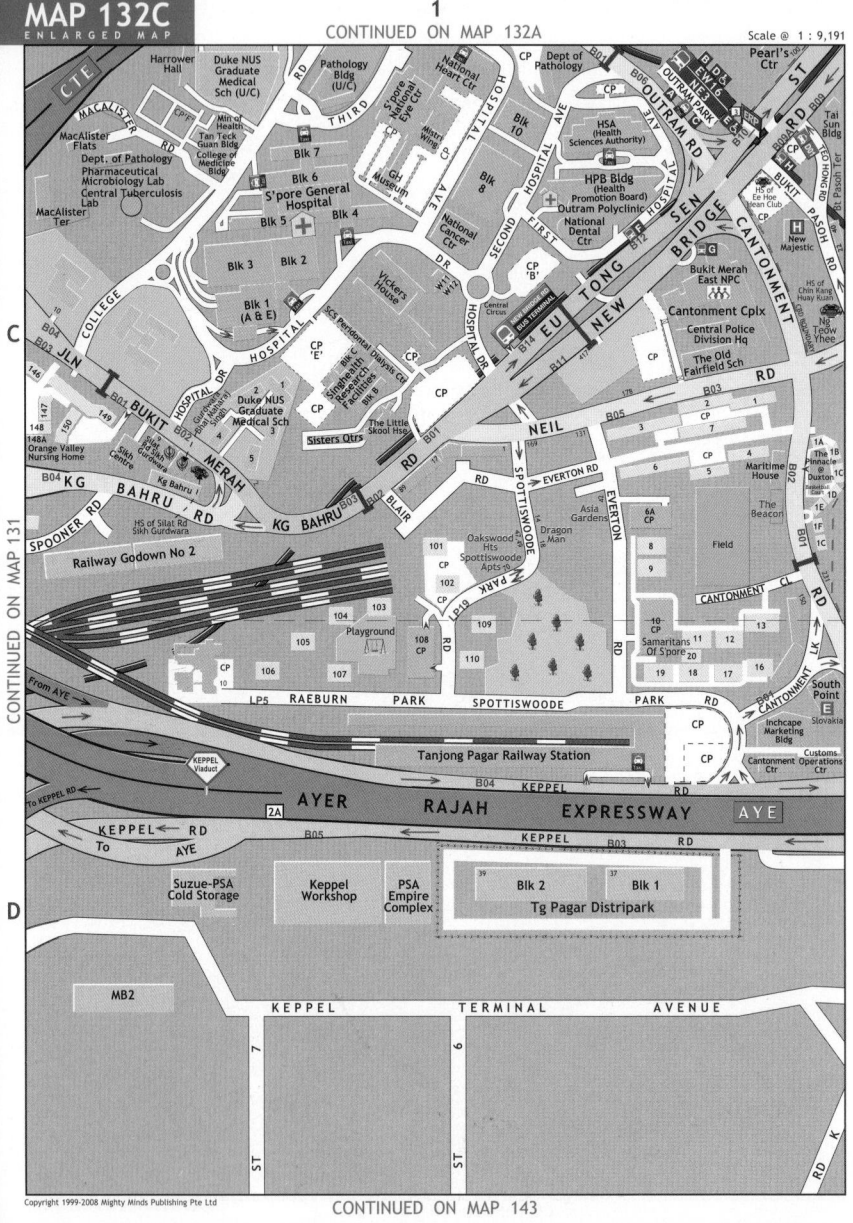

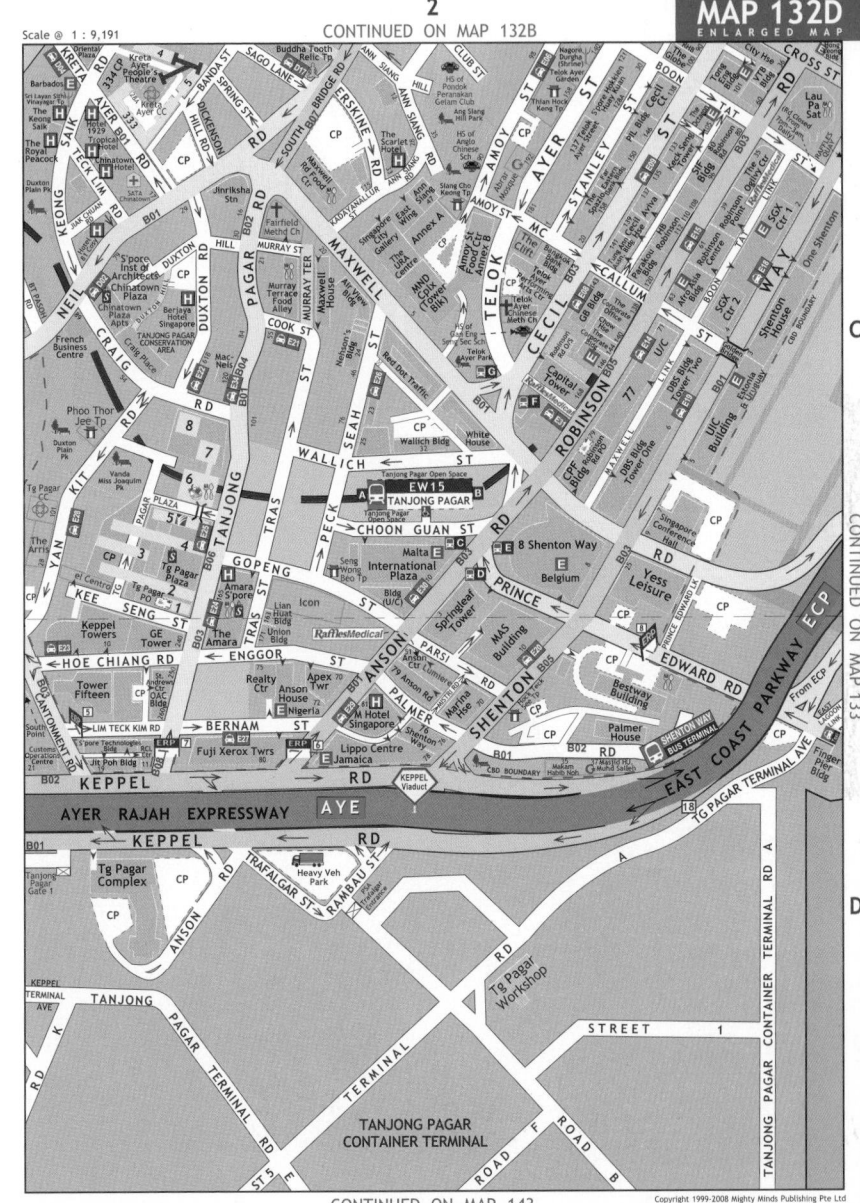

CONTINUED ON MAP 132B

CONTINUED ON MAP 133

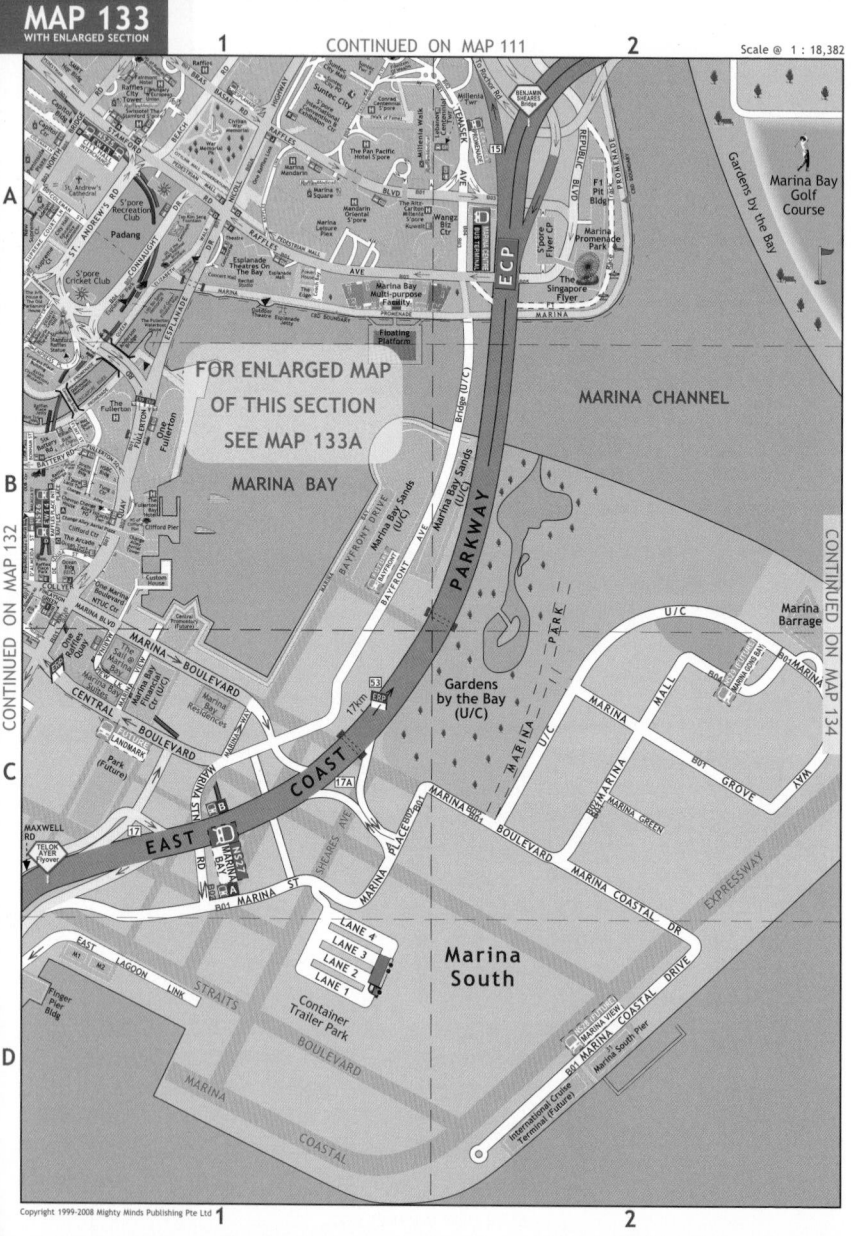

Gardens by the Bay

Marina Bay Golf Course

MARINA CHANNEL

FOR ENLARGED MAP OF THIS SECTION SEE MAP 133A

MARINA BAY

CONTINUED ON MAP 132
CONTINUED ON MAP 134

Marina Barrage

Gardens by the Bay (U/C)

MARINA BOULEVARD

EAST COAST PARKWAY

Marina South

Container Trailer Park

LANE 4
LANE 3
LANE 2
LANE 1

EAST LAGOON LINK

STRAITS

Finger Pier Bldg

MARINA COASTAL

BOULEVARD

International Cruise Terminal (Future)

Marina South Pier

Scale @ 1 : 9,191

SMRT Hqtr Bldg
PEDESTRIAN MALL
Fairmont Hotel
Raffles City Tower
Raffles City
Hungary
European Union
RafflesMedical
Swissotel The Stamford S'pore
Capitol Bldg
Capitol Ctr
BRIDGE RD
NORTH BUS
STAMFORD RD
NS25
CITY HALL INTERCHANGE
EW13 NS25
Hs of Raffles Institution
Raffles H
BRAS BASAH RD
BEACH RD
ESPLANADE
HIGHWAY
RAFFLES
Suntec City Mall
Suntec Twr 5
Suntec City
Suntec City PO
S'pore International Convention & Exhibition Ctr
(Walk of Fame)
Conrad Centennial S'pore
Fountain Of Wealth
Millenia Walk
RafflesMedical

Peninsula Plaza
St. Andrew's Cathedral
COLEMAN ST
City Hall Education Commission
ST. ANDREW'S RD
Padang
S'pore Recreation Club
CITYLINK MALL (UNDERGROUND)
War Memorial Pk
Civilian War Memorial
PEDESTRIAN MALL
NICOLL
One Raffles Link
RAFFLES
The Pan Pacific Hotel S'pore
BLVD
Marina Mandarin
Marina Square
Mandarin Oriental S'pore
The Ritz-Carlton Millenia S'pore
Kuwait
A

New Supreme Court
Supreme Court Ln
Supreme Ct
PARLIAMENT
CONNAUGHT
Esplanade Park
ELIZABETH WALK
QUEEN
Art House Old Parliament House
Sir Stamford Raffles Statue
S'pore Cricket Club
Tan Kim Seng Fountain
Hs of the Indian National Army Monument
Lim Bo Seng Memorial
DR
RAFFLES
Theatre
Esplanade Concourse
Esplanade Theatres On The Bay
Concert Hall
Recital Studio
Esplanade Mall
B01
Power House
The Edge
Coach Bay
PEDESTRIAN MALL
AVE
B03
Marina Leisure Plex
Marina Bay Multi-purpose Facility
CONTINUED ON MAP 133 GRID 2A & 2B

CONTINUED ON MAP 133B
EMPRESS PL
Asian Civilisations Museum
Dalhousie Memorial
Cavenagh Bridge
SINGAPORE RIVER
Anderson Bridge
Raffles Place Jetty
River Taxi
The Fullerton Waterboat House
MARINA
Outdoor Theatre
Esplanade Jetty
CBD BOUNDARY
PROMENADE
Floating Platform

Merlion Park
PROMENADE
ESPLANADE RD
The Fullerton
ERP ERP
One Fullerton
BONHAM ST
Six Battery Rd
BATTERY RD
FULLERTON RD
FULLERTON SQ
Bank of China
Straits Exchange Bldg
HSBC Bldg
Tung Ctr
BOAT QUAY
Republic Plaza
Prudential Tower
D'ALMEIDA ST
MALACCA ST
EN26
EW14
Raffles Place
RAFFLES PLACE
Chevron House
Change Alley Hitachi Twr
S'pore Land Twr
Change Alley Aerial Plaza
Change Alley Aerial Tower
The Arcade
Clifford Ctr
Ocean Twr
Hs of Clifford Pier
The Fullerton Hotel
Clifford Pier
MARINA BAY
B

DE SOUZA ST
Ocean Bldg (U/C)
Raffles Place Park
COLLYER QUAY
FINLAYSON GREEN
Custom House
One Marina Boulevard
NTUC Ctr
MARINA BLVD
One Raffles Quay
Central Promontory (Future)
FUTURE BAYFRONT
MARINA BAYFRONT DRIVE
BAY
BAYFRONT AVE
Marina Bay Sands (U/C)
Marina Bay Sands (U/C)
PROMENADE

Copyright 1999-2008 Mighty Minds Publishing Pte Ltd

Tyre Rotation

Why is tyre rotation important?

Tyre rotation is the practice of swapping the front tyres of a vehicle with the rear tyres at regular intervals. The purpose is to extend tyre life by allowing more even treadwear.

The front tyres of a vehicle accomplish different tasks from the rear tyres. The tasks encountered on a front wheel drive vehicle are different from those of a rear wheel drive. The front tyres also respond to steering by altering the vehicle's momentum in one direction or another. The result of all this friction is a gradual loss of tread. When the vehicle is moving, the front tyres take more abuse than the rear tyres. To prevent the front tyres from wearing out much faster than the rear tyres, a periodic tyre rotation is necessary.

Tyre rotation will help all of your vehicle's tyres wear out at the same rate. This prolongs the tyres' life and keeps the tyres performing equally on all four corners. Furthermore, you can get a new pair of tyres without being compelled to buy all four tyres.

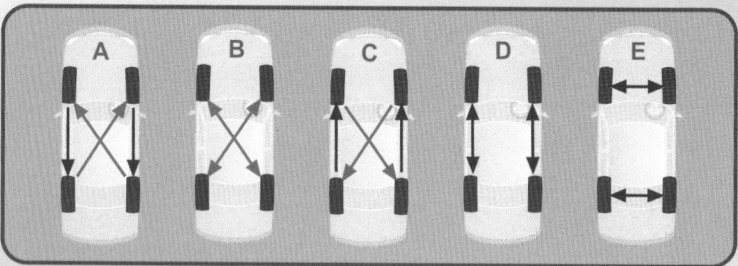

Four Tyre Rotation

1. On front wheel drive vehicles, rotate the tyres in a forward cross pattern (Diagram A) or the 'X' pattern (Diagram B).

2. On rear wheel or four wheel drive vehicles, rotate the tyres in a rearward cross pattern (Diagram C) or the 'X' pattern (Diagram B).

3. For vehicles with directional tyres, rotate as shown in Diagram D.

4. For vehicles with front tyres that are different in size to the rear tyres (non directional tyres), rotate as shown in Diagram 'E'.

Five Tyre Rotation

If your vehicle has a spare tyre that matches the other four tyres, it should be included in the tyre rotation pattern. This results in equally distributed use that will help maintain tread depths on all five tyres throughout their life.

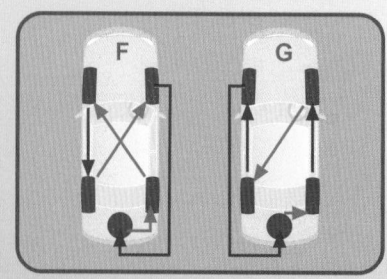

MAP 134

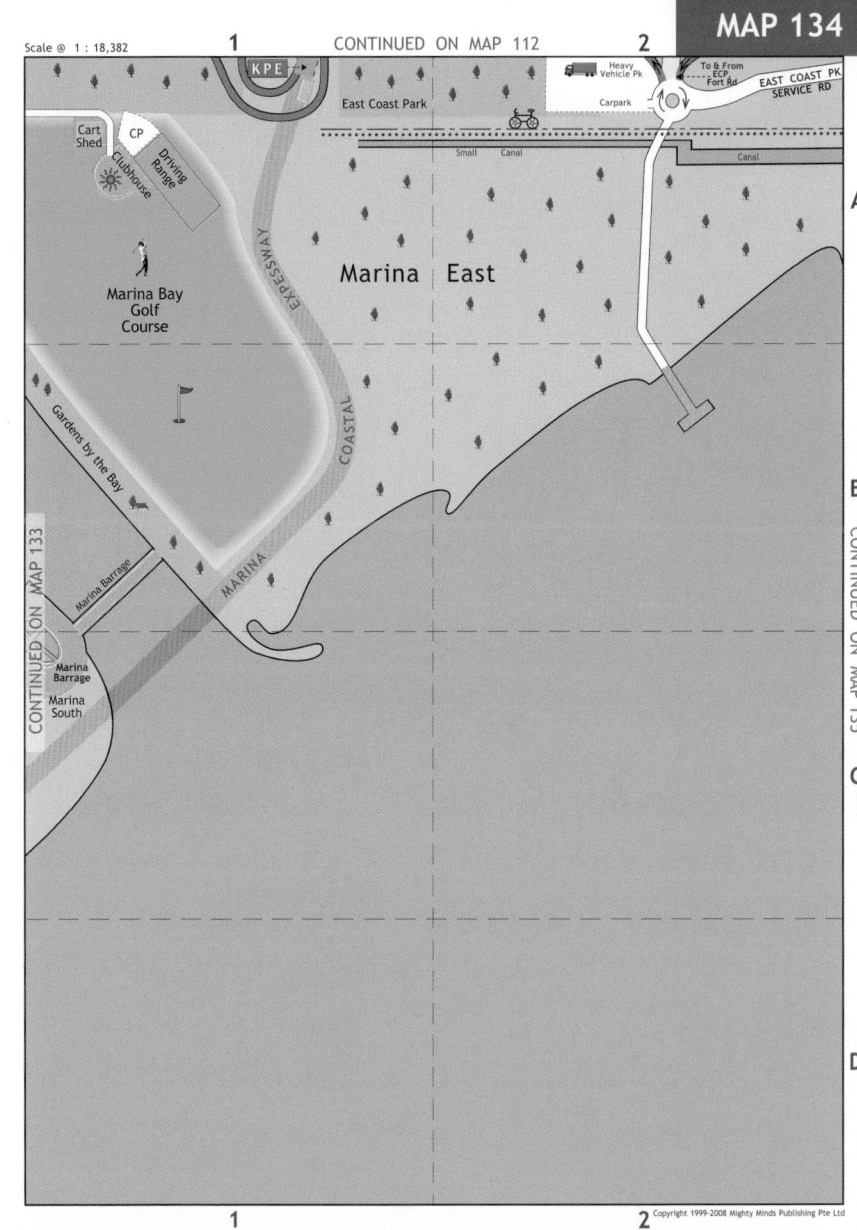

Scale @ 1 : 18,382

KPE

East Coast Park

Heavy Vehicle Pk

To & From ECP Fort Rd

EAST COAST PK SERVICE RD

Carpark

Cart Shed

CP

Clubhouse

Driving Range

Small Canal

Canal

EXPRESSWAY

Marina East

Marina Bay Golf Course

A

COASTAL

Gardens by the Bay

B

MARINA

CONTINUED ON MAP 133

Marina Barrage

Marina Barrage

Marina South

CONTINUED ON MAP 135

C

D

MAP 135

CONTINUED ON MAP 113

Scale @ 1 : 18,382

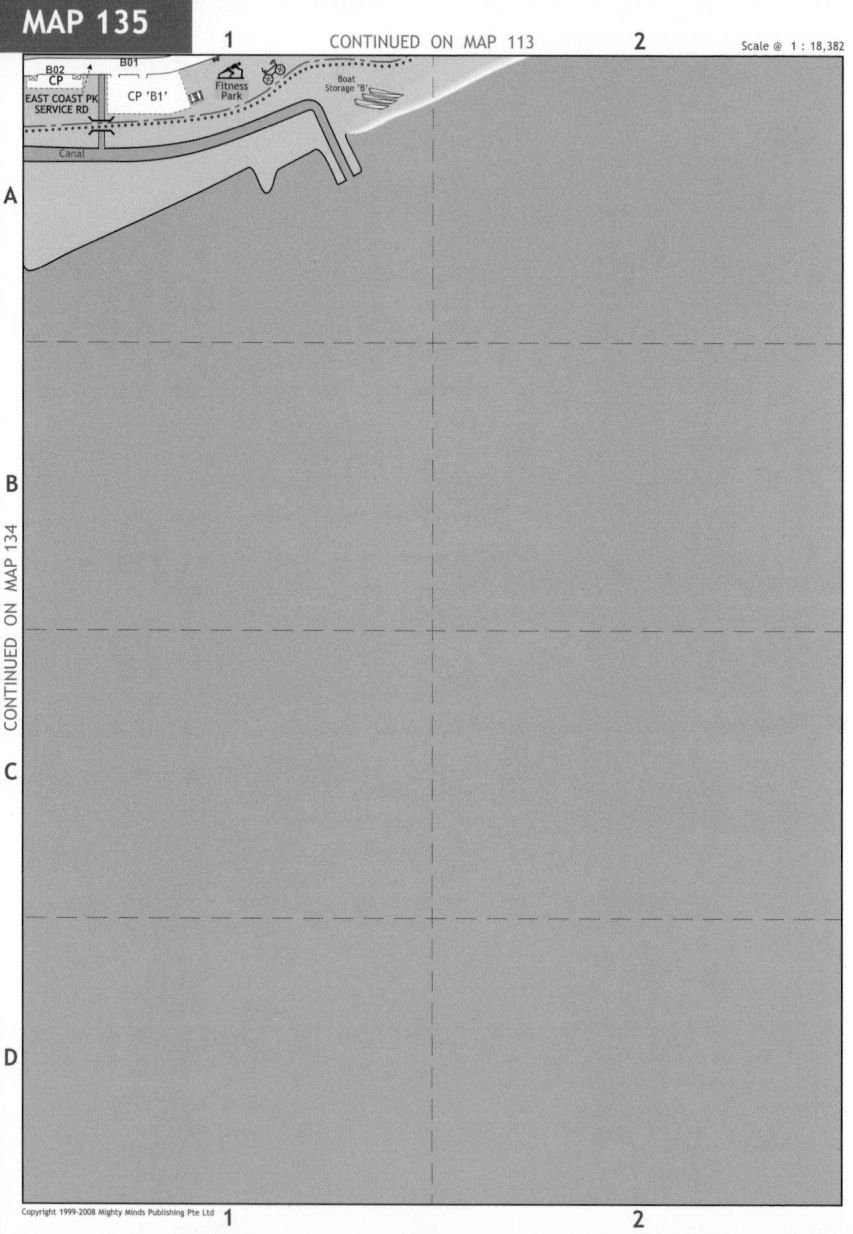

CONTINUED ON MAP 134

A

B

C

D

MAP 136

Scale @ 1 : 18,382   1   CONTINUED ON MAP 120   2

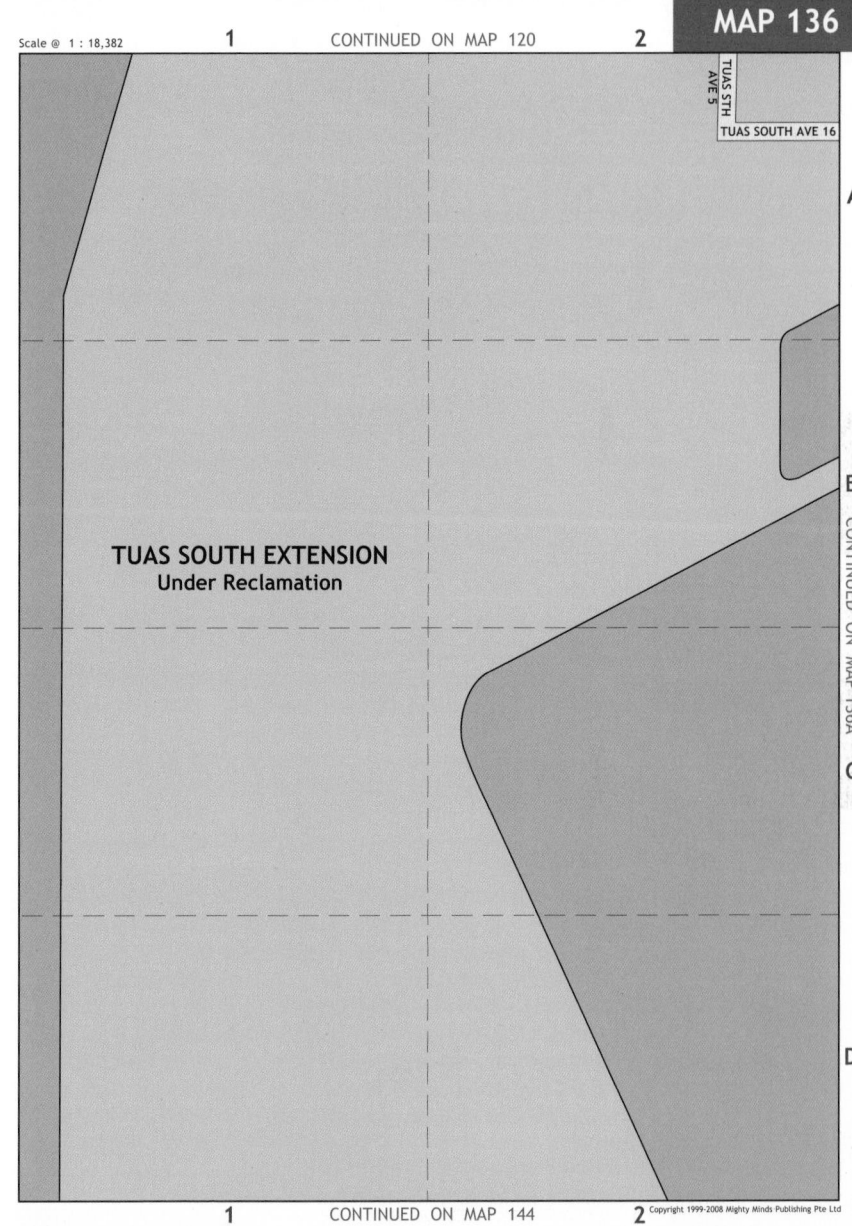

TUAS STH AVE 5

TUAS SOUTH AVE 16

A

B

CONTINUED ON MAP 136A

C

D

TUAS SOUTH EXTENSION
Under Reclamation

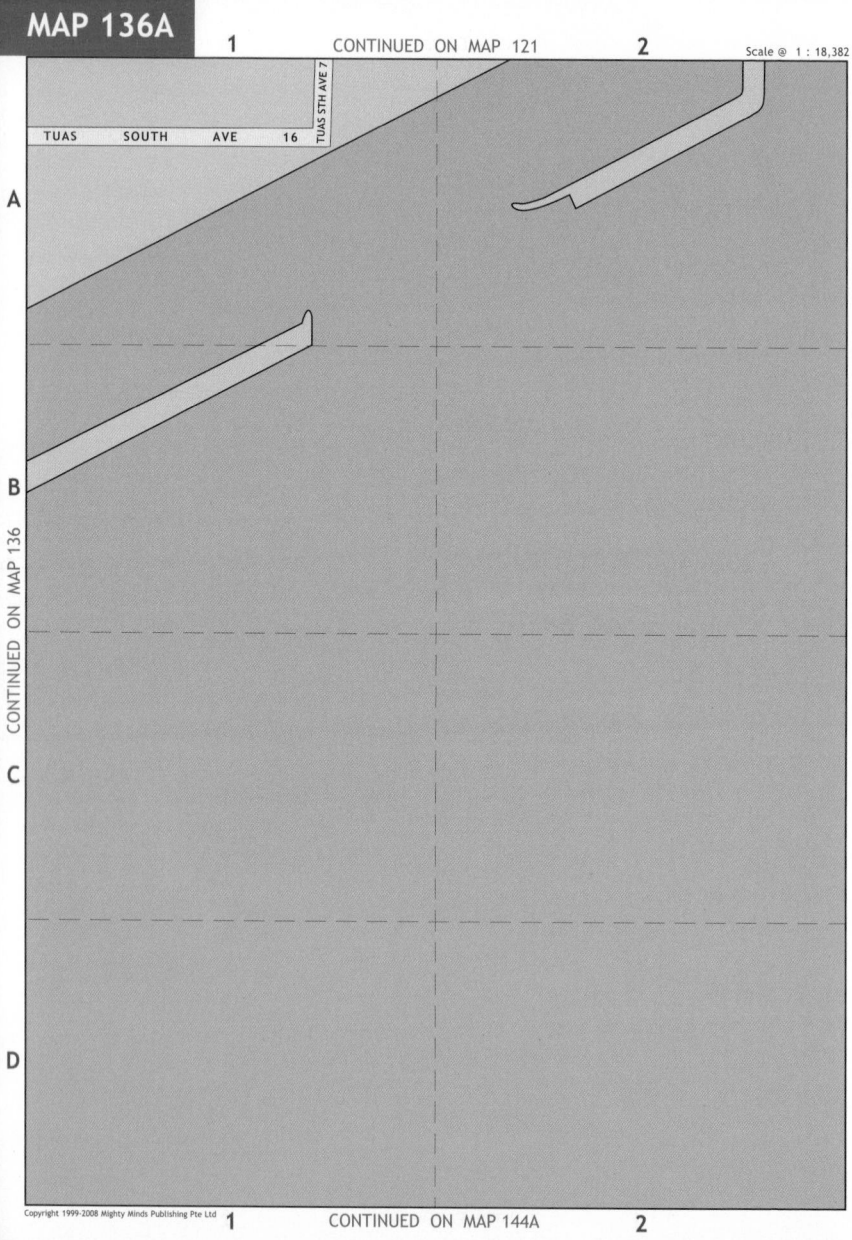

TUAS   SOUTH   AVE   16

TUAS STH AVE 7

CONTINUED ON MAP 136

CONTINUED ON MAP 144A

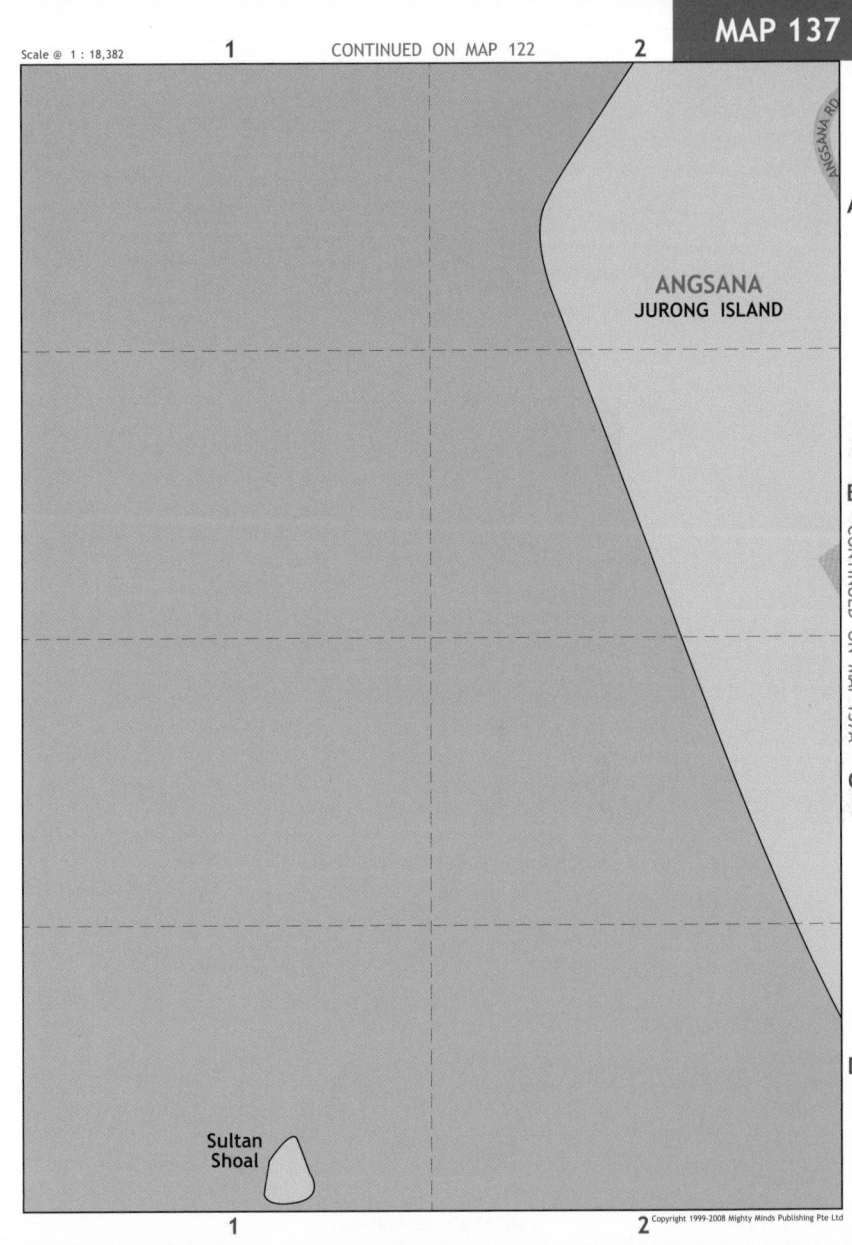

ANGSANA
JURONG ISLAND

ANGSANA RD

A

CONTINUED ON MAP 137A

B

C

D

**Sultan
Shoal**

CONTINUED ON MAP 123

Scale @ 1 : 18,382

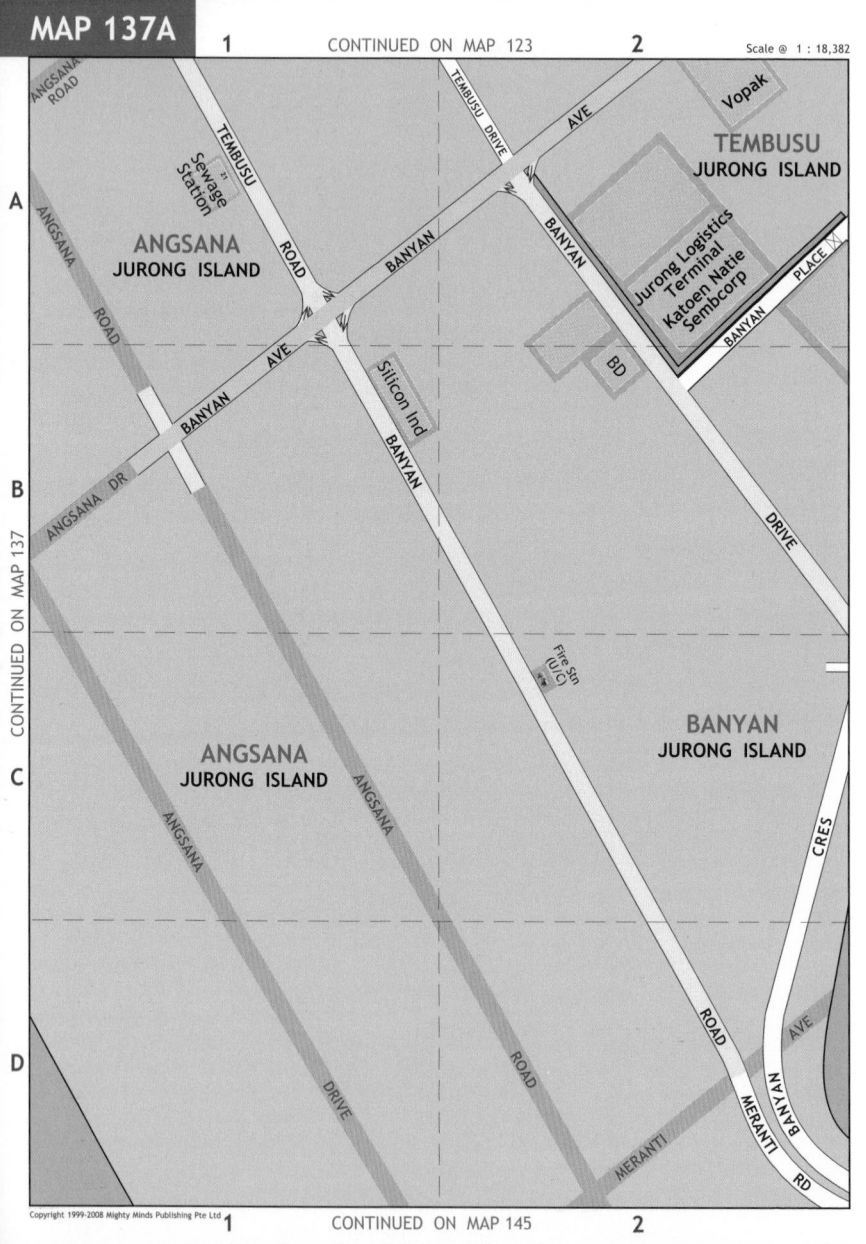

ANGSANA ROAD

TEMBUSU DRIVE

AVE

Vopak

TEMBUSU
JURONG ISLAND

Sewage Station

TEMBUSU ROAD

ANGSANA
JURONG ISLAND

BANYAN

BANYAN

Jurong Logistics Terminal
Katoen Natie
Sembcorp

PLACE

ANGSANA ROAD

AVE

BANYAN

BD

CONTINUED ON MAP 137

ANGSANA DR.

BANYAN

Silicon Ind

BANYAN

DRIVE

Five Stn (U.C)

BANYAN
JURONG ISLAND

ANGSANA
JURONG ISLAND

ANGSANA

ANGSANA

CRES

ROAD

AVE

DRIVE

ROAD

MERANTI

BANYAN

MERANTI RD

CONTINUED ON MAP 145

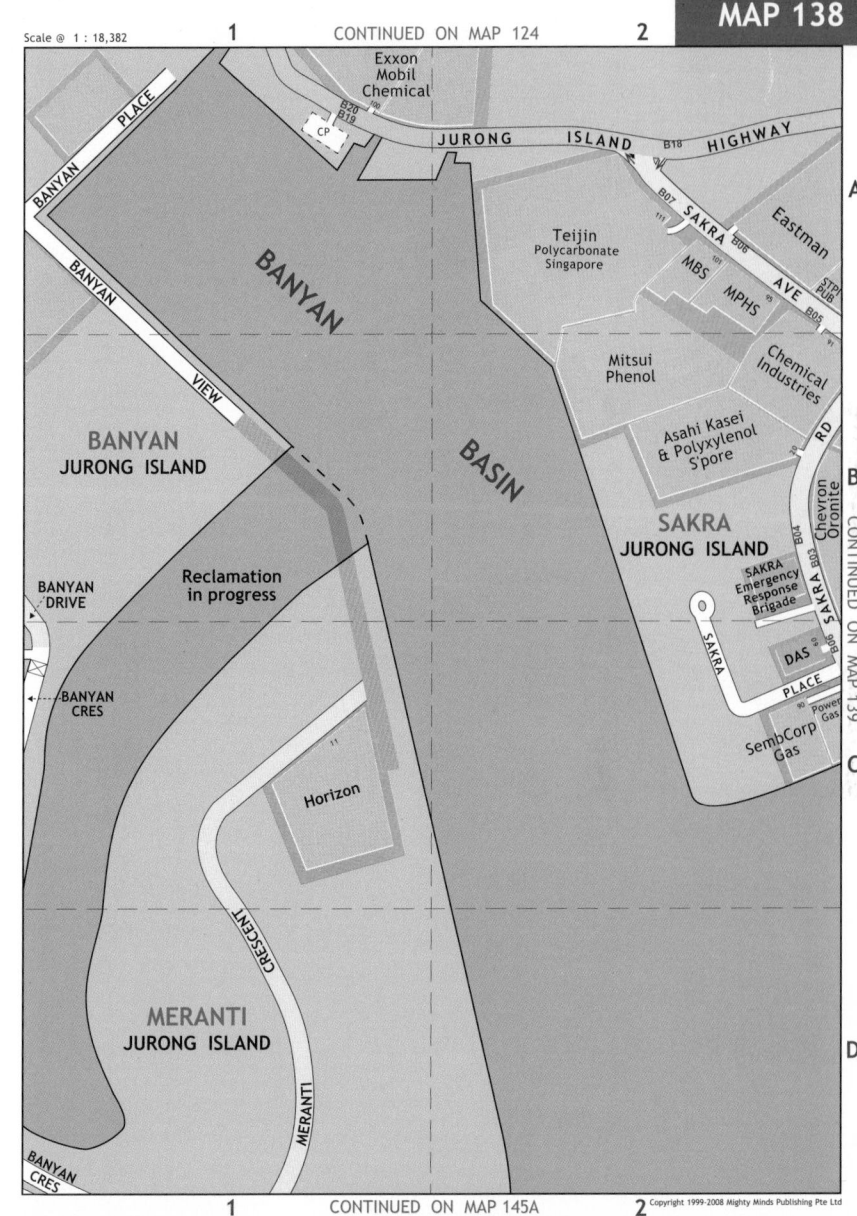

Exxon Mobil Chemical

CP

B20
B19

JURONG ISLAND HIGHWAY

B18

B07

SAKRA

B06

111

Eastman

STPI PUB

B05

Teijin
Polycarbonate
Singapore

MBS

MPHS

BANYAN PLACE

BANYAN VIEW

BANYAN

BASIN

Mitsui Phenol

Chemical Industries

Asahi Kasei & Polyxylenol S'pore

BANYAN
JURONG ISLAND

SAKRA
JURONG ISLAND

R D

B04

Chevron Oronite

BANYAN DRIVE

Reclamation in progress

SAKRA
Emergency
Response
Brigade

B03

SAKRA

B02

BANYAN CRES

SAKRA

DAS

PLACE

90

Power Gas

SembCorp Gas

Horizon

11

CRESCENT

MERANTI
JURONG ISLAND

MERANTI

BANYAN CRES

MAP 139

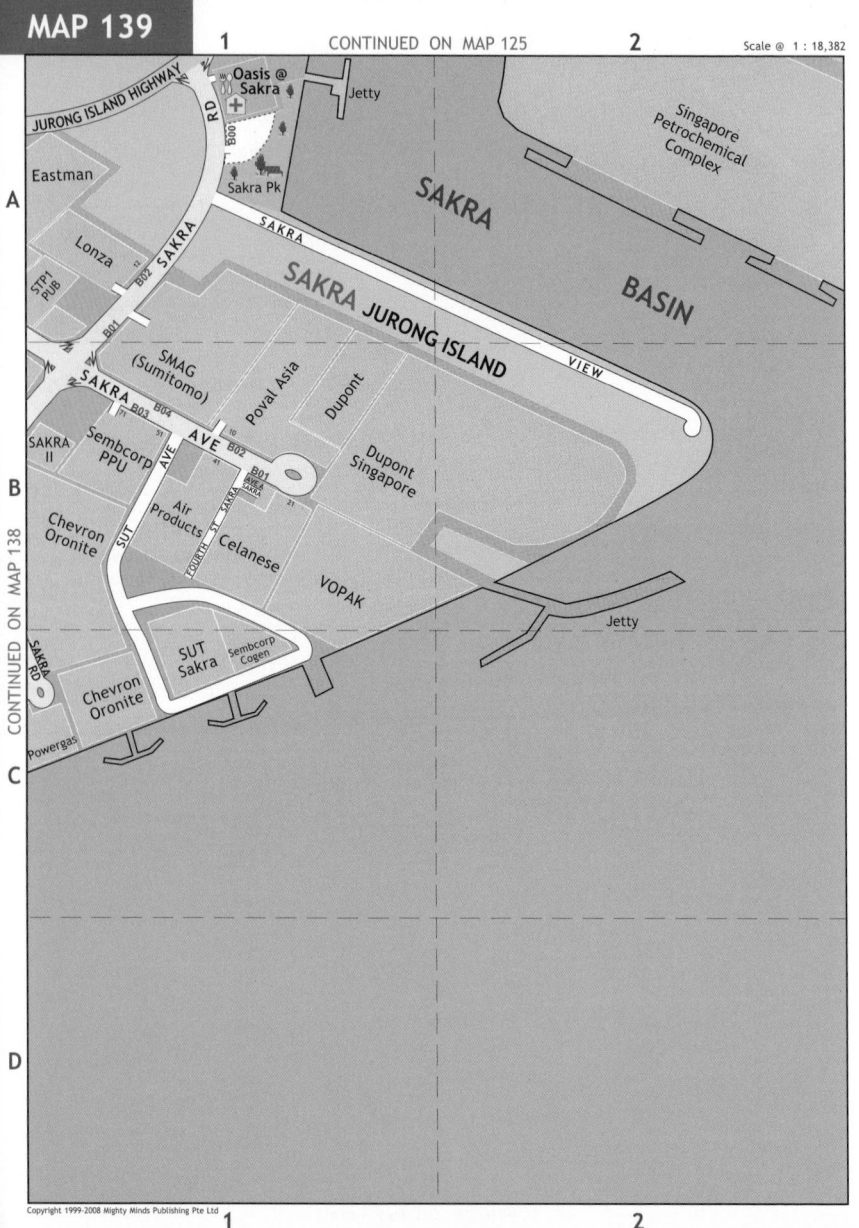

JURONG ISLAND HIGHWAY

Oasis @ Sakra

Jetty

Eastman

Sakra Pk

SAKRA

Singapore
Petrochemical
Complex

A

Lonza

STP1
PUB

SAKRA

B02

SAKRA

SAKRA JURONG ISLAND

VIEW

SAKRA

BASIN

B01

SMAG
(Sumitomo)

SAKRA

Poval Asia

Dupont

Dupont
Singapore

B04 B03

SAKRA
II

Sembcorp
PPU

AVE

B02

B01

B

Air
Products

Celanese

VOPAK

Chevron
Oronite

SUT

FOURTH ST. SAKRA

SAKRA
RD

SUT
Sakra

Sembcorp
Cogen

Jetty

Chevron
Oronite

Powergas

C

D

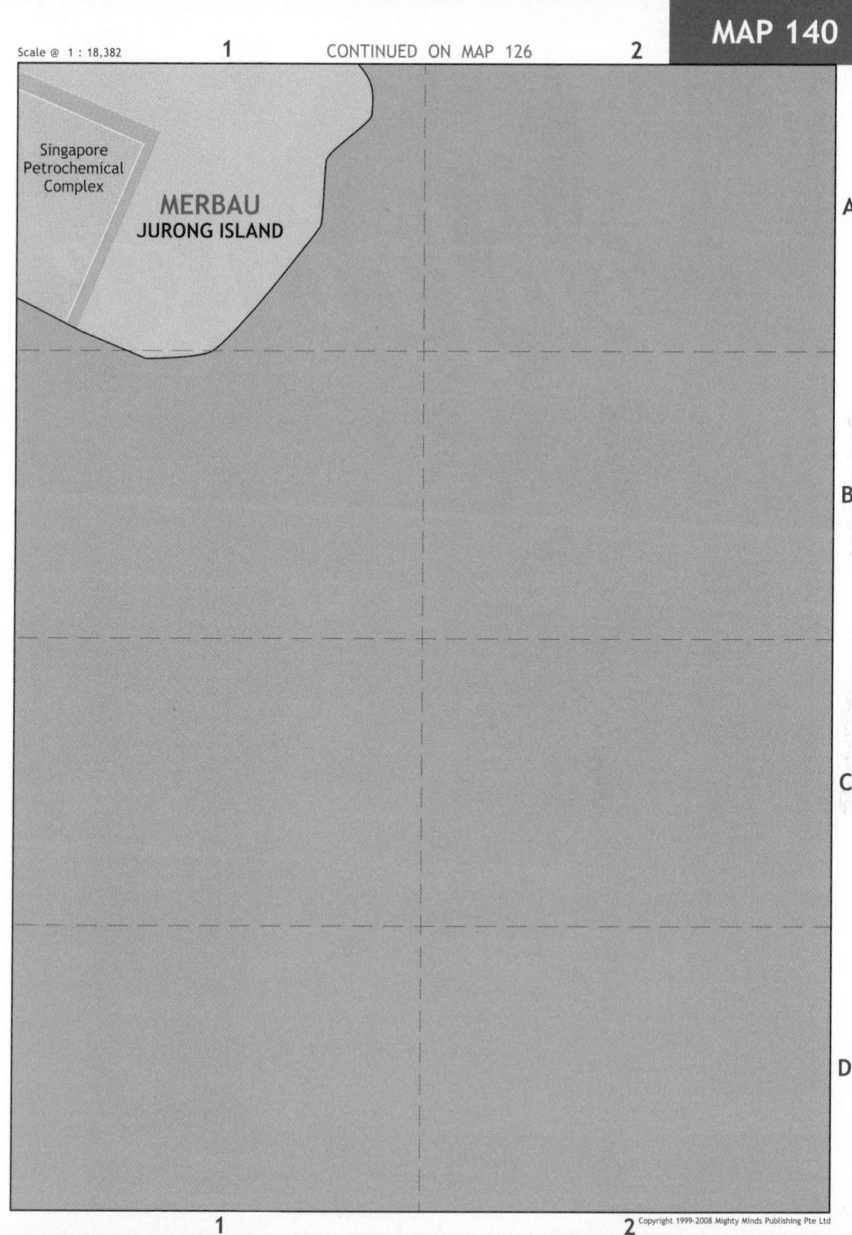

Singapore
Petrochemical
Complex

MERBAU
JURONG ISLAND

A

B

C

D

WHY
infringe
our map
Copyright?

Why risk paying thousands of dollars when you can use our maps *FREE** with our permission!

Be it for a website, catalogue, brochure, poster, an invitation card or a wedding card.

Whether you're an individual, an organisation or a business. Do it the safe way. Seek our permission before you use our maps.

*Conditions apply

Conditions for free use of maps with our permission

- Maps must depict the following statement "Map reproduced from Mighty Minds Street Directory - Singapore's Most Updated Street Directory."
- Maps are not to be resold and must not form part of a product/ publication / image that is to be sold commercially.
- All enquiries and requests are to be made by email with name, designation, organisation name, address, tel, fax and website.
- Our written permission is required before using.
- We reserve the right to reject any request without giving any reason whatsoever.

Kindly read our copyright notice on Page 2. Contact us and we will gladly help you.
Email: mighty@singnet.com.sg

Scale @ 1 : 18,382

CONTINUED ON MAP 130

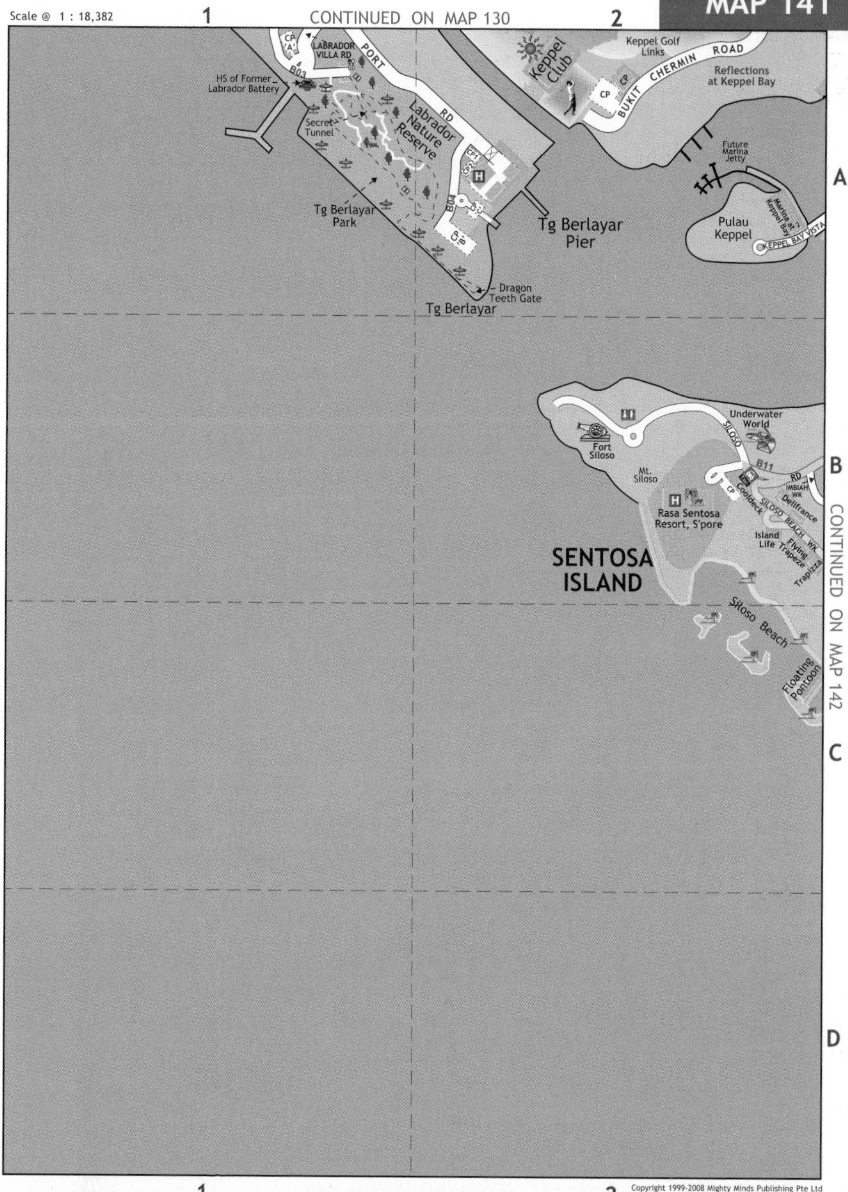
1
2
CP 'A'
LABRADOR VILLA RD
PORT RD
B03
HS of Former Labrador Battery
Secret Tunnel
Labrador Nature Reserve
CP1
CP2
H
B04
CP B
Tg Berlayar Park
Tg Berlayar Pier
Dragon Teeth Gate
Tg Berlayar
Keppel Club
Keppel Golf Links
CP
BUKIT CHERMIN ROAD
Reflections at Keppel Bay
Future Marina Jetty
Pulau Keppel
Marina at Keppel Bay
KEPPEL BAY VISTA
A
B
C
D
Underwater World
SILOSO
Fort Siloso
Mt. Siloso
B11
RD
IMBIAH WK
Cooldeck
Delifrance
SILOSO BEACH WK
H
Rasa Sentosa Resort, S'pore
Island Life
Flying Trapeze
Trapizza
SENTOSA ISLAND
Siloso Beach
Floating Pontoon

CONTINUED ON MAP 142

MAP 142

CONTINUED ON MAP 131

Scale @ 1 : 18,382

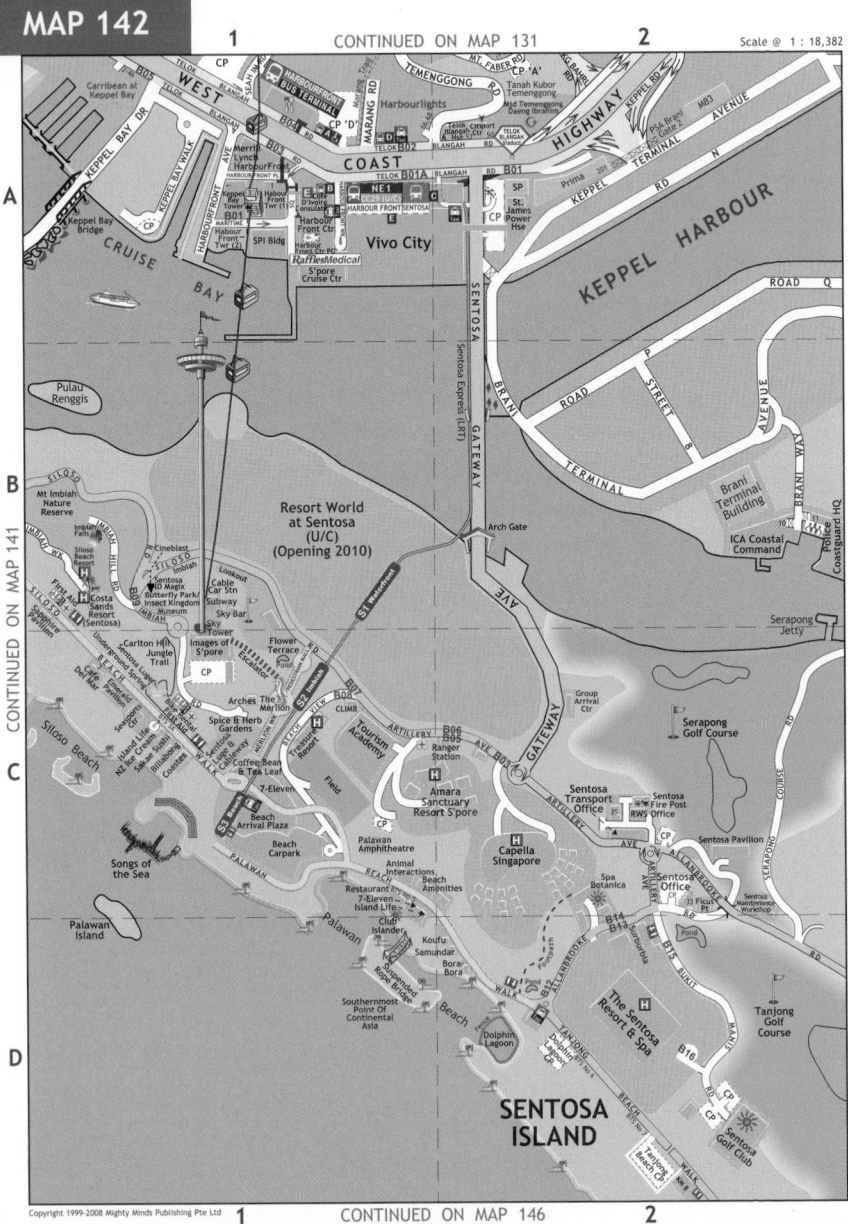

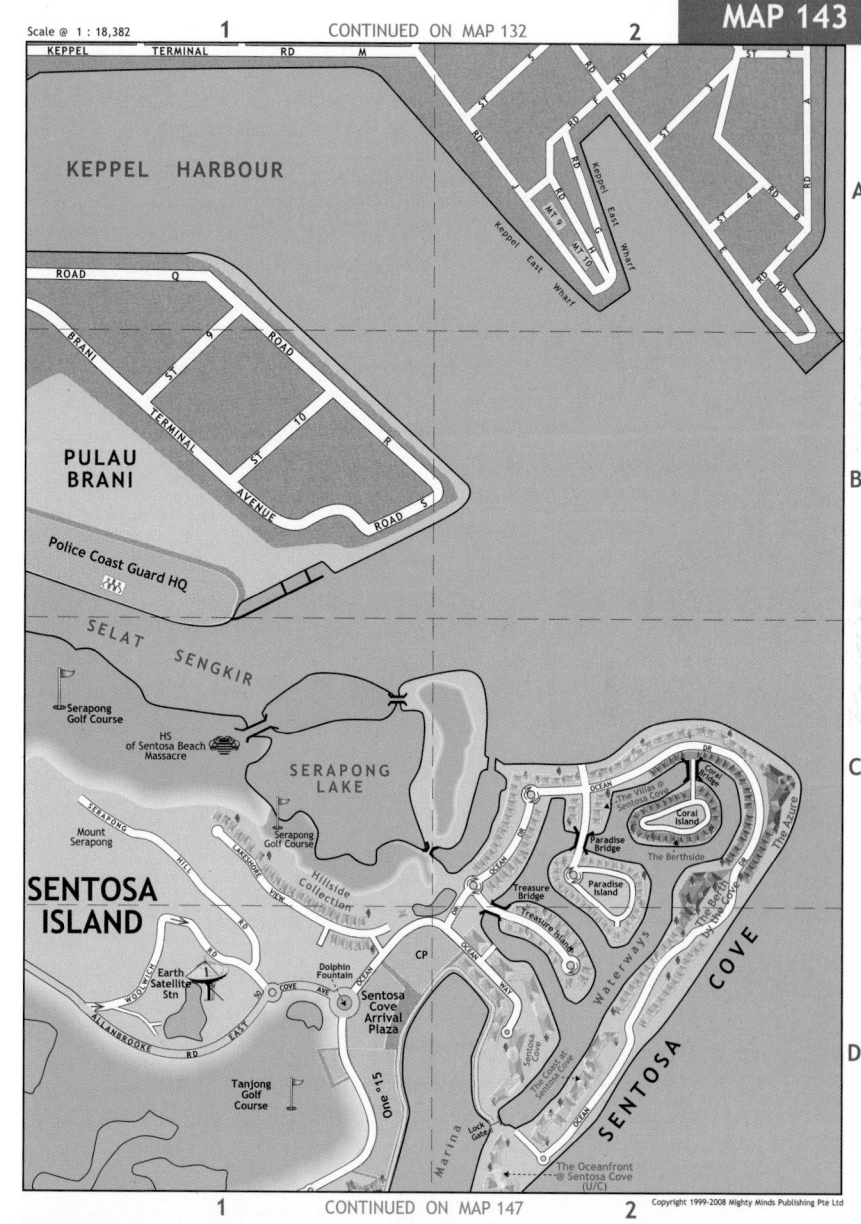

KEPPEL TERMINAL RD M

KEPPEL HARBOUR

Keppel East Wharf
MT 9
MT 10
Keppel East Wharf

ROAD Q

BRANI

TERMINAL

ST 9 ROAD 10 R

AVENUE ST 8 ROAD S

PULAU
BRANI

Police Coast Guard HQ

SELAT SENGKIR

Serapong
Golf Course

HS
of Sentosa Beach
Massacre

SERAPONG
LAKE

Serapong
Golf Course

Hillside
Collection

SERAPONG

Mount
Serapong

HILL RD

LAKESIDE VIEW

SENTOSA
ISLAND

Earth
Satellite
Stn

WOOLLERTON RD

ALLANBROOKE RD

COVE AVE

SO EAST

Dolphin
Fountain

CP

Sentosa
Cove
Arrival
Plaza

OCEAN

OCEAN DR

OCEAN WAY

Treasure
Bridge

Treasure Island

The Villas @
Sentosa Cove

Paradise
Bridge

Paradise
Island

OCEAN DR

Coral
Island

Coral Isle DR

The Berthside

Waterways

The Berth
by the Cove

SENTOSA COVE

The Azure

Tanjong
Golf Course

One °15

Marina
Lock Gate

The Coast @
Sentosa Cove

OCEAN DR

The Oceanfront
@ Sentosa Cove
(U/C)

MAP 144   1   CONTINUED ON MAP 136   2   Scale @ 1 : 18,382

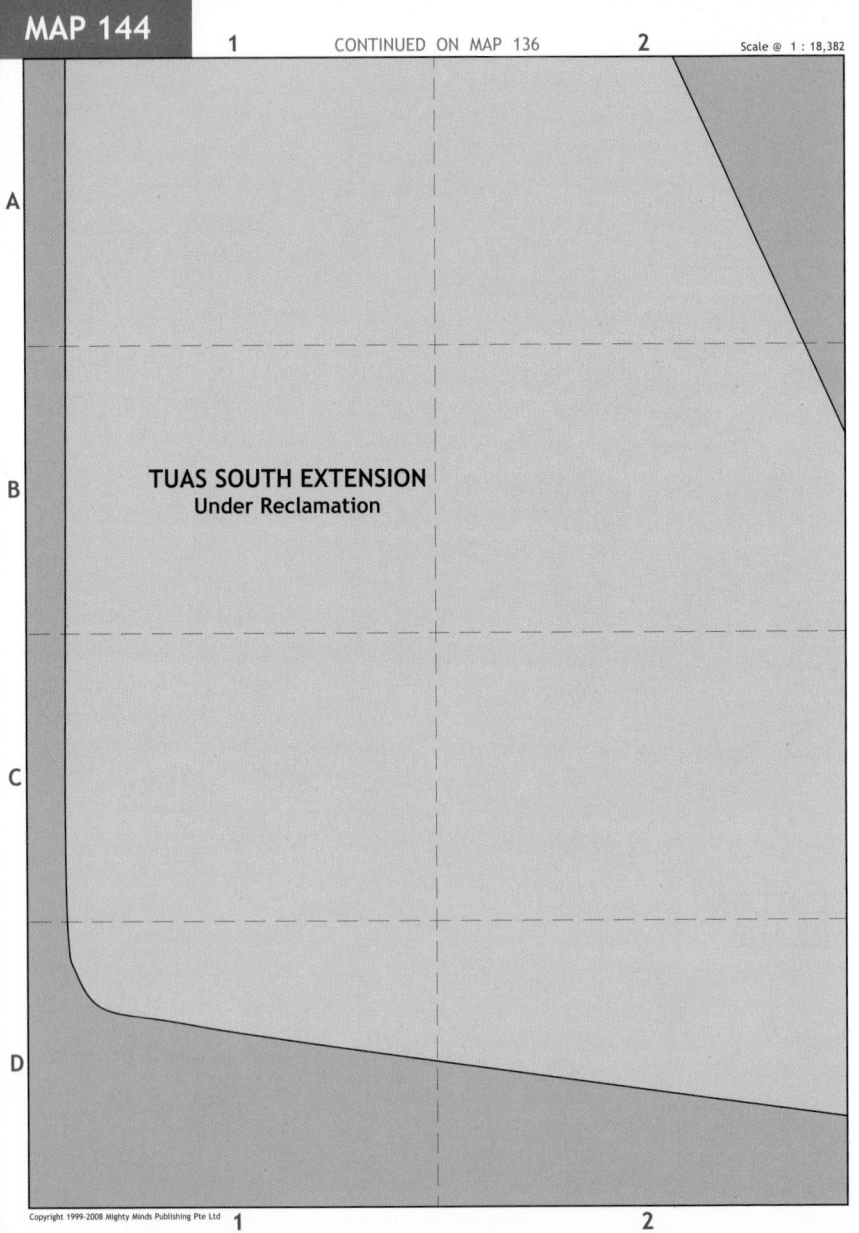

TUAS SOUTH EXTENSION
Under Reclamation

A

B

C

D

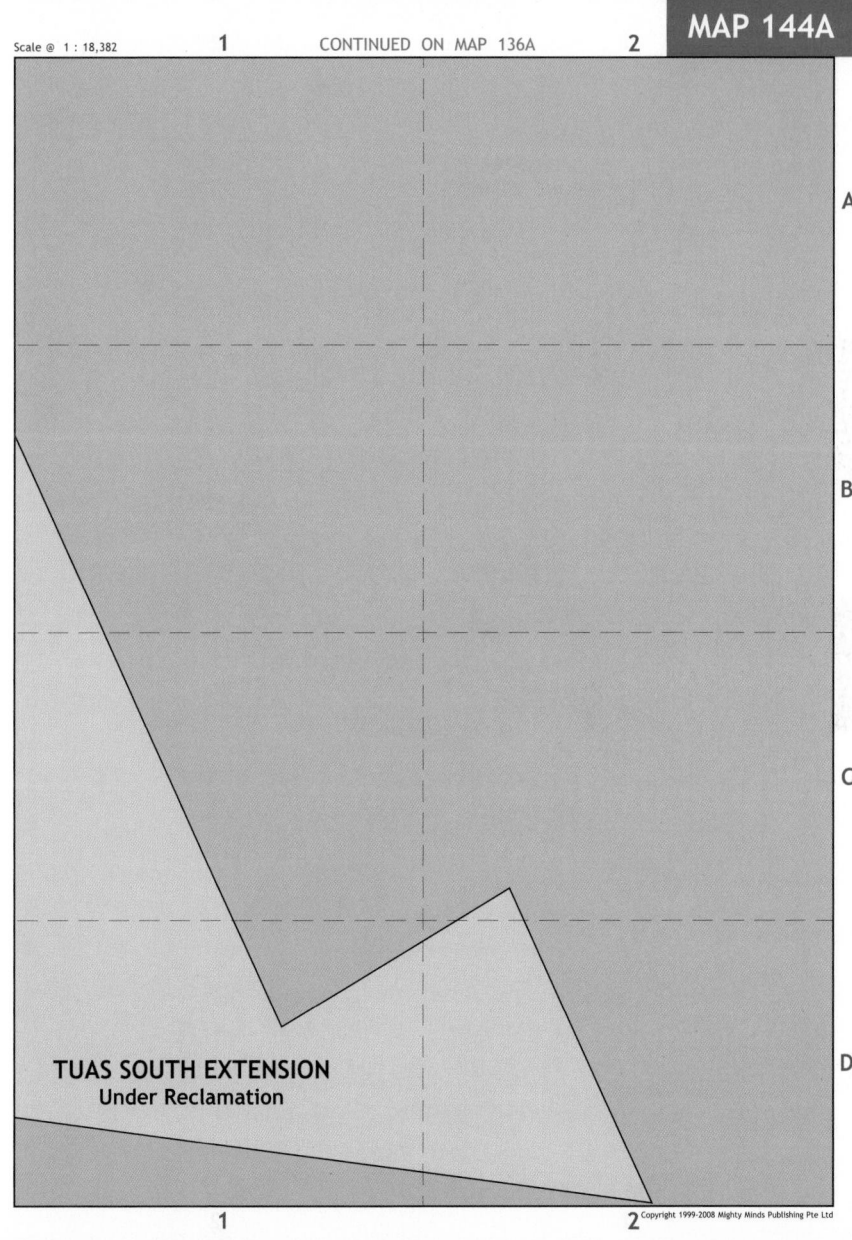

A

B

C

TUAS SOUTH EXTENSION
Under Reclamation

D

MAP 145

1   CONTINUED ON MAP 137A   2

Scale @ 1 : 18,382

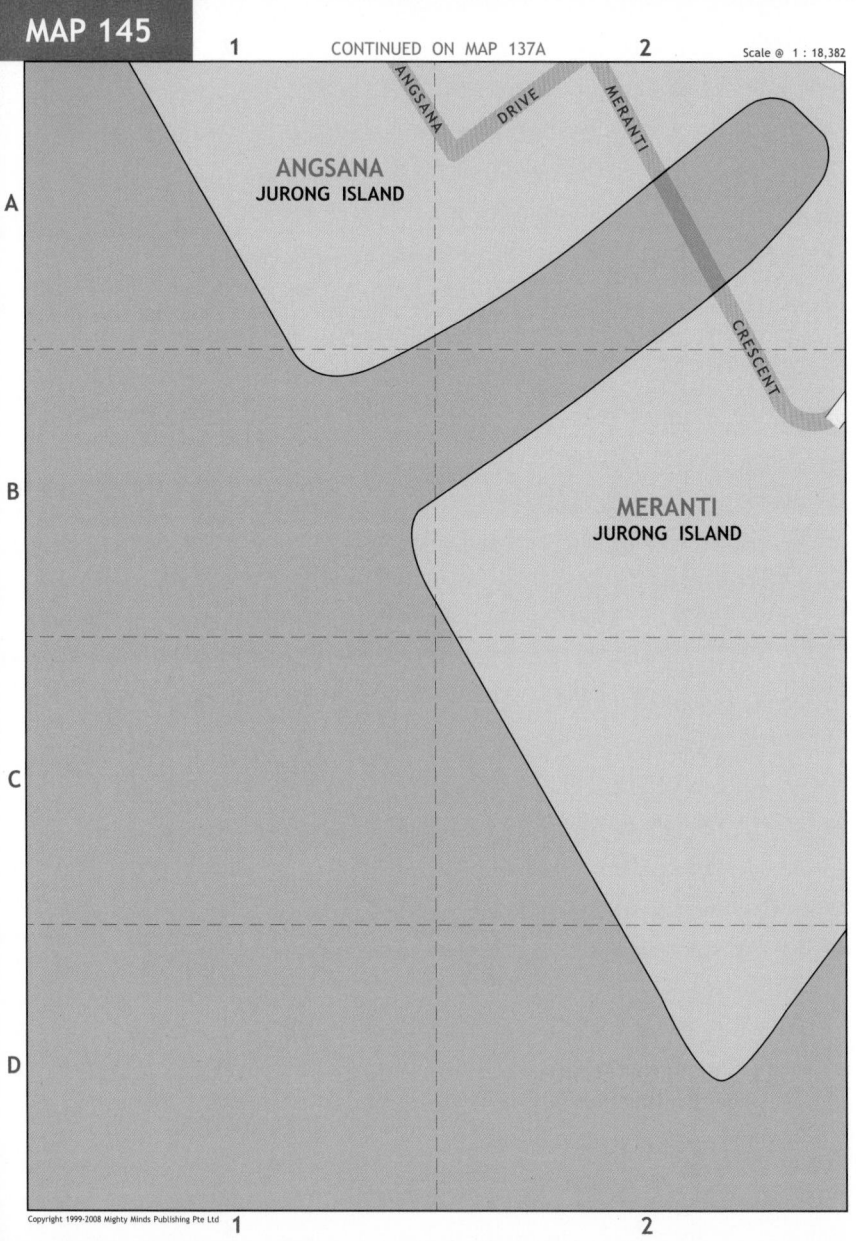

ANGSANA
JURONG ISLAND

MERANTI
JURONG ISLAND

ANGSANA

DRIVE

MERANTI

CRESCENT

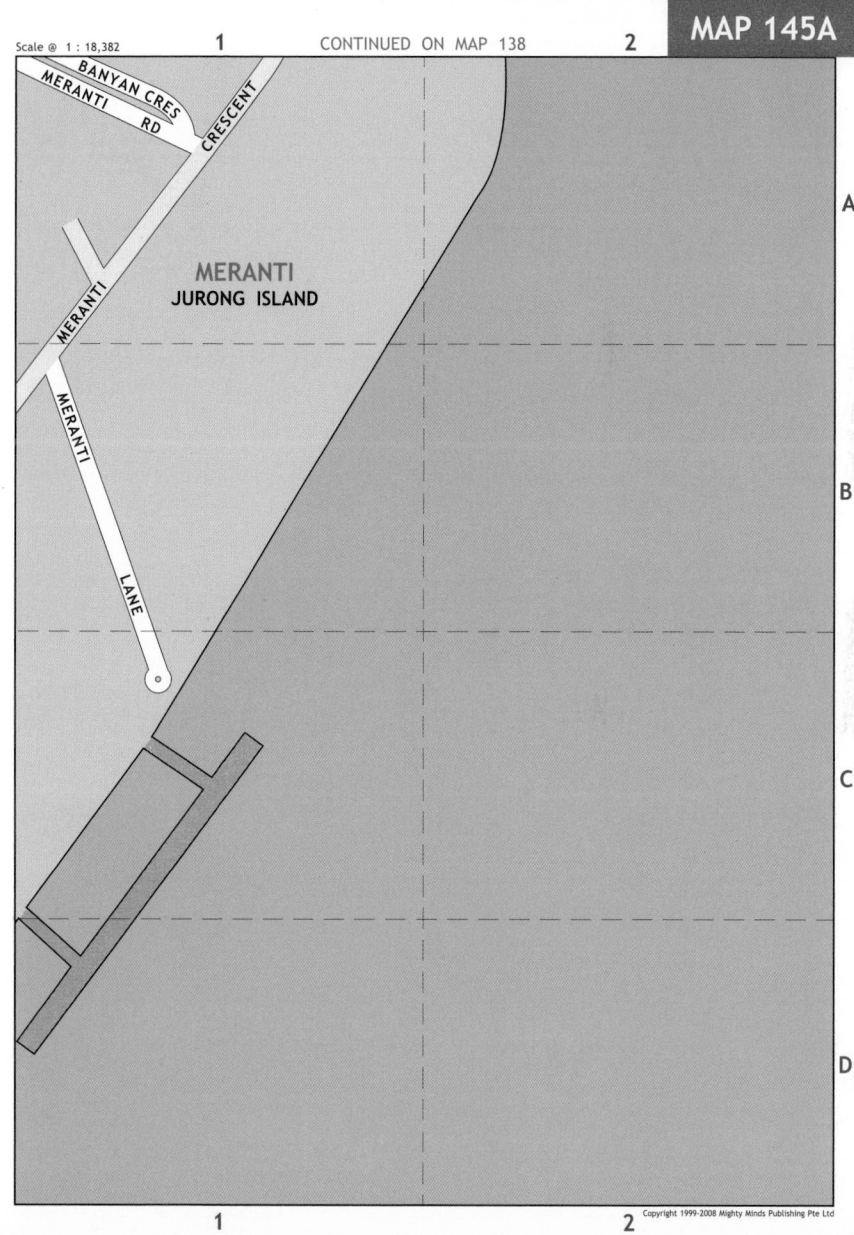

MERANTI
JURONG ISLAND

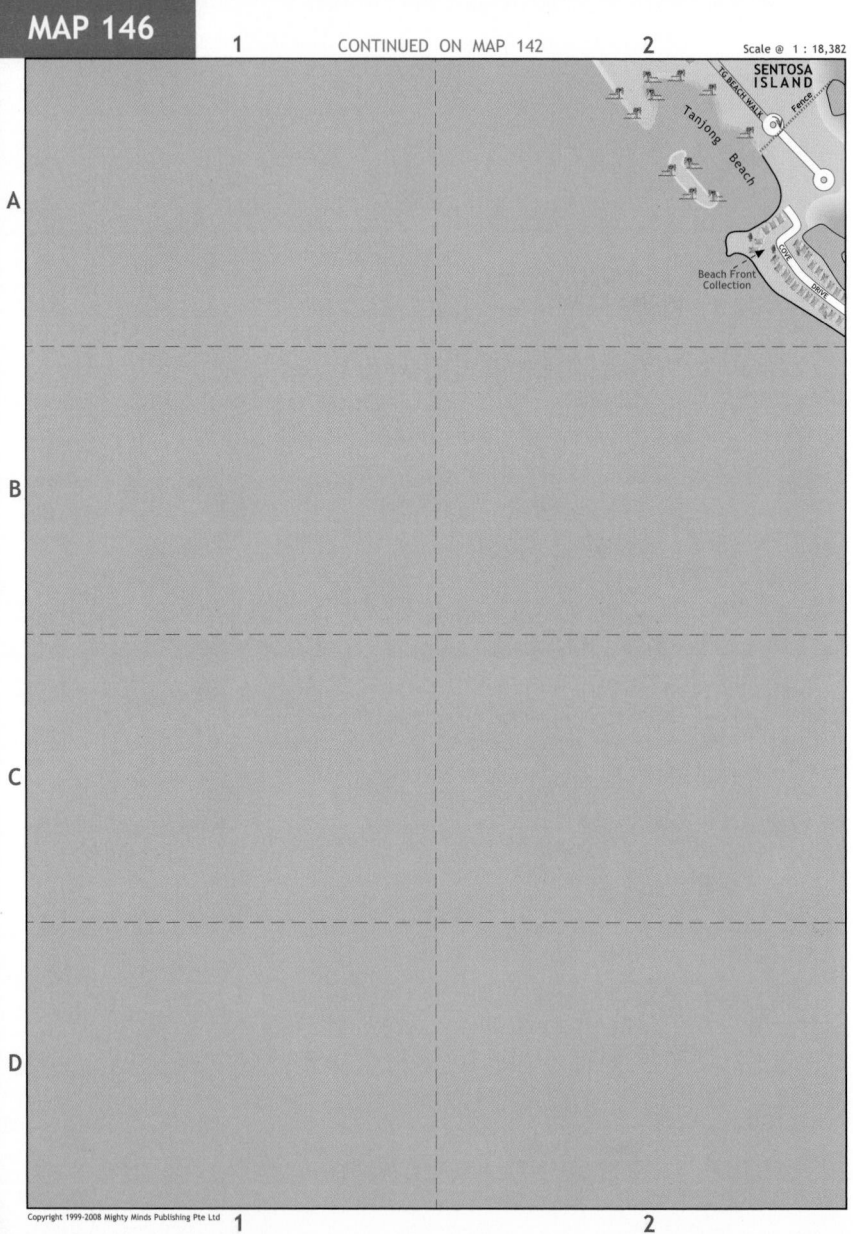

SENTOSA
ISLAND

TG BEACH WALK

Fence

Tanjong Beach

Beach Front
Collection

DRIVE

A

B

C

D

MAP 147

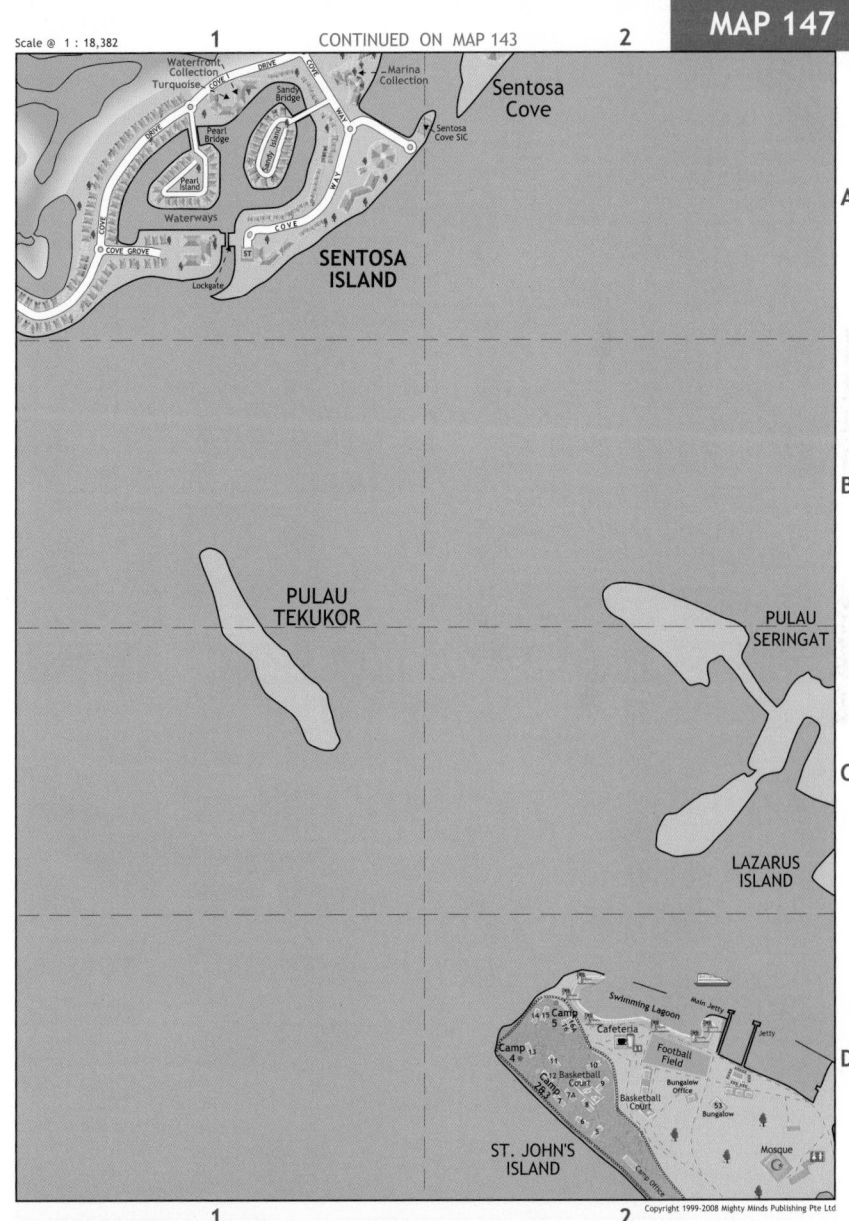

WaterFront,
Collection
Turquoise

Marina
Collection

Sentosa
Cove

Sandy
Bridge

Pearl
Bridge

Pearl
Island

Sentosa
Cove SIC

Waterways

COVE GROVE

SENTOSA
ISLAND

Lockgate

PULAU
TEKUKOR

PULAU
SERINGAT

LAZARUS
ISLAND

Swimming Lagoon

Main Jetty

Camp
5

Camp
13

Cafeteria

Football
Field

Jetty

Camp
4

Camp
2&3

Basketball
Court

Bungalow
Office

53
Bungalow

Basketball
Court

Mosque

ST. JOHN'S
ISLAND

MAP 148

PULAU TEKONG

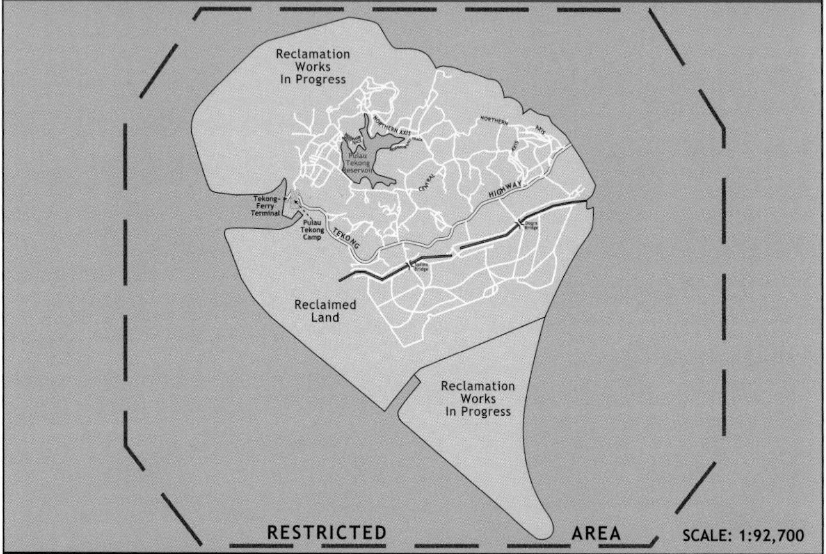

Reclamation Works In Progress

SUNGEI AYER

NORTHERN

NYE

Pulau Tekong Kenangan

TEKONG

HIGHWAY

Tekong Ferry Terminal

Pulau Tekong Camp

Reclaimed Land

Reclamation Works In Progress

RESTRICTED AREA

SCALE: 1:92,700

SINGAPORE SOUTHERN ISLANDS

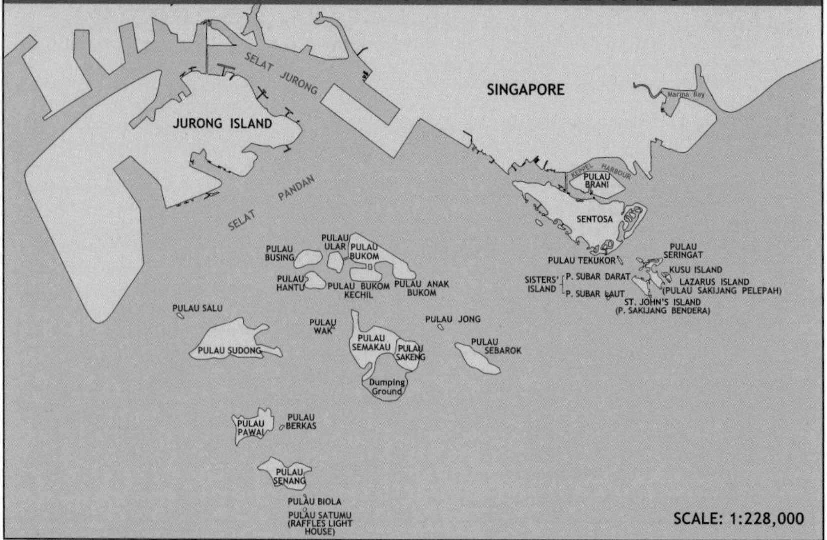

SELAT JURONG

SINGAPORE

Marina Bay

JURONG ISLAND

SELAT PANDAN

KEPPEL HARBOUR

PULAU BRANI

SENTOSA

PULAU TEKUKOR

PULAU SERINGAT

KUSU ISLAND

SISTERS' ISLAND

P. SUBAR DARAT

P. SUBAR LAUT

LAZARUS ISLAND (PULAU SAKIJANG PELEPAH)

ST. JOHN'S ISLAND (P. SAKIJANG BENDERA)

PULAU BUSING

PULAU ULAR

PULAU BUKOM

PULAU HANTU

PULAU BUKOM KECHIL

PULAU ANAK BUKOM

PULAU SALU

PULAU WAK

PULAU JONG

PULAU SUDONG

PULAU SEMAKAU

PULAU SAKENG

PULAU SEBAROK

Dumping Ground

PULAU PAWAI

PULAU BERKAS

PULAU SENANG

PULAU BIOLA

PULAU SATUMU (RAFFLES LIGHT HOUSE)

SCALE: 1:228,000

MAP 149

KUSU ISLAND

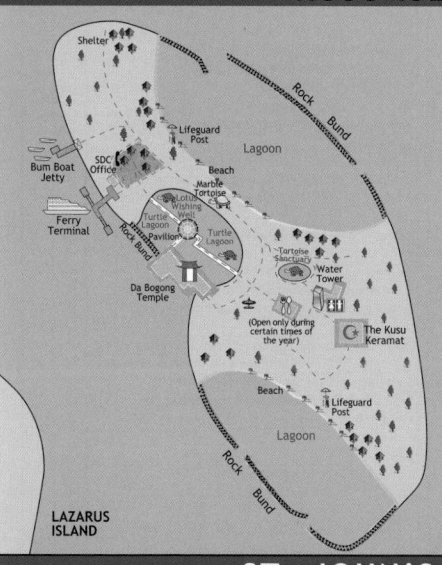

Shelter
Rock Bund
Lagoon
Lifeguard Post
Bum Boat Jetty
SDC Office
Ferry Terminal
Beach
Marble Tortoise
Lotus Wishing Well
Turtle Lagoon
Pavilion
Rock Bund
Turtle Lagoon
Da Bogong Temple
Tortoise Sanctuary
Water Tower
(Open only during certain times of the year)
The Kusu Keramat
Beach
Lifeguard Post
Lagoon
Rock Bund
LAZARUS ISLAND

FERRY SCHEDULE

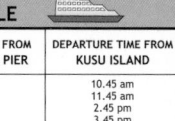

DAYS	DEPARTURE TIME FROM MARINA SOUTH PIER	DEPARTURE TIME FROM KUSU ISLAND
Monday to Saturday	10.00 am 2.00 pm	10.45 am 11.45 am 2.45 pm 3.45 pm
Sunday and Public Holiday	9.00 am 11.00 am 1.00 pm 3.00 pm 5.00 pm	9.50 am 11.50 am 1.50 pm 3.50 pm 5.50 pm

*Departure times are correct as at publishing date and may have changed. Kindly confirm at Marina South Pier before your departure.

FERRY ROUTE

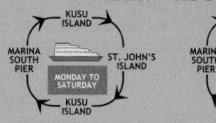

KUSU ISLAND
MARINA SOUTH PIER — ST. JOHN'S ISLAND
MONDAY TO SATURDAY
KUSU ISLAND

KUSU ISLAND
MARINA SOUTH PIER — ST. JOHN'S ISLAND
SUNDAY AND PUBLIC HOLIDAY
KUSU ISLAND

SCALE: 1:8,500

ST. JOHN'S ISLAND

FERRY ROUTE

KUSU ISLAND
MARINA SOUTH PIER — ST. JOHN'S ISLAND
MONDAY TO SATURDAY
KUSU ISLAND

KUSU ISLAND
MARINA SOUTH PIER — ST. JOHN'S ISLAND
SUNDAY AND PUBLIC HOLIDAY
KUSU ISLAND

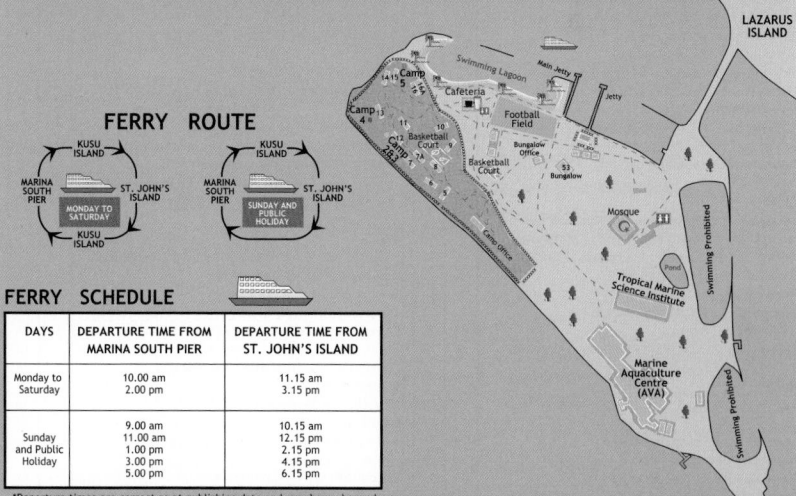

LAZARUS ISLAND
Swimming Lagoon
Main Jetty
Camp
Cafeteria
Jetty
Camp
Football Field
Basketball Court
Basketball Court
Bungalow Office
Bungalow
Camp Office
Mosque
Pond
Tropical Marine Science Institute
Swimming Prohibited
Marine Aquaculture Centre (AVA)
Swimming Prohibited

FERRY SCHEDULE

DAYS	DEPARTURE TIME FROM MARINA SOUTH PIER	DEPARTURE TIME FROM ST. JOHN'S ISLAND
Monday to Saturday	10.00 am 2.00 pm	11.15 am 3.15 pm
Sunday and Public Holiday	9.00 am 11.00 am 1.00 pm 3.00 pm 5.00 pm	10.15 am 12.15 pm 2.15 pm 4.15 pm 6.15 pm

*Departure times are correct as at publishing date and may have changed. Kindly confirm at Marina South Pier before your departure.

SCALE: 1:14,300

ABN AMRO ATM LOCATIONS (ATM 5)

LOCATION	MAP	GRID
CENTRAL		
Bishan Junction 8 (Behind City Chain, Level 1)	67	2D
•Thomson Plaza, 301 Upper Thomson Road #01-38/41	66	2C
SOUTH		
Midpoint Orchard, 220 Orchard Road #01-10	110	1C
One Raffles Quay, South Tower Level 1	133	1C
Orchard Tower, 400 Orchard Road Front Block, Level 1	109	2C
Paragon Shopping Centre, 290 Orchard Road (Basement 1)	110	1C
Sentosa Island, 42 Cable Car Rd Sentosa (Cable Car Plaza)	142	1B
Singapore Flyer (opposite Ticketing Counter)	133	2A
•Singapore Land Tower, 50 Raffles Place #01-03	133	1C
Tanglin Mall, 163 Tanglin Road (Main entrance)	109	2C
EAST		
Changi Airport Terminal 1 Arrival Meeting Hall East (Near Burger King)	75	1B
Changi Airport Terminal 2 Arrival Meeting Hall, Airport Boulevard (Near Taxi Stand)	75	1C
Changi Airport Terminal 3, Airport Boulevard (near Coach Stand, opposite McDonald's)	75	1C
87 Marine Parade Central, level 1	113	2C
Tampines Giant Complex, 21 Tampines North Drive 2 #01-01	72	1A
WEST		
Haw Par Technocentre, Commonwealth Drive, Level 6	108	1C
Holland Village Shopping Centre (Next to BreadTalk, Level 1)	108	1B

CITIBANK ATM LOCATIONS (ATM 5)

LOCATION	MAP	GRID
CENTRAL		
•AMK Hub Br, 53 Ang Mo Kio Ave 3 (facing AMK MRT Stn)	67	2A
Ang Mo Kio MRT Stn, 2450 Ang Mo Kio Ave 8 (Beside UOB ATM)	67	2A
•Bishan MRT Stn, 200 Bishan Rd #01-03	67	2D
Braddell MRT Stn, 379 Lor 1 Toa Payoh	88	2B
Junction 8, 9 Bishan Place #01-K11 (Outside Prima Vera)	67	2D
SPH News Centre, 1000 Toa Payoh North	88	2A
Toa Payoh MRT Stn, 510 Lor 6 Toa Payoh	88	2C
TYCO Electronics, 26 Ang Mo Kio Industrial Pk 2	47	2D
Yio Chu Kang MRT Stn, 3000 Ang Mo Kio Ave 8 (Directly outside the control station)	46	2C
NORTH		
Admiralty MRT Stn, 70 Woodlands Ave 7 (Just outside the stn)	12	1B
Khatib MRT Stn, 201 Yishun Ave 2 (Left of stn control room)	27	1B
Kranji MRT Stn, 960 Woodlands Road (Beside UOB ATM)	46	2C
Marsiling MRT Stn, 71 Woodlands Ave 3	10	2C
Sembawang MRT Stn, 11 Canberra Rd	13	1A
Woodlands MRT Stn, 30 Woodlands Ave 2	11	2C
Yio Chu Kang MRT Stn	46	2C
Yishun MRT Stn, 301 Yishun Ave 2 (Left of stn control room)	14	1D
SOUTH		
Bugis MRT, 220 Victoria St #B1-02 (Next to TransitLink Ticket Office)	111	1D
Chevron House, 30 Raffles Place #01-K8	133	1B
•Capital Square Branch, 23 Church Street #01-01	132	2B
City Hall MRT Stn, 150 North Bridge Rd #B1-01	133	1A
•Cuscaden Rd Branch, HPL House, 50 Cuscaden Rd #02-02	109	2C
Dhoby Ghaut MRT Stn, 11 Orchard Rd (Near escalators to SMU)	110	2D

CITIBANK ATM LOCATIONS (ATM 5)

LOCATION	MAP	GRID
•Esplanade Branch, One Raffles Link Bldg #01-01, 1 Raffles Link	133	1A
Esplanade Mall, 1 Esplanade Dr, #02-K1	133	1A
Funan DigitaLife Mall, 109 North Bridge Road, #01-K1A	132	2A
•Great World City Branch, 1 Kim Seng Promenade #01-51	132	1A
Marina Bay MRT Stn, 21 Marina Stn Rd	133	1C
Millenia Walk, 9 Raffles Boulevard #01-13A/B	133	1A
Newton MRT Stn, 49 Scotts Rd	110	1B
Novena MRT Stn, 250 Thomson Rd	110	2A
•Orchard Branch, 40A Orchard Road #01-00 (Opposite Dhoby Ghaut MRT)	110	2D
Orchard MRT Stn, 437 Orchard Road (Beside ticket office)	110	1C
Outram Park MRT Stn, 10 Outram Rd (Beside stn control room)	132	1C
Paragon CitiGold Ctr, 290 Orchard Road #01-25B, #14-07/09, #01-K2, #B1-K9	110	1C
Raffles Place MRT Stn, 5 Raffles Place (Left of stn control room)	132	1B
Redhill MRT Stn, 920 Tiong Bahru Rd (In front of stn control room)	131	1A
Shaw House, 350 Orchard Rd #01-02	109	2C
Somerset MRT Stn, 1 Somerset Rd (Left of stn control room)	110	1D
Tangs Plaza, 310-320 Orchard Rd, Level 1 (Next to Tangs entrance)	110	1C
Tangs Studio, Basement 1 (Next to Orchard underpass to MRT)	110	1C
Tanjong Pagar MRT Stn, 120 Maxwell Rd (on mezzanine level)	132	2C
Tiong Bahru MRT Stn, 300 Tiong Bahru Road #B1-02	131	2B
The American Club, 10 Claymore Hill (for Members Only)	109	2B
•VivoCity Branch, 1 Harbourfront Walk #01-143, #01-05	142	1A
EAST		
Aljunied MRT Stn, 81 Lor 25 Geylang	112	2A
Bedok MRT Stn, 315 New Upp Changi Rd	93	1D
Changi Airport Terminal 2 Arrival Meeting Hall	75	1C
Changi Airport Terminal 2 Departure Hall , Transit Lounge	75	1C
Changi Airport Terminal 3, Check-in Hall South	75	1C
Changi Airport Terminal 3, Departure Hall (Transit Lounge Sth)	75	1C
Eunos MRT Stn, 30 Eunos Crescent	113	2A
Expo MRT Stn, 21 Changi South Ave 1	94	2B
Kallang MRT Stn, 5 Sims Avenue (In front of stn control room)	112	1B
Kembangan MRT Stn, 55 Sims Ave East (In front of stn control room)	92	1D
Lavender MRT Stn, 50 Kallang Rd	111	2B
•Parkway Parade Br, 80 Marine Parade Rd #01-02, #01-11	113	2C
Pasir Ris MRT Stn, 10 Pasir Ris Central (near 7 Eleven)	52	1D
Paya Lebar MRT Stn, 30 Paya Lebar Road	113	1A
Simei MRT Stn, 30 Simei St 3 (at ground level turn left)	94	1A
Tampines MRT Stn, 20 Tampines Central 1	72	2C
Tampines Plaza, Compaq Ctr Ground Floor 5 Tampines Ctrl 1	72	2C
Tanah Merah MRT Stn, 920 New Upper Changi Road	94	1D
WEST		
31 Biopolis Way #01-08 Nanos Building (In front of Epicentre)	107	2C
Boon Lay MRT Stn, 301 Boon Lay Way	81	1B
Bt Batok MRT Stn, 10 Bt Batok Ctrl	62	2D
Bt Gombak MRT Stn, 802 Bt Batok West Ave 5	62	2C
Chinese Garden MRT Stn, 3150 Clementi Ave West	82	2A
Choa Chu Kang MRT Stn, 10 Choa Chu Kang Avenue 4	41	1C
Clementi MRT Stn, 3150 Clementi Ave West	106	1A
Commonwealth MRT Stn, 375 Commonwealth Ave	108	1C
Dover MRT Stn, 200 Commonwealth Ave West	107	1B
Holland Village, Holland Road Shopping Ctr, 211 Holland Ave	108	1B
•Jurong East Branch, CPF Jurong Building, #01-02, 21 Jurong East St 13	83	1B
Lakeside MRT Stn, 201 Boon Lay Way	82	1A
Queenstown MRT Stn, 301 Commonwealth Ave 3	108	2D
Yew Tee MRT Stn, 61 Choa Chu Kang Drive	41	2A

DBS & POSB ATM LOCATIONS

LOCATION	MAP	GRID
CENTRAL		
●AMK Hub, 53 Ang Mo Kio Ave #B1-01 & #03-01/27	67	2A
Ang Mo Kio Avenue 1, Blk 226G #01-687	67	1B
Ang Mo Kio Avenue 1, Blk 339	67	2B
Ang Mo Kio Avenue 4, Blk 160 #01-404a	46	1D
●Ang Mo Kio Avenue 4, Blk 629 #01-1018	46	1C
Ang Mo Kio Avenue 6, Blk 729 #01-4272a	46	2D
Ang Mo Kio Avenue 10, Blk 409	68	1B
Ang Mo Kio Avenue 10, Blk 453A	68	1A
Ang Mo Kio Avenue 10, Blk 528 #01-2385a	68	1A
●Ang Mo Kio Central, Blk 712A #01-4066	67	2A
Ang Mo Kio Driving Ctr, 3 Ang Mo Kio Street 62	46	2C
Ang Mo Kio MRT Stn, 2450 Ang Mo Kio Ave 8	67	2A
Ang Mo Kio Street 21, Blk 250 #01-00	67	1A
Ang Mo Kio Street 53, Blk 505 #01-00	47	1D
Ang Mo Kio Street 54, Blk 554 #01-2052a	68	1A
Ang Mo Kio Thye Hua Kwan Hosp, 17 Ang Mo Kio Ave 9, 1st Storey	46	1C
Bishan Bus Interchange, Bishan Street 13, Blk 514 #01-00	67	2D
Bishan Street 11, Blk 151 #01-187	89	1A
●Bishan Street 11, Blk 507 #01-392	67	2D
Boon Keng MRT Station, 900 Serangoon Road	111	2A
Braddell MRT Stn, 379 Lorong 1 Toa Payoh	88	2B
Burger King, 243 Holland Avenue	108	1B
Cheers Balestier, 269 Balestier Road #01-20	89	1D
Cheers Bishan, Bishan Street 22, Blk 282 #01-101	67	2C
Cheers Novena, Novena Ville, 275 Thomson Road #01-06	88	2D
Empress Road, Blk 7 #01-35A	108	2A
Esso Stn, 2761 Ang Mo Kio Avenue 5	46	1D
Esso Stn, 384 Lorong Chuan	68	2B
Esso Stn, 399 Lorong 2 Toa Payoh	88	2B
Esso Stn, 1001 Lorong 5 Toa Payoh	89	1B
Esso Stn, 114 Macpherson Road	90	1C
Esso Stn, 560 Thomson Road	88	1B
Esso Stn, 373 Upper Aljunied Road	90	2C
Esso Stn, 866 Upper Serangoon Rd	69	2C
Esso Stn, 353 Upper Thomson Road	66	2C
Esso Stn, 553 Upper Thomson Road	66	2A
Esso Stn, 594 Upper Thomson Road	45	2D
●HDB Hub, 480 Lorong 6 Toa Payoh #01-09	88	2C
HDB Hub, 500 Lorong 6 Toa Payoh #01-32	88	2C
●HDB Hub, 500 Lorong 6 Toa Payoh #02-50	88	2C
Hersing Hub, 743 Lorong 5 Toa Payoh	89	1B
JTC Ang Mo Kio Techplace II Ind Pk 2, Blk 5004 Ang Mo Kio Ave 5	47	2D
●Junction 8 Shopping Centre, 9 Bishan Place #01-14	67	2D
Kallang Bahru, Blk 71 #01-529	90	1D
Lorong 1 Toa Payoh, Blk 107 #01-266	88	2A
Lorong 1 Toa Payoh, Blk 128 #01-819	88	2B
Lorong 4 Toa Payoh, Blk 93 #01-80A	88	2B
Lorong 8 Toa Payoh, Blk 211 #01-01A	89	1A
●45 Macpherson Road	90	1C
MCDS Building, 512 Thomson Road	88	1C
Mecs Matsushita, 22 Ang Mo Kio Industrial Park II	47	2D
Mediacorp Caldecott Hill, 2nd Sty Next To Reception	88	1B
Mount Alvernia Hospital, 820 Thomson Rd 1st Storey Lobby Area	88	1B
Nanyang Poly, 180 Ang Mo Kio Avenue 8 Blk A Unit No.A.208	46	2C
News Centre, 1000 Toa Payoh North	88	2A
Novena MRT Station, 250 Thomson Road #B1-00	110	2A
NTUC AMK Hub, 53 Ang Mo Kio Avenue 3 #B2-26	67	2A
NTUC Bishan, Bishan Street 13, Blk 510 #01-520	67	2D
NTUC Coronation Shopping Plaza, 587 Bukit Timah Road #01-01	86	2D
NTUC Junction 8, 9 Bishan Place #B1-01	67	2D
NTUC Kallang Bahru, Blk 71 #02-531	90	1D
NTUC Lorong 6 Toa Payoh, Blk 192 #01-670 Blk 672	88	2C

LOCATION	MAP	GRID
NTUC Shaw Plaza, 360 Balestier Road #B1-01	89	1D
NTUC Toa Payoh Ctrl, HDB Hub, 500 Lorong 6 Toa Payoh #B1-32	88	2C
NUS Bt Timah Campus, 469 Bukit Timah Road MPA01-01	87	1D
Philip's Singapore Pte Ltd (Security Post), 620 Toa Payoh Lor 1	88	2A
Potong Pasir Avenue 1, Blk 147 #01-85A	89	2C
Revenue House, 55 Newton Rd 1st Storey Security Control Room	110	2A
Seagate, 7000 Ang Mo Kio Avenue 5	48	1D
Shunfu Road Food Ctr, Shunfu Road, Blk 320	67	1D
Singapore Island Country Club (Bukit), 240 Sime Road	86	2A
Singapore Island Country Club (Island),180 Island Club Road	66	1B
SPC Stn, 317 Braddell Rd	88	2A
St. Georges Road, Blk 14 #01-76A	89	2D
●Square 2, 10 Sinaran Drive #02-19/20	88	2D
Tan Tock Seng Hospital, 11 Jalan Tan Tock Seng 1st Storey	88	2D
Techpoint, 10 Ang Mo Kio Street 65	46	2B
The Grassroot Club, 190 Ang Mo Kio Avenue 8	46	2C
Thomson Medical Ctr, 339 Thomson Road	88	1D
●Thomson Plaza, 301 Upper Thomson Road #01-37	66	2C
●Thomson Plaza, 301 Upper Thomson Road #01-45	66	2C
Toa Payoh East, Lorong 6 Toa Payoh, Blk 19 #01-280A	89	1B
Toa Payoh MRT Stn, 510 Lorong 6 Toa Payoh	88	2C
●Towner Road, Blk 101 #01-238	111	2A
Turf City, 200 Turf Club Road	86	1A
Upper Boon Keng Road, Blk 18 #01-1139A	112	1A
Whampoa Drive, Blk 74 #01-344A	89	1D
Yio Chu Kang MRT Stn, 300 Ang Mo Kio Avenue 8	46	2C
NORTH		
Admiralty MRT Station, 70 Woodlands Avenue 7 1st Storey	12	1B
Admiralty Place, Woodlands Avenue 6, Blk 678 #01-716A	12	1B
Admiralty Place, Woodlands Avenue 6, Blk 678A #01-K1	12	2D
●Bangkit Road, Blk 260 #01-15	42	2D
Beauty World Centre, 144 Upper Bukit Timah Road #01-4769A	85	1A
●Beauty World Centre, 144 Upper Bukit Timah Road #03-06A	85	1A
Bukit Panjang Plaza, 1 Jelebu Road #01-K4	42	1C
Causeway Point, 1 Woodlands Square Basement 1	11	2C
Cheers, Yishun Ring Road, Blk 110 #01-389	13	2C
Cheers, Yishun Ring Road, Blk 846 #01-3629	27	1B
Esso Stn, 215 Jalan Kayu	48	1A
Esso Stn, 590 Sembawang Road	13	2A
Esso Stn, 593 Sembawang Road	13	2A
Esso Stn, 50 Woodlands Avenue 1	11	1D
Esso Stn, 1091 Woodlands Road	10	1C
Esso Stn, 10 Yishun Avenue 9	14	1D
Fajar Road, Blk 410 #01-467A	42	2C
Greenridge Shopping Ctr, Jelapang Road, Blk 524A #01-K1	42	2C
JTC Kranji Loop Shophouse	9	2C
Khatib MRT Stn, 201 Yishun Avenue 2	27	1B
Kranji MRT Stn, 960 Woodlands Rd	10	1D
Marsiling Lane, Blk 20 #01-169A	11	1B
Marsiling MRT Station, 71 Woodlands Avenue 3, 1st Storey	10	2C
Marsiling Rise, Blk 131 #01-206A	11	1B
Northpoint, 930 Yishun Avenue 2 Basement 2	14	1D
NTUC Bukit Panjang Plaza, 1 Jelebu Road #01-15	42	1C
NTUC Marsiling MRTStation, 71 Woodlands Avenue 3 #01-01	10	2C
NTUC Sembawang MRT Station, 11 Canberra Road #01-05	13	1A
NTUC Senja Road, Blk 628 #01-01	42	1C
NTUC The Woodgrove, 30 Woodlands Avenue 1 #01-11	11	1D
NTUC Woodlands Centre, Blk 5A #02-180	10	2B
NTUC Woodlands Civic Centre, 900 South Woodlands Dr #B1-01	11	2C
NTUC Woodlands Drive 50, Blk 888 #01-757	12	1C
NTUC Yew Tee MRT Station, 61 Choa Chu Kang Drive #01-01	41	2A
NTUC Yishun MRT Station, Blk 301 Yishun Avenue 2 #01-02	14	1D

DBS & POSB ATM LOCATIONS

LOCATION	MAP	GRID
NTUC Yishun Ring Road, Blk 239 #01-1150	14	1C
NTUC Yishun Ring Road, Blk 414 #01-1853	14	2D
NTUC Yishun Street 81, Blk 849 #01-3701	27	1B
Pending Road, Blk 128 #01-344A	42	2D
Republic Polytechnic, 9 Woodlands Avenue 9	11	2A
Sembawang MRT Station, 11 Canberra Road 1st Storey	13	1A
Sembawang Shipyard, Admiralty Road West (Main Gate)	3	1A
Sembawang Way, Blk 355 #01-03	13	1A
Senja LRT Station, 90 Bukit Panjang Ring Road	42	1B
Singapore Zoo, 80 Mandai Lake Road	24	2D
SPC Stn, 599 Yishun Ring Rd	27	1B
Sun Plaza, 30 Sembawang Drive	13	1A
Ten Mile Junction Level 1, 1 Woodlands Rd	42	1C
Vista Point, Woodlands Drive 44, Blk 548 #01-K2	12	1C
●Woodlands Centre Road, Blk 2A #01-134	10	2B
Woodlands Centre Road (Near Blk 5A #01-00)	10	2B
●Woodlands Civic Centre, 900 South Woodlands Drive #02-01	11	2C
Woodlands Mart, Woodlands Avenue 6, Blk 768 #01-K1	12	1A
Woodlands MRT Station, 30 Woodlands Avenue 2, 2nd Storey	11	2C
Woodlands North Plaza, Woodlands Street 82, Blk 883 #01-K2	11	2B
359 Woodlands Road, Yew Tee Shophouse	41	2A
●Woodlands Street 31, Blk 303 #01-191	10	2D
Woodlands Street 81, Blk 802 #01-00	11	2B
Woodlands Town Centre, Blk 4A #01-00A	10	2B
●Yew Tee MRT Stn, 61 Choa Chu Kang Drive, #01-04	41	2A
Yishun Avenue 2, Blk 837 #01-00	27	1B
●Yishun Avenue 5, Blk 101 #01-05	13	2D
●Yishun Avenue 5, Blk 101 #01-33A	13	2D
190 Yishun Avenue 7, Int'l Video Product	14	1B
Yishun Central, Blk 322 #01-00	14	2D
●Yishun Central 1, Blk 926 #01-183	14	1D
Yishun MRT Station, 301 Yishun Avenue 2	14	1D
Yishun Ring Road, Blk 799 #01-3410A	27	1A
Yishun Street 22, Blk 290 #01-401	14	1C
Yishun Street 72, Blk 744 #01-197A	14	1D
Yishun Street 81, Blk 844 #01-166	27	1B
SOUTH		
●Alexandra Village, Bukit Merah Lane 1, Blk 123 #01-78	130	2B
Amoy Street Food Centre, Telok Ayer Street	132	2C
Banda Street, Blk 5 #01-52A	132	2C
Beach Road, Blk 1	111	2C
BHG Bugis Junction, 230 Victoria Street Basement 1	111	1D
Bras Basah Complex, Blk 231 #01-21A	111	1D
●73 Bras Basah Road	111	1D
Bugis MRT Stn, 220 Victoria Street	111	1D
●Bukit Merah Central, Blk 161 #01-3727	131	1B
Bukit Merah View, Blk 115 #01-375A	131	1B
Bukit Purmei Road, Blk 112 #01-00A	131	2C
Burlington Square, 175 Bencoolen Street Level 1	111	1C
Cathay Cineleisure Orchard, 8 Grange Road Basement 1	110	1C
●Centrepoint, 176 Orchard Road #01-27	110	1C
Centrepoint, 176 Orchard Road Basement 1	110	1C
Change Alley, Chevron House, 30 Raffles Place	133	1B
Cheers, Bugis Entertainment Centre, ABFL Blk C52 Queens St	111	1D
Cheers, Prime Centre, 200 Middle Road #02	111	1C
Cheers, Singapore Finance House, 470 North Bridge Rd #01-01	111	1D
Cheers, Stamford Court, 61 Stamford Road #01-03	110	2D
Cheers, The Central, 6 Eu Tong Sen Street #01-03/04	132	2A
Chinatown MRT Stn, 151 North Bridge Road	132	2B
Clarke Quay, Blk 30 River Valley Rd #01-51	132	2A
Comcentre 3, 31 Exeter Road B1 Canteen	110	1D
CPF Building, 79 Robinson Rd	132	2C

DBS & POSB ATM LOCATIONS

LOCATION	MAP	GRID
DBS Building Tower One, 6 Shenton Way	132	2C
●DBS Building Tower Two, 6 Shenton Way 1st Storey	132	2C
Dhoby Ghaut MRT Stn, 11 Orchard Rd	110	2D
Esplanade Mall, 8 Raffles Avenue #01-K2	133	1A
Esso Stn, 141 Bukit Timah Road	110	2B
Esso Stn, 1 Jervois Road	131	2A
Esso Stn, 2991 Jalan Bukit Merah	131	1B
Esso Stn, 353 Tanglin Road	109	1D
Esso Stn, 396 Telok Blangah Road	131	1D
Esso Stn, 237 Whitley Road	87	2D
Everton Park Cantonment Road, Blk 1 #01-27A	132	1C
Far East Plaza, 14 Scotts Rd level 1	110	1C
Forum The Shopping Mall, 583 Orchard Road Basement 1	109	2C
●Funan The DigitaLife Mall, 109 North Bridge Road #03-31	132	2A
Gateway West Tower #B1, 150 Beach Road	111	1C
Gleneagles Medical Centre, 6 Napier Road #02-01	109	1B
Golden Shoe Carpark, 50 Market Street 1st Storey	132	2B
●Great World City, 1 Kim Seng Promenade #02-32	132	1A
Great World City B1, 1 Kim Seng Promenade Basement 1	132	1A
Great World City S1, 1 Kim Seng Promenade #01-K5	132	1A
●Harbourfront Centre, 1 Maritime Square #02-122	142	1A
Havelock Road, Blk 40 Beo Crescent	131	2A
●Hong Lim Complex, Upper Cross Street, Blk 531 #01-51	132	1B
298 Jalan Besar	111	1B
Jalan Bukit Merah, Blk 111 #01-1672A	131	2C
Jalan Bukit Merah, Blk 146 #01-1082	131	2C
Jalan Bukit Merah Food Ctr, Blk 6 #01-K2	130	2B
Keppel Club, Bukit Chermin	141	2A
●Key Point, 371 Beach Road #01-03/04	111	2C
KK Hospital, 100 Bukit Timah Road Lift Lobby	110	2B
Lau Pa Sat Festival Market, 18 Raffles Quay	132	2C
Liang Court Complex, 177 River Valley Road 1st Storey	132	2A
Little India Arcade, 48 Serangoon Road #01-K1 Serangoon Block	111	1C
Lucky Plaza, 304 Orchard Road #03-61	110	1C
Marina Bay MRT Stn, 21 Marina Bay Rd	133	1C
Marina Bay Sands IR, 12A Bayfront Avenue	133	1B
Marina Square, 6 Raffles Boulevard Level 3	133	1A
●1 Maritime Square #02-103	142	1A
MAS Building, 10 Shenton Way 1st Storey	132	2D
Millenia Walk, 9 Raffles Boulevard 1st Storey	133	1A
Ministry of Manpower, 18 Havelock Road Ground Floor Entrance	132	2B
Mount Elizabeth Hospital, 3 Mount Elizabeth	110	1A
Newton Building (Kiosk), 135 Bukit Timah Road	110	2B
Newton Food Centre, 500 Clemenceau Avenue North	110	1B
Newton MRT Stn, 49 Scotts Road Basement 1	110	1B
●Ngee Ann City, 391 Orchard Road #04-14	110	1C
Ngee Ann City, 391 Orchard Rd, Podium Blk #05-23A	110	1C
Ngee Ann Polytechnic, 535 Clementi Road Canteen	85	1C
NTUC, Bukit Merah Central, Blk 166 #02-3531	131	1B
NTUC, Cambridge, Blk 43 #01-15	110	2A
NTUC, Dawson Place, Dawson Road, Blk 57 #01-07	130	2A
NTUC, Depot Road, Blk 108 #01-01	130	2C
NTUC, Havelock Road, Blk 50 #01-755	131	2A
NTUC, 131 Killiney Road #01-01	110	1D
NTUC, MDIS, 501 Stirling Rd	108	1D
NTUC, Queenstown, Margaret Drive, Blk 34A #01-342	108	2D
NTUC, Rochor Road, Blk 3 #01-640	111	1C
NTUC, Square 2, 10 Sinaran Drive #04-46/56	110	2A
NTUC, Stirling Rd, Blk 170 #01-1147	130	1B
NTUC, Tanjong Pagar Plaza, Tanjong Pagar Road, Blk 5 #01-01	132	2C
NTUC, Telok Blangah Street 32, Blk 78A #01-01	130	2D
NTUC, Tiong Bahru Plaza, 302 Tiong Bahru Road #B1-01	131	2B
OG Albert Complex, 60 Albert Street Level 1	111	1C

LOCATION	MAP	GRID
Orchard MRT Station, 437 Orchard Road #B2-02	110	1C
Orchard Towers, 1 Claymore Drive	109	2C
Outram Park MRT Stn, 10 Outram Road	132	1C
Paragon, 290 Orchard Road #B1-K1	110	1C
Park Mall, 9 Penang Road #B1-08	110	2D
Parklane Shopping Mall, 35 Selegie Road 1st Storey	110	2C
Pearl's Centre, 100 Eu Tong Sen Street #01-11	132	1C
Peninsula Plaza, 111 North Bridge Road #02-54	133	1A
People's Park Centre, 101 Upp Cross Street #B1	132	2B
People's Park Complex, 1 Park Road	132	2B
●Plaza Singapura, 68 Orchard Road #B1-25	110	2D
PSA Tanjong Pagar Complex, 7 Keppel Road (Glutton's Corner)	132	2D
PWC Building, 8 Cross Street #01-01K	132	2B
Queen Street, Blk 270 #01-137A	111	1D
Queensway Shopping Centre, 1 Queensway 1st Storey	130	1B
Raffles City Shopping Centre, 252 North Bridge Road #B1-K3	133	1A
●Raffles City Shopping Centre, 252 North Bridge Road #02-26A/B	133	1A
Raffles Hospital, 585 North Bridge Road	111	1C
Raffles Hotel, 328 North Bridge Road 1st Storey	111	1D
Raffles Junior College, 10 Bishan Street 21	67	2D
Raffles Place MRT Station, 5 Raffles Place #B1-09	133	1B
Redhill Lane, Blk 79 #01-336A	131	1B
Redhill MRT Stn, 920 Tiong Bahru Rd	131	1A
●Rochor Centre, Blk 1 Rochor Road #01-544	111	1C
●Royal Brothers Building, 22 Malacca Street #01-00	132	2B
Sentosa Golf Club, Sentosa Island, 27 Bukit Manis	142	2D
Sentosa Island, Beach Station Arrival Plaza	142	1C
Shaw House, 350 Orchard Road #B1-00	109	2C
Shaw Tower, 100 Beach Road	111	1D
Shell House, 83 Clemenceau Avenue	132	2A
Singapore Cruise Centre, 1 Maritime Square Lobby D Level 1	142	1A
Singapore General Hospital, Blk 1 Outram Road	132	1C
Singapore General Hospital, Wards Building, Blk 4 Outram Road	132	1C
Singapore Power Building, 111 Somerset Road	110	1D
SMU Bras Basah, 80 Stamford Road #B1-03	110	2D
Somerset MRT Stn, 1 Somerset Road Basement 1	110	1D
SPC Stn, 3800 Jalan Bukit Merah	131	1B
Spottiswoode Park Road, Blk 108 #01-00	132	1D
Suntec City Mall, 3 Temasek Boulevard Basement 1	133	1A
●Suntec City Mall, 3 Temasek Boulevard #01-054	133	1A
●Suntec City Mall, 3 Temasek Boulevard #02-003/005/007	133	1A
Suntec City Mall, 3 Temasek Boulevard Level 2	133	1A
Takashimaya Shopping Centre, 391 Orchard Road Basement 1	110	1C
Takashimaya Shopping Centre, 391 Orchard Road 1st Storey	110	1C
Tang Plaza, 320 Orchard Road Basement 1	110	1C
Tanglin Mall, 163 Tanglin Road 2nd Storey	109	2C
Tanjong Pagar MRT Stn, 120 Maxwell Road #B1	132	2C
●Tanjong Pagar Plaza, Tanjong Pagar Road, Blk 1 #01-41	132	2C
Telok Blangah Crescent, Blk 6 #01-420	131	1C
Telok Blangah Drive, Blk 77 #01-K1	130	2D
Telok Blangah Rise, Blk 36 #01-103A	131	2D
●The Arcade, 11 Collyer Quay #02-22	133	1B
The Cathay, 2 Handy Rd	110	2D
The Comtech, 60 Alexandra Terrace	130	1C
The Heeren (Outside Main Ent), 260 Orchard Road #01-ATM 2	110	1C
The Tanglin Club, 5 Stevens Road	110	1B
Tiong Bahru Market, 30 Seng Poh Road	132	1B
Tiong Bahru Plaza, 302 Tiong Bahru Road #B1-13A	131	2B
●Tiong Bahru Plaza, 302 Tiong Bahru Road #01-17	131	2B
United Square, 101 Thomson Rd	110	2A
●Upper Cross Street, Blk 531 #01-01	132	2B
Veerasamy Road, Blk 634 #01-00	111	1C
Wisma Atria, 435 Orchard Road 3 Storey	110	1C

LOCATION	MAP	GRID
Zion Road, Blk 92 #01-197A	132	1A
EAST		
Airline House, Sia Engineering 1st Storey	54	2D
Bedok Market Place, Shop N Save Bedok, 348 Bedok Road	94	1C
Bedok MRT Stn, 315 New Upper Changi Road #01-01	93	1D
Bedok North Avenue 3, Blk 133 #01-138A	93	2C
Bedok North Street 1, Blk 204 #01-393A	93	1D
●Bedok North Street 1, Blk 213 #01-103	93	1D
Bedok North Street 3, Blk 509 #01-131A	93	1C
Bedok North Street 4, Blk 87 #01-191A	93	2C
Bedok Reservoir Road, Blk 124 #01-1093A	92	1C
Bedok Reservoir Road, Blk 616 #01-K1	92	1B
Bedok Reservoir Road, Blk 715 #01-3000A	92	2B
Bedok Reservoir View, Blk 775 #01-K1	93	2B
Bedok South Avenue 3, Blk 73 #01-452A	115	2A
Bedok South Road, Blk 18 #01-45A	115	1A
Budget Terminal 30 Airport Boulevard	96	1B
Budget Terminal Departure Hall, 30 Airport Boulevard	96	1B
Chai Chee Complex, 750E Chai Chee Technopark @ Chai Chee	92	2D
Chai Chee Road, Blk 25A #01-455	92	2D
Chai Chee Street, Blk 42 #01-68A	92	2C
Changi Airport Terminal 1, Arrival Hall	75	1B
Changi Airport Terminal 1, Departure Hall	75	1B
Changi Airport Terminal 1, Departure Transit West	75	1B
Changi Airport Terminal 2, Arrival Hall	75	1C
Changi Airport Terminal 2, Basement 1	75	1C
Changi Airport Terminal 2, Departure Check-in Hall North	75	1C
Changi Airport Terminal 2, Departure Transit Lounge	75	1C
Changi Airport Terminal 2, Departure Transit Lounge North	75	1C
Changi Airport Terminal 2, Departure Transit Lounge North Level 3	75	1C
Changi Airport Terminal 3, Arrival Hall North	75	1C
Changi Airport Terminal 3, Departure Check-in Hall North	75	1C
Changi Airport Terminal 3, Departure Transit Lounge North	75	1C
Changi Airport Terminal 3, Departure Transit Lounge South	75	1C
51 Changi Business Park Central, The Signature #01-K3	95	1B
Chai Chee Complex, 750E Chai Chee Technopark @ Chai Chee	92	2D
Changi General Hospital, 2 Simei Street 3	94	1A
Changi Village, Blk 2 #01-70A	54	1B
Cheers, Aljunied Avenue 2, Blk 119 #01-74	112	2A
Cheers, Bedok North Street 3, Blk 539 #01-625	92	2C
Cheers, Haig Road, Blk 12 #01-333	113	1A
Cheers, Hougang Central, Blk 810 #01-214	70	1A
Cheers, Hougang Point, 1 Hougang Street 91 #01-01	48	2D
Circuit Road, Blk 37 #01-393A	90	2C
Circuit Road, Blk 79A #01-00	90	2D
Cisco Hq, 20 Jalan Afifi	91	1D
City Plaza, 810 Geylang Road 1st Storey	113	1A
Compass Point, 1 Sengkang Square #01-01 Blk 02	49	1B
●Compass Point, 1 Sengkang Square #01-18	49	1B
Courts Megastore, 50 Tampines North Drive 2	51	1D
Daichi Foodmart, Tampines Street 21, Blk 201B #01-1091	73	1D
Dunman Food Court, 271 Dunman Road	113	2B
East Coast Lagoon Food Village, 1220 East Coast Parkway	115	1C
East Coast RC, 1000 East Coast Parkway	114	1C
●914 East Coast Road #01-03/04	114	2B
●Eastpoint Shopping Centre, 3 Simei Street 6 #01-37	94	1A
East Shore Hospital, 321 Joo Chiat Road	114	1A
Elias Mall, Elias Road, Blk 625 #01-K5	51	2D
Esso Stn, 630 Aljunied Road	90	2C
Esso Stn, 611 Aljunied Road	90	2D
Esso Stn, 799 Bedok South Avenue 1	93	1D
Esso Stn, 649 Changi Road	114	1A
Esso Stn, 239 East Coast Road	113	2C

DBS & POSB ATM LOCATIONS

LOCATION	MAP	GRID
Esso Stn, 590 East Coast Road	114	2B
Esso Stn, 345 Geylang Lorong 21	112	2B
Esso Stn, 638 Geylang Road	113	1A
Esso Stn, 225 Guillemard Road	112	2B
Esso Stn, 600 Hougang Avenue 3	70	1D
Esso Stn, 216 Lavender Street	111	2B
Esso Stn, 708 Mountbatten Road	112	2C
Esso Stn, 61 Pasir Ris Drive 1	51	2D
Esso Stn, 211 Punggol Road	49	2C
Esso Stn, 9 Tampines Avenue 7	72	2C
Esso Stn, 40 Tampines Avenue 9	73	1B
Esso Stn, 189 Tanjong Katong Road	113	1B
Esso Stn, 943 Upper Changi Road North	74	1C
Esso Stn, 955 Upper Changi Road North	74	1C
Esso Stn, 251 Upper East Coast Road	115	1A
Esso Stn, 1027 Upper Serangoon Road	70	1B
Esso Stn, 160 Yio Chu Kang Road	69	1B
Esso Stn, 299 Yio Chu Kang Road	48	1C
Eunos Crescent, Blk 9 #01-2709A	91	2D
Expo MRT Stn, 21 Changi South Ave 1	94	2B
Fernvale Point, 21 Sengkang West Ave #01-01	48	1A
French Road, Blk 809	111	2B
Haig Road, Blk 10 #01-351A	113	1A
•Heartland Mall, Hougang St 21, Blk 205 Level 3	69	2C
Hougang Avenue 1, Blk 106 #01-1227	70	1C
Hougang Avenue 1, Blk 124 #01-K1	69	2D
Hougang Avenue 3, Blk 23 #01-311A	70	1B
Hougang Avenue 6, Blk 521 #01-37A	49	1D
Hougang Avenue 7, Blk 9 #01-01A	70	1B
Hougang Avenue 8, Blk 631 #01-20A	69	2A
Hougang Avenue 8, Blk 683 #01-947A	48	2D
Hougang Avenue 10, Blk 401 #01-00	49	1D
•Hougang Central, Blk 805 #01-102	70	1A
Hougang Green Shopping Mall, 21 Hougang Street 51	48	2D
Hougang Mall, 90 Hougang Avenue 10 1st Storey	70	1A
•Hougang Street 21, Blk 204 #01-107	69	2C
Institute of Mental Health, 10 Buangkok View	48	2C
ITE College East, 10 Simei Avenue	94	2B
Jalan Empat, Blk 13 #01-49A	112	2B
Joo Chiat Complex, Joo Chiat Road, Blk 1 #01-1019A	113	2A
Blk 514 JTC Factory Chai Chee Lane	92	2C
JTC Tai Seng, Blk 124 Hougang Avenue 1	69	2D
Katong Mall, 112 East Coast Road	113	2C
Katong Shopping Centre, 865 Mountbatten Road #01	113	2C
Kembangan MRT Station, 55 Sims Avenue East	92	1D
Laguna Country Club, 11 Laguna Golf Green	94	2D
Lavender Station, 50 Kallang Road 1st Storey	111	2B
Lorong Lew Lian, Blk 2 #01-56A	69	1D
Loyang Point, Pasir Ris Street 21, Blk 258 #01-K1	74	1B
•Marine Parade Road, Blk 83 #01-584	113	2C
Marine Terrace, Blk 57 #01-107A	114	2C
New Upper Changi Road, Blk 59 #01-1218A	93	2D
•New Upper Changi Road, Blk 210 #01-707	93	1D
NTUC, Aljunied Avenue 2, Blk 114 #01-75	90	2C
NTUC, Bedok North Street 1, Blk 212 #01-147	93	1D
NTUC, Bedok North Street 4, Blk 89 #01-77	93	2C
NTUC, Bedok Reservoir Road, Blk 745 #01-3015	92	2B
NTUC, Chai Chee Avenue, Blk 29B #01-62	92	2D
NTUC, Changi Airport Terminal 1 #B12-58 (East Wing)	75	1B
NTUC, Compassvale Link, Blk 277C #01-13	49	1C
NTUC, 934 East Coast Road, Siglap New Market	114	2B
NTUC, Eastpoint, 3 Simei Street 6 #B1-04	94	1A
NTUC, Hougang Avenue 4, Blk 682 #01-310	48	2D
NTUC, Hougang Mall, 90 Hougang Avenue 10 #B1-07	70	1A
NTUC, Hougang Point, 1 Hougang Street 91 #02-01	48	2D
NTUC, Hougang Street 21, Blk 202 #01-00	69	2C
NTUC, Jalan Tiga, Blk 41 #01-05	112	2B
NTUC, 6 Marine Parade Central	113	2C
NTUC, New Upper Changi Road, Blk 57 #01-1334	93	2D
NTUC, Pasir Ris E!Hub, 1 Pasir Ris Close #02-127	52	1D
NTUC, Pasir Ris West Plaza, Pasir Ris Street 72, Blk 735 #01-37	51	2C
NTUC, Punggol Field Plaza, Punggol Field Road, Blk 168 #03-01	50	1A
NTUC, Rivervale Mall, 11 Rivervale Crescent #03-01	49	2B
NTUC, Rivervale Plaza, Rivervale Drive, Blk 118 #01-08	49	2C
NTUC, Serangoon Central Avenue 4, Blk 253 #01-241	69	1C
NTUC, Serangoon Garden, 9 Portchester Avenue	68	2B
NTUC, Serangoon North Avenue 1, Blk 152B #01-384	69	1A
NTUC, Singapore Post Centre, 10 Eunos Road 8 #B2-13	113	1A
NTUC, Tampines CC, Tampines St 83, Blk 866A #01-01	72	1C
NTUC, Tampines Mall, 4 Tampines Central 5 #B1-12	72	2D
NTUC, Tampines Street 11, Blk 107 #01-353	73	1D
NTUC, Tampines Street 11, Blk 138 #01-136	94	1A
NTUC, Tampines Street 44, Blk 475 #01-145	73	1B
NTUC, Upper Boon Keng Rd, Blk 5 #01-105	112	1B
•Parkway Parade, 80 Marine Parade Road #01-12	113	2C
Parkway Parade, 80 Marine Parade Road #03-K1	113	2C
Pasir Ris Drive 4, Blk 440 #01-01A	73	2A
Pasir Ris MRT Station, 10 Pasir Ris Central AM-04	52	1D
Pasir Ris NTUC Resort, 1 Pasir Ris Close	52	1C
Pasir Ris West Plaza, Pasir Ris Street 72, Blk 735 #01-K1	51	2C
Paya Lebar MRT Stn, 30 Paya Lebar Rd	113	1A
Punggol Field, Blk 198 #01-K1	30	2D
Punggol MRT Station, 70 Punggol Central	30	2D
Rivervale Mall, 11 Rivervale Crescent #01-K1	49	2B
Rivervale Plaza, Rivervale Drive, Blk 118 #01-21	49	2C
SAFRA Resort, 10 Changi Coastal Walk, 1st Storey Main Lobby	117	2A
Serangoon Avenue 2, Blk 304 #01-14A	68	2D
Serangoon Avenue 4, Blk 214 #01-88A	69	1C
•Serangoon Central Drive, Blk 254 #01-203	69	1C
•Serangoon Garden, 1 Maju Avenue #01-02	68	2B
Serangoon MRT Station, 600 Upper Serangoon Road	69	1D
Serangoon North Avenue 1, Blk 153 #01-536	69	1A
Serangoon North Avenue 3, Blk 542B #01-K1	48	1D
SIA Training Centre, 720 Upper Changi Road	95	1A
Simei MRT Stn, 30 Simei Street 3	94	1A
Simei Street 2, Blk 146 #01-18A	94	2A
•250 Sims Avenue #01-01	112	2A
Sims Avenue, Blk 417 #01-04A	113	1A
Sims Drive, Blk 60 #01-00	112	2A
Singapore Expo Centre, 1 Expo Drive #01-01	94	2B
Singapore Post Centre, 10 Eunos Road 8 #B1-K4	113	1A
SPC Stn, 1001 Bedok North Rd	93	2C
SPC Stn, 120 Hougang Avenue 2	69	2A
SPC Stn, 429 MacPherson Rd	90	2C
SPC Stn, 710 Mountbatten Rd	112	2C
SPC Stn, 100 Punggol Central	31	1A
SPC Stn, 157 Upper East Coast Rd	115	1A
Tampines Avenue 2 Street 23, Blk 211 #01-105A	73	2C
Tampines Avenue 4, Blk 811 #01-00A	93	2A
Tampines Avenue 5, Blk 938 #01-161A	72	2D
Tampines Central 1, Blk 503 #01-351A	73	1C
•Tampines Central, Blk 513 #01-160	72	2C
•Tampines Mall, 4 Tampines Central 5 #01-42/43/44	72	2D
Tampines Mart, 9 Tampines Street 32	73	2C
Tampines MRT Stn, 12 Tampines Central 1 #01-12	72	2A
•Tampines Street 21, Blk 201A #01-1051	73	1D

LOCATION	MAP	GRID
Tampines Street 11, Blk 138 #01-98	94	1A
Tampines Street 23, Blk 201E #01-100	73	1D
Tampines Street 11, Blk 406 #01-00	73	1C
Tampines Street 42, Blk 447 #01-62A	73	1C
Tampines Street 44, Blk 478 #01-K1	73	1B
Tampines Street 72, Blk 717 #01-00	72	1C
Tampines Street 81, Blk 825 #01-76A	72	1D
•Tampines Street 81, Blk 827 #01-138	72	1D
Tampines Street 82, Blk 844 #01-00	72	2D
Tanah Merah Country Club, 25 Changi Coast Road	95	2C
Tanah Merah Ferry Terminal, 50 Tanah Merah Ferry Road, Departure Lounge	118	1B
Tanah Merah MRT Station, 920 New Upper Changi Road	94	1D
Tanjong Katong Complex, 845 Geylang Road #01-ATM	113	1A
Techlink Kaki Bukit Techpark, 31 Kaki Bukit Road 3	91	2B
•Telepark, 5 Tampines Central 6 #01-24	72	2C
Temasek Polytechnic, 21 Tampines Ave 1, 1st Storey	72	1D
•Ubi Avenue 1, Blk 301 #01-257	91	2C
Ubi Avenue 1, Blk 304 #01-115	91	2C
Upper Aljunied Rd, Blk 1 #01-K1	90	2B
•White Sands, 1 Pasir Ris Central Street 3 #02-05/06	52	1D
WEST		
Alexandra Hospital, 378 Alexandra Road #01-04 (Main Lobby)	130	1B
Alexandra Technopark, 438A Alexandra Road	130	1C
Boon Lay MRT Station, 301 Boon Lay Way	60	1B
•Bukit Batok Central, Blk 636 #01-02	62	2D
Bukit Batok East Avenue 4, Blk 272 #01-60	63	1D
Bukit Batok MRT Stn, 10 Bukit Batok Central #01-08	62	2D
Bukit Batok Street 11, Blk 148 #01-00	62	1D
•Bukit Batok Street 11, Blk 153 #01-290	62	1D
Bukit Batok Street 21, Blk 206 #01-01	83	2A
Bukit Batok Street 31, Blk 374, McDonalds	62	2C
Bukit Batok West Avenue 4, Blk 415 #01-274A	62	1B
Bukit Gombak MRT Station, 802 Bukit Batok West Avenue 5	62	2C
•Bukit Timah Plaza, 1 Jalan Anak Bukit #01-19	85	1B
Buona Vista MRT Station, 100 North Buona Vista Road #01	107	2C
Cheers, Bukit Batok Central, Blk 642 #01-54	62	2D
Cheers, Choa Chu Kang Avenue 4, Blk 303 #01-723	41	1C
Chinese Garden MRT Station, 151 Boon Lay Way 1st Storey	82	2A
Choa Chu Kang Avenue 3, Blk 475 #01-K2	41	1D
•Choa Chu Kang Avenue 4, Blk 304 #01-657	41	1C
Choa Chu Kang MRT Station, 10 Choa Chu Kang Avenue 4	41	1C
Choa Chu Kang Road, Blk 253 #01-K1	41	1D
Choa Chu Kang Street 51, Blk 533 #01-K2	41	1D
Clementi Avenue 3, Blk 443 #01-51A	106	1A
•Clementi Avenue 3, Blk 449 #01-243	106	1A
•Clementi Avenue 3, Blk 450 #01-293	106	1A
Clementi Avenue 5, Blk 324 #01-129A	106	2A
Clementi Avenue 5, Blk 379 #01-370A	106	2A
Clementi MRT Station, 3150 Commonwealth Avenue West #02	106	1A
Clementi Street 12, Blk 107A	84	2D
Clementi West Street 1, Blk 609 #01-00	106	1C
Clementi West Street 2, Blk 701 #01-339A	106	1B
Clementi West Street 2, Blk 726 #01-75A	106	1C
Cold Storage, Village Centre, 3 South Buona Vista Road #01-01	129	2C
Cold Storage Jelita, 293 Holland Road 1st Storey	107	2A
Commonwealth Avenue, Blk 27 #01-268A	108	2D
Commonwealth Drive, Blk 46-3 #01-398A	108	1D
Commonwealth Crescent, Blk 97 #01-18A	108	1C
Commonwealth MRT Station, 375 Commonwealth Avenue #02-01	108	1B
•CPF Jurong Building, 21 Jurong East Street 13 #01-03	83	1C
•97 Corporation Drive	82	1C

DBS & POSB ATM LOCATIONS

LOCATION	MAP	GRID
Dover MRT Station, 200 Commonwealth Avenue West	107	1B
Dover Road, Blk 32 #01-01A	107	1D
Esso Stn, 145 Alexandra Road	131	1A
Esso Stn, 813 Bukit Batok West Avenue 5	62	2A
Esso Stn, 751 Bukit Timah Road	86	1C
Esso Stn, 50 Choa Chu Kang Avenue 3	41	1D
Esso Stn, 50 Choa Chu Kang Drive	41	2A
Esso Stn, 31 Choa Chu Kang Way	41	2D
Esso Stn, 126 Clementi Avenue 2	106	2A
Esso Stn, 30 Dunearn Road	110	1A
Esso Stn, 650 Dunearn Road	86	1C
Esso Stn, 870 Dunearn Road	85	2B
Esso Stn, 174 Holland Road	108	1B
Esso Stn, 302 Jalan Ahmah Ibrahim	82	1D
Esso Stn, 253 Jalan Buroh	105	2B
Esso Stn, 37 Jalan Jurong Kechil	84	2A
Esso Stn, 150 Jurong East Avenue 1	82	2A
Esso Stn, 10 Jurong West Avenue 1	61	1D
Esso Stn, 242A Pasir Panjang Road	129	2C
Esso Stn, 19 Pioneer Road	102	1A
Esso Stn, 262 Queensway	130	1A
Esso Stn, 622 Queensway	108	1C
Esso Stn, 213 Upper Bukit Timah Road	84	2A
Esso Stn, 217 Upper Bukit Timah Road	84	2A
Esso Stn, 926 Upper Bukit Timah Road	42	1D
Esso Stn, 181 West Coast Road	106	1B
Gek Poh Shopping Centre, Jurong West St 75, Blk 762 #01-K2	59	2D
Ghim Moh Road, Blk 19 #01-263A	107	2B
Guthrie House, 1 Fifth Avenue #01-05	86	1C
•Holland Drive, Blk 43 #01-59	107	2B
•Holland Village, 257 Holland Avenue	108	1B
Holland Village Shopping Mall, 3 Lorong Liput	108	1B
HomeTeam Academy, 501 Old Choa Chu Kang Road	40	1D
Ikea Building, 317 Alexandra Road #01-00	130	2A
•IMM, 2 Jurong East Street 21 #01-22	83	2B
6 International Business Park #01-K1	83	2C
Jurong East Avenue 1, Blk 340 #01-00	61	2D
Jurong East MRT Station, 10 Jurong East Street 12, 2nd Storey	83	1B
Jurong East Street 13, Blk 135 #01-315A	83	1B
Jurong East Street 24, Blk 252 #01-127	83	1A
Jurong East Street 31, Blk 347 #01-29A	82	2A
•Jurong Point, 1 Jurong West Central 2 #B1-20	81	1A
Jurong West Avenue 1, Blk 502 #01-831A	61	1D
Jurong West Street 25, Blk 276 #01-K1	60	1C
Jurong West Street 41, Blk 494 #01-130A	61	1D
•Jurong West Street 51, Blk 501 #01-279	61	1D
Jurong West Street 72, Blk 731 #01-35A	80	2A
Jurong West Street 92, Blk 923 #01-33A	80	1A
•Jurong West Street 92, Blk 960 #01-174	80	2A
Keppel Offshore & Marine, 50 Gul Road	101	1D
Keppel Shipyard Tuas, 51 Pioneer Sector 1 Shipyard's Canteen	100	2C
Lakeside MRT Station, 201 Boon Lay Way 1st Storey	82	1A
McDonald's Place, 11 King Albert Park 1st Storey	85	1B
Mei Ling Street, Blk 158 #01-74A	130	1A
Mindef Bukit Gombak 1st Sty Canteen, Blk 2	63	1A
MOE Building, 1 North Buona Vista 1st Storey	107	2C
NIE, 1 Nanyang Walk Blk 4 Canteen Library	58	2D
Nanyang Technological University Admin Ofc & Canteen, Blk N1.2	58	2D
Nanyang Technological University Canteen B	80	1A
Nanyang Technological University Library Block	58	2D
NTUC, Boon Lay Shopping Ctr, Boon Lay Place, Blk 221 #02-200	60	2D
NTUC, 10 Bukit Batok Central #01-08	62	2D
NTUC, Bukit Batok East Avenue 3, Blk 280 #01-315	63	1D

DBS & POSB ATM LOCATIONS

LOCATION	MAP	GRID
NTUC, Bukit Timah Plaza, 1 Jalan Anak Bukit #B1-01	85	1B
NTUC, Clementi Avenue 2, Blk 352 #01-141	106	2A
NTUC, Clementi Avenue 3, Blk 451 #01-307	106	1A
NTUC, Dover Crescent, Blk 28 #01-83	107	1C
NTUC, Holland Drive, Blk 15 #01-80	107	2B
NTUC, Jurong Point Shopping Ctr, 1 Jurong West Ctrl 2 #B1-09	81	1A
NTUC, Jurong Street 13, Blk 135 #01-337	83	1B
NTUC, Jurong West Street 41, Blk 498 #01-434	61	1D
NTUC, Limbang Shopping Ctr, Choa Chu Kang St 51, Blk 533 #01-11	41	1B
NTUC, Lot 1 Shoppers' Mall, 21 Choa Chu Kang Avenue 4	41	1C
NTUC, Taman Jurong Shopping Ctr, Yung Sheng Rd, Blk 399 #01-35	82	1B
NTUC, Teban Gardens Road, Blk 37 #01-304	83	1D
NTUC, Teck Whye Lane, Blk 140 #01-351	41	2D
NTUC, Yung Kuang Road, Blk 63 #01-119	82	1C
NUH Kent Ridge Wing, 5 Lower Kent Ridge Road	129	1A
NUH, 5 Lower Kent Ridge Road (Main Lobby)	129	1A
NUS, 10 Kent Ridge Crescent Admin Building	106	2D
NUS Science Faculty, 2 Medical Drive	107	1D
NUS Yusof Ishak House, 10 Kent Ridge Crescent	106	2D
Pandan Garden, Blk 412 #01-107A	83	2D
Pioneer Mall, Blk 638 Jurong West Street 61	80	2A
PSA Building, 460 Alexandra Road #02-03B	130	1D
Safti MI (Near Canteen), Upper Jurong Road 1st Storey	80	1C
Science Park, Main Lobby, Blk 16 The Pastuer Science Park Drive	129	2A
SIM HQ, 461 Clementi Road	85	1C
Singapore Polytechnic, Near Canteen Polycentre, 500 Dover Rd	107	1B
Taman Jurong Market & Food Centre, 3 Yung Sheng Rd	82	1B
Teban Gardens Road, Blk 38 #01-315A	83	1D
Teck Whye Lane, Blk 141 #01-273	41	2C
Teck Whye Lane, Blk 16 #01-101A	41	2D
The Alpha, 10 Science Park Road Level 1 Main Lobby	129	1A
The Chevrons, 48 Boon Lay Way	83	2C
Toh Guan Road, Blk 286E	83	1B
Toh Yi Drive, Blk 18 #01-113A	84	2A
Tuas Amenity Centre, 71 Pioneer Road #01-K1	100	2A
Tuas Food Ctr, Tuas Avenue 13, Blk 37	77	2D
West Coast Food Ctr, West Coast Drive, Blk 502 #01-K1	106	1B
West Mall, 1 Bukit Batok Central Link #01-K4	62	2D
Yung Kuang Road, Blk 64 #01-00	82	1C

HSBC ATM LOCATIONS (ATM 5)

LOCATION	MAP	GRID
CENTRAL		
HDB Hub, 500 Lorong 6 Toa Payoh (Level 1, facing NTUC)	88	2C
●Jubilee Entertainment Cplx, 61 Ang Mo Kio Ave 8 #01-05 / 01-05A	67	2A
●Serangoon Garden, 62/62A Serangoon Garden Way	68	2B
SOUTH		
CityLink Mall - Guardian #B1 One Raffles Link	133	1A
●Claymore Plaza, 6 Claymore Hill #01-01	109	2C
6 Eu Tong Sen Street #01-73	132	2A
Great World City, 1 Kim Seng Promenade Cold Storage Checkout Counter, Basement 1	132	1A
●HSBC Building, 21 Collyer Quay #01-01	133	1B
Ngee Ann City, Tower B Level 1 391 Orchard Road	110	1C
Paragon Shopping Centre, 290 Orchard Road #B1	110	1C
●Park Hotel, 270 Orchard Road #01-01	110	1C
Tang Plaza, 320 Orchard Road #B1	110	1C
●The Atrium@Orchard, 60A Orchard Road #01-02	110	2D
●Suntec City Mall (Tower 4), 3 Temasek Boulevard #01-154	111	1D
●VivoCity, 1 Harbourfront Walk #01-52	142	1A

HSBC ATM LOCATIONS (ATM 5)

LOCATION	MAP	GRID
EAST		
Changi Airport Terminal 2 Airport Boulevard Departure/Check-in Hall North (level 2 near MRT escalator)	75	1C
Changi Airport Terminal 2 Airport Boulevard Departure/Transit Lounge North	75	1C
Changi Airport Terminal 3 Airport Boulevard Departure/Transit Lounge North	75	1C
Giant Tampines, 21 Tampines North Drive 2	72	1A
●Parkway Parade, 80 Marine Parade Road #01-92	113	2C
WEST		
●Holland Village, 263 Holland Avenue	108	2B
●131 Jurong East Street 13 #01-257/259	83	1B

MAYBANK ATM LOCATIONS (ATM 5)

LOCATION	MAP	GRID
CENTRAL		
●Ang Mo Kio Avenue 8, Block 710A #01-2627	67	2A
●Balestier Plaza, 400 Balestier Road #01-13	89	1D
●HDB Hub, Block 480 Lorong 6 Toa Payoh #01-11	88	2C
Lorong 6 Toa Payoh #01-K1 Blk 520	88	2C
NORTH		
●888 Plaza, Woodlands Drive 50, Block 888 #01-K5 (near NTUC Fairprice) & #02-731	12	1C
SOUTH		
●Hong Leong Building, 16 Raffles Quay #01-04	132	2C
Lucky Plaza, 304 Orchard Road Basement 1	110	1C
●Maybank Tower, 2 Battery Road	133	1B
●North Bridge Shopping Ctr, 420 North Bridge Road #01-36/02-36	111	1D
●Peace Centre, 1 Sophia Road #01-20	110	2C
●Pek Chuan Building, 116 Lavender Street #01-08	111	2B
●People's Park Centre, 101 Upper Cross Street #01-22	132	2B
Plaza Singapura, 68 Orchard Road #B2-K3	110	2D
●Queensway Shopping Ctr, 1 Queensway #01-56	130	1B
●Textile Centre, 200 Jalan Sultan #01-02	111	2C
EAST		
Changi Airport Terminal 2 Arrival Meeting Hall (Near MRT entrance)	75	1C
●62 Changi Road #01-01	113	2A
●707 East Coast	114	2B
●Marine Parade Central, Block 87 #01-502	113	2C
New Upp Changi Rd, Blk 210 #01-699	93	1D
●Tampines Street 11, Block 139 #01-44/46/48	93	2A
●996 Upper Serangoon Road	69	2B
WEST		
●Choa Chu Kang Avenue 4, Block 303 #01-723	41	1C
●247 Holland Avenue	108	1C
IMM Building, 2 Jurong East St 21 #01-C12	83	2B
●Jurong East Street 13, Block 131 #01-249	83	1B
Jurong Point Shopping Centre, 1 Jurong West Central 2 #B1-19	81	1A
●114/116 Upper Bukit Timah Road	85	1A

OCBC ATM LOCATIONS

LOCATION	MAP	GRID
CENTRAL		
Ang Mo Kio / Jalan Leban		
AMK Hub Cheers, 53 Ang Mo Kio Avenue 3 #B1-82 (●#B1-32)	67	2A
AMK Hub Cheers, 53 Ang Mo Kio Avenue 3 #01-37	67	2A
AMK Hub Fairprice, 53 Ang Mo Kio Avenue 3 #B2-26	67	2A

LOCATION	MAP	GRID
Ang Mo Kio Ave 1, Blk 226C #01-651	67	1A
Ang Mo Kio Ave 1, Blk 339, 7-Eleven #01-1579	67	2B
Ang Mo Kio Ave 3, Blk 202 #01-1668	67	2A
Ang Mo Kio Ave 4, Blk 157 #01-578	46	1D
●Ang Mo Kio Ave 4, Blk 629 #01-1006	46	1C
Ang Mo Kio Ave 6, Blk 712 #01-4056	67	2A
Ang Mo Kio Ave 8, Blk 710A #01-2629	67	2A
Ang Mo Kio Ave 10, Blk 407 #01-741	68	1B
Ang Mo Kio Ave 10, Blk 449 #01-1709	68	1A
Ang Mo Kio Ave 10, Blk 531 #01-2441	47	1D
Ang Mo Kio Ave 10, Blk 532, 7-Eleven #01-2455	47	1D
Ang Mo Kio MRT, 2450 Ang Mo Kio Ave 8	67	2A
Nanyang Polytechnic, 180 Ang Mo Kio Ave 8, Blk A Level 2	46	2C
14 Jalan Leban, 7-Eleven	66	2A
Balestier		
580 Balestier Road, 7-Eleven	88	2D
Shaw Plaza, 360 Balestier Road #B1-01 (Fairprice)	89	1D
●Shaw Plaza Twin Heights, 360 Balestier Rd #01-41	89	1D
Bishan		
Bishan Junction 8 Shopping Centre, 9 Bishan Place #01-K7	67	2D
Bishan St 11, Blk 151 #01-187	89	1A
●Bishan St 11, Blk 501 #01-372	67	2D
Prime Supermarket, Bishan St 22, Blk 282 #01-149	67	2C
Boon Keng		
Towner Road, Blk 101, 7-Eleven #01-234	111	2A
Novena		
Fairprice, Square 2, 10 Sinaran Drive #04-03	88	2D
Tan Tock Seng Hospital, 7-Eleven, 11 Jalan Tan Tock Seng #01-03	88	2D
Sennett		
16 Tai Thong Crescent, 7-Eleven	90	1C
Serangoon		
3 Kensington Park, 7-Eleven	68	2A
9 Portchester Avenue, Fairprice	68	2 B
Serangoon Ave 3, Blk 326, 7-Eleven #01-378	68	2D
Serangoon Bus Interchange, Serangoon Ctrl, Blk 264 #01-215A	69	1D
Serangoon Central Drive, Blk 253 #01-241 (Fairprice)	69	1C
●Serangoon Garden, 86 Serangoon Garden Way	68	2B
Serangoon North Ave 1, Blk 152B #01-384 (Fairprice)	69	1A
19 Serangoon North Ave 5, Sheng Siong Supermarket	48	1D
999 Serangoon Road, 7-Eleven	89	2D
Toa Payoh / Kim Keat / Potong Pasir		
Hersing Hub, 743 Lorong 5 Toa Payoh	89	1B
Lorong 1 Toa Payoh, 7-Eleven, Blk 111 #01-358	88	2A
Lorong 1 Toa Payoh, Blk 128 #01-821	88	2B
Lorong 6 Toa Payoh, Blk 190, 7-Eleven #01-564	88	2C
Lorong 8 Toa Payoh, Blk 212 #01-29	89	1A
●Toa Payoh Central, 520 Lorong 6 Toa Payoh #02-53	88	2C
Toa Payoh HDB Hub, Fairprice, Lor 6 Toa Payoh, Blk 500 #B1-32	88	2C
Toa Payoh MRT Station, 510 Lorong 6 Toa Payoh #B1-02	88	2C
Kim Keat Avenue, Blk 260 #01-00	89	1C
Potong Pasir Ave 3, Blk 136, 7-Eleven #01-166	89	2B
Upper Thomson Road		
Thomson Plaza, Fairprice, 301 Upper Thomson Road #03-25	66	2C
Thomson Plaza, 301 Upper Thomson Road Level 1	66	2C
●181 Upper Thomson Road	67	1D
244H Upper Thomson Road, 7-Eleven	67	1C
912 Upper Thomson Road, 7-Eleven	45	1A
NORTH		
Sembawang		
Sembawang Mart, Canberra Road, Blk 511 #01-K2	3	1D
Sembawang Way, Blk 355 Level 1 (Fairprice)	13	1A
●Sun Plaza, 30 Sembawang Drive #02-23	13	1A

OCBC ATM LOCATIONS

LOCATION	MAP	GRID
US Naval Regional PSA Sembawang Terminal, 7-4 Deptford Rd	3	2C
Woodlands / Marsiling		
Admiralty Place, 1 Woodlands Avenue 6, Blk 678A #01-K2	12	1B
●Causeway Point, 1 Woodlands Square #01-18	11	1C
North Plaza, Woodlands St 82, Blk 883 #01-K1	11	2B
888 Plaza, Woodlands Dr 50, Blk 888 #01-K3	12	1C
888 Plaza, Woodlands Drive 50 #01-757 (Fairprice)	12	1C
The Woodgrove, Fairprice, 30 Woodlands Ave 1 #01-11	11	1D
Vista Point, Woodlands Drive 44, Blk 548 #01-K1	12	1C
Woodlands Centre Road, Blk 1A #01-68	10	2B
Woodlands Civic Centre, Fairprice, 900 South W'lands Dr #B1-01	11	2C
Woodlands Mart, Woodlands Ave 6, Blk 768 #01-K4	12	1A
●Woodlands St 31, Blk 303 #01-159	10	2D
Marsiling Lane, Blk 18 #01-271	11	1B
Yishun		
Khatib MRT Station, 201 Yishun Ave 2 S/N 107	27	1B
Northpoint Shopping Centre, 930 Yishun Ave 2 #B2-00	14	1D
●Northpoint Shopping Centre, 930 Yishun Ave 2 #01-07	14	1D
Yishun Ave 5, Blk 102, 7-Eleven #01-137	13	2D
●Yishun Ring Road, Blk 103 #01-67	13	2C
Yishun Ring Road, Blk 239, Fairprice, #01-1150	14	1C
Yishun Ring Road, Blk 413, 7-Eleven #01-1873	14	1D
Yishun Ring Road, Blk 414, Fairprice, #01-1853	14	2D
Yishun Ring Road, Blk 807, 7-Eleven #01-4217	26	2B
●Yishun Ring Road, Blk 846 #01-3619	27	1B
Yishun Ring Road, Blk 846, Yunnan Medical Hall & Dept Store #01-3655	27	1B
Yishun Ring Road, Blk 849 #01-K2	27	1B
Yishun St 22, Blk 291, 7-Eleven #01-337	14	1C
Yishun St 72, between Blk 731 & 732	13	2D
SOUTH		
Alexandra Road / Queenstown		
●Alexandra Village, Bukit Merah Lane 1, Blk 123 #01-98	130	2B
Dawson Place, Dawson Road, Blk 57 #01-K2	130	2A
Dawson Place, Dawson Road, Blk 57 #01-01 (Fairprice)	130	2C
Depot Height Shopping Ctr, Fairprice, Blk 108 Depot Rd #01-01	130	2C
Ikea Building, 317 Alexandra Road level one	130	2A
Queenstown Fairprice, Blk 34A Margaret Drive #01-342	108	2D
Queenstown MRT Station, 301 Commonwealth Avenue S/N 507	108	2D
Queensway Shopping Centre, 1 Queensway level one	130	1B
Bencoolen		
Fortune Centre, 190 Middle Road Ground floor	111	1D
Bugis / Rochor Road		
BHG Bugis Junction, 230 Victoria St #B1-33	111	1D
Bugis Junction, 230 Victoria Street Level Two	111	1D
Bugis MRT Station, 320 Victoria St S/N 523	111	1D
Rochor Road, Blk 1, 7-Eleven #01-518	111	1C
Rochor Road, Blk 1, Fairprice #01-640	111	1C
Sim Lim Square, 1 Rochor Canal Road Level 1	111	1C
Bukit Merah		
Bukit Merah Central, Blk 162, 7-Eleven #01-3547	131	1B
Bukit Merah Central Blk 166 #01-3531 (Fairprice)	131	1B
CMPB, 3 Depot Road	131	1C
Stirling Rd, Fairprice, Blk 170 #01-1147	130	1A
Bukit Timah		
KK Women's & Children's Hospital, 100 Bukit Timah Road	110	2B
Chinatown / Outram Park		
Chinatown MRT Station, 151 New Bridge Road	132	2B
New Bridge Centre, Smith Street Level one, Blk 336	132	2B
Pearl's Centre, 100 Eu Tong Sen St Main lobby	132	1C
●People's Park Centre, 101 Upper Cross St #01-27 & #B1-49	132	2B
People's Park Complex, 1 Park Road Level One	132	2B

LOCATION	MAP	GRID
People's Park Food Centre, New Market Road, Blk 32 #01-K3	132	2B
City Hall / North Bridge Road / Bras Basah		
City Hall MRT Station, 150 North Bridge Road	133	1A
●City Link Mall, 1 Raffles Link #B1-07	133	1A
Funan The DigitaLife Mall, 109 North Bridge Road #01-K9	132	2A
●460 North Bridge Road #01-00	111	1D
Peninsula Plaza Foodcourt, 111 North Bridge Road #B1-07A	133	1A
Raffles City Shopping Centre, 252 North Bridge Road Basement 1	133	1A
●SMU (Li Ka Shing Library), 70 Stamford Road, #B1-43	110	2D
●The Adelphi, 1 Coleman St #01-09 & #02-08	133	1A
Bras Basah Complex, Bain Street, Blk 231 #01-17	111	1C
HarbourFront		
●HarbourFront Centre, 1 Maritime Square #02-99	142	1A
Singapore Cruise Centre, 1 Maritime Square #01-30A	142	1A
Jalan Besar / Jalan Berseh		
●Sim Lim Tower, 10 Jalan Besar #01-01	111	1C
New World Centre, 1 Jalan Berseh, #01-06	111	1B
Jalan Sultan		
●Textile Centre, 200 Jalan Sultan #01-05	111	2C
Kim Seng / River Valley		
Great World City, 1 Kim Seng Promenade #B1-K6	132	1A
Liang Court Shopping Centre, 177 River Valley Road #L1-K3	132	2A
423 River Valley Road, 7-Eleven	109	2D
Lavender		
Lavender MRT Station, 50 Kallang Road #B1-02	111	2B
Little India		
Little India Arcade, 7-Eleven, 48 Serangoon Road, #01-19	111	1C
Little India MRT Station, 6 Bukit Timah Road	110	2C
Serangoon Road, 7-Eleven, 320 Serangoon Road, #01-29	111	1B
Marina Square / Esplanade / Suntec City		
Esplanade Mall, 8 Raffles Ave #01-K1	133	1A
Suntec City Mall, 5 Temasek Boulevard #B1-A02	133	1A
Suntec City Mall, 5 Temasek Boulevard, #02-105A	133	1A
Orchard / Tanglin		
Cathay Cineleisure Orchard, 8 Grange Road #01-K2	110	1C
Centrepoint, 170 Orchard Road Level 1	110	1C
Chevron House, 30 Raffles Place Level 1	133	1B
China Square Foodcourt, 51 Telok Ayer St Level 1	132	2B
Dhoby Ghaut MRT Stn, 11 Orchard Rd Basement 1, Dhoby Ghaut Xchange	110	2D
Forum The Shopping Mall, 583 Orchard Road basement one	109	2C
Great Eastern Centre, 1 Pickering Street #01-00	132	2B
●Lucky Plaza, 304 Orchard Road Level 1 #01-95	110	1C
1 Marina Boulevard, Basement 1	133	1B
63 Market St	132	2B
Mt Elizabeth Medical Centre, 3 Mt Elizabeth level 1	110	1C
Ngee Ann City, 391B Orchard Road #B1-36 facing Delifrance	110	1C
Ngee Ann City, 391B Orchard Road #B2-14	110	1C
Ngee Ann City, 391B Orchard Road Level 4	110	1C
●OCBC Centre, Raffles Place, 65 Chulia St #01-00	132	2B
Orchard Grand Court, Fairprice, 131 Killiney Rd #01-01	110	1D
Orchard MRT Station, 437 Orchard Rd #B2-01	110	1C
●Orchard Point, 160 Orchard Rd #B1-12	110	1C
Orchard Shopping Centre, 7-Eleven, 321 Orchard Road #01-01	110	1C
Orchard Tower, 1 Claymore Drive	109	2C
Paragon, 290 Orchard Road #B1-K12	110	1C
Plaza Singapura, 68 Orchard Road #B2-K2	110	1C
Raffles Place MRT Station, 5 Raffles Place #B1-K13	133	1B
●SIA Building, 77 Robinson Road #01-03	132	2C
Tang Plaza, 320 Orchard Road Basement 1	110	1C
Tanglin Mall, 163 Tanglin Road #02-K6	109	2C
The Heeren, 260 Orchard Road #K1-01	110	1C
●The Octagon, 105 Cecil St	132	2C
Wisma Atria Shopping Centre, 435 Orchard Road Basement 1	110	1C

LOCATION	MAP	GRID
Scotts Road		
Far East Plaza, 14 Scotts Road Basement 1 entrance	110	1C
Newton MRT Station, 49 Scotts Road	110	1B
Shaw Centre, Near Isetan entrance, 1 Scotts Road	109	2C
Shaw House, Lobby area, 1 Scotts Road	109	2C
Selegie		
Parklane Shopping Mall, 35 Selegie Road, Ground floor	110	2C
Singapore General Hospital		
Blk 1 Level 1 (near pharmacy)	132	1C
Blk 4 Level 1 (near cafeteria)	132	1C
Somerset		
Somerset MRT Stn, 1 Somerset Rd, #B1-02	110	1D
South Bridge Road		
Fook Hai Building, 150 South Bridge Road Level 1	132	2B
Tanjong Pagar		
International Plaza, 10 Anson Road Level one	132	2C
Tanjong Pagar Plaza, 7-Eleven, Tanjong Pagar Rd, Blk 1 #01-32	132	2C
●260 Tanjong Pagar Road #01-01	132	2D
Telok Blangah		
Telok Blangah Crescent, Blk 9, Besprof Holdings #01-119	131	1C
Tiong Bahru		
Havelock Rd, Blk 50 #01-755 (Fairprice)	131	2A
Link Hotel, 50 Tiong Bahru Rd, Cheers #01-03	132	1B
Tiong Bahru MRT Station, 300 Tiong Bahru Road S/N 522	131	2B
Tiong Bahru Plaza, 302 Tiong Bahru Road Level 1	131	2B
Tiong Bahru Plaza, 302 Tiong Bahru Road #B1-01 (Fairprice)	131	2B
EAST		
Aljunied		
●Aljunied Ave 2, Blk 119 #01-40	112	2A
●Aljunied Ave 2, Blk 114 #01-75 Fairprice	90	2D
Bedok / Chai Chee		
Bedok Bus Interchange, New Upper Changi Road, Blk 207 #01-00	93	1D
●Bedok North St 1, Blk 204 #01-403	93	1D
Bedok North St 1, Blk 212, #01-147 (Fairprice)	93	1D
Bedok North St 3, Blk 539A, Shing Song Supermarket #01-477	92	2C
Bedok North St 4, Blk 89, #01-77 (Fairprice)	93	2C
●Bedok North St 4, Blk 88 #01-163	93	2C
Bedok Reservoir Road, Blk 631, 7-Eleven #01-934	92	1A
Bedok Reservoir Road, Blk 632, McDonald's #01-850	92	1B
Bedok Reservoir Road, Blk 744, 7-Eleven #01-3061	92	2B
Bedok Shopping Complex, 7-Eleven, 346 Bedok Road	94	1B
Bedok South Road, Blk 18, 7-Eleven #01-65	115	1A
Chai Chee Ave, Blk 29B #01-62 (Fairprice)	92	2D
Chai Chee Road, Blk 25A, Prime Supermarket #01-459	92	2D
New Upper Changi Road, Blk 57, #01-1334 (Fairprice)	93	2D
New Upper Changi Road, Blk 59, Wei Kien Medical Hall #01-1240	93	2D
Changi		
Changi Airport Terminal 1, Arrival Hall (near info counter)	75	1B
Changi Airport Terminal 1, Arrival Hall (near Burger King)	75	1B
Changi Airport Terminal 2, Arrival Hall	75	1C
Changi Airport Terminal 2, Basement South	75	1C
Changi Airport Terminal 2, Departure / Check-In Hall North	75	1C
Changi Airport Terminal 2, Departure / Transit Lounge South	75	1C
Changi Airport Terminal 3, Arrival Hall North	75	1C
Changi Airport Terminal 3, Basement 2 South	75	1C
Changi Airport Terminal 3, Departure Check-in Hall North	75	1C
Changi Airport Terminal 3, Departure Check-in Hall South	75	1C
Changi Airport Terminal 3, Departure / Transit Lounge South	75	1C
●40 Changi Road	113	2A
38A Changi Road, 7-Eleven	113	2A
Changi Village Road, Blk 1, 7-Eleven #01-2014	54	1B
Singapore Expo, 1 Expo Drive Foyer 2	94	2B

OCBC ATM LOCATIONS

LOCATION	MAP	GRID
East Coast / Marine Parade		
●174 East Coast Road	113	2C
55 East Coast Road, 7-Eleven	113	2C
705 East Coast Road, 7-Eleven	114	2B
6 Marine Parade Central, Fairprice	113	2C
Marine Parade Central, Blk 83 #01-550A	113	2C
●Marine Parade Central, Blk 83 #01-576	113	2C
Marine Terrace, Blk 59 #01-89	114	1C
Parkway Parade, 80 Marine Parade Road Level 3	113	2C
Parkway Parade, 80 Marine Parade Road, Next to info counter	113	2C
Siglap New Market, Fairprice, 934 East Coast Rd	114	2B
Eunos / Kembangan		
Eunos Bus Interchange, 409 Eunos Road 2	113	2A
Eunos Crescent, Blk 1A, 7-Eleven #01-2469	91	2D
Singapore Post Centre, Fairprice, 10 Eunos Road 8 #B2-13	113	1A
Kembangan MRT, 55 Sims Ave East S/N 206	92	1D
Geylang / Kallang / Jalan Tiga		
Aljunied MRT Station, 81 Lorong 25 Geylang S/N 202	112	2A
City Plaza, 810 Geylang Road, #01-00	113	1A
Geylang Bahru, Blk 68 #01-3225	90	1D
●325 Geylang Road	112	2B
348 Geylang Road, 7-Eleven	112	2B
●Hoa Nam Building, 27 Foch Road #01-02 & #02-01	111	1B
Kallang Bahru, Blk 71 #02-531 (Fairprice)	90	1D
Sims Place, Blk 53 #01-174	112	2A
Singapore Immigration Building, 10 Kallang Road, Main lobby	111	2C
Upper Boon Keng Road, Blk 18 #01-1153	112	1A
Upper Boon Keng Road, Blk 5 #01-05 (Fairprice)	112	1B
Jalan Tiga, Blk 41 #01-05 (Fairprice)	112	2B
Hougang		
Heartland Mall, Hougang Street 21, Blk 205 Level One	69	2C
Hougang Ave 1, Blk 106, 7-Eleven #01-1223	70	1C
Hougang Ave 3, Blk 23, #01-281 (Cheers)	70	1B
Hougang Ave 4, Blk 682, #01-310 (Fairprice)	48	2D
Hougang Ave 7, Blk 10, Current & Electrical Maintenance Co #01-51	70	1B
Hougang Ave 8, Blk 644, 7-Eleven #01-273	69	2A
Hougang Central, Blk 811 #01-208	70	1A
Hougang Green Shopping Mall, 21 Hougang St 51 #01-34	48	2D
●Hougang Mall, 90 Hougang Ave 10 #01-01	70	1A
Hougang Point, Fairprice, 1 Hougang St 91 #02-02	48	2D
Hougang St 21, Blk 202, #01-00 (Fairprice)	69	2C
Hougang St 21, Blk 210, 7-Eleven #01-275	70	1C
●Hougang St 21, Blk 211 #01-295	70	1C
Hougang St 61, Blk 685 #01-160	48	2D
Macpherson		
Circuit Road, Blk 36, 7-Eleven #01-422	90	2C
385 Upper Aljunied Road, Prime Supermarket	90	2C
Pasir Ris		
Downtown East, 1 Pasir Ris Close	52	1D
Elias Mall, 625 Elias Road #01-K5	51	2D
Fairprice E!Hub Downtown East, 1 Pasir Ris Close #02-127	52	1D
Loyang Point, Pasir Ris St 21, Blk 258 #01-K1	74	1A
Pasir Ris Bus Interchange, 10 Pasir Ris Central	52	1D
Pasir Ris Drive 4, Blk 440 #01-01	73	2A
Pasir Ris Drive 6, Blk 446, 7-Eleven #01-112	73	2A
Pasir Ris West Plaza, Fairprice, Pasir Ris St 72, Blk 735 #01-300	51	1C
Pasir Ris West Plaza, Pasir Ris St 72, Blk 735 #01-K3	51	1C
●White Sands Shopping Mall, 1 Pasir Ris Central St 3 #01-16	52	1D
White Sands Shopping Mall, 1 Pasir Ris Ctrl St 3 #B1-10 (Fairprice)	52	1D
Punggol / Sengkang / Rivervale		
●Punggol Plaza, Punggol Field, Blk 168 #01-11	50	1A
Punggol Plaza, Punggol Field Level 1, Blk 168 outside Koufu FC	50	1A
●Compass Point, 1 Sengkang Square #01-40	49	1B

LOCATION	MAP	GRID
Rivervale Mall, 11 Rivervale Crescent #01-K2	49	2B
Rivervale Plaza, Rivervale Drive, Blk 118 #01-K2	49	2C
Rivervale Plaza, Rivervale Drive, Blk 118 #01-08 (Fairprice)	49	2C
Compassvale Link, Blk 277C #01-13	49	1C
Simei		
●Eastpoint Mall, 3 Simei St 6 #B1-06	94	1A
Simei MRT Station, 30 Simei Street AM-05	94	1A
Simei St 3, Blk 248 #01-130	94	1A
Tampines		
IKEA Building, 60 Tampines North Drive 2	51	1D
Tampines Ave 4, Blk 802, 7-Eleven #01-09	93	2A
Tampines Bus Interchange, 512 Tampines Central 1	72	2C
Tampines Central 1, Blk 506 #01-K1	73	1C
Tampines Central CC, Fairprice, Tampines St 83, Blk 866A #01-01	72	1C
●Tampines CPF Building, 1 Tampines Central 5 #01-02	73	1D
Tampines Mart, 5 Tampines St 32 Level 1	73	2C
Tampines MRT Station, 20 Tampines Central 1 S/N 210	72	2C
Tampines St 11, Blk 107 #01-353 (Fairprice)	73	1D
Tampines St 11, Blk 138 #01-136 (Fairprice)	94	1A
●Tampines St 11, Blk 138 #01-108	94	1A
Tampines St 11, Blk 139, 7-Eleven #01-20	93	2A
Tampines St 21, Blk 201A #01-1059	73	1D
Tampines St 21, Blk 201B #01-1091	73	1D
Tampines St 44, Blk 475 #01-143	73	1B
Tampines St 44, Blk 475 #01-145 (Fairprice)	73	1B
Tampines St 81, Blk 823, Prime Supermarket #01-160	72	1D
Tanah Merah		
50 Tanah Merah Ferry Road, Departure Hall	118	1B
Tanah Merah MRT Station, 920 New Upper Changi Road S/N 302	94	1C
Tanjong Katong		
Oriental Emporium, 15 Tanjong Katong Road Level 1	113	1A
366 Tanjong Katong Road, 7-Eleven	113	1C
Ubi		
Ubi Ave 1, Blk 302 #01-59	91	2C
Ubi Ave 1, Blk 306 #01-185	91	2C
Upper Serangoon		
●777 Upper Serangoon Road #01-01	69	2C
WEST		
Bukit Batok		
●Bukit Batok Central, Blk 634 #01-108	62	2C
●Bukit Batok Central, Blk 634 #01-112	62	2C
Bukit Batok East Ave 3, Blk 283 #01-281	63	1D
Bukit Batok East Ave 3, Fairprice, Blk 280 #01-317	63	1D
Bukit Batok MRT Station, 10 Bukit Batok Ctrl #01-08 (Fairprice)	62	2D
Bukit Batok MRT Station, 10 Bukit Batok Central S/N 539 #01-07	62	2D
Bukit Batok St 31, Blk 373, Prime Supermarket #01-248	62	2C
Bukit Batok West Ave 6, Blk 132, 7-Eleven #01-304	62	2C
Bukit Batok West Ave 8, Blk 154A #01-K1	62	1D
Bukit Panjang		
●Bangkit Road, Blk 257 #01-51	42	2D
Bukit Gombak Camp, 54 Gombak Rise	63	1A
Bukit Panjang Plaza, 1 Jelebu Road Level 2	42	1C
Bukit Panjang Ring Road, Blk 259, 7-Eleven #01-20	42	2D
Fajar Shopping Centre, Fajar Road, Blk 445 #01-K1	42	2C
Greenridge Shopping Centre, Jelapang Rd, Blk 524A #01-K2	42	2C
Senja Grand, Fairprice, Blk 628 Senja Rd #01-01	42	1C
Bukit Timah / Sixth Avenue		
Bukit Timah Plaza, Fairprice, 1 Jalan Anak Bukit, Basement 2	85	1B
Bukit Timah Plaza - Level 1, 1 Jalan Anak Bukit	85	1B
●Bukit Timah Shopping Centre, 170 Upper Bukit Timah Rd #01-01	85	1A
Coronation Plaza, Fairprice, 587 Bt Timah Rd #01-01	86	2D
6 Sixth Avenue, 7-Eleven	86	1C

OCBC ATM LOCATIONS

LOCATION	MAP	GRID
●Sixth Avenue Ctr, 827 Bukit Timah Road	86	1C
Buona Vista / Holland		
Buona Vista, Fairprice, Blk 15 Holland Drive #01-80	107	2B
Buona Vista MRT Station, 100 North Buona Vista Road	107	2C
Ghim Moh Road, Blk 19 #01-245	107	2B
●Holland Drive, Blk 43 #01-47	107	2B
Jelita Shopping Centre- Level 2, 293 Holland Road	107	2A
4 Lorong Mambong, 7-Eleven	107	2B
Choa Chu Kang / Yew Tee / Teck Whye		
●Choa Chu Kang Ave 4, Blk 304 #01-663	41	1C
Choa Chu Kang Ave 4, Blk 423, 7-Eleven #01-260	41	1C
Choa Chu Kang MRT Station, 10 Choa Chu Kang Ave 4 #01-K2	41	1C
Limbang Shopping Centre, Choa Chu Kang St 51, Blk 532 #01-K1	41	1B
Limbang Shopping Centre, CCK St 51, Blk 533 #01-11 (Fairprice)	41	1B
Sunshine Place, Choa Chu Kang Ave 3, Blk 475 #01-K3	41	1D
Teck Whye Lane, Blk 140 #01-351 (Fairprice)	41	2C
Teck Whye Lane, Blk 141 #01-247	41	2C
Clementi		
Clementi Ave 2, Blk 352, Fairprice #01-141	106	2A
Clementi Ave 3, Blk 443, 7-Eleven #01-71	106	1A
●Clementi Ave 3, Blk 446 #01-193	106	1A
Clementi Ave 3, Blk 451, Fairprice #01-307	106	1A
Clementi Ave 5, Blk 325, Breadwinner Bakery Shop #01-137	106	2A
Clementi St 11, Blk 109, 7-Eleven #01-15	84-	2D
Clementi West St 2, Blk 727, 7-Eleven #01-284	106	1C
Ngee Ann Poly 2, 535 Clementi Road Blk 7 (opp swimming pool)	85	1B
Commonwealth / Dover		
Commonwealth Drive, Blk 46-3 #01-388	108	1D
Commonwealth MRT Station, 375 Commonwealth Ave	108	1C
Dover Crescent, Blk 28 #01-83 (Fairprice)	107	1D
Jurong		
●Yung Kuang Road, Blk 65 #01-95	82	1C
3 Yuan Ching Road, Sheng Siong Supermarket #01-01A	82	1C
Jurong East		
IMM Building, 2 Jurong East St 21 Level 1	83	2B
Jurong East Bus Interchange, 155 Jurong East Street 13	83	1B
●Jurong East St 13, Blk 130 #01-235	83	1B
Jurong East St 13, Blk 130, 7-Eleven #01-233	83	1B
Jurong East St 13, Blk 135, Fairprice #01-337	83	1C
Jurong East St 24, Blk 252, 7-Eleven #01-129	83	1A
Jurong East St 31, Blk 345, 7-Eleven #01-13	82	2A
Jurong West / Boon Lay		
Jurong Point, 1 Jurong West Ctrl 2 #B1-21 (in front of Coffee Bean)	81	1A
●Jurong Point, 1 Jurong West Central 2 #B1-31	81	1A
●Jurong West Ave 1, Blk 502 #01-821	60	2D
Jurong West St 41, Blk 463 #01-00	61	1D
Jurong West St 41, Blk 495, JianXin Medical #01-104	61	1D
Jurong West St 41, Blk 498 Fairprice #01-434	61	1D
Jurong West St 51, Blk 501, 7-Eleven #01-225	61	1D
Jurong West St 75, Blk 763, Prime Supermarket #01-01	59	2D
Jurong West St 91, Blk 962 #01-300	80	2A
Jurong West St 91, Next to Blk 964	80	2A
Pioneer Mall, Jurong West St 61, Blk 638 Level One	80	2A
Boon Lay MRT Station, 301 Boon Lay Way	81	1B
Boon Lay Shopping Centre, Boon Lay Place, Blk 221	60	2A
Boon Lay Shopping Ctr, Boon Lay Pl, Blk 221 #02-200 (Fairprice)	60	2A
NTU		
Academic Complex North, 50 Nanyang Ave NS3 01-01	58	2D
NTU Canteen 2, Nanyang Drive	59	1D
NTU Canteen B, Nanyang Link	80	1A
NUS		
NUS, 10 Kent Ridge Road, Near Arts & Social Science Faculty	106	2D
Singapore Polytechnic Foodcourt 2, 500 Dover Road	107	1B

OCBC ATM LOCATIONS

LOCATION	MAP	GRID
Taman Jurong / Lakeside		
Lakeside MRT Station, 201 Boon Lay Way	82	1A
Taman Jurong Shopping Centre, Fairprice, Yung Sheng Rd, Blk 399 #01-35	82	1B
Taman Jurong Shopping Centre, Yung Sheng Rd, Blk 399 #01-K2	82	1B
West Coast		
Teban Gardens Road, Blk 37 #01-307	83	1D
Teban Gardens Road, Fairprice, Blk 37 #01-304	83	1D
West Coast Drive, Blk 505, 7-Eleven #01-216	106	1B

RHB BANK ATM LOCATIONS

LOCATION	MAP	GRID
CENTRAL		
●Upper Serangoon Branch, 1 Yio Chu Kang Road	69	1C
SOUTH		
●Bt Merah Branch, Jalan Bukit Merah, Blk 131 #01-1577/1579	131	2C
●Cecil St Branch, Ground Floor 90 Cecil Street	132	2B
●Jalan Besar Branch, Sim Lim Tower, 10 Jalan Besar #01-03	111	1C
EAST		
●Geylang Branch, 537 Geylang Road	112	2B
●Katong Branch, 14-18 East Coast Road	113	2C
WEST		
●Bt Timah Branch, The Rail Mall, 440/442 Upper Bukit Timah Rd	63	2B

STANDARD CHARTERED ATM LOCATIONS (ATM 5)

LOCATION	MAP	GRID
CENTRAL		
●Fook Hai Building, 150 South Bridge Road #01-12	132	2B
HDB Hub, Lorong 2 Toa Payoh Blk 520 #01-K3	88	2C
●67 Serangoon Garden Way	68	2B
Suntec City Mall, 3 Temasek Boulevard Level 2 Entertainment Ctr Atrium #02-116	133	1A
●Suntec City Mall, 3 Temasek Boulevard #02-108	133	1A
●Suntec Tower 4, 6 Temasek Boulevard #32-05	111	1D
NORTH		
●246R Upper Thomson Road	67	1C
●Woodlands Civic Centre, 900 South Woodlands Drive #02-07	11	2C
SOUTH		
●Anchorpoint, 370 Alexandra Road #01-33	130	2A
●6 Battery Road	133	1B
●Peace Centre, 1 Sophia Road #01-01/08	110	2C
Plaza by the Park, 51 Bras Basah Rd #01-02C	110	2D
●Shaw Centre, 1 Scotts Road #01-01	109	2C
●Vivo City, 1 HarbourFront Walk #B2-01 & #01-03	142	1A
EAST		
●Abacus Plaza, 3 Tampines Central 1 #01-01	72	2D
●City Plaza, 810 Geylang Road #01-67/74	113	1A
●Hougang Street 21, Blk 210 #01-251/253	70	1C
●Marine Parade Central, Blk 87 #01-500	113	2C
●New Upper Changi Road, Blk 210 #01-703/705	93	1D
WEST		
●2 Hillview Road Bukit Timah	63	2B
●261 Holland Avenue	108	1B
●Yung Kuang Road, Blk 66 #01-83/91	82	1C

LOCATION	MAP	GRID
CENTRAL		
●AMK Hub, 53 Ang Mo Kio Ave 3 #B1-34	67	2A
226C Ang Mo Kio Ave 1, Yin Siew Choon Koon Kee Medical, #01-651	67	1A
339 Ang Mo Kio Ave 1, #01-1573/1575	67	2B
632 Ang Mo Kio Ave 4, Yong Seng Eng Fruits Trading Co, #01-966	46	2C
163 Ang Mo Kio Ave 4, Gateway Self Service Market, #01-434	46	1D
531 Ang Mo Kio Ave 10, #01-2441	47	2D
449 Ang Mo Kio Ave 10, #01-1715	68	1A
Ang Mo Kio Ave 10, Between Blk 407 & 408	68	1B
Ang Mo Kio Bus Interchange, 57 Ang Mo Kio Ave 8	67	2A
Ang Mo Kio MRT Stn, 2450 Ang Mo Kio Ave 8	67	2A
●25 Bendemeer Road, #01-561/563	111	2A
150A Bishan St 11, Delightful Trading, #01-173	89	1A
●501 Bishan St 11, #01-368/370	67	2D
513 Bishan St 13, Eaton Patisserie, #01-506	67	2D
282 Bishan St 22, Prime Supermarket, #01-149	67	2C
Boon Keng MRT Stn, 900 Serangoon Rd #B1 Concourse Level	111	2A
Braddell MRT Stn, 379 Lorong 1 Toa Payoh	88	2B
79A Circuit Rd	90	2D
●Coronation Plaza, 587 Bukit Timah Road, #01-02	86	2D
Jubilee Entertainment Complex, 61 Ang Mo Kio Ave 8	67	2A
Junction 8 Shopping Centre, 9 Bishan Place, #01-K7A	67	2D
Junction 8 Shopping Centre - Level 1, 9 Bishan Place	67	2D
71 Kallang Bahru, #01-529A	90	1D
KK Hospital, 100 Bukit Timah Road, Children Twr Podium 1	110	2B
109 Lor 1 Toa Payoh, Cheers Store, #01-310	88	2A
181 Lor 4 Toa Payoh #01-608A, near Smart Emporium	89	1B
85 Lor 4 Toa Payoh, Hong Ern Corporation, #01-320	88	2B
20 Lor 7 Toa Payoh, Da Lee Minimart, #01-736	89	1B
211 Lor 8 Toa Payoh, #01-11/15	89	1A
●181-185 MacPherson Road	90	1C
McDonald's - Big Mac Centre, 51 Ang Mo Kio Ave 3	67	2A
Mount Alvernia Hospital, 820 Upper Thomson Rd, Ground Floor - near Main Lobby	88	1A
148 Potong Pasir Ave 1, McDonald's, #01-43	89	2C
●69 Serangoon Garden Way	68	2B
Shaw Plaza, 360 Balestier Rd, #01-K2	89	1D
8 Sixth Ave, KJ Colourlab & Studio	86	1C
Tech Chong Medical Hall, 2 Lorong Lew Lian, #01-40	69	1D
Toa Payoh Bus Interchange, 530 Lor 6 Toa Payoh	88	2C
Toa Payoh Hub - 1st storey HDB Hub, 520 Lor 6 Toa Payoh	88	2C
Toa Payoh MRT Stn, 510 Lor 6 Toa Payoh	88	2C
Thomson Plaza - NTUC Fairprice, 301 Upper Thomson Rd	66	2C
United Square Auto Lobby, 101 Thomson Rd, #01-K11	110	2A
United Square, Basement 1, 101 Thomson Rd	110	2A
381 Upper Aljunied Rd, Prime Supermarket	90	2B
●251-253 Upper Thomson Road	67	1C
86 Whampoa Drive, Winners Hair Cut, #01-945	89	1D
Yang Cheng Medical Hall, 153 Serangoon North Ave 1, #01-484	69	1A
Yio Chu Kang MRT Stn, 3000 Ang Mo Kio Ave 8	46	2C
NORTH		
888 Plaza, Woodlands Drive 50, #01-K1 Woodlands	12	1C
●Admiralty MRT Stn, 70 Woodlands Ave 7, #01-02	12	1B
Admiralty MRT Stn, 70 Woodlands Ave 7	12	1B
●Bukit Panjang Plaza, 1 Jelebu Rd, #02-02	42	1C
Bukit Panjang Plaza, 1 Jelebu Rd, #02-K7	42	1C
259 Bukit Panjang Ring Rd, #01-32	42	2D
Causeway Point, 1 Woodlands Square Level 2	11	2C
Fajar Shopping Centre, 445 Fajar Rd, #01-K3	42	2C
Greenridge Shopping Ctr, 524A Jelapang Rd #01-K1	42	2C
Khatib MRT Stn, 201 Yishun Ave 2	27	1B
Kranji MRT Stn, 960 Woodlands Rd	10	1D

LOCATION	MAP	GRID
18 Marsiling Lane, Milky Confectionary (S) Pte Ltd, #01-271	11	1B
Marsiling MRT Stn, 71 Woodlands Ave 3	10	2C
Northpoint Shopping Centre, 930 Yishun Ave 2, Level 1 (near Delifrance Outlet)	14	1D
Sembawang MRT Stn, 11 Canberra Rd	13	1A
Senja Grand, 628 Senja Rd, #01-K2	42	1C
Sun Plaza, 30 Sembawang Drive	13	1A
Ten Mile Junction, beside entrance, 1 Woodlands Rd	42	1C
Vista Point, 548 Woodlands Drive 44, #01-K3	12	1C
4A Woodlands Centre Rd	10	2B
●Woodlands Civic Ctr, 900 South Woodlands Drive #01-06	11	2C
Woodlands Mart, 768 Woodlands Ave 6, #01-K2	12	1B
Woodlands MRT Stn, 30 Woodlands Ave 2	11	2C
Woodlands North Plaza, 883 Woodlands St 82, #01-K3	11	2B
306 Woodlands St 31 #01-43	10	2C
101 Yishun Ave 5, #01-41A	13	2D
743 Yishun Ave 5, Cambridge Book Centre, #01-548	14	1D
●924 Yishun Central 1, #01-348	14	1D
Yishun Golden Village, 51 Yishun Central 1, #01-K1	14	1D
Yishun MRT Stn, 301 Yishun Ave 2	14	1D
849 Yishun Ring Rd, #01-K1	27	1B
●291 Yishun St 22, #01-351/353/355	14	1C
293 Yishun St 22, Shop N Save, #01-261	14	1C
SOUTH		
Anchorpoint, 370 Alexandra Rd Basement 1	130	2A
BHG Bugis Junction, 230 Victoria Street, #B1-K1	111	1D
BHG Bugis Junction, 230 Victoria Street, #01-K1	111	1D
BP Tower, 396 Alexandra Rd	130	1C
●Bras Basah Complex, 231 Bain St, #01-29/39	111	1D
Bras Basah Complex - Seng Yew Book Store, 231 Bain St, #01-17	111	1D
Bugis MRT Stn, 220 Victoria St	111	1D
Bukit Merah Bus Interchange, 3591 Bukit Merah Central	131	1B
●162 Bukit Merah Central, #01-3543	131	1B
166 Bukit Merah Central (near NTUC)	131	1B
116 Bukit Merah View, Seah Koon Huat Dept Store, #01-233	131	1B
112 Bukit Purmei Rd	131	2C
Capitol Centre, 141 North Bridge Rd	133	1A
Cathay Cineleisure Orchard - Basement 1, 8 Grange Rd, #B1-K3	110	1C
●Central Plaza, 298 Tiong Bahru Rd, #01-01/02	131	2B
Centrepoint Shopping Centre, 176 Orchard Rd	110	1C
Chevron House Change Alley - Level 1, 30 Raffles Place	133	1B
Chinatown MRT Stn, 151 New Bridge Rd, Concourse level	132	2B
City Hall MRT Stn, 150 North Bridge Rd	133	1A
CityLink Mall, 1 Raffles Link #B1-K1	133	1A
Clarke Quay, 3D River Valley Rd, #01-K2	132	2A
Clifford Centre - Level 2, 24 Raffles Place	133	1B
Dhoby Gaut MRT Station, 11 Orchard Rd	110	2D
●Faber House, 320 Orchard Rd, #01-230	110	1C
Far East Plaza - Level 2, 14 Scotts Rd	110	1C
Far East Shopping Centre, 545 Orchard Rd	109	2C
Far East Square, 137 Amoy Street	132	2B
●FEB Building, 156 Cecil St, #01-00	132	2C
Fortune Centre, 190 Middle Road	111	1D
Forum The Shopping Mall, 583 Orchard Rd, #B1-K4	109	2C
●Fu Lu Shou Complex, 149 Rochor Rd, #01-26	111	1C
Funan Digitalife Mall, 109 North Bridge Rd, #01-K1	132	2A
Golden Mile Complex - Wah Hai Marine Supplies, 5001 Beach Rd #01-14	111	2C
Great World City - Basement 1, 1 Kim Seng Promenade	132	1A
●Great World City, 1 Kim Seng Promenade, #01-34	132	1A
HarbourFront Bus Interchange, 4 Seah Im Rd	142	1A
HarbourFront Centre Autolobby, 1 Maritime Square, #02-107	142	1A

LOCATION	MAP	GRID
HarbourFront MRT Stn, 81 Telok Blangah Rd	142	1A
• Hong Lim Complex, 531 Upper Cross St, #01-07	132	2B
Hotel Meridien - Great Pastor Food Court, 100 Orchard Rd, #01-02	110	2D
Ikea Building, 317 Alexandra Rd, Level 1 - Lift Lobby	130	2A
• International Plaza, 10 Anson Rd	132	2C
International Plaza (near Soo Kee), 10 Anson Rd	132	2C
6 Jln Bukit Merah, #01-K1	130	2B
Keypoint, 371 Beach Rd, #01-04A	111	2C
• 803 King George's Avenue, #01-242/244	111	2B
Liang Court Shopping Centre, 177 River Valley Rd, #01-K2	132	2A
Lucky Plaza, 304 Orchard Rd, Level 1	110	1C
Marina Bay MRT Stn, 21 Marina Station Rd	133	1A
• Marina Square, 6 Raffles Boulevard, #01-210/211	133	1A
Marina Square - Marina Food Loft, 6 Raffles Boulevard, #04-101	133	1A
Ministry of Manpower, 18 Havelock Rd	132	2B
Mount Elizabeth Medical Centre, 3 Mount Elizabeth, #01-03/05	110	1C
32 New Market Rd, #01-K2	132	2B
Newton Food Centre, 500 Clemenceau Ave North, #01-AXS	110	1B
Newton MRT Stn, 49 Scotts Rd	110	1B
Ngee Ann City - Basement 2 (near #B2-35), 391 Orchard Rd	110	1C
Ngee Ann City 1, 391B Orchard Rd, #B1-A1	110	1C
Novena MRT Stn, 250 Thomson Rd	110	2A
• Novena Square, 238A Thomson Rd, #01-38	110	2A
OG Albert Complex, 60 Albert St	111	1C
Orchard MRT Stn, 437 Orchard Rd	110	1C
Orchard Twr Level 1, 400 Orchard Rd (entrance to the Rear Block)	109	2C
OUB Centre - Basement 1 (near BK), 1 Raffles Place	132	2B
OUB Centre Office Left (Autolobby), 1 Raffles Place	132	2B
Outram MRT Stn, 10 Outram Rd	132	1C
44 Owen Rd, #01-301	111	1A
Peace Centre, 1 Sophia Rd	110	2C
Pearl Centre - Near Entrance, 100 Eu Tong Sen St, #01-01	132	1C
People's Park Centre - Level 2, 101 Upper Cross St	132	2B
• People's Park Complex, 1 Park Rd, #01-01/02	132	2B
Plaza Hotel - Near Watson's, 7500A Beach Rd, #01-K1	111	2D
Plaza Singapura, 68 Orchard Rd, #B2-K1	110	2D
Plaza Singapura, 68 Orchard Rd, #06-10	110	2D
Raffles City Shopping Centre, 252 North Bridge Rd, #B1-23C	133	1A
• Raffles City Shopping Centre, 252 North Bridge Rd, #B1-04/05	133	1A
50 Raffles Place MRT Stn - #B1-K13 (next to 7-Eleven)	133	1B
50 Raffles Place MRT Stn - B2 (next to SAM Machine)	133	1B
50 Raffles Place MRT Stn - Shopping Level (next to EC House)	133	1B
Redhill MRT Stn, 920 Tiong Bahru Rd	131	1A
Rochor Centre - New A C Radio Pte Ltd, 1 Rochor Rd, #01-552	111	1C
58 Seng Poh Rd, #01-27	132	1B
Sentosa Visitor Arrival Ctr, 21 Gateway Ave	142	2C
• SGX Centre, 2 Shenton Way, #01-01	132	2C
Shaw House - Basement 1, 350 Orchard Rd	110	1C
Shaw Leisure Gallery - Level 1, 100 Beach Rd	111	1D
Sim Lim Square - Level 1, 1 Rochor Canal Rd	111	1C
Sim Lim Tower, 10 Jalan Besar	111	1C
Singapore General Hospital - Level 1, 4 Outram Rd	132	1C
• SMU Campus Branch (UOB), 70 Stamford Rd, #B1-42	110	2D
St. James Power Station, 3 Sentosa Gateway #01-06	142	2A
Somerset MRT Station, 1 Somerset Rd	110	1D
Suntec City Mall - Carrefour Supermarket, 3 Temasek Boulevard	133	1A
Suntec City Mall, 3 Temasek Boulevard, #02-105B	133	1A
Suntec City Mall, 3 Temasek Boulevard, #B1-K4	133	1A
Takashimaya Shopping Centre - Basement 2, 391 Orchard Rd	110	1C
Takashimaya Shopping Centre - Level 1, 391 Orchard Rd	110	1C
Tanglin Mall, 163 Tanglin Rd, #02-K3	109	2C
• Tanglin Shopping Centre, 19 Tanglin Rd, #01-19	109	2C
Tang Plaza Autolobby, 320 Orchard Rd	110	1C

LOCATION	MAP	GRID
Tangs Superstore, 320 Orchard Rd	110	1C
Tanjong Pagar MRT Stn, 120 Maxwell Rd	132	2C
• 1 Tanjong Pagar Plaza, #01-37/40	132	2C
Tekka Mall - Level 1, 2 Serangoon Rd, #01-K1	111	1C
9 Telok Blangah Crescent, #01-121	131	1C
79 Telok Blangah Drive	130	2D
• Textile Centre, 200 Jalan Sultan, #01-06	111	2C
• The Adelphi, 1 Coleman St, #01-14	133	1A
The Paragon, 290 Orchard Rd, #B1-K10	110	1C
Tiong Bahru Market, 30 Seng Poh Rd	132	1B
Tiong Bahru MRT Stn, 302 Tiong Bahru Rd	131	2B
UOB Plaza 1 - near Singapore River, 80 Raffles Place	133	2B
UOB Plaza 2, Atrium Autolobby, 80 Raffles Place	133	2B
• UOB Plaza 1, 80 Raffles Place	132	2B
• Vivo City, 1 HarbourFront Walk, #B2-35/36	142	1A
Wisma Atria - Basement 1, 435 Orchard Rd	110	1C
Zhujiao Centre, 662 Buffalo Rd, #01-00	110	2C
Zouk Discotheque, 17 Jiak Kim St	132	1A
EAST		
113 Aljunied Ave 2, McDonald's Restaurant, #01-01	90	2D
• 119 Aljunied Ave 2, #01-80/82/84	112	2A
Aljunied MRT Stn, 81 Geylang Lor 25	112	2A
Bedok Bus Interchange, 207 New Upper Changi Rd, #01-00A	93	1D
Bedok MRT Station, 315 New Upper Changi Rd	93	1D
• 204 Bedok North St 1, #01-417/419	93	1D
213 Bedok North St 1, Adonis Nuskin Pte Ltd, #01-111	93	1D
539 Bedok North St 3, Kong Hock TV Electric Co, #01-623	92	2C
510 Bedok North St 3, Prima Deli Cake Shop, #01-59	93	1C
85 Bedok North St 4, Near NTUC	93	2C
348 Bedok Rd, Shop N Save - The Market Place, #01-01	94	1A
632 Bedok Reservoir Rd, McDonald's, #01-850	92	1C
744 Bedok Reservoir Rd, #01-3063	92	2B
18 Bedok South Rd, Golden Town Trading Pte Ltd, #01-63	115	1A
Century Square Shopping Centre - Basement 1, 2 Tampines Ctrl 5	72	2D
25A Chai Chee Rd, Prime Supermarket Ltd, #01-459	92	2D
Changi Airport - Airline House Cargo Complex, SIA Basement Canteen	54	2D
Changi Airport Budget Terminal - Arrival Meeting Hall	96	1B
Changi Airport Terminal 1 Departure / Check-in Hall Central East	75	1B
Changi Airport Terminal 1 - Arrival Meeting Hall Ctrl - near Info Ctr	75	1B
Changi Airport Terminal 1 - Departure Hall Building 1 East Wing	75	1B
• Changi Airport, Terminal 2, #B16-17	75	1C
Changi Airport Terminal 2 - Departure Transit Lounge South	75	1C
Changi Airport Terminal 2 - Departure Transit Lounge South	75	1C
Changi Airport Term 2 - Arrival Meeting Hall Sth - near Burger King	75	1C
Changi Airport Term 2 - Arrival Meeting Hall Nth - near Spice Express	75	1C
Changi Airport Terminal 3 - Departure Transit Lounge North	75	1C
Changi Airport Terminal 3 - Departure Transit Lounge South	75	1C
Changi Airport Terminal 3 - Basement 2 South	75	1C
Changi Airport Terminal 3 - Arrival North	75	1C
Changi Airport Terminal 3 - Departure Check-in Hall North	75	1C
Changi Airport Terminal 3 - Departure Check-in Hall South	75	1C
Changi General Hospital - Main Lobby Level 1, 2 Simei St 3	94	1A
4 Changi Village Rd, Subway, #01-2072	54	1B
• City Plaza, 810 Geylang Rd, #01-51/55	113	1A
• 895/897 East Coast Road	114	2B
East Point Mall - Level 1, 3 Simei St 6, #01-K2	94	1A
East Shore Hospital, 321 Joo Chiat Place	114	1A
E!Hub Downtown East, 1 Pasir Ris Close	52	1D
Elias Mall, 625 Elias Rd, #01-K3	51	2D
Eunos MRT Stn, 30 Eunos Crescent	113	2A
321 Geylang Rd, 7-Eleven Store	112	1B
• 439-443 Geylang Rd	112	2B

LOCATION	MAP	GRID
102 Hougang Ave 1, Jen Ann Medical Store, #01-1191	70	1C
106 Hougang Ave 1, Prima Deli Cake Shop, #01-1231	70	1C
●108 Hougang Ave 1, #01-1313/1315	70	1C
121 Hougang Ave 1, #01-1340	69	2C
●683 Hougang Ave 8, #01-903/905/907	48	2D
809 Hougang Central, #01-164	70	1A
840 Hougang Central Bus Interchange	70	1A
Hougang Green Shopping Mall - Theory G, 21 Hougang St 51, #01-59	48	2D
Hougang MRT Stn, 80 B1	70	1A
●Hougang MRT Stn, 80 Hougang Central, #01-01	70	1A
Hougang Point - NTUC, 1 Hougang St 91	48	2D
208 Hougang St 21, McDonald's, #01-217	69	2C
Heartland Mall, 205 Hougang St 21, #01-K1	69	2C
IKEA Tampines, 60 Tampines North Drive 2	51	1D
1 Joo Chiat Rd, #01-K1	113	2A
Kallang Leisure Park, 5 Stadium Walk 1st Storey	112	1C
Kallang MRT Stn, 5 Sims Ave	112	1B
Kembangan MRT Stn, 55 Sims Ave East	92	1D
Lavender MRT Stn, 50 Kallang Rd	111	2B
Loyang Amenity Centre, 4A Loyang Lane, #01-K1	74	1A
Loyang Point, 258 Pasir Ris St 21	74	1A
181-185 MacPherson Rd	90	1C
83 Marine Parade Central, #01-552A	113	2C
59 Marine Terrace, Smile Dental Clinic, #01-91	114	1C
57 New Upper Changi Rd, #01-00	93	2D
●210 New Upper Changi Rd, #01-711	92	2D
NTUC Hougang Mall, 90 Hougang Ave 10 Level 1	70	1A
NTUC Lifestyle World Downtown East, 1 Pasir Ris Close	52	1D
●Odeon Katong Shopping Complex, 11 East Coast Rd, #01-01	113	2C
51 Old Airport Rd, Hawker Ctr #01-K1	112	2B
●Parkway Parade, 80 Marine Parade Rd, #01-13	113	2C
Pasir Ris Bus Interchange, 501 Pasir Ris Drive 3	52	1D
Pasir Ris MRT Stn, 10 Pasir Ris Central	52	1D
443 Pasir Ris Dr 6, #01-04A	73	2A
●443 Pasir Ris Dr 6, #01-20/22	73	2A
Punggol Plaza, 168 Punggol Field	50	1A
●Rivervale Mall, 11 Rivervale Crescent, #01-33	49	2B
Rivervale Plaza, 118 Rivervale Drive, #01-K3	49	2C
Safra Resort Country Club - Golfers Wing, 10 Changi Coast Walk	95	2A
SDB Centre - Bedok 416 Bedok North Ave 2, #01-09	93	1C
Sengkang Bus Interchange, 13 Sengkang Square	49	1B
Sengkang MRT Stn Autolobby, 5 Sengkang Square, #01-03	49	1B
301 Serangoon Ave 2, Asia Photo Supplier, #01-340	68	2D
267 Serangoon Ave 3, McDonald's, #01-37	69	1D
262 Serangoon Central Drive, #01-109 Autolobby	69	1D
Simei MRT Stn, 30 Simei St 3	94	1A
248 Simei St 3, Simei Clinic & Surgery, #01-132	94	1A
Sims Place, Between Blk 48 & 49	112	2A
Singapore Post Centre - Basement 2, 10 Eunos Rd 8	113	1A
811 Tampines Ave 4	93	2A
Tampines Bus Interchange, 512 Tampines Central 1, #01-174	72	2C
503 Tampines Central 1, Chye Soon Pawnshop PL, #01-285	73	1C
20 Tampines Central 1, Vending Arcade	72	2C
Tampines Mall Auto Lobby, 4 Tampines Central 5, #01-K5	72	2D
Tampines Mart, 9-11 Tampines St 32	73	2C
139 Tampines St 11, Boss Ice Cream Cake House, #01-86	93	2A
201C Tampines St 21, #01-10	73	1D
476 Tampines St 44, Adonis Beauty Consultant, #01-201	73	1B
829 Tampines St 81, Yes Supermarket Pte Ltd, #01-272	72	1D
Tanah Merah MRT Stn, 920 New Upper Changi Rd	94	1D
Tanjong Katong Complex - Level 1, 845 Geylang Rd	113	1A
301 Ubi Ave 1, Duet Trading & Gift Shop, #01-251	91	2C
304 Ubi Ave 1, Muayli Hair Studio, #01-117	91	2C

LOCATION	MAP	GRID
UMCI Pte Ltd 5th Storey Canteen, 3 Pasir Ris Dr 12	51	1C
●UOB Tampines Centre, 1 Tampines Central, #01-01	72	1D
West Plaza, 735 Pasir Ris St 72, #01-K2	51	2C
WEST		
●325 Boon Lay Place	81	2A
221 Boon Lay Place, Jurong Far East Watch Co, #01-110	60	2D
221 Boon Lay Place, Yeng Seng Chan Medical Hall, #01-190	60	1B
Boon Lay MRT Stn, 301 Boon Lay Place	81	1B
Boon Lay Temporary Bus Interchange, 10 Jurong West St 64	81	1A
●634 Bukit Batok Central, #01-104/106	62	2D
632 Bukit Batok Central, McDonald's, #01-138/140/142	62	2D
272 Bukit Batok East Ave 4, Prima Deli Cake Shop, #01-76	63	1D
157 Bukit Batok St 11, #01-202	62	1D
375 Bukit Batok St 31, #01-140	62	2C
Bukit Gombak MRT Stn, 802 Bukit Batok West Ave 5	62	2C
Bukit Timah Plaza - Level 1, 1 Jln Anak Bukit, #01-K33	85	1C
911 Bukit Timah Rd, Tan Chong Motor Showroom	85	2B
Chinese Garden MRT Stn, 151	82	2A
253 Choa Chu Kang Ave 1, #B1-00	41	1D
Choa Chu Kang MRT Stn, Auto Lobby, #01-13, 10 CCK Ave 4	41	1C
354 Clementi Ave 2, Sin Onn Goldsmiths & Watch, #01-171	106	1A
●450 Clementi Ave 3, #01-287/289	106	1A
451 Clementi Ave 3, #01-K1	106	1A
Clementi Bus Interchange, 3161 Commonwealth Ave West	106	1A
Clementi MRT Stn, 3150 Commonwealth Ave West	106	1A
Commonwealth Ave, Clementi West St 2, #01-256	106	1C
46-3 Commonwealth Dr, Weng Cheong Optics & Contact Lens, #01-394	108	1D
Commonwealth MRT Stn, 375 Commonwealth Ave	108	1C
Dover MRT Stn, 200 Commonwealth Ave West	107	1B
35 Dover Rd, Eng Aik Seng Provision Store, #01-169	107	1D
Gek Poh Shopping Centre, 762 Jurong West St 75, #01-K1	59	2D
19 Ghim Moh Rd, 7-Eleven Store, #01-237	107	2B
●Holland Rd Shopping Ctr, 211 Holland Ave, #01-12	108	1B
Holland Village - Outside Burger King, 243A Holland Ave	108	1B
IMM Building, 2 Jurong East St 21, #01-36 Autolobby	83	2B
IMM Building, 2 Jurong East St 21 #01-03	83	2B
Jurong East MRT Stn, 10 Jurong East St 12	83	1B
Jurong East MRT Stn, 10 Jurong East St 12 (Guardian Pharmacy)	83	1B
●130 Jurong East St 13, #01-213/215/217	83	1B
135 Jurong East St 13, #01-325	83	1B
256 Jurong East St 24, McDonald's, #01-381	83	1A
253 Jurong East St 24, Photo Bugs, #01-217	83	1A
346 Jurong East St 31, #01-75	82	2A
Jurong Point, 1 Jurong West Central 2, #01-13A	81	1A
●Jurong Point, 1 Jurong West Central 2, #01-16C	81	1A
502 Jurong West Ave 1, #01-819	61	1D
494 Jurong West St 41, Pretty Care De Beauty, #01-136	61	1D
501 Jurong West St 51, Kheng Guan Hang Minimart, #01-277	61	1D
960 Jurong West St 92, #01-178	80	2A
McDonald's Place, 11 King Albert Park	85	1B
Nanyang Drive, NTU Canteen A	58	2D
National University Hospital Main Building, 5 Lower Kent Ridge Rd	129	1A
Ngee Ann Polytechnic, 535 Clementi Rd, Blk 73 #01-06	85	1B
NTUC - Choa Chu Kang, 303 Choa Chu Kang Ave 4	41	1C
NUS Forum - Footpath to Arts Faculty, 10 Kent Ridge Crescent	106	2D
NUS Science Faculty - Lecture Rm 26, 10 Kent Ridge Crescent	106	2D
One-North, The Matrix Block 30 Biopolis St, #01-01A	107	2C
Pioneer Mall, 638 Jurong West St 61	80	2A
Queenstown MRT Station, 301	108	2D
1 Queensway Shopping Centre, Level 1	130	1B
Singapore Institute of Management, level 2, 461 Clementi Rd	85	1C

UOB ATM LOCATIONS

LOCATION	MAP	GRID
Singapore Poly FC2, 500 Dover Rd	107	1B
Sunshine Place, 475 Choa Chu Kang Ave 3, #01-K1	41	1D
Taman Jurong Shopping Centre, 399 Yung Sheng Rd, #01-K5	82	1B
37 Teban Gardens	83	1D
61 Teban Gardens Rd, #01-K1	83	1D
141 Teck Whye Lane, #01-247	41	2C
•UOB Centre, 148 Upper Bukit Timah Rd, #01-0/ #02-01	85	1A
•501 West Coast Drive, #01-302	106	1B
West Mall, 1 Bukit Batok Central Link, #01-K3	62	2D
Yew Tee MRT Station, 61 Choa Chu Kang Drive	41	1A

AXS STATION LOCATIONS

LOCATION	MAP	GRID
CENTRAL		
Adam Rd		
SPC Stn, 31 Adam Rd	87	1C
Ang Mo Kio		
AMK Hub, Citibank Micro Branch	67	2A
AMK West TC Office, Ang Mo Kio Ave 4, Blk 161	46	1D
AMKTC Ofc, Ang Mo Kio Ave 1, Blk 342 #01-1561	67	2B
Ang Mo Kio Ave 1, Blk 226G (next to POSB ATMs)	67	1A
Ang Mo Kio Ave 6, Blk 712	67	2A
Ang Mo Kio Ave 6, Blk 715	67	2A
Ang Mo Kio Ave 10, Blk 532 (outside 7-Eleven)	47	1A
Ang Mo Kio MRT Stn	67	2A
Ang Mo Kio Polyclinic	67	2A
Cheers Ang Mo Kio, Ang Mo Kio Ave 10, Blk 407	68	1A
Cheng San CC	67	2A
Esso Stn, 2761 Ang Mo Kio Ave 5	46	1D
iEcon Minimart, Ang Mo Kio Ave 4, Blk 632 #01-952	46	2C
iEcon Piak Lan Teng, Ang Mo Kio Ave 1, Blk 338 #01-1609	67	2B
iEcon Wei Ann Minimart, Ang Mo Kio Ave 4, Blk 107	67	1A
S11, Clementi Ave 3, Blk 450	106	1A
SPC Stn, 793 Ang Mo Kio Ave 1	67	1B
The Grassroots' Club	46	2C
TYCO Electronics, 26 Ang Mo Kio Ind Pk 2 (Employee only)	47	2D
WOW! Minimart, Ang Mo Kio Ave 4, Blk 632 #01-966	46	2C
Balestier		
Shaw Plaza, 360 Balestier Rd (entrance, security counter)	89	1D
SPC Stn, 462 Balestier Rd	88	2D
Bishan		
Bishan Bus Interchange (near POSB ATM)	67	2D
Bishan Junction 8	67	2D
Bishan MRT Citibank Micro Branch, 200 Bishan Rd	67	2D
Bishan North Shopping Mall, Bishan St 22, Blk 282	67	2C
Bishan St 11, Blk 150A (outside 7-Eleven)	89	1A
CPF Bishan Branch, 3 Bishan Place #01-01	67	2D
Raffles Junior College	88	2A
TC Ofc, Bishan St 13, Blk 197 #01-585	68	1D
Boon Keng		
iEcon Minimart, Upp Boon Keng Rd, Blk 11	111	2A
iEcon Yong Teck Seng, Boon Keng Rd, Blk 22	111	2A
Braddell		
SPC Stn, 317 Braddell Rd	88	2A
Serangoon North		
Yio Chu Kang Amenity Ctr, 19 Serangoon Nth Ave 5 (Sheng Siong)	48	1D
Sin Ming		
LTA Sin Ming, 10 Sin Ming Dr (main lobby)	67	1C
Thomson		
Caldecott Broadcast Centre, Andrew Rd (food court)	87	2B
SPC Stn, 327 Thomson Rd	88	2D
Thomson Plaza, 301 Upp Thomson Rd (near DBS Bank)	66	2C

AXS STATION LOCATIONS

LOCATION	MAP	GRID
Toa Payoh		
Braddell MRT Stn	88	2B
BTPTC Main Office, Toa Payoh Lor 2, Blk 125A #01-134	88	2B
HDB Hub, DBS Autolobby	88	2C
HDB Hub, Citibank	88	2C
Hersing Hub	89	1C
iEcon Ban Seng Provisions, Toa Payoh Lor 2, Blk 116 #01-146	88	2A
iEcon Tong Seng Huat, Toa Payoh Lor 8, Blk 234	89	1B
Kim Keat Ave, Blk 260 (beside Shop N Save)	89	1C
SAFRA Toa Payoh	89	1C
SPC Stn, 180 Toa Payoh Lor 6	89	1B
Toa Payoh Central, Blk 178 (outside Bata)	88	2B
Toa Payoh Lor 1, Blk 109 (near letterboxes)	88	2A
Toa Payoh Lor 1, POSB Autolobby, Blk 107 #01-266	88	2A
Toa Payoh MRT Stn	88	2C
Toa Payoh Polyclinic	89	1B
Upper Thomson		
MBE Nee Soon, 916 Upp Thomson Rd (outside MBE shop)	26	2D
SPC Stn, 1 Jln Leban	66	2A
SPC Stn, 98 Upp Thomson Rd	67	1D
Whampoa		
Whampoa Constituency Office	89	1D
Yio Chu Kang		
SPC Stn, 76 Yio Chu Kang Rd	69	1C
Yio Chu Kang MRT Stn	46	2C
NORTH		
Bukit Panjang		
Bukit Panjang Plaza (Level 1), 1 Jelebu Rd (near McDonalds)	42	1C
Bukit Panjang Plaza (Level 2, info counter)	42	1C
Fajar Shopping Centre, Fajar Rd, Blk 445 (Concourse)	42	2C
Greenridge Shopping Centre, Jelepong Rd, Blk 524A	42	2C
HBPTC Office, Bangkit Rd, Blk 256	42	2C
Kranji		
Kranji MRT Stn	10	1D
Marsiling		
iEcon Bmart 168, Marsiling Rd, Blk 136 #01-2186	11	1B
Marsiling Lane, Blk 19 (beside #01-299, facing market)	11	1B
Marsiling MRT Stn	10	2C
S11 Woodlands, Woodlands St 31, Blk 302	10	2C
Woodlands St 31, Blk 303 (next to POSB)	10	2D
Sembawang		
Blk 355 Sembawang Way	13	1A
Sembawang MRT Stn	13	1A
SPC Stn, 588 Sembawang Rd	13	2B
Sun Plaza, 30 Sembawang Dr (B1, beside POSB ATM)	13	1A
Teo Chuan Kee Minimart, Admiralty Dr, Blk 468B #01-29	3	1D
Ulu Pandan		
Laurels Supermarket Pandan Valley, Ulu Pandan Rd #B1-204	107	1A
Woodlands		
Admiralty MRT Stn	12	1B
Admiralty Place, Woodlands Ave 6, Blk 678 (beside POSB ATM)	12	1B
Chartered Semiconductor, 60 Woodlands Ind Pk D St 2	10	1C
(Building 3 beside Citibank ATM)		
CPF W'lands Branch (W'lands Civic Ctr), 900 Sth W'lands St #01-02	11	2C
Esso Stn, 50 Woodlands Ave 1	11	1D
iEcon Yeong-Heng Minimart, Woodlands Dr 50, Blk 895B	11	2C
NorthTech, 29 Woodlands Ind Pk E 1 (main entrance)	2	1D
888 Plaza (outside KFC), Woodlands Dr 50, Blk 888	12	1C
Republic Polytechnic, 9 Woodlands Ave 9 (beside 7-Eleven)	11	2C
SPC Stn, 250 Admiralty Rd	11	1B
The Woodgrove, 30 Woodlands Ave 1 (near 7-Eleven)	11	1D
Vista Point, Woodlands Dr 14, Blk 548 (next to shop #01-30)	12	1C

AXS STATION LOCATIONS		
LOCATION	**MAP**	**GRID**
Woodlands Civic Centre (1), 900 Sth Woodlands Dr #02-06	11	1C
(SP Services Cust Ctr)		
Woodlands Mart, Woodlands Ave 6, Blk 768	12	1A
Woodlands MRT Stn	11	2C
Woodlands North Plaza, W'lands St 82, Blk 883	11	2B
Woodlands Polyclinic	11	1D
Yishun		
Esso Yishun, 10 Yishun Ave 9	14	1D
GV Yishun, 51 Yishun Ctrl 1 (opp Burger King)	14	1D
iEcon Ann Teng Heng, Yishun St 72, Blk 761	14	1D
iEcon Chan Lian Seng Provision, Yishun St 72, Blk 748 #01-224	14	1D
iEcon Hock Tai Cheong, Yishun Ave 4, Blk 664	27	2A
iEcon Piak Lan Hiong, Yishun St 61, Blk 605 #01-311	27	1A
Khatib MRT Stn	27	1B
Nee Soon South CC, 30 Yishun St 81 (outside ofc)	27	2D
Northpoint (basement 1), 930 Yishun Ave 2 (near POSB ATM)	14	1D
Northpoint (basement 2), 930 Yishun Ave 2 (beside lift)	14	1D
POSB Autolobby, Yishun St 20, Blk 290	14	1B
POSB Autolobby, Yishun St 81, Blk 844	27	1B
S11, Yishun St 72, Blk 744	14	1D
SAFRA Yishun	27	2A
SPC Stn, 599 Yishun Ring Rd	27	1B
Stats ChipPac, 5 Yishun St 23 (Employee only)	14	2B
Up-Mart Trading Minimart, Yishun St 71, Blk 717	13	2D
Yishun Ave 5, Blk 102 (outside 7-Eleven)	13	2D
Yishun Central, Blk 934	14	1D
Yishun MRT Stn	14	1D
Yishun Ring Rd, Blk 414 (outside NTUC)	14	2D
Yishun Sapphire, 44 Canberra Dr (Club House)	13	2B
SOUTH		
Alexandra		
Alexandra Technopark (Blk A)	130	1C
Dawson Place, Dawson Rd, Blk 57 (outside NTUC)	130	2A
PSA Building, 460 Alexandra Rd	130	1D
The Comtech, 60 Alexandra Terrace (main lobby)	130	1C
Beach Road		
Gateway West, 150 Beach Rd (basement)	111	1D
The Concourse, 298 Beach Rd (ground level)	111	2C
The Plaza, 7500E Beach Rd (outside main office)	111	2D
Bendemeer Road		
iEcon San Chung Minimart, Bendemeer Rd Blk 24 #01-547	111	2A
Bras Basah Road		
NTUC Income Centre, 75 Bras Basah Rd (main entrance)	111	1D
Bugis		
Bugis Junction, 230 Victoria St (level 3)	111	1D
Bugis MRT Stn	111	1D
Bugis Village, 165/166 Rochor Rd (outside KFC)	111	1D
Bukit Merah		
Alexandra Hospital, 378 Alexandra Rd (beside POSB ATM)	130	1B
Bukit Merah Central, Blk 166 (level 1, outside NTUC)	131	1B
Esso Stn, 2991 Jln Bt Merah	131	1B
iEcon Chong's & Family, Jln Bt Merah, Blk 133 #01-1526	131	2C
iEcon Chop Chuan Leong, Jln Bt Merah, Blk 28 #01-4466	131	2C
NEA Ctrl Regional Ofc, 4545 Jln Bt Merah	130	2B
Redhill MRT Stn	131	1A
SPC Stn, 3800 Jln Bt Merah	131	1B
Chinatown		
Chinatown Point, 133 New Bridge Rd (level 1, passageway to	132	2B
Hong Lim Complex)		
People's Park Complex, 1 Park Rd (level 1 outside CK dept store)	132	2B
City Hall		
City Hall MRT Stn	133	1A

AXS STATION LOCATIONS		
LOCATION	**MAP**	**GRID**
Clemenceau Avenue		
GE Money House, 182 Clemenceau Ave	110	2D
Cluny Rd		
Singapore Botanic Gardens NParks HQ office, 1 Cluny Rd	109	1A
Cross Street		
China Square Central, 18 Cross St (level 1 near escalator)	132	2B
DBS Autolobby China Square (PWC Bldg)	132	2B
S11 Upper Cross Street Blk 34	132	2B
Cuppage		
StarHub Shop Cuppage, 51 Cuppage Rd #01-05	110	1C
Harbour Front		
Citibank, Vivo City #01-05 Branch	142	1A
DBS HarbourFront	142	1A
Giant Vivo City, 1 HarbourFront Walk #01-23	142	1A
GV Vivo City, Vivo City Level 2	142	1A
Havelock		
SPC Stn, 397 Havelock Rd	132	1A
Subordinate Courts, 1 Havelock Sq (main foyer)	132	2B
Jalan Besar		
S21 Foodcourt, 30 Jln Besar (Lavender Food Square)	111	1B
Sim Lim Square	111	1C
Sim Lim Tower, 10 Jln Besar	111	1C
Kallang		
Kallang MRT Stn	112	1B
Kampong Java		
KK Hospital, 100 Bt Timah Rd (outside FC)	110	2D
LTA Hampshire, no.1 Hampshire Rd (main lobby)	110	2B
Kim Seng Road		
GV Grand Great World City, level 3 (main entrance)	132	1A
Lavender		
Lavender MRT Stn	111	2B
Marina		
Carrefour Suntec, 2 Temasek Blvd, (level 1 main entrance)	111	1D
Citibank Esplanade Branch, Raffles Link #01-01	133	1A
GV Marina Square, Marina Leisureplex level 3	133	1A
Marina Food Loft, 6 Raffles Blvd, Marina Sq #04-101	133	1A
Millenia Walk, 9 Raffles Blvd (level 2)	133	1A
Suntec City, 3 Temasek Blvd (Crystal Jade & Siam Kitchen)	133	1A
Maxwell Road		
Mohamed Sultan Ad, AIG Bldg	132	1A
URA Centre, 45 Maxwell Rd (customer svc counter)	132	2C
Newton		
Newton MRT Stn	110	1B
North Bridge Road		
DBS Autolobby, Peninsula Plaza, level 2	133	1A
Funan The Digitalife Mall, 109 Nth Bridge Rd	132	2A
Novena		
Novena MRT Stn	110	2A
Revenue House, 55 Newton Rd (level 2, outside canteen)	110	2A
Tan Tock Seng Hospital, 11 Jln Tan Tock Seng (level 1 atrium)	88	2D
United Square, 101 Thomson Rd (level 1)	110	2A
Orchard		
Centrepoint, 176 Orchard Rd (basement opposite Guardian Pharmacy)	110	1C
Citibank Orchard Rd Branch	110	2D
Citibank Paragon Branch	110	1C
Dhoby Ghaut MRT Stn	110	2D
Environment Building, 40 Scotts Rd (outside canteen)	110	1B
GV Plaza, Plaza Singapura level 7	110	2D
International Building, 360 Orchard Rd (facing escalator)	109	2C
Orchard MRT Stn	110	1C
Plaza Singapura level B1	110	2D
Singapore Power Building, 111 Somerset Rd (customer svc ctr)	110	1D
Singapore Tourism Board (Tourism Court)	109	2C

AXS STATION LOCATIONS

LOCATION	MAP	GRID
SMU, 80 Stamford Rd (Sch of Information System Basement)	110	2D
Somerset MRT Stn	110	1D
StarHub Shop Plaza Singapura, 68 Orchard Rd #B2-17	110	2D
Wisma Astria Orchard Rd	110	1D
Outram		
Outram MRT Stn	132	1C
Singapore General Hospital, Outram Rd, Blk 2	132	1C
Singapore General Hospital, Outram Rd, Blk 4	132	1C
Queenstown		
Queenstown MRT Stn	108	2D
Queensway		
Anchorpoint, 370 Alexandra Rd (level 1)	130	2A
MDIS UniCampus, 501 Stirling Rd (canteen)	108	1D
Queensway Shopping Centre, 1 Queensway (pillar outside #01-47)	130	1B
SPC Stn, 264 Queensway	130	1A
Raffles Place		
Capital Square (Citibank), 23 Church Street #01-01	132	2B
Chevron House, 30 Raffles Place (beside OCBC ATM)	133	1B
Golden Shoe Car Park, 50 Market St (lift lobby A)	132	2B
Market Street Carpark, 146 Market St	132	2B
One Marina Boulevard, 1 Marina Blvd (basement)	133	1B
Raffles City Shopping Centre, 252 North Bridge Rd #B1-00	133	1A
Raffles Place MRT Stn	133	1B
Republic Plaza, 9 Raffles Place (shopping arcade)	132	2B
StarHub Shop OUB Centre, 1 Raffles Place #B1-02	132	2B
The Arcade level 2, POSB Autolobby	133	1B
River Valley		
Liang Court, 177 River Valley Rd (level 1, near bubble lift)	132	2A
NTUC FairPrice Orchard Grand Court, 131 Killiney Rd	110	1D
SPC Stn, 132 Killiney Rd	110	1D
SPC Stn, 2 Jervois Rd	131	2A
The Pier, 80 Mohamed Sultan Rd (outside #01-12)	132	1A
Selegie		
Parklane Shopping Mall, 35 Selegie Rd (level 1)	110	2C
Tanjong Pagar		
CPF Building, 79 Robinson Rd (outside main entrance)	132	2C
CPF Building, 79 Robinson Rd Level 2	132	2C
DBS Autolobby, DBS Bldg Tower One	132	2C
Fuji Xerox Towers, 80 Anson Rd (beside #01-04)	132	2D
Tanjong Pagar Complex, 7B Keppel Rd (facing escalator)	132	2C
Tanjong Pagar MRT Stn	132	2C
Tg Pagar Plaza, Blk 1 (beside 7-Eleven)	132	2C
Tiong Bahru		
GV Tiong Bahru Plaza, 302 Tiong Bahru Rd, level 4	131	2B
Tiong Bahru Market & Food Centre, 30 Seng Poh Rd	132	1B
Tiong Bahru MRT Stn	131	2B
Tiong Bahru Plaza, 302 Tiong Bahru Rd (basement, lift lobby)	131	2B
EAST		
Aljunied		
Aljunied Ave 2, Blk 119 (beside #01-03)	112	2A
Esso Stn, 630 Aljunied Rd	90	2C
Upp Aljunied Lane, Blk 1 (entrance to market)	90	1B
Bedok		
Bedok North St 1, Blk 201A	93	1D
Bedok North St 1, Blk 213	93	1D
Bedok North St 4, Blk 89 (outside 7-Eleven)	93	2C
Bedok Reservoir View, Blk 775	93	2B
East Coast TC Main Ofc, Bedok Nth St 1 Blk 206 #01-353	93	1D
Esso Bedok South, 799 Bedok Sth Ave 1	93	1D
Bedok MRT Stn	93	1D
Bedok North St 1, Blk 204 (beside NTUC foodfare)	93	1D
Cheers Bedok North St 3, Blk 539	92	2C

AXS STATION LOCATIONS

LOCATION	MAP	GRID
SPC Stn, 101 Bedok North Rd	93	2C
Bedok Reservoir		
Bedok Reservoir Rd, Blk 745 (outside NTUC)	92	2B
Bedok Reservoir Rd, Blk 632 (outside McDonalds)	92	1C
Buangkok		
Buangkok Cres, Blk 982	48	2C
Institute of Mental Health, 10 Buangkok View (main lobby)	48	2C
Chai Chee		
MBE Technopark @ Chai Chee, Chai Chee Rd, Blk 750 #01-03	92	2D
Changi		
Airline House, 25 Airline Rd (canteen)	54	2D
Airport Police Station, 35 Airport Blvd (main lobby)	95	2A
Changi Airport Budget Terminal, 30 Airport Blvd (Departure Hall)	96	1B
Changi Airport Terminal 1 (Departure Hall near check-in gate)	75	1B
Changi Airport Terminal 2 (Departure Hall near Starbucks)	75	1C
Changi Beach Park (NParks info ctr near carpark 1)	54	1B
Lian Soon Amenity Centre, 91 Alps Ave (level 3 near lift)	55	1D
SIA Training Centre, 720 Upp Changi Rd East	95	1A
Changi Business Park		
The Signature, 51 Changi Business Park (level 1, near lift lobby)	95	1B
Circuit Road		
iEcon Li Feng Yuan, Circuit Rd, Blk 78 #01-484	90	2C
East Coast		
East Coast Park (outside blade shop near carpark C3)	114	1C
Esso Stn, 255 East Coast Rd	113	2B
Esso Stn, 251 Upp East Coast Rd	115	1A
SPC Stn, 157 Upp East Coast Rd	115	1A
Eunos		
Eunos Cres, Blk 7 (passageway between coffeeshop #01-2651)	91	2D
Eunos MRT Stn	113	2A
Expo		
Expo MRT Stn	94	2B
Geylang		
Aljunied MRT Stn	112	2A
Esso Stn, Lor 38, 638 Geylang Rd	113	1A
Haig Road		
Haig Rd, Blk 12 (between Bengawan Solo & Watsons)	113	1A
Hougang		
Cheers Hougang, Hougang Ave 3, Blk 23	70	1B
Heartland Mall-Kovan, Hougang St 21, Blk 205 (level 2)	69	2C
Hougang Central, Blk 809 (beside UOB ATM)	70	1A
Hougang Green Shopping Mall, 21 Hougang St 51 (beside Guardian)	48	2D
Hougang HDB Branch Ofc	70	1B
Hougang Mall, 90 Hougang Ave 10 (level 5)	70	1A
Hougang Plaza	70	1A
Hougang Polyclinic	70	1A
iEcon Chin Huat Siong Kee, Hougang Ave 1, Blk 124 #01-1432	69	2A
iEcon Chng Wah Seng Minimart, Lor Lew Lian, Blk 2 #01-42	69	1D
iEcon Our Minimart, Hougang Ave 1, Blk 108	70	1D
SPC Stn, 120 Hougang Ave 2	69	2A
Stan. Chart. Bank Hougang, Hougang St 21, Blk 210 #01-251/253	70	1C
Joo Chiat		
Joo Chiat Complex, Joo Chiat Rd, Blk 1 (main entrance)	113	2A
Kaki Bukit		
Techlink, 31 Kaki Bukit Rd 3 (corridor to food court)	91	2B
Katong		
Katong Mall, 112 East Coast Rd, #L1-00	113	2C
Kembangan		
Kembangan MRT Stn	92	1D
Lorong Chuan		
New Tech Park, 151 Lor Chuan (main lobby)	68	2D
Macpherson		
Esso Stn, 110 Macpherson Rd	90	1C

LOCATION	MAP	GRID
SPC Stn, 429 Macpherson Rd	90	2C
Marine Parade		
Marine Parade TC Main Office, Marine Terrace, Blk 50 #01-265	115	1C
Parkway Parade (1), 80 Marine Parade (Waterfall Plaza entrance)	113	2C
Mountbatten		
Equatorial Apt	112	2D
Esso Stn, 708 Mountbatten Rd	112	2C
SPC Stn, 710 Mountbatten Rd	112	2C
Old Airport Road		
Old Airport Rd, Blk 51	112	2B
Pasir Ris		
Downtown East, 1 Pasir Ris Close (outside Food Court)	52	1D
Downtown East Hub (level 2)	52	1D
Elias Mall, Elias Rd, Blk 625 (beside UOB ATM)	51	2D
Loyang Point, Pasir Ris At 21, Blk 258	74	1A
Esso Stn Pasir Ris, 61 Pasir Ris Dr 1	51	2D
SPC Stn, 11 Pasir Ris Dr 4	73	2A
Pasir Ris Blk 443 (outside UOB Bank)	73	2A
Pasir Ris MRT Stn	52	1D
Pasir Ris Park (NParks info ctr near carpark E)	51	2C
Pasir Ris West Plaza (1), Pasir Ris St 72, Blk 735 (near 7-Eleven)	51	2C
White Sands, 1 Pasir Ris Ctrl St 3 (level 2)	52	1D
Paya Lebar		
CISCO Ctr, 20 Jln Afifi	90	1D
Paya Lebar MRT Stn	113	1A
Trinity Christian Centre	91	1C
Pipit Road		
Pipit Rd, Blk 54 (next to Macpherson NPP)	90	2D
Potong Pasir		
Potong Pasir Ave 1, Blk 148	89	2C
Punggol		
Marina Country Club, 600 Punggol Seventeenth Ave	30	2B
Punggol Drive, Blk 639	31	1D
Punggol Field, Blk 110A	50	1A
Punggol Field, Blk 198	30	2D
Punggol Plaza, POSB Autolobby	50	1A
Punggol Plaza, Punggol Field, Blk 168 (near Food Court)	50	1A
SPC Stn, Punggol	31	1D
Sengkang		
Compassvale Link, Blk 267	49	1C
Compassvale St, Blk 263	49	1A
Compass Point (1), 1 Sengkang Sq (beside Charles & Keith)	49	1B
Esso Stn, 211 Punggol Rd	49	2C
Fernvale Point, 21 Sengkang West Ave	48	1A
iEcon Minimart, Anchorvale Link, Blk 303 #01-04	49	1B
Rivervale Mall, 11 Rivervale Cres (level 2)	49	2B
Rivervale Plaza, Blk 118 Rivervale Dr (near KFC)	49	2C
Rivervale Plaza, POSB Autolobby	49	2C
Serangoon		
Serangoon Ave 3, Blk 326 (staircase beside clinic)	68	2D
Serangoon Ave 4, Blk 226 (in front of #01-149)	69	1C
Serangoon Bus Interchange	69	1D
Serangoon Central Dr, Blk 266 (opp Shop N Save)	69	1D
Serangoon North Ave 1, Blk 153 (beside POSB ATMs)	69	1A
Serangoon Garden		
Serangoon Garden Village, 9 Portchester Ave	68	2B
Simei		
Changi General Hospital, 2 Simei St 3 (opp A & E dept)	94	1A
City Harvest Church S'pore Expo Hall 8	94	2B
Eastpoint Mall (1), 3 Simei St 6 (level opp Starbucks)	94	1A
Simei MRT Stn	94	1A
Tampines		
Century Square, 2 Tampines Ctrl 5 (basement lift lobby)	72	2D

AXS STATION LOCATIONS

LOCATION	MAP	GRID
Courts Megastore	51	1D
CPF Tampines Branch, 1 Tampines Ctrl 5 #01-01	72	2D
Esso Stn, 9 Tampines Ave 7	73	2C
GV Tampines Mall, Tampines Mall Shopping Ctr level 4	72	2D
Tampines Central, Blk 510	72	2C
Tampines Mall	72	2D
Tampines Mart, 7 Tampines St 32 (outside Guardian)	73	2C
Tampines MRT Stn	72	2C
Tampines St 11, Blk 139 (at coffeeshop near carpark entrance)	93	2A
Tampines St 21, Blk 201C (next to POSB & OCBC ATM)	73	1D
Tampines St 44, Blk 475 (outside NTUC Fairprice)	73	1B
Tampines St 81, Blk 823A (outside Freshmart)	72	1D
Temasek Polytechnic, 21 Tampines Ave 1	72	1D
(Plaza, outside sch of Applied Science Gen. ofc)		
Tanah Merah		
Tanah Merah MRT Stn	94	1D
Tanjong Katong		
SPC Stn, 1 Swanage Rd	113	1B
Ubi		
DHL Air Express Centre, 1 Tai Seng Dr (canteen)	91	1B
Traffic Police HQ, 10 Ubi Ave 3 (main lobby)	91	1C
Ubi Ave 1, Blk 304 (staircase landing next to #01-111)	91	2C
Ubi Ave 1, Blk 306 (outside G'value)	91	2C
Ubi Ave 1, Blk 341 (next to Kampong Ubi CC library)	91	2D
Upper Serangoon		
SPC Stn, 849 Upp Serangoon Rd	69	2C
WEST		
Ayer Rajah		
Ayer Rajah Amenity Centre, 69 Ayer Rajah Cres (level 1)	107	2D
Gemplus (Employees only), 12 Ayer Rajah Cres	107	2D
Bukit Batok		
Bukit Batok Central, Blk 630 (Outside Town Council Ofc)	62	2D
Bt Batok MRT Stn	62	2D
Bt Batok Polyclinic	62	2D
Bt Batok St 31, Blk 372 (next to 7-Eleven)	62	2C
Bt Batok West Ave 8, Blk 154A (outside NTUC)	62	1D
Bt Gombak MRT Stn	62	2C
Econ Minimart Evermeed, Bt Batok East Ave 3, Blk 284	63	1D
Esso Stn, 813 Bt Batok West Ave 5	62	2A
HomeTeamNS Bukit Batok Clubhouse, 2 Bt Batok West Ave 7	62	2B
S11 Bukit Batok Central Blk 640	62	2D
Bukit Timah		
Bukit Timah Plaza, 1 Jln Anak Bukit (outside #01-11)	85	1A
Bukit Timah Shopping Ctr	85	1A
Esso Stn, 213 Upp Bt Timah Rd	84	2A
SPC Stn, 623A Bt Timah Rd	86	2D
Buona Vista / Ghim Moh		
Biopolis @ One-North Matrix Block, 30 Biopolis St	107	2C
iEcon Ban Joo Loong, Ghim Moh Rd, Blk 11	107	2C
Choa Chu Kang		
Cheers Choa Chu Kang, Ave 4, Blk 303	41	1C
Choa Chu Kang MRT Stn	41	1C
Choa Chu Kang Polyclinic	41	2C
Esso Stn, 50 Choa Chu Kang Ave 3	41	1D
Keat Hong Shopping Centre, Choa Chu Kang Ave 1, Blk 253	41	1D
Limbang Shopping Centre, Choa Chu Kang St 51, Blk 533	41	1B
Lot 1 Shopper's Mall, 21 Choa Chu Kang Ave 4 (basement)	41	1C
Esso Stn 50 Choa Chu Kang Dr	41	2A
S11 Choa Chu Kang, Choa Chu Kang Dr, Blk 787B	41	2A
Sunshine Place, Choa Chu Kang Ave 3, Blk 475 (near ATMs)	41	1D
Teck Whye Lane, Blk 140 (opp NTUC)	41	2C
Ten Mile Junction, 1 Woodlands Rd (near taxi stand)	42	1C

AXS STATION LOCATIONS

LOCATION	MAP	GRID
Yew Tee MRT Stn	41	2A
Yew Tee Shopping Centre (1) Choa Chu Kang St 62, Blk 622 (near 7-Eleven)	41	2A
Clementi		
Clementi Ave 3, Blk 451 (outside NTUC)	106	1A
Clementi Ave 4, Blk 308 (linkway, near bus stop)	84	2D
Clementi MRT Stn	106	1A
Clementi West St 2, Blk 726 (facing hawker ctr, near bus stop)	106	1C
Esco Stn, 126 Clementi Ave 2	106	2A
iEcon 99JA Enterprise, Clementi West St 2, Blk 710	106	1C
iEcon Sin Yeow Leong, Clementi Ave 2, Blk 354	106	2A
SIM, 461 Clementi Rd (level 2, near library)	85	1C
West Coast TC Main Ofc, Clementi Ave 3, Blk 444 #01-123	106	1A
Commonwealth		
Commonwealth MRT Stn	108	1C
iEcon Chua Yan Kee, Tanglin Halt Rd, Blk 49	108	1D
SPC Stn, 490 Commonwealth Ave	108	1C
Dover		
Dover MRT Stn	107	1B
Singapore Polytechnic, 500 Dover Rd (Blk 71A, beside admin ofc)	107	1B
Dunearn		
SPC Stn, 260 Dunearn Rd	87	1D
Holland Avenue		
Civil Service College, 31 North Buona Vista Rd	107	2B
HDB Buona Vista Branch Ofc, Holland Ave, Blk 14 #01-55	107	2B
International Business Park		
iQuest@IBP, 27 Int'l Business Park	83	2D
The Atrium, 6 Int'l Business Park (level 1)	83	2C
Jalan Ahmad Ibrahim		
Esso Stn, 302 Jln Ahmad Ibrahim	82	1D
Jalan Buroh		
SPC Stn, 33 Jln Buroh	103	2A
Jalan Jurong Kechil		
Esso Stn, 37 Jln Jurong Kechil	84	2A
Jurong East		
Chinese Garden MRT Stn	82	2A
CPF Jurong Branch, 21 Jurong East St 13 #01-01	83	1B
Esso Stn, 150 Jurong East Ave 1	82	2A
iEcon Lim Thiong Beng, Jurong East St 32, Blk 303	82	2A
iEcon Soon Seng, Jurong East St 21, Blk 217A #01-595	83	1A
IMM, 2 Jurong East St 21 (level 1, beside Mini Toon)	83	2B
IMM, 2 Jurong East St 21 (level 1, Opp Starhub)	83	2B
IMM, 2 Jurong East St 21 (level 2, Opp Challenger)	83	2B
IMM, 2 Jurong East St 21 (level 3, SingPost)	83	2B
JTC Summit, 8 Jurong Town Hall Rd (level 3 FC)	83	1C
Jurong East MRT	83	1B
Jurong East St 13, Blk 135 (next to NTUC)	83	1B
Jurong East St 24, Blk 252 (near POSB ATM)	83	1A
Jurong East St 24, Blk 255	83	1A
Jurong East St 31, Blk 345 (beside bakery)	82	2A
Jurong Polyclinic	61	2D
M1 Shop IBP	83	2D
S11 Jurong East, Jurong East St 13, Blk 132	83	1B
SPC Stn, 91 Jurong East Ave 1	83	1A
Toh Guan Rd, Blk 286E (beside coffeeshop)	83	1B
Jurong West		
Boon Lay MRT Stn	81	1B
City Harvest Church, no.1 Jurong West St 91 (level 1)	80	2A
Gek Poh Shopping Centre, Jurong West St 75, Blk 762	59	2A
GV Jurong Point, level 4 (diagonally opposite candy bar)	81	1A
Jurong Spring CC, 8 Jurong West St 52	60	2D
Jurong West St 41, Blk 492 (near bicycle shop)	61	1D
Jurong West St 91, Blk 962 (outside Prime Mart)	80	2A

AXS STATION LOCATIONS

LOCATION	MAP	GRID
Lakeside MRT Stn	82	1A
Esso Stn, 10 Jurong West Ave 1	61	1D
Pioneer Mall, Jurong West St 61, Blk 638	80	2A
Sheng Siong, 9 Jurong West Ave 5, #01-09	60	1D
SPC Stn, 100 Jurong West Ave 1	60	2D
Star 5 Technologies, Jurong Point, 1 Jurong West Ctrl 2, #02-28	81	1A
West Coast TC Branch (1), Jurong West St 51, Blk 509	61	1D
Nanyang Technology University, NTU North Spine Canteen A	58	2D
Nanyang Technology University, NTU South Spine Canteen B	80	1A
National University Hospital		
NUH Kent Ridge Wing	129	1A
NUH Main Building	107	1D
National University of Singapore		
NUS Block Admin, 10 Kent Ridge Cres (beside POSB ATM)	106	2D
NUS LT 27, 10 Kent Ridge Cres	107	1D
Pasir Panjang		
SPC Stn, 158 Pasir Panjang Rd	129	2C
Science Hub		
Science Hub 1, 87 Science Park Dr	129	2B
Sunset Way		
iEcon Minimart, Clementi St 12, Blk 105 #01-02	84	2D
Taman Jurong		
Taman Jurong Shopping Centre, Yung Sheng Rd, Blk 399	82	1B
S11 Taman Jurong, 101 Yung Sheng Rd	82	1B
Telok Blangah		
Depot Heights Shopping Ctr, Depot Rd, Blk 108 (outside NTUC)	130	2C
iEcon Teck Guan Minimart, Telok Blangah Dr, Blk 77	130	2D
SAFRA Mount Faber	131	1C
SPC Stn, 616 Telok Blangah Rd	130	2D
Tuas		
SPC Stn, 8 Pioneer Rd	102	2A
SPC Stn, 16 Tuas Rd	78	2D
Turf City		
Turf Club, 200 Turf Club Rd	86	1B
West Coast		
Esso Stn, 181 West Coast Rd	106	1B
McDonald's West Coast Park, 71 West Coast Highway	106	1D
West Coast Dr, Blk 502 (outside market)	106	1B

WESTERN UNION LOCATIONS

LOCATION	TEL NO.	MAP	GRID
CENTRAL			
RHB Bank, 1 Yio Chu Kang Rd	6288 8053	69	1C
SingPost, Ang Mo Kio Ave 6, Blk 727 #01-4246	6453 7899	67	2A
SingPost, HDB Hub Biz Two, 520 Lor 6 Toa Payoh, #02-55	6251 8899	88	2C
SingPost, 70 Macpherson Rd	6746 8899	90	1C
SingPost, Serangoon Ctrl Dr, Blk 261 #01-05/07	6283 6899	69	1C
SingPost, Serangoon Garden Way	6282 5899	68	2B
SingPost, Toa Payoh North, Blk 203 #01-1117/1119	6355 7899	88	2A
SingPost, Thomson Rd, 246T Upper Thomson Rd	6454 7899	67	1C
SingPost, Towner Road, Blk 101 #01-204/206	6299 8899	111	2A
Western Union, Balestier Pt, 279 Balestier Rd, #01-01	6353 4830	89	1D
NORTH			
SingPost, Sun Plaza, 30 Sembawang Drive #01-07	6753 8600	13	1A
SingPost, Woodlands Civic Ctr, 900 South Woodlands Dr #02-05	6765 9010	11	2C
SingPost, Yishun Central 1, Blk 924 #01-304	6756 7899	14	1D

WESTERN UNION LOCATIONS

LOCATION	TEL NO.	MAP	GRID
SOUTH			
RHB Bank, Bt Merah, Jalan Bt Merah, Blk 131 #01-1577/1579	6278 5388	131	2C
RHB Bank, Cecil Street, 90 Cecil Street, Ground Floor	6320 0602	132	2B
RHB Bank, Jln Besar, Sim Lim Tower, 10 Jln Besar, #01-03	6296 6233	111	1C
SingPost, 110 Alexandra Road	6365 6899	131	1A
SingPost, Beach Rd, Blk 15 #01-4685	6292 7899	111	2C
SingPost, Bras Basah Cplx, Bain St, Blk 231 #01-03	6339 8899	111	1D
SingPost, Bukit Merah Central, Blk 165 #01-3689	6270 7899	131	1B
SingPost, Change Alley, Hitachi Tower, 16 Collyer Quay, #02-02	6538 6899	133	1B
SingPost, Chinatown Point, 133 New Bridge Rd, #02-42/44	6538 7899	132	2B
SingPost, CPF Bldg, 79 Robinson Rd #01-06	6222 8899	132	2C
SingPost, Harbourfront Ctr,1 Maritime Square, #02-52	6270 6899	142	1A
SingPost, 1 Killiney Rd	6734 7899	110	1D
SingPost, New Park Hotel, 181 Kitchener Rd, #01-26/28	6293 8899	111	1B
SingPost, Ngee Ann City, 391 Orchard Rd, #04-15	6738 6899	110	1C
SingPost, POSB Newton Branch Bldg, 135 Bukit Timah Rd, #01-01	6734 6899	110	2B
SingPost, Rochor Road, Blk 1 #01-560	6293 7899	111	1C
SingPost, Suntec City Mall, 3 Temasek Boulevard #03-001/003	6332 0289	133	1A
SingPost, 56 Tanglin Road	6743 5899	109	2C
SingPost, Tanjong Pagar Plaza, Blk 1 #01-25	6221 7899	132	2C
Tang Plaza American Express - Tangs, Fes Retail, 320 Scotts Rd	6735 2069	110	1C
The Concourse American Express, Fes Retail The Concourse, 300 Beach Rd, #18-01	6735 2069	111	2C
Western Union, Golden Mile Complex, 5001 Beach Rd, #01-02	6295 3501/ 6295 3502	111	2C
Western Union, Kerbau - 81 Serangoon Rd	6391 9272/ 6391 9273	111	1C
Western Union, Lucky Chinatown 211 New Bridge Rd, #01-08	6325 3627/ 6325 3628	132	2B
Western Union, Lucky Plaza 304 Orchard Rd, #02-18	6336 2000	110	1C
Western Union, 113 Serangoon Rd	6336 2000	111	1B
Western Union, Tekka Mall, 2 Serangoon Rd, #02-08	6391 0282	111	1C
Western Union, The Claremont Hotel, 301 Serangoon Rd, #01-01	6391 0280	111	1C
EAST			
RHB Bank, 537 Geylang Rd	6747 8966	112	2B
RHB Bank, Katong, 14-18 East Coast Rd	6344 8044	113	2C
Singapore Post Centre, 10 Eunos Rd 8, West Entrance, #01-02	6741 8857	113	1A
SingPost, 350 Bedok Rd	6442 6899	94	1C
SingPost, Bedok North Street 1, Blk 218 #01-49	6442 7899	93	1C
SingPost, Changi Airport, Terminal 2 Departure Hall, Unit 026-39	6542 7899	75	1C
SingPost, CPF Tampines Building, 1 Tampines Ctrl 5, #01-03	6787 7899	72	2D
SingPost, 447 Geylang Rd	6756 7899	112	2B
SingPost, Hougang Mall, 90 Hougang Ave 10, #04-15A	6282 7899	70	1A
SingPost, Marine Parade Central, Blk 86 #01-670	6345 7899	113	2C
SingPost, 10 Palm Avenue	6443 7899	115	1B
SingPost, Sengkang Community Hub, Sengkang Sq, Blk 2 #03-01	6315 3498	49	1B
SingPost, 373 Tanjong Katong Rd	6344 7899	113	1C
SingPost, 755 Upper Serangoon Rd	6282 6899	69	2C
SingPost, White Sands, 1 Pasir Ris Ctrl St 3, #04-13	6581 7899	52	1D

WESTERN UNION LOCATIONS

LOCATION	TEL NO.	MAP	GRID
WEST			
RHB Bank, Bt Timah, The Rail Mall, 440/442 Upper Bt Timah Rd	6769 1766	63	2B
SingPost, Bt Batok Ctrl, West Mall, 1 Bukit Batok Ctrl Link, #05-09	6791 0799	62	1C
SingPost, Bt Timah, 22 Sixth Avenue	6468 8899	86	1C
SingPost, 309 Choa Chua Kang Ave 4, #01-03	6769 8108	41	1C
SingPost, 10 Choa Chu Kang Rd Track 10	6769 7899	42	1C
SingPost, Clementi Avenue 3, Blk 449 #01-241	6775 8899	106	1A
SingPost, Ghim Moh Road, Blk 21 #01-225	6462 7899	107	2B
SingPost, IMM Bldg, 2 Jurong East St 21 #02-07A	6665 0699	83	2B
SingPost, Jurong Point, 1 Jurong West Ctrl 2, B1-45	6792 7899	81	1A
SingPost, Jurong West St 41, Blk 492 #01-42	6665 3599	61	1D
SingPost, Teban Gdn, Blk 38 #01-136	6665 0499	83	1D

⊗ CALTEX PETROL STATIONS

LOCATION	MAP	GRID
CENTRAL		
1351 Ang Mo Kio Avenue 1	67	2B
3551 Ang Mo Kio Avenue 3	68	2D
542 Balestier Road	88	2D
319 Braddell Rd	88	2A
277 Lor Chuan Road	68	2C
68 MacPherson Road	90	1C
465 MacPherson Road	90	2C
555 Upper Thomson Road	66	2A
236 Whitley Road	87	2D
NORTH		
62 Sembawang Road	26	1D
337 Woodlands Road	41	2A
SOUTH		
360 Alexandra Road	130	2A
4870 Beach Road	111	2C
130 Dunearn Road	110	1A
3781 Jalan Bukit Merah	131	1B
EAST		
66 Aljunied Road	112	2A
78 Changi Road	113	2A
355 East Coast Road	114	1B
71 Frankel Avenue	114	2A
128 Paya Lebar Road	91	1D
1 Tampines Ave 8	72	1D
265 Tanjong Katong Road	113	1C
559 Upper Serangoon Road	69	1D
818 Upper Serangoon Road	69	2C
WEST		
50 Bukit Batok East Avenue 3	84	1A
836 Dunearn Road	85	2B
297 Holland Road	107	2A
400 Jalan Ahmad Ibrahim	80	2D
210 Jalan Buroh	105	1C
27 Jurong Port Road	104	1C
21 Jurong West Street 93	80	2B
450 North Buona Vista Road	107	2C
112 Pasir Panjang Road	129	2C

EXXONMOBIL PETROL STATIONS

LOCATION	MAP	GRID
CENTRAL		
2761 Ang Mo Kio Avenue 5	46	1D
384 Lorong Chuan	68	2B
114 Macpherson Road	90	1C
560 Thomson Road	88	1B
399 Toa Payoh Lorong 2	88	2B
1001 Toa Payoh Lorong 5	89	1B
353 Upper Thomson Road	66	2C
553 Upper Thomson Road	66	2A
594 Upper Thomson Road	45	2D
237 Whitley Road	87	2D
NORTH		
590 Sembawang Road	13	2B
593 Sembawang Road	13	2B
213 Upper Bukit Timah Road	84	2A
217 Upper Bukit Timah Road	84	2A
926 Upper Bukit Timah Road	42	1D
10 Yishun Avenue 9	14	1D
50 Woodland Avenue 1	11	1D
1091 Woodland Road	10	1C
SOUTH		
145 Alexandra Road	131	1A
141 Bukit Timah Road	110	2B
30 Dunearn Road	110	1A
174 Holland Road	108	1B
2991 Jalan Bukit Merah	131	1B
1 Jervois Road	131	2A
262 Queensway	130	1A
622 Queensway	108	1B
353 Tanglin Road	109	1D
396 Telok Blangh Road	131	1D
EAST		
611 Aljunied Road	90	2D
630 Aljunied Road	90	2C
799 Bedok South Avenue 1	93	1D
649 Changi Road	114	1A
239 East Coast Road	113	2B
590 East Coast Road	114	2B
345 Geylang Road	112	2B
638 Geylang Road	113	1B
225 Guillemard Road	112	2B
600 Hougang Avenue 3	70	1D
215 Jalan Kayu	48	1A
216 Lavender Street	111	2B
708 Mountbatten Road	112	2C
61 Pasir Ris Drive 1	51	2D
211 Punggol Road	49	2C
9 Tampines Avenue 7	73	2C
40 Tampines Avenue 9	73	1B
189 Tanjong Katong Road	113	1B
263 Tanjong Katong Road	113	1B
373 Upper Aljunied Road	90	2C
943 Upper Changi Road North	74	1C
955 Upper Changi Road North	74	1C
251 Upper East Coast Road	115	1A
866 Upper Serangoon Road	69	2C
1027 Upper Serangoon Road	70	1B
160 Yio Chu Kang Road	69	1B
299 Yio Chu Kang Road	48	1C
WEST		
813 Bukit Batok West Avenue 5	62	2A
751 Bukit Timah Road	86	1C
50 Choa Chu Kang Avenue 3	41	1D

EXXONMOBIL PETROL STATIONS

LOCATION	MAP	GRID
50 Choa Chu Kang Drive	41	2A
31 Choa Chu Kang Way	41	2D
126 Clementi Avenue 2	106	2A
650 Dunearn Road	86	1C
870 Dunearn Road	85	2B
302 Jalan Ahmad Ibrahim	82	1D
253 Jalan Buroh	105	2B
37 Jalan Jurong Kechil	84	2A
150 Jurong East Avenue 1	82	2A
10 Jurong West Avenue 1	61	1D
242A Pasir Panjang Road	129	2C
19 Pioneer Road	102	1A
181 West Coast Road	106	1B

SPC PETROL STATIONS

LOCATION	MAP	GRID
CENTRAL		
31 Adam Road	87	1C
793 Ang Mo Kio Ave 1	67	1B
462 Balestier Road	88	2D
317 Braddell Road	88	2A
1 Jalan Leban	66	2A
429 Macpherson Road	90	2C
327 Thomson Road	88	2D
180 Toa Payoh Lor 6	89	1B
98 Upper Thomson Road	67	1D
NORTH		
250 Admiralty Road	11	1B
588 Sembawang Road	13	2B
599 Yishun Ring Road	27	1B
SOUTH		
490 Commonwealth Road	108	1C
397 Havelock Road	132	1A
3800 Jalan Bukit Merah	131	1B
2 Jervois Road	131	2A
132 Killiney Road	110	1D
264 Queensway	130	1A
616 Telok Blangah Road	130	2D
EAST		
101 Bedok North Road	93	2C
337 Changi Road	114	1A
120 Hougang Ave 2	69	2A
710 Mountbatten Road	112	2C
11 Pasir Ris Drive 4	73	2A
100 Punggol Central	31	1D
1 Swanage Road / Tanjong Katong	113	1B
157 Upper East Coast Road	115	1A
849 Upper Serangoon Road	69	2C
76 Yio Chu Kang Road	69	1C
WEST		
331 Bukit Timah Road	110	1A
623A Bukit Timah Road	86	2D
260 Dunearn Road	87	1D
33 Jalan Buroh (CNG Available)	103	2A
91 Jurong East Ave 1	83	1A
100 Jurong West Ave 1	60	2D
158 Pasir Panjang Road	129	2C
8 Pioneer Road	102	2A
16 Tuas Road	78	2D

SHELL PETROL STATIONS

LOCATION	MAP	GRID
CENTRAL		
2225 Ang Mo Kio Ave 8	68	1B
110 Braddell Rd	89	2A
54 Lavender St	111	2B
182 Lornie Rd	88	1B
259 Macpherson Rd	90	1C
103 Moulmein Rd	110	2A
49 Serangoon Garden Way	68	2B
324 Thomson Rd	88	2D
248 Toa Payoh Lor 1	88	2A
862 Upper Serangoon Rd	69	2C
80 Upper Thomson Rd	67	1D
183A Upper Thomson Rd	67	1D
551 Upper Thomson Rd	66	2A
NORTH		
695 Mandai Rd	22	2C
10 Marsiling Rd	11	1B
595 Sembawang Rd	13	2B
35 Upper Bt Timah Rd	85	1B
219 Upper Bt Timah Rd	84	2A
772 Upper Bt Timah Rd	42	1D
1200 Upper Thomson Rd	26	1D
20 Woodlands Ave 9	11	2B
3700 Yishun Ring Rd	13	2D
1 Yishun St 11	14	1D
SOUTH		
358 Alexandra Rd	130	2A
143 Bt Timah Rd	110	2B
150 Bt Timah Rd	110	2B
548 Havelock Rd	132	1A
305 Outram Rd	132	1B
260 Queensway	130	1A
509 Serangoon Rd	111	1A
450 Telok Blangah Rd	130	2D
603 Tiong Bahru Rd	131	1A
EAST		
79 Aljunied Rd	112	2A
99 Bedok Nth Rd	93	2C
331 Bedok Rd	94	1C
460 Changi Rd	114	1A
743 Dunman Rd	113	2B
338 East Coast Rd	114	1B
203 Geylang Rd	112	1B
340 Geylang Rd	112	2B
132 Guillemard Rd	112	2B
1 New Loyang Link	74	1B
98 Paya Lebar Rd	91	1D
255 Paya Lebar Rd	91	1C
61 Sengkang East Rd	49	1B
9 Tampines Ave 2	73	1D
10 Tampines Ave 4	72	2D
191 Tanjong Katong Rd	113	1B
685 Upper Changi Rd	94	2A
40 Upper East Coast Rd	114	2B
158 Yio Chu Kang Rd	69	1A
298 Yio Chu Kang Rd	48	1C
WEST		
2 Boon Lay Avenue	81	1A
28 Bt Batok East Ave 6	63	1D
11 Bt Batok West Ave 3	62	1D
20 Choa Chu Kang Dr	41	1B
355 Commonwealth Ave	108	2D
314 Dunearn Rd	87	1D

SHELL PETROL STATIONS

LOCATION	MAP	GRID
648 Dunearn Rd	86	1C
311 Jln Ahmad Ibrahim	82	1D
70 Jln Jurong Kechil	84	2A
21 Jurong West Ave 5	60	1D
168 Pasir Panjang Rd	129	2C
328 Pasir Panjang Rd	129	1A

CNG Stations

	MAP	GRID
SMART - 1 Mandai Link	23	1C
SPC - 33 Jalan Buroh	103	1D
SembCorp - 10 Merlimau Place (Jurong Island)	125	2C

24-HOUR CLINIC LOCATIONS

LOCATION		MAP	GRID
CENTRAL			
Medihealth Bishan 24 Hours Clinic and Surgery	6258 3212	68	1D
Block 121 Bishan Street 12 #01-95			
Novena Clinic 24 Hours	6307 9959	110	2A
10 Sinaran Drive (Novena Sq 2) #08-18			
NORTH			
Central Clinic and Surgery (Yishun)	6759 7985	13	2D
Block 701A Yishun Avenue 5 #01-04			
EAST			
Central Clinic and Surgery (Hougang)	6387 6965	48	2D
Block 681 Hougang Avenue 8 #01-831			
Lifelink 24hrs Clinic and Surgery	6281 3977	69	1A
Block 153 Serangoon North Avenue 1 #01-534			
Mediline Wei Min Clinic	6247 9221	113	2C
Block 81 Marine Parade Ctrl #01-634			
Raffles Medical Group	6241 8818	75	1C
S'pore Changi Airport #B2-MS-15, Passenger Term 3			
Silver Cross Family Clinic (Serangoon)	6287 8702	69	1D
Block 262 Serangoon Central Drive #01-109			
Tampines 24-Hr Family Clinic	6786 7228	73	1D
Block 201D Tampines Street 21 #01-1151			
WEST			
CCK 24-hr Family Clinic	6891 0338	41	1C
Block 304 Choa Chu Kang Avenue 4 #01-653			
Central Clinic and Surgery (Clementi)	6773 2925	106	1A
Block 450 Clementi Avenue 3 #01-291			
Prohealth 24-Hour Medical Clinic	6765 2115	42	2D
Block 259 Bukit Panjang Ring Road #01-18			
Shenton Family Medical Clinic (Bukit Gombak)	6566 5671	62	2C
Block 372 Bukit Batok Street 31 #01-378			

24-HOUR MOBILE MEDICAL SERVICES

The HouseCall GP - Dr Choo Wei Chieh	6247 9247
MW Medical - Dr Madeleine Chew	6250 0625

Contents

ATM LOCATIONS   Page
- ABN Amro ---------------------------------- CG1
- Citibank ------------------------------------ CG1
- DBS & POSB ------------------------------ CG2
- HSBC -------------------------------------- CG7
- Maybank ---------------------------------- CG7
- OCBC -------------------------------------- CG7
- RHB -- CG11
- Standard Chartered ----------------------- CG11
- UOB -- CG12

- AXS Stations ------------------------------ CG15

- Western Union Remittance Ctrs ---------- CG19

PETROL STATIONS
- CALTEX ----------------------------------- CG20
- EXXONMOBIL ----------------------------- CG21
- SPC -- CG21
- SHELL ------------------------------------- CG22
- CNG -- CG22

- 24-hour Clinics --------------------------- CG22
- 24-hour Mobile Medical Services --------- CG22

Information

1 The featured services are divided into five zones by location: Central, North, South, East and West.

2 Every location has a **Map** and **Grid** reference for your quick search in the map pages.

3 For ATMs, a red dot on the left indicates that the particular ATM is located at a bank branch of the particular bank.

4 ATMs listed under **DBS** include **POSB** ATMs.

5 A **DBS** location appearing with a red dot but with blue text indicates that the ATM is located at a **POSB** bank branch.

The information provided is accurate as at printing date. The Publisher, the Banks and Service Providers accept no liability for any inconvenience, injury or loss sustained by any person using this guide.